John A. Scigliano

John A. Scigliano
Rm 134   1:20

PULSE CIRCUITS:
Switching and Shaping

PRENTICE-HALL INTERNATIONAL, INC., LONDON
PRENTICE-HALL OF AUSTRALIA, PTY., LTD., SYDNEY
PRENTICE-HALL OF CANADA, LTD., TORONTO
PRENTICE-HALL OF INDIA (PRIVATE) LTD., NEW DELHI
PRENTICE-HALL OF JAPAN, INC., TOKYO
PRENTICE-HALL DE MEXICO, S.A., MEXICO CITY

PULSE CIRCUITS:

Switching and Shaping

DANIEL S. BABB

PROFESSOR OF ELECTRICAL ENGINEERING
UNIVERSITY OF ILLINOIS

Contributing Author

PAUL F. SCHWARZLOSE
PROFESSOR OF ELECTRICAL ENGINEERING
UNIVERSITY OF ILLINOIS

PRENTICE-HALL, INC.
ENGLEWOOD CLIFFS, N.J.

Second printing....... August, 1964

Library of Congress
Catalog No. 64–16028
Printed in the
United States of America
74109C

Preface

The title selected for this text implies a gamut of circuit functions that include: limiting, clipping, clamping, peaking, delaying, comparing, sweeping, differentiating, integrating, summing, gating, timing, triggering, rectifying, shaping, storing, blocking, synchronizing, counting, pulsing, and pulse stretching.

These kinds of circuit functions are frequently essential in electrical systems for the automatic control of many manufacturing processes (e.g., sorting, routing, mixing, packaging, assembling); for the operation of a number of finished products and systems (e.g., television, radar, aircraft, missiles, computers, electronic instruments); and for the continuous measurement of many nonelectrical as well as electrical quantities (e.g., position, direction, velocity, temperature, altitude, distance, blood pressure).

It is enlightening to survey technical periodicals, and to examine published reports in the broad areas of automation, automatic controls, automatic operations, and automatic measurements. All types of engineering and scientific endeavors are actively interested in electronic systems. The reader is invited to inspect the "References for Electronic Control and Measurement Systems," near the close of the text. Even an inspection of the titles for these references is suggestive of the wide coverage and frequent complexity of electronic control systems.

Circuits that can perform or assist in performing the functions initially referred to in this preface are sufficiently important to deserve a special study. In general, these circuit functions require the electronic switching of any one, or more, of a number of electronic devices (e.g., diodes, tubes, transistors, saturable reactors).

It is these circuit functions that place a special requirement on the contents and organization of a text on electronic switching circuits. They account for the rather unconventional organization of this text, a result of classroom experience over the years.

Unfortunately, only a few electronic switching type circuits are clearly identified by name. A great majority of the circuits are identified, if identified at all, in accordance with the functions performed in a complete system. Any one of these circuits, divorced from a system, may have any one of a number of different names. In many instances a circuit configuration means very little. Much depends on the nature of the driving voltages, magnitude of circuit parameters, and the type of electronic device that is used as an electronic switch. The author has the viewpoint that any attempt to classify electronic switching circuits by name and to organize chapters entirely around these "named" circuits is futile. If this were done, certain basic types of circuit analysis problems will appear repeatedly and will never be solved to the complete satisfaction of the students.

The nature of electronic switching circuits is such that partial understanding is intolerable. Consequently, a certain amount of backtracking or review is required; Chapter 2 on exponentials is an example. It is dangerous to assume that students, at any level, are completely familiar with exponentials. Throughout the text it is frequently necessary to calculate a voltage, the slope, or a time interval on an exponential. A few class periods on this chapter is time well spent. In addition, students may repeatedly refer back to this chapter for assistance. The problems at the close of the chapter are RC circuits with mechanical type switches represented. Normally, students have the ability to solve these circuit problems, but it is also normal to use entirely too much time in the solution. Such circuits, involving single time-constant exponentials, must be solved with ease, mentally if possible.

Chapter 3, which is concerned with switching in RC circuits, still has no electronic switches represented. The resistance switching in a circuit is *defined* for different types of driving voltages. The one objective is to concentrate on the results attainable when resistances in a circuit are changed at defined instants of time, independent of how electronic devices might similate the defined switching conditions. Chapter 3 is a prerequisite to the remaining chapters.

Chapter 4 is on clamping circuits, a "named" circuit. However, Chapter 5 on input circuits for grounded cathode triodes returns to the "unnamed" circuits for the purpose of studying various means of driving triodes into conduction or nonconduction and of observing the results with the various circuitry techniques. Once this is done, the results of various loading circuits can be examined, as in Chapter 6. Chapter 8 is a similar treatment for transistors. It is preceded by Chapter 7 on semiconductor electronics in order to provide the necessary background on semiconductor characteristics. An understanding of vacuum tube characteristics is assumed and is, therefore, given no special treatment in the earlier chapters. The remainder of the text takes on a more conventional form.

The author has used the material of this text in a four-hour, one-semester course, with laboratory, at the advanced undergraduate level for a number of years. The course has been actually identified as "Industrial Electronics." Perhaps "Industrial Electronics" (by its usual meaning from past history) and *Pulse Circuits: Switching and Shaping* do not appear to be synonymous terms, but the author would define industrial electronics as all control and measurement problems that have been, or could be solved with electronic systems. A concentrated study of circuitry techniques in the broad area of electronic switching and pulse forming is one of the prerequisites for developing an ability to analyze, or synthesize, electronic control systems. Each time the course is given, each student, at the end of the course, gives a seminar-type report on an involved control or measurement system that requires the use of the basic material of this book.

The author is especially grateful to Professor Paul F. Schwarzlose for the preparation of Chapter 7 on "Semiconductor Electronics" and for his suggestions and assistance in getting the remainder of the text in its final form. The author is also grateful to Professor M. S. Helm for his suggestions and to others for encouraging words and the necessary amount of prodding. The figures for the text were prepared by Charles G. Preston, Urbana, Illinois.

D. S. BABB

Contents

Chapter 4 Diode Clamping Circuits, 43

Chapter 5 Input Circuits to Grounded Cathode Amplifiers, 53

Chapter 6 Output Circuits for Grounded Cathode Amplifiers, 85

Chapter 7 Semiconductor Electronics, 118

Chapter 7 Semiconductor Electronics—Cont.

Chapter 8 Input and Output Circuits for Grounded Emitter Transistors, 140

Chapter 9 Effects of Feedback in Switching Circuits, 158

Chapter **9 Effects of Feedback in Switching Circuits—Cont.**

Chapter **10 Dual-Tube Switching and Pulse Forming Circuits, 193**

Chapter **11 Dual-Transistor Switching Circuits, 227**

Chapter **12 Triggering, Gating, Synchronizing (Part I, Tubes), 245**

Chapter 12 Triggering, Gating, Synchronizing (Part I, Tubes)—Cont.

Chapter 13 Triggering, Gating, Synchronizing (Part II, Semiconductor Devices), 269

Chapter 14 Other Solid State Circuitry and Techniques for Electronic Switching and Pulse Shaping, 290

Chapter **14 Other Solid State Circuitry and Techniques for Electronic Switching and Pulse Shaping—Cont.**

Chapter **15 Rectification and Magnetic Amplifiers, 316**

To the Student

These pages, addressed "to the student," are written to provide some assistance for the studies of the text. After scanning the pages of the text to get a general impression of the contents, the student will likely have some questions to which he would like to have answers before getting involved in the detailed studies. Let us anticipate some of these questions and attempt to give satisfactory answers.

To What Types of Applications Are the Studies of This Text Directed?

The electronic circuits and related problems of this text are directed toward applications of automatic control systems, automatic measurement systems, and automatic computing systems in which electronic-switching and pulse-shaping circuits are used. Electrical systems, employing these kinds of circuits, find application in practically any area of technology. A number of applications are referenced immediately following Chapter 15. It is worthwhile to inspect this list to observe the kinds and variety of problems that have been solved with electrical systems.

Are These or Similar Applications Incorporated in the Formal Studies of This Text?

The referenced applications are not directly incorporated in the studies of this text. There are a number of reasons for not concentrating on these and similar applications. There are just too many and too wide a variety of applications. In addition, any one electrical system could require many hours of study and may even be impossible to understand and analyze without a knowledge of the basic circuitry included in these systems. It seems most desirable to concentrate our studies on the types of circuits that might be used in electrical systems before attempting to analyze, or synthesize, any complete system.

Is One Area of Technology More Unique Than Any Other Area as to the Kinds of Basic Circuits Required?

Any one area of technology is no more unique than any other area as to the kinds of basic circuits that may be required in the over-all system. No two systems, of course, are exactly identical. Still, the circuitry techniques for a system of one area of technology could be very similar to that of many other areas of technology. There are many basic types of electronic-switching and pulse-shaping circuits that are common to systems of many areas, whether these areas of technology be the processing industries, the medical profession, guided missiles, automatic production lines, traffic control, computers, or others. Each area of technology is only unique in the *kinds* of problems to be solved with electronic control systems and perhaps in the restricted use of certain electrical-electronic devices.

What Is Pulse Circuits: Switching and Shaping?

Pulse Circuits: Switching and Shaping is a study of electrical circuits in which electronic devices perform as switches in accordance with the demands of electrical signals. Two general results are possible with electronic switching actions in circuits. One general result is the generation of special types of waveforms (voltage or current) that are needed in automatic control systems, automatic measurement systems, and automatic computing systems. The second general result is the possibility of having a circuit behave simply as a switch, rather than as a waveform generator, in which case the circuit will have an output or will not have an output in accordance with the demands of electrical signals.

These two general results, generation of waveforms and similation of switches, lead to a great number of practical circuitry configurations as needed and used in electrical systems.

How Are Electronic Switching and Pulse Shaping Circuits Identified?

Each electronic switching circuit, as used in automatic control, measurement, and computing systems, is identified, most frequently, in accordance with the function performed by the particular basic circuit in the system. The *circuit function* is normally dictated by the system and may be meaningless when the circuit is divorced from the system. There are only a few circuits that are *clearly* identified, in or out of a system, by assigning particular names to particular circuit configurations. If you, the student, can accept this situation, then the studies of this text will be much more satisfying than they would be by wanting to know just where and why each particular circuit is used. If we can study each circuit and understand its behavior under different conditions of operation, then we need not be too concerned when a particular circuit is identified differently in different systems.

After a few weeks of study, you should begin to take a real interest in reading and studying a few applications as published in technical periodicals. Only by doing this can you fully appreciate the problem of identifying circuits always by name except as they perform certain functions in a complete system.

What Are Some of the Circuit Functions?

Let us list some of the functions that electronic switching circuits may be required to perform. Although these circuit functions, as listed here, cannot be defined at this time, the words will have some meaning and will provide some insight for the studies of the text. A few of the circuit functions are:

Clipping	Scanning	Timing
Limiting	Detecting	Restoring
Clamping	Averaging	Inverting
Summing	Subtracting	Sweeping
Storing	Synchronizing	Dumping
Comparing	Triggering	Delaying
Blocking	Counting	Syncing
Gating	Pulse stretching	Peaking

What Electronic Devices Can Serve as Electronic Switches?

Offhand, one may wish to believe that only two-terminal devices (diodes) can serve as electronic switches. This is not true. There are a number of multiterminal electrical devices that are used in switching and pulse shaping circuits. Vacuum triodes, multielement vacuum tubes, transistors, unijunction transistors, thyratrons (gas tubes or solid state devices), ignitrons, saturable reactors, and silicon-controlled-rectifiers are some of the multiterminal devices that are incorporated in such circuits. The many practical electrical systems of control, of measurement, and of computers would not be possible without multiterminal devices.

The point here is to give a warning to the student not to be surprised over the kinds of electronic devices that might be used in switching circuitry of any complete electrical system.

What Is the Language of Electronic-Switching and Pulse-Shaping Circuits?

The language of electronic-switching and pulse-shaping circuits is peculiar to these kinds of circuits. Some of the circuit functions have been previously listed, but when assigning identifying names to particular circuits, one is confronted with an added choice of words to describe the circuits. It seems desirable to provide an early acquaintance with the language of these circuits by listing here some of the identifying names that are used. This listing also presents the opportunity to give important warnings.

(1) Each identifying name does not necessarily imply a different circuit nor a different circuit function.

(2) There may be several circuit configurations for a particular circuit function.

(3) Any one identified circuit does not necessarily define the complete circuit configuration. Each identified circuit may have a number of modifications or additions to the basic circuit configuration.

(4) Identifications that are used for particular circuits may be peculiar to the area of technology.

A partial list of circuit identifications follows (most, but not all of these are used in the text):

Counter	Frequency divider
Decade counter	Timing slicer
Rotating electronic switch	Sync separator
Shift register	Mixer
Ringing circuit	Coincidence circuit
Sweep circuit	Memory circuit
Blocking oscillator	AND circuit
Clock oscillator	OR circuit
Astable multivibrator	NOR circuit
Relaxing oscillator	NOT circuit
Monostable multivibrator	Inverter
Univibrator	Voltage level discriminator
Single-shot multivibrator	Difference amplifier
Bistable multivibrator	Peaking circuit
Flip-flop circuit	Adder
Binary	Notch inserter

What Educational Background Must One Have to Analyze, or Synthesize, a Complete System in Which Electronic-Switching Circuits Are Used?

Four prerequisites to the analysis, or design, of complete electronic systems are stated and briefly discussed, as follows:

1. It is essential to know the physical properties and the electrical characteristics of each and every electrical-electronic device that might be used in the electrical system under consideration. With some exceptions, this knowledge is assumed for the studies of the text.

2. Familiarity with circuit techniques for accomplishing the various circuit functions is essential. One must develop an ability to analyze

and design the circuits that are required to perform particular functions. It is the major objective of this text to concentrate on this second prerequisite.

3. Familiarity with a number of complete systems and the circuitry techniques used in these systems, is very helpful. Getting familiar with the circuitry techniques of complete systems is the personal responsibility of each individual. One very important way to obtain this kind of information is to read and study technical periodicals that describe such systems. This is not so very difficult, especially after one has *thoroughly analyzed at least one involved control system,* in any area of technology. You may be required to do this as a supplement to the studies of this text. If not required, then you must determine to do this for yourself at the earliest opportunity.

4. The analysis, or design, of the electronic circuitry for a complete control or measurement system requires a knowledge of each and every variable, electrical and nonelectrical, that are pertinent to the system. Know the variables; then the circuitry of a working system is more easily understood and the need for particular circuits within the system are recognized. The design of a new system may require the assistance of someone who is trained in the area of technology for which the system is intended. A systems designer cannot be expected to know the variables, quantities to be controlled, and the nature of signal sources for a system to be designed for the medical profession, for example, without the assistance of a licensed specialist in this profession.

1

Diode

Switching Circuits

Nonreactive

1.1 General Discussion

The diode is one type of electronic device that has a significant role in electronic switching and pulse shaping circuits. This is true because the diode, as a two-terminal device, can exhibit either a low resistance or a high resistance depending on the polarity and perhaps the magnitude of the voltage across the diode.

The importance of causing a resistance magnitude to quickly and automatically change from a low value to a high value, or the inverse, will be appreciated more and more as we proceed through the studies of this text. Mastery of the circuitry and problems in this chapter will be very helpful for later studies.

The diode circuits of this chapter are presented with two objectives in mind. One of the objectives is to illustrate *some* of the results that can be obtained with diodes. These circuits are necessarily restricted, at this early stage of study, to nonreactive circuits. The effects, if any, of capacitance or inductance are not considered. Further, the diodes are regarded as ideal, having either a negligible or a constant forward resistance and an infinite reverse resistance.

1

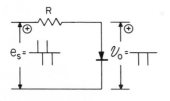

Fig. 1.1. A diode clipping circuit.

The second and probably more impor-tant objective is to develop a procedure for determining when a particular diode is conducting or is not conducting; i.e., when is the resistance of the diode at a low value and when is the resistance at a high value? The procedure is not difficult with only one diode in a circuit. Increase the number of diodes in a circuit, however, and it becomes more important to develop a plan of attack.

1.2 Basic Diode Clipping and/or Limiting Circuits

A nonreactive circuit with one diode is shown in Figure 1.1. In such a circuit, only the negative portions of the signal voltage will appear as the output voltage. The positive portions are, in a sense, clipped. The circuit could be identified, therefore, as a clipping circuit. Actually, complete clipping of the positive pulses is not possible, and is approximated only if the forward resistance of the diode is small and much less than the series resistance R. In this event the positive pulses of voltage will appear across R with very little attenuation. The negative pulses for the output voltages are only slightly attenuated provided the reverse resistance of the diode is large and much greater than the series resistance R.

Diode clipping circuits become much more versatile when one considers the four possible configurations illustrated by the four circuits of Figure 1.2.

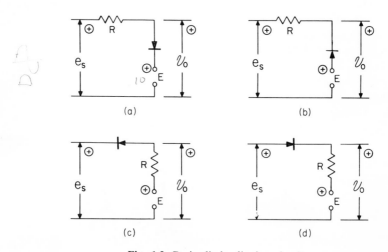

Fig. 1.2. Basic diode clipping circuits.

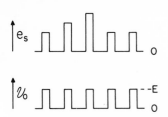

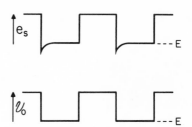

Fig. 1.3. Output voltage pulses with an upper *limit* of *E*.

Fig. 1.4. Clipping of objectionable spikes to form a square wave.

Each of these circuits suggests the possible use of a d-c biasing voltage to control the voltage level at which a diode changes operation from a nonconducting to a conducting state or the inverse. The biasing voltages can be positive, negative or zero. In circuit (a), only those portions of e_s that are less than the biasing voltage E will appear at the output as the voltage v_o. The voltage E is the *upper limit* for the output voltage, as is also true for circuit (c). In circuits (b) and (d), the voltage E is the *lower limit* for the output voltage.

These circuits are often referred to as limiters rather than as clippers. The two identifications are not necessarily interchangeable. Their use depends on the particular reason for using one of these diode circuits. One example of identifying one of the diode circuits as a limiter is illustrated by the waveforms of Figure 1.3. Here, the source voltage is represented by positive pulses that are not of the same magnitude consistantly, but are never less than E. Either circuit (a) or circuit (c) of Figure 1.2 will limit these pulses to the desired voltage level E. A particular application may dictate a preference of one of these two circuits over the other. If circuit (a) is used, the internal resistance of the biasing voltage must be low.

One example of the identification of one of the diode circuits as a clipper was illustrated with Figure 1.1. Another example is shown by the voltage waveforms of Figure 1.4. In this figure, the source voltage has a waveform suggesting an attempt to generate a square wave. The undershoots on this waveform may be objectionable. They can be *removed* with a clipper. Diode circuit (b) or circuit (d) will perform this function. Again, the choice of the two diode circuits is dictated by the over-all circuit in which the clipping circuit is included. Loading effects on other circuits should be examined.

1.3 A Clipping Circuit to Convert a Sine Wave to a Square Wave

The clipping circuit of Figure 1.5 illustrates one method of generating a square wave, which is so often needed for pulsing and switching circuits.

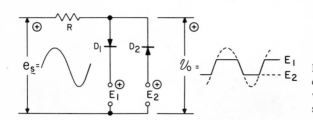

Fig. 1.5. A diode clipping circuit to convert a sine wave to an approximate square wave.

Actually, a square wave is only approximated, but this is a practical condition that exists for any type of square-wave generator.

The output voltage, referring to Figure 1.5, has an upper limit of E_1 and a lower limit of E_2. Obviously, E_1 must be algebraically greater than E_2. If the sinusoidal driving voltage is symmetrical about a zero voltage level, then the output voltage is completely symmetrical if $E_1 = -E_2$. The circuit requires a large driving voltage in order to better approximate a square wave for the output voltage.

The time required for the output voltage to rise from E_2 to E_1, or to fall from E_1 to E_2, is a significant measure of the steepness of the leading and trailing edges. Representing the rise time as t_r,

$$t_r = \frac{T}{\pi} \sin^{-1} \frac{E_1}{E_m} \tag{1.1}$$

$$= \frac{T\theta_1}{\pi} \tag{1.2}$$

where T is the period of the driving voltage. The angle θ_1 is defined in Equation (1.1).

For certain types of circuit problems where the approximate square wave is the driving voltage, it is convenient to represent the leading and trailing edges as linear functions of time. Such a voltage is sometimes referred to as a *ramp voltage*. The assumed ramp voltage is permissable, for this example, provided the rise time is a small fraction of the period. The slopes of the leading and trailing edges, expressed as volts per microsecond, are then significant portions of the output waveform.

1.4   A Current Biased Diode Circuit

The diode in the circuit in Figure 1.6 is current biased. The magnitude of the biasing current is E/R_2, assuming negligible forward resistance for the diode. An inspection of the circuit indicates a lower limit of zero for the output voltage.

The major problem in this circuit is in determining the critical value of the source voltage at which the diode becomes nonconducting. The diode

is nonconducting when the source voltage
is greater than its critical value. The circuit
is analyzed by assuming the diode is conducting or by assuming the diode is not
conducting. With either procedure, the
conditions necessary to cause the transition
from diode conduction to nonconduction,
or the inverse, is easily determined.

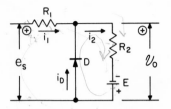

Fig. 1.6. The diode is current biased.

When the diode is not conducting, the
output voltage may be obtained by application of the principle of superposition.

$$v_o = \frac{e_s R_2}{R_1 + R_2} - \frac{ER_1}{R_1 + R_2} \qquad (1.3)$$

For an assumed ideal diode, the critical value of the source voltage is the
value of e_s when v_o is zero. Thus,

$$e_s \text{ (critical)} = \frac{ER_1}{R_2} \qquad (1.4)$$

The diode is conducting for values of the source voltage less than the critical value.

The same critical value of source voltage is obtained, of course, by
assuming the ideal diode is conducting. Referring to the current and voltage
notations in the circuit diagram,

$$i_D = i_2 - i_1 \qquad \qquad +\frac{E}{R_2} R_1 = e \quad (1.5)$$

$$0 = \frac{E}{R_2} - \frac{e_s}{R_1} \qquad \qquad R_2 \qquad (1.6)$$

The current i_2 can be greater than or equal to i_1, but not less than i_1. The
transition occurs about i_D equal to zero. Consequently, the critical value
of source voltage is again expressed by Equation (1.4).

From one practical viewpoint, the output voltage is assuredly clamped
to zero for values of the source voltage that are less than the critical value.
Small spurious signals are thereby prevented from appearing at the output.
The output voltage is expressed by Equation (1.3) when the source voltage
is greater than its critical value.

1.5   Thevenin's Equivalence

A Thevenin's equivalent circuit is freely used throughout the text to
facilitate the analysis of switching circuits: the diode circuit in Figure
1.7a is chosen as one example. The circuit is very similar to the diode
circuit in Figure 1.6 except for the presence of R_D. From this information
it may be assumed that the diode has a constant forward resistance of

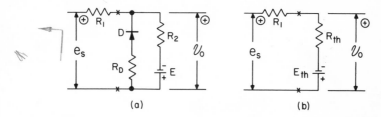

Fig. 1.7. An equivalent circuit (b) when the diode of circuit (a) is conducting.

R_D, or that perhaps R_D includes a resistance that is inserted in series with the diode.

A portion of the circuit, as indicated in the figure, is replaced with a Thevenin's equivalent circuit. The equivalent circuit is shown in Figure 1.7b and applies only when the diode is conducting and the circuit parameters are assumed to be *constant*. Otherwise, Thevenin's theorem is not applicable. R_{th} represents the parallel combination of R_D and R_2, and $E_{th} = ER_D/(R_D + R_2)$. The output voltage is expressed by Equation (1.3) when the diode is not conducting. If the diode is conducting, the output voltage is

$$v_o = \frac{e_s R_{th}}{R_1 + R_{th}} - \frac{E_{th} R_1}{R_1 + R_{th}} \qquad (1.7)$$

and the output voltage is not firmly clamped to zero with R_D not equal to zero. Since the diode current is zero when the output voltage is zero, the transition occurs about v_o equal to zero. The critical value of the source voltage, therefore, is

$$e_s \text{ (critical)} = \frac{E_{th} R_1}{R_{th}} \qquad (1.8)$$

Inserting the identities for E_{th} and R_{th}, the critical value of the source voltage, as determined from Equation (1.7), reverts to ER_1/R_2 as represented by Equation (1.4).

1.6   A Current Biased Diode Circuit with Two Source Voltages

Remove the source voltage branch for e_{s2} in the circuit in Figure 1.8 and the remaining circuit is identical to that in Figure 1.6 except for the presence of diode D_1. The response of the circuit in Figure 1.6 is not changed by this diode, and expressions for the output voltage, v_o, remain the same. The only possible effect of the series diode in that circuit is the blocking of the source current i_1 if the source voltage is ever negative.

Perhaps the circuit of Figure 1.8 has the function of blocking, or not blocking, the current i_3. To block this current, v_o must be equal to or greater

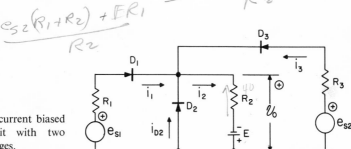

$$\frac{e_{s2}(R_1+R_2) + ER_1}{R_2}$$

$$\frac{\left(e_{s2} + \frac{ER_1}{R_1+R_2}\right)(R_1+R_2)}{R_2}$$

Fig. 1.8. A current biased diode circuit with two source voltages.

than e_{s2}. The critical value of e_{s1} (to block e_{s2}) is more easily determined by assuming diode D_3 is not conducting, rather than by assuming it is conducting. The voltage v_o is then expressed by Equation (1.3) where e_s is now e_{s1}. Thus, with diode D_3 on the verge of conducting,

$$e_{s2} = \frac{e_{s1}R_2}{R_1 + R_2} - \frac{ER_1}{R_1 + R_2} \tag{1.9}$$

Then, to block the current i_3, e_{s1} has the critical value of

$$e_{s1}\,(\text{critical}) = \frac{e_{s2}(R_1 + R_2)}{R_2} + \frac{ER_1}{R_2} \tag{1.10}$$

For any smaller value of e_{s1}, diode D_3 is conducting. Notice that the last term of Equation (1.10) is the critical value of e_{s1} that causes transition for diode D_2. Of course, only positive values of source voltages are significant for this particular circuit.

The blocking of a source current, such as i_3, has greater meaning when R_3 is regarded as the only desired loading for the source e_{s2}; i.e., the resistance loading is either R_3 or the loading is infinite. This condition can be satisfied in the circuit. Assume that e_{s2} (positive) is always present. Then $i_3 = e_{s2}/R_3$ provided that diode D_2 is conducting. Diode D_2 is certainly conducting if e_{s1} is zero and i_3 is less than i_2. Now, if e_{s1} (positive) is present and greater than the value given by Equation (1.10), i_3 is zero. The current i_1, however, is $(e_{s1} + E)/(R_1 + R_2)$. As required, the resistance loading for e_{s2} is either R_3 or infinite, if the reverse resistance of the diode D_3 is assumed to be infinite.

1.7 OR Circuit with Diodes

The diode circuit in Figure 1.8, described in the preceding section, can also be regarded as an OR circuit. An OR circuit is one that will yield an output voltage whenever one or more of a number of signal voltages is applied. Such a circuit is often used as a part of electronic control systems, computers, and automatic measurement systems.

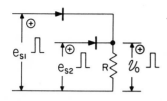

Fig. 1.9. A diode OR circuit.

The circuit in Figure 1.9 illustrates a simplified diode OR circuit for positive pulses. The circuit is nearly identical to that of Figure 1.8. It omits the current biased diode (which is not necessarily a requirement). The omitted resistors, R_1 and R_3, could represent the source resistance. The circuit of Figure 1.8 is also applicable to negative pulses by inverting the voltage polarity of E as well as inverting all diodes.

By removing one of the diodes in the OR circuit in Figure 1.9, the remaining circuit is recognized as one of the basic types of diode clipping circuits.

1.8   AND Circuit with Diodes

The AND circuit is a circuit that will yield an output voltage only if all source voltages are simultaneously present with the same polarities.

Remove the current biased diode D_2 and the circuit in Figure 1.8 can be an AND circuit provided that the source voltages are all negative pulses. The resistances R_1 and R_3, which could represent the source resistances, should be small. With diode D_2 removed, diodes D_1 and D_3 of that circuit become current biased assuming the voltage E is retained with the indicated polarity. Consequently, the output voltage v_o is firmly clamped to zero so long as either source voltage is zero and R_1 and R_3 are negligible. Negative pulses at both sources must be present to establish a negative pulse for the output voltage. As stated previously, with diode D_2 removed, the circuit is an AND circuit for negative pulses only. For positive pulses only, the circuit is an OR circuit.

To avoid the possibility of positive output pulses, and therefore to avoid the possibility of an OR circuit when an AND circuit is desired, the diode D_2 is inverted and replaced in the circuit. The circuit is now the same as is shown in Figure 1.10. Compare the circuit with that in Figure 1.8 and observe that diode D_2 has been inverted, and positive pulses for v_o are now impossible. The circuit can only be an AND circuit; it cannot be

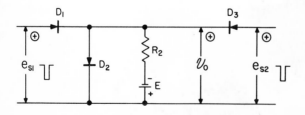

Fig. 1.10. A diode AND circuit.

an OR circuit.

The circuit in Figure 1.10 is shown in a more conventional configuration in Figure 1.11, and a small d-c bias voltage E_2 is included. With R_2 having the indicated polarity, diodes D_1 and D_3 are now current biased. The output voltage is firmly clamped to the negative voltage represented by E_2 unless all input voltages are sufficiently negative to block the input diodes D_1 and D_3 and any other input diodes. The output voltage v_o is equal to E_1 (a negative voltage) when all input diodes are blocked. To make the circuit an AND circuit for positive pulses, invert all diodes and voltages.

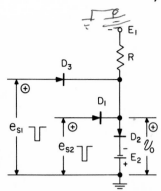

Fig. 1.11. Same as Figure 1.10 with voltage E_2 included.

PROBLEMS

1.1 Assume ideal diodes for each of the circuits of Figure 1.2. If e_s is a sinusoidal voltage having a peak value of 40 volts, plot v_o for each circuit. The bias voltage, E, is a positive 10 volts for each circuit.

1.2 Repeat Problem 1.1 for E equal to a negative 10 volts.

1.3 Repeat Problem 1.1 for $R = 1900$ ohms, the forward resistance of the diodes $= 100$ ohms, and assume infinite reverse resistance for the diodes.

1.4 Repeat Problem 1.3 with the internal resistance of the bias voltage equal to 400 ohms.

1.5 For the circuit of Figure 1.5, $e_s = 100 \sin 2\pi(1000)t$, $E_1 = 5$ volts, $E_2 = -5$ volts, $R = 1$ Meg, and the forward resistance of each diode is 1000 ohms. Plot v_o and calculate the rise time for this output voltage.

1.6 For the circuit of Figure 1.6, $R_1 = 2$ K, $R_2 = 100$ K, $E = 40$ volts, and the diode is ideal. What is the minimum value of the source voltage for which the diode is nonconducting?

1.7 For the circuit of Figure 1.6, $e_s = 2 \sin \omega t$, and the other quantities are as given in Problem 1.6. For what fraction of a period T is the diode nonconducting? Plot v_o.

1.8 For the circuit of Figure 1.6, $R_1 = 10$ K, $R_2 = 50$ K, $E = 30$ volts, and the source voltage is a positive pulse of 10 volts. What is the magnitude of the output pulse?

1.9 Repeat Problems 1.6, 1.7, and 1.8, with a 5 K resistance in series with the ideal diode. Discuss the results.

1.10 For the circuit of Figure 1.8, $R_1 = 3$ K, $R_2 = 24$ K, $R_3 = 2$ K, $E = 50$ volts, e_{s2} is a positive pulse of 20 volts and the diodes are ideal. Determine the minimum value of e_{s1} to block the current i_3.

1.11 For the circuit of Figure 1.8, The quantities are the same as for Problem 1.10 except that e_{s2} is not given. It is desired to have a positve pulse of 10

develop a procedure to determine when a particular diode is on or off.

volts for v_o whenever a positive pulse occurs at either source. What magnitude of e_{s1} and of e_{s2} will give this response?

1.12 For the results of Problem 1.11, what is the magnitude of the pulse for v_o when the two source pulses are simultaneously present?

1.13 With the use of a diode limiting circuit, modify the circuit of Figure 1.8 to limit the positive output pulses to 10 volts. This corresponds to assuming that the source pulses are greater than the calculated values of Problem 1.11.

1.14 Design a diode AND circuit for positive pulses with three inputs. The internal resistance for each source is 1500 ohms. The output pulse is to be 60 volts when all inputs are present, but no more than 2 volts otherwise. The circuit is to be nonreactive.

1.15 Refer to the four circuits of Figure 1.2, and consider the possibility of combining any two of these circuits in tandem. Analyze any selected combination, in general terms, by deriving expressions for limiting voltages, anywhere in the circuit, and the expressions for the source voltage required to give these limiting voltages. (This kind of study is valuable for much of the work of this text.)

1.16 Refer to the circuit represented for this problem. The source voltage is indicated with the figure. Plot v_o and e_s to the same time base, indicating significant voltages on each waveform.

$e_{s1} = e_{s2} \dfrac{(R_1 + R_2)}{R_2}$

$e_{s1} = e_{s2} \dfrac{10 - 60.2}{12}$

$e_{s1} = \dfrac{e_{s2}}{12}$

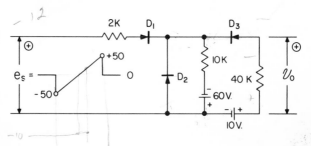

Fig. P1.16.

1.17 Refer to the circuit represented for this problem. For the given source voltage, plot v_o and e_s to the same time base indicating significant voltages on each waveform if
(a) $E = 30$ volts.
(b) $E = 10$ volts.
(c) $E = 0$.

$\dfrac{100 - 10}{12}$

$\dfrac{12 \cdot 100}{96}$

$\dfrac{10 \times 12}{10}$

operation of the time

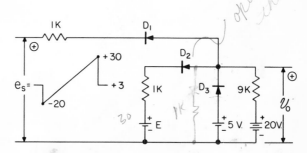

Fig. P1.17.

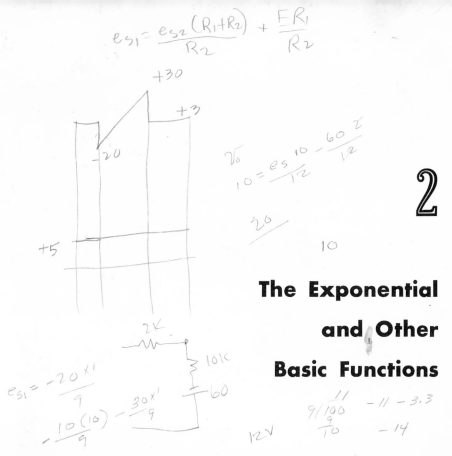

2

The Exponential
and Other
Basic Functions

2.1 General Discussion

It is the primary purpose of this chapter to study the properties of an exponential, of the form e^{kt}, as an essential preparation for the material that is to follow in later chapters. The exponential function is so frequently exhibited in the response of electronic switching and pulse shaping circuits, for the types of driving voltages required, that it becomes very important to know the characteristics of an exponential. A thorough working knowledge of the exponential will permit a rapid analysis of the circuits that are presented for study. Rapid analysis, almost to the point of reading a circuit (oral analysis), is valuable. The circuit problems in this chapter are included to develop the kind of adeptness necessary for later studies.

A ramp voltage or current has the function of a straight line of finite slope. The ramp can be generated by taking a small portion of some other function, usually an exponential. A step function is a ramp function having infinite slope. A constant might be regarded as a ramp function with zero slope. It seems significant that only a few general types of functions are used to describe the response of circuits, the most significant functions being the exponential, ramp, constant, step, and sinusoid. The complete response could include more than one of these functions.

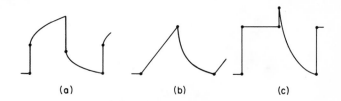

(a)   (b)   (c)

Fig. 2.1. Three periodic waveforms (one steady-state cycle shown) with
a sequence of basic functions.

Of the five significant functions listed, only the sinusoid is periodic
and repetitive. A sinusoidal function and/or a constant can represent a
steady state solution of a circuit. The step, ramp, and exponential are not
repetitive, and the steady state solution of a circuit cannot be represented
in terms of one of these alone. Somehow, a circuit voltage must be returned
to an initial state in order to repeat a step, a ramp, or an exponential. It is
possible, however, to represent a steady state solution of a circuit in terms
of a combination of steps, ramps and exponentials. The graphs of Figure
2.1 represent three possible types of periodic waveforms involving steps,
ramps and exponentials. In Figure 2.1a, for example, each cycle of the
waveform contains a step followed by an exponential, then by a second
step, and finally by a second exponential which returns the waveform to
the initial state that existed before the first step.

Periodic waveforms such as those of Figure 2.1 suggest the need for
switching or for sudden changes of parameters in a circuit. A linear circuit,
or a circuit with constant parameters, cannot always get the job done.
When these sort of things happen in a circuit, we are confronted with a
need for unique techniques for analyzing such circuits. If a circuit experiences
a change in its parameters at some instant, or for a particular time interval,
then the instant of time or the time interval must be known, but not necessarily known in advance of a solution. In certain types of circuit problems,
these significant times are determined in the process of and as a part of
the circuit evaluation.

2.2 Graphical Representation of Voltage Functions

The five diagrams of Figure 2.2 are graphical representations of the five
significant voltage functions. These graphs are shown to emphasize the
importance of regarding constant coefficients (ϕ, k, or A on the graphs)
as positve and negative real numbers. Each constant coefficient then results
in a pair of graphs. Failure to regard a constant coefficient in this manner
is often the reason for errors of interpretation and of calculations in circuit
problems. Assigning both positve and negative real numbers to constant
coefficients, where permissible, almost automatically prevents such errors.

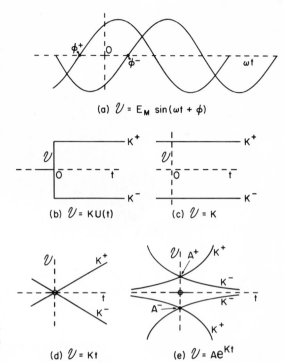

(a) $v = E_M \sin(\omega t + \phi)$

(b) $v = KU(t)$

(c) $v = K$

Fig. 2.2. Five basic voltage functions to emphasize the sign of coefficients.

(d) $v = Kt$

(e) $v = Ae^{Kt}$

Of course, a numerical solution of a circuit problem will clearly indicate whether a coefficient is positive, negative, or of zero value. Above all one must guard against forcing (assuming) a solution in advance of the numerical solution. The forcing of a solution is very easy to do since it is not always convenient to sketch a set of graphs for every general function. Even so, it is very helpful to have a mental image of a *set* of graphs.

2.3   A General Expression for an Exponential Voltage

A voltage that is a function of time according to the expression

$$v = E_{as} - (E_{as} - E_o)e^{-t/\tau_c} \qquad (2.1)$$

is illustrated in Figure 2.3. Here, E_o is the initial value and E_{as} is the asymptotical value of the exponential. Unhappily, the one graph (not a set) forces a solution by representing E_{as} as a positive value and E_o as a negative value. In general, these two quantities of Equation (2.1) should be regarded as representing either positive or negative real numbers including zero. As an example, the equation yields 24.24 volts for a particular t/τ_c ratio of 1.0 if E_{as} is 50 volts and E_o is − 20 volts. As another example, the equation yields − 35 volts for a particular t/τ_c ratio of 2.3 if E_{as} is − 40 volts and

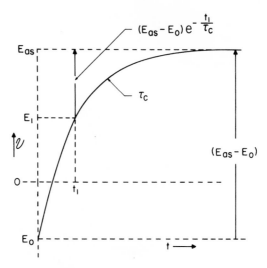

Fig. 2.3. An exponential voltage.

$$v_t = E_{as} - (E_{as} - E_o)e^{-t/\tau_c}.$$

or

$$v_t = E_o + (E_{as} - E_o)(1 - e^{-t/\tau_c}).$$

E_o is 10 volts.

The general expression of Equation (2.1) reduces to

when you *short a cap*

$$v = E_o e^{-t/\tau_c} \quad \left(\text{for } E_{as} = 0\right) \tag{2.2}$$

when $E_{as} = 0$ *$V = E_o e^{-t/\tau_c}$*

Also,

when you charge

$$v = E_{as}(1 - e^{-t/\tau_c}) \quad \text{for } E_o = 0 \tag{2.3}$$

These last two equations are *special* cases for the general expression and should be regarded as such.

2.4   Slope of an Exponential

The derivative of the general expression for an exponential, Equation (2.1), gives

$$\frac{dv}{dt} = \frac{1}{\tau_c}(E_{as} - E_o)e^{-t/\tau_c} \tag{2.4}$$

as the slope of the exponential at any time t. At a given time t_1 and representing the resulting voltage as E_1 at this instant, the

$$\text{slope at } t_1 = \frac{(E_{as} - E_1)e^{-t/\tau_c}}{\tau_c} = \frac{E_{as} - E_1}{\tau_c} \tag{2.5}$$

which is illustrated in Figure 2.4. It is interesting to observe that the straight line representing the slope at any time t_1 intercepts the E_{as} level exactly τ_c seconds after the time t_1. Also, from Equation (2.5), the initial slope of

$$v = E_{as} - (E_{as} - E_0)\epsilon^{-t/\tau_c}$$

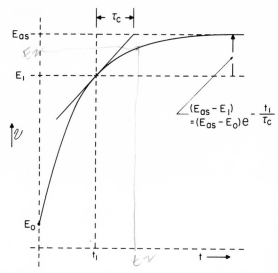

$$(E_{as} - E_1) = (E_{as} - E_0)\epsilon^{-\frac{t_1}{\tau_c}}$$

Fig. 2.4. Slope of an exponential.

the exponential, for $t = 0$, is $(E_{as} - E_0)/\tau_c$. This is of particular interest since the first portion of an exponential is often used to approximate a ramp voltage.

2.5 Per Cent Slope Deviation

With time t_2 later than time t_1 and defining the per unit (multiplied by 100 it is called *per cent*) slope deviation from 1 to 2 as

$$\text{p.u. slope deviation} = \frac{\text{slope at time } t_1 - \text{slope at time } t_2}{\text{slope at time } t_1} \quad (2.6)$$

then, recalling Equation (2.5),

$$\text{p.u. slope deviation (1 to 2)} = \frac{E_2 - E_1}{E_{as} - E_1} \quad .01 \quad (2.7)$$

where E_2 is the voltage on the exponential at time t_2. Normally, however, the first small portion of an exponential is used to represent a ramp voltage or a sweep voltage. Thus,

$$\text{p.u. slope deviation (0 to 1)} = \frac{E_1 - E_0}{E_{as} - E_0} \quad (2.8)$$

The per unit slope deviation of Equation (2.8) is also expressed as

$$\text{p.u. slope deviation (0 to 1)} = 1 - e^{-t_1/\tau_c} \quad (2.9)$$

which is true since

$$E_1 - E_0 = (E_{as} - E_0)(1 - e^{-t_1/\tau_c}) \quad (2.10)$$

$$.01 = \frac{150}{15000}$$

$$E_{as} = \frac{E_{as}}{15000}$$

If the identity of Equation (2.10) is not immediately recognizable, then observe the second form of the general expression for an exponential as given with Figure 2.3.

Both expressions of Equation (2.8) and Equation (2.9) are usable forms. The former equation stresses an initial interest in the voltage ratios required for a desired limit of per cent slope deviation. The latter equation stresses an interest in the maximum time interval for a desired limit of per cent slope deviation.

The per unit slope deviation as given by Equation (2.9) is approximated by the t_1/τ_c ratio provided this ratio is small. Observe the series expansion,

$$1 - e^{-t_1/t_c} = \frac{t_1}{\tau_c}\left(1 - \frac{t_1}{2\tau_c} + \frac{t_1^2}{6\tau_c} - \cdots\right) \tag{2.11}$$

Thus, for small t_1/τ_c ratios,

$$\text{p.u. slope deviation (0 to 1)} \cong \frac{t_1}{\tau_c} \tag{2.12}$$

Equations (2.8), (2.9), and (2.12) are three possible expressions for the per unit slope deviation of an exponential where the initial point, (E_o, t_o), is taken as reference.

2.6   Time Intervals on an Exponential

Using the subscripts 1 and 2 as in the preceding section,

$$\begin{aligned} E_1 &= E_{\text{as}} - (E_{\text{as}} - E_o)\, e^{-t_1/\tau_c} \\ E_2 &= E_{\text{as}} - (E_{\text{as}} - E_o)\, e^{-t_2/\tau_c} \end{aligned} \tag{2.13}$$

Solving for t_1 and t_2 gives

$$\begin{aligned} t_1 &= \tau_c \ln \frac{E_{\text{as}} - E_o}{E_{\text{as}} - E_1} \\ t_2 &= \tau_c \ln \frac{E_{\text{as}} - E_o}{E_{\text{as}} - E_2} \end{aligned} \tag{2.14}$$

The voltage ratios in these two expressions of Equation (2.14) are always positive ratios greater than unity regardless of the polarities of the various voltages. Consequently, the times t_1 and t_2 are positive quantities measured from the instant of E_o, the initial voltage of the exponential.

From Equations (2.14) we obtain the time interval from t_1 to t_2 as

$$t_2 - t_1 = \tau_c \ln \frac{E_{\text{as}} - E_1}{E_{\text{as}} - E_2} \tag{2.15}$$

Again, the voltage ratio is positive and greater than unity provided t_2 is a later time than t_1.

To obtain an expression for calculating small time intervals on an exponential, observe from the series expansion that

$$e^{-t/\tau_c} = 1 - \frac{t}{\tau_c} + \frac{t^2}{2\tau_c^2} - \frac{t^3}{6\tau_c^3} + \cdots \tag{2.16}$$

Saving the first two terms of the series for small t/τ_c ratios and substituting in the Equations of (2.13) then,

$$\begin{aligned} E_1 &\cong E_{\mathrm{as}} - (E_{\mathrm{as}} - E_o)(1 - t_1/\tau_c) \\ E_2 &\cong E_{\mathrm{as}} - (E_{\mathrm{as}} - E_o)(1 - t_2/\tau_c) \end{aligned} \tag{2.17}$$

Solving for t_1 and t_2, each measured from the (E_o, t_o) point, gives

$$\begin{aligned} t_1 &\cong \tau_c \frac{E_1 - E_o}{E_{\mathrm{as}} - E_o} \\ t_2 &\cong \tau_c \frac{E_2 - E_o}{E_{\mathrm{as}} - E_o} \end{aligned} \tag{2.18}$$

for small t/τ_c ratios as defined.

Now, writing Equations (2.18) as a proportion,

$$\frac{t_2}{t_1} \cong \frac{E_2 - E_o}{E_1 - E_o} \tag{2.19}$$

which is true provided the assumption of small t/τ_c ratios is applicable. The time ratio is independent of τ_c but this is also true in the general case regardless of the t/τ_c ratios. See Equations (2.14).

A small time interval between any two points on an exponential is obtained simply by regarding the point (E_1, t_1) as an initial point on the exponential and replacing E_o with E_1 and t_o with t_1 in the second expression of Equations (2.18). Thus,

$$t_2 - t_1 \cong \tau_c \frac{E_2 - E_1}{E_{\mathrm{as}} - E_1} \tag{2.20}$$

2.7   The Ramp Voltage

A ramp voltage has the function of a straight line with a finite slope.

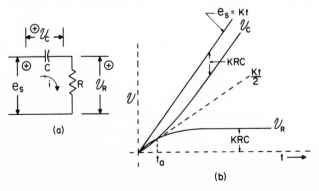

Fig. 2.5. Voltages of an RC series circuit with a ramp voltage applied.

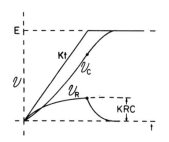

Fig. 2.6. Same as Figure 2.5(b) with the ramp voltage limited to E volts.

Let us consider the response of an RC series circuit with a ramp voltage applied. The RC series circuit, with the voltage and current references necessary for writing voltage equations, is shown in Figure 2.5a. The applied ramp voltage is expressed by

$$e_s = kt \qquad (2.21)$$

The voltage equation for the circuit is

$$kt = iR + \frac{1}{C} \int i \, dt \qquad (2.22)$$

Solving for the current,

$$i = kC(1 - e^{-t/RC}) \qquad (2.23)$$

where kC is the asymptotical value of the current. The constant k has the measure of volts/microsecond when C is in microfarads and t is in microseconds.

The voltages v_R and v_C, as a function of time, are

$$v_R = kRC(1 - e^{-t/RC}) \qquad (2.24)$$

$$v_C = kt - v_R \qquad (2.25)$$

The three voltages kt, v_R and v_C are shown graphically in Figure 2.5b. Observe that the resistor voltage is an exponential voltage with an asymptotical value of kRC. Further, after steady state operation, the capacitor voltage continues to be displaced from the applied voltage by kRC volts as indicated on the graph. If the ramp voltage is stopped after steady state has been attained for the ramp, and the applied voltage is then held constant at the voltage E, as indicated in Figure 2.6, then the three voltages are as shown in Figure 2.6. With this constant voltage being applied, the resistor voltage returns exponentially to zero and the capacitor voltage continues exponentially to E as its asymptotical value.

2.8 Transcendental Equations

When dealing with exponential functions, sinusoidal functions or any other type of function in which the derivative includes the function, one is sometimes confronted with a mathematical expression that is not solvable by algebraic means. Even so, the expression can have a particular solution or solutions. For example, how does one find the value of x for which $e^{-x} = x$? Certainly there is a value of x that satisfies this stated equality. The two members of this equality are plotted on the graph of Figure 2.7. From this graph, the value of x is read as 0.565. A method of successive

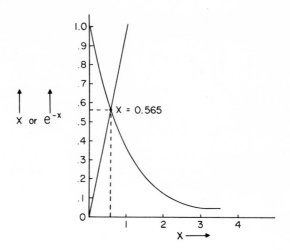

Fig. 2.7. Graphical solution of $e^{-x} = x$.

approximations, rather than a graphical solution, could also be used.

This discussion on transcendental equations is given here because the voltage graphs of Figure 2.5, associated with the preceding section, could inspire an academic interest in the instant of time when the capacitor and resistor voltages are equal. This instant of time is indicated as t_a on Figure 2.5. At this instant,

$$v_C = v_R = kt_a - v_R$$

or,

$$v_R = \frac{kt_a}{2} \qquad (2.26)$$

The point of intersection of the v_R and v_C graphs is then somewhere on the $kt/2$ line as indicated in Figure 2.5. From Equations (2.24) and (2.26),

$$\frac{kt_a}{2} = kRC\,(1 - e^{-t_a/RC}) \qquad (2.27)$$

This is a transcendental equation where t_a/RC, evaluated graphically or by successive approximations, has the value of 1.5933.

2.9 From a Ramp to a Step Voltage

Consider an applied voltage to an RC series circuit that is a ramp voltage until a limiting voltage of E is reached at time t_1. Further, consider a family of input voltages with different slopes for the ramp voltage, as indicated in Figure 2.8. Then, a plot of the family of curves for the resistor voltage is represented in Figure 2.9. The locus of this family of v_R curves, as the ramp voltage converges to a step voltage, is of particular interest. The slope of the ramp voltage, which can have different values, is

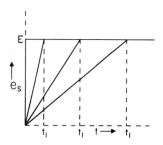

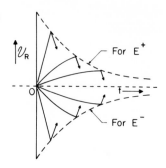

Fig. 2.8. Ramp voltages with limiting value of E at time t_1. See Figure 2.9.

Fig. 2.9. Locus (dashed line) of V_{R1}. See Equation (2.29).

$$k = \frac{E}{t_1} \qquad (2.28)$$

The resistor voltage at the instant of t_1 when the ramp voltage arrives at E, is expressed by

$$\begin{aligned} v_{R1} &= kRC\,(1 - e^{-t_1/RC}) \\ &= \frac{ERC}{t_1}(1 - e^{-t_1/RC}) \end{aligned} \qquad (2.29)$$

which is the locus of V_{R1} as represented in Figure 2.9.

An examination of Equation (2.29) which is of the form

$$y = \frac{1 - e^{-x}}{x} \qquad (2.30)$$

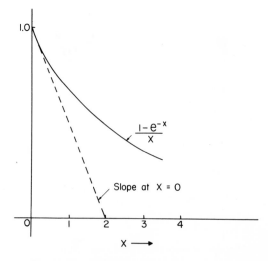

Fig. 2.10. A graphical study of $(1 - e^{-x})/x$.

reveals that V_{R1} is equal to E when t_1 is zero. Also, the slope of the locus when t_1 is zero, is $-E/2RC$. These facts are shown in Figure 2.10 but with reference to Equation (2.30).

2.10   The Problems

The circuit problems, Problem 2.9 through Problem 2.20, have single time-constant exponentials involved in their solutions. It is very important to develop an ability to solve such circuits with ease. There is no need to use differential equations, operational calculus, or LaPlace transforms to obtain a solution. The form of the solution is identical for each circuit. For each switch position there is an exponential of the form represented by Equation (2.1). The E_{as} and τ_c values are easily determined by applying Thevenin's theorem for each switch position, if necessary. Except for a circuit like the one in Problem 2.19, applying Thevenin's theorem reduces the circuit (for each switch position) to a simple series circuit. For example, v_o in the circuit of Problem 2.11 has an E_{as} value of zero with the switches in position 1 and a value of 35.5 volts with the switches in position 2. The τ_c values are 400 μs and 44.4 μs, respectively.

The initial voltage E_o for each exponential is also easily determined for the conditions given in each of these circuit problems. The given conditions for each circuit allow an exponential to be completed, practically, in at least one of the switch positions. This means that all voltages in a circuit are known for at least one instant of time, simply by comparing time constants and time intervals. A starting point for evaluating a steady state cycle of operation is thereby provided. Returning to the circuit of Problem 2.11, v_o has the final value of 35.5 volts at the end of time T_2. So, initially in the time interval T_1, v_o has the value of -64.5 volts. At the end of time T_1, v_o is -23.7 volts. Initially, in time T_2, v_o is 76.3 volts.

The circuit of Problem 2.19 is different from the other circuit problems in that it has two capacitors rather than one capacitor. Thevenin's theorem is not conveniently applicable to the solution of this circuit, but, it should be recognized that the circuit has a single time-constant solution. Let the driving voltages go to zero and observe that the four circuit parameters are all in parallel. With the driving voltages present, the E_{as} values are determined by the resistance network. The applied step voltages are attenuated at the output by the capacitance network. Evaluate the circuit by any familiar procedure and these facts are found to be true. The form of the solution will contain exponentials of the form represented by Equation (2.1). For the actual values given on the circuit of Problem 2.19, the applied step voltage is 150 volts. The magnitude of the step at v_o is 75 volts, since the two capacitances are equal. The two E_{as} values for v_o are 33.3 volts and -16.7 volts, which are realizable final values for v_o in the two switch positions. The 75-volt steps on v_o are measured from these two values for v_o that exist immediately before switching.

PROBLEMS

2.1 For $\tau_c = 100 \ \mu s$ and $t = 200 \ \mu s$, evaluate v of Equation (2.1) if
  (a) $E_{as} = \quad 0, \qquad E_o = -100$ volts.
  (b) $E_{as} = \quad 50, \qquad E_o = -50$
  (c) $E_{as} = 100, \qquad E_o = 0$
  (d) $E_{as} = 120, \qquad E_o = 20$

2.2 Repeat Problem 2.1 with E_{as} and E_o of the opposite polarity.

2.3 For $\tau_c = 500 \ \mu s$, $E_{as} = 300$ and $E_o = -100$, evaluate v of Equation (2.1) if
  (a) $t = 100 \ \mu s$.
  (b) $t = 50 \ \mu s$.
  (c) $t = 10 \ \mu s$.

2.4 A voltage increases from zero exponentially [See equation (2.1)]. At 150 volts, the per unit slope deviation is 0.01. What is the E_{as} value of the exponetial?

2.5 For $\tau_c = 400 \ \mu s$, $E_o = -170$, and $E_{as} = 300$ volts. Find t, on the exponential, for $v = -20$ volts.

2.6 Repeat Problem 2.5 for $\tau_c = 100 \ \mu s$.

2.7 Repeat Problem 2.5 for $\tau_c = 20 \ \mu s$.

2.8 For the exponential of Problem 2.5; find $t_2 - t_1$ if $E_2 = -10$, and $E_1 = -20$ volts.

2.9–2.20 Plot a steady-state cycle for each indicated voltage in each of the circuits in Figures P2.9 through P2.20. The times T_1 and T_2 are the time intervals that each switch is in the indicated positions 1 and 2. The switching cycle is repetitive and the switching times, between positions, are instantaneous. For each waveform indicate all significant voltages, time intervals, and time constants.

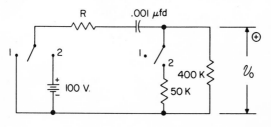

Fig. P2.9.
$T_1 = T_2. = 400 \ \mu s$.
(a) $R = 0$. (b) $R = 10$ K.

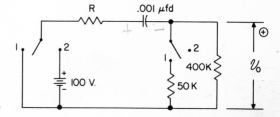

Fig. P2.10.
$T_1 = T_2 = 400 \ \mu s$.
(a) $R = 0$. (b) $R = 10$ K.

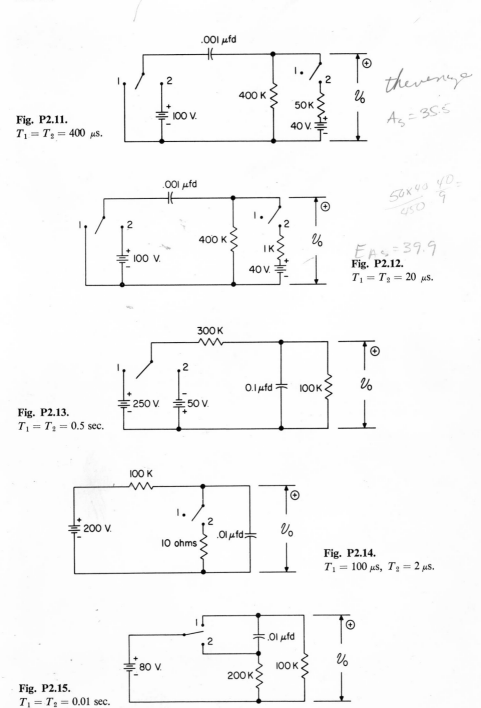

Fig. P2.11.
$T_1 = T_2 = 400 \ \mu s.$

thevenye
$A_s = 35.5$

$\frac{50 \times 40}{450} = \frac{40}{9} =$

$E_{As} = 39.9$

Fig. P2.12.
$T_1 = T_2 = 20 \ \mu s.$

Fig. P2.13.
$T_1 = T_2 = 0.5 \ sec.$

Fig. P2.14.
$T_1 = 100 \ \mu s, \ T_2 = 2 \ \mu s.$

Fig. P2.15.
$T_1 = T_2 = 0.01 \ sec.$

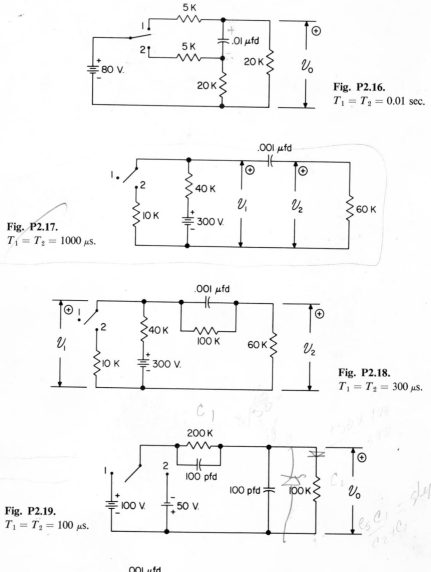

Fig. P2.16.
$T_1 = T_2 = 0.01$ sec.

Fig. P2.17.
$T_1 = T_2 = 1000\ \mu s.$

Fig. P2.18.
$T_1 = T_2 = 300\ \mu s.$

Fig. P2.19.
$T_1 = T_2 = 100\ \mu s.$

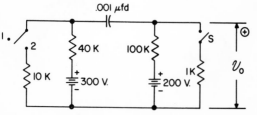

Fig. P2.20.
$T_1 = T_2 = 200\ \mu s$ and the
switch S is closed only if
v_o is positive.

3

Resistance Switching
in RC Circuits

3.1 General Discussion

Many electronic switching and pulse-shaping circuits use RC coupling in order to obtain the responses that are required. A simplified circuit representation of RC coupling from a source to a load is shown in Figure 3.1. In this figure, R_o of the source and R_{in} of the load are indicated as variables. Actually, R_o and R_{in} of switching and pulse shaping circuits are usually variable in the sense that they are multivalued, having two or more different values for each cycle of operation. They are not continuously variable as a function of time, for ideal operation. They are resistances that *switch* from one value to another.

Later chapters will describe or assume the use of electronic devices in performing the automatic switching functions that are required in many measurement and control systems. The studies of the later chapters will be enhanced, however, with a general study of the responses that are possible with resistance switching in RC circuits.

Resistance switching in the circuits of this chapter is presented under *defined* conditions. The absence of electronic devices

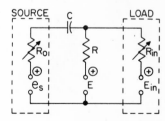

Fig. 3.1. An RC-coupled circuit in which R_o of the source and R_{in} of the load are not constants.

25

will permit the student to concentrate on the details of analysis and on the responses of a circuit, without the added burden of being required to know the properties and characteristics of a particular electronic device that might be used to perform the defined switching operations. The techniques of analysis that are learned in this chapter are very often repeated in the analysis of circuits, with electronic devices, in the later chapters.

The driving voltages of this chapter are of three types: rectangular, sinusoidal and trapezoidal.

3.2 A Periodic Rectangular Wave Source Voltage

Several interesting facts can be discovered about the circuit of Figure 3.2 by representing the source voltage, e_s, as a periodic rectangular wave and by letting R take on either of two values, R_a or R_b. The resistance is defined as R_a when the current, i, has positive instantaneous values and as R_b when the current has negative instantaneous values. Positive currents result in a positive change of voltage on the capacitor while negative currents result in a negative change of voltage on the capacitor. This is significant in that it is the key to establishing a general method of analysis. For any periodic waveform of e_s (a periodic rectangular wave is assumed for the studies of this section) the capacitor voltage, for steady state conditions, will vary between the same upper and lower limits in each cycle.

A possible waveform for v_o, when e_s is a periodic rectangular wave, is illustrated in Figure 3.3. The zero voltage reference for e_s is not shown to emphasize that the zero level for v_o is independent of the zero level for e_s. All that is known for the moment, using subscripts a and b as defined in the

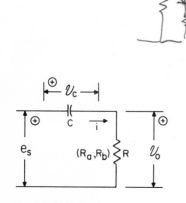

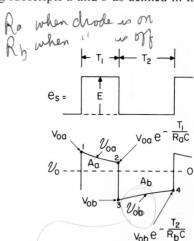

Fig. 3.2. RC circuit.
$R = R_a$ if i is positive.
$R = R_b$ if i is negative.

Fig. 3.3. e_s and v_o for the circuit in Figure 3.2.

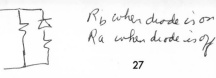
R_b when diode is on
R_a when diode is off

preceding paragraph (subscript a if i is positive and subscript b if i is negative) is

$$\Delta v_{ca} = - \Delta v_{cb} \tag{3.1}$$

which states that the positive change of capacitor voltage is equal to the negative change of the capacitor voltage in each steady state cycle. The actual upper and lower limits of the capacitor voltage have no importance for the present.

Referring to the notations of Figure 3.3, the positive change of capacitor voltage is expressed in various forms as follows:

$$\Delta v_{ca} = \frac{1}{C} \int \frac{v_{oa}}{R_a} \, dt \tag{3.2}$$

$$= \frac{1}{R_a C} \int_o^{T_1} V_{oa} \, e^{-t/R_a C} \, dt \tag{3.3}$$

$$= \frac{\text{Area } A_a}{R_a C} \tag{3.4}$$

$$= V_{oa} (1 - e^{-T_1/R_a C}) \tag{3.5}$$

Equation (3.4) is true for any periodic waveform, while Equation (3.5) is true only for the indicated rectangular wave of input voltage. Two corresponding equations for the negative change of capacitor voltage are

$$\Delta v_{cb} = \frac{\text{Area } A_b}{R_b C} \tag{3.6}$$

$$= V_{ob} (1 - e^{-T_2/R_b C}) \tag{3.7}$$

Consequently, recalling Equation (3.1), the area ratio is

$$\frac{A_a}{A_b} = - \frac{R_a}{R_b} \tag{3.8}$$

Further, the ratio of the positive to negative peak values of the output voltage is

you can make V_{oa} large by making denominator small or num large for small

$$-\frac{V_{oa}}{V_{ob}} = \frac{1 - e^{-T_2/R_b C}}{1 - e^{-T_1/R_a C}} \tag{3.9}$$

Equation (3.8) is true for any periodic waveform of e_s, but Equation (3.9) results only if e_s is a periodic rectangular wave. Other source voltage waveforms are considered later in the chapter. The output voltage waveform is easily evaluated from Equation (3.9) since it is known that the step in voltage from point 2 to point 3 (see Figure 3.3) has the magnitude of E, a *given* value on the source voltage. Thus, all significant points on the output voltage waveform can be expressed in terms of one unknown, either V_{oa} or V_{ob}.

Several interesting facts are observed from a study of Equations (3.8) and (3.9). These are itemized for ease of reference in later studies, as follows:

(a)   The output voltage averages to zero only if the circuit is linear; i.e., $R_a = R_b = R$.

(b)   The positive and negative changes of v_o are equal in magnitude. See Equation (3.9).

(c)   The output voltage, v_o, has equal positive and negative maximum values ($V_{oa} = V_{ob}$) provided

$$R_a T_2 = R_b T_1 \qquad\qquad (3.10)$$

or provided

$$T_2 \gg R_b C \quad \text{and} \quad T_1 \gg R_a C \qquad\qquad (3.11)$$

(d)   The positive and negative maximum values of v_o have the approximate ratio,

$$\frac{V_{oa}}{V_{ob}} \cong - \frac{R_a T_2}{R_b T_1} \qquad\qquad (3.12)$$

provided $T_1 \ll R_a C$ and $T_2 \ll R_b C$.

(e)   Also,

$$\frac{V_{oa}}{V_{ob}} \cong - \frac{R_a C}{T_1} \qquad\qquad (3.13)$$

provided $T_1 \ll R_a C$ and $T_2 \gg R_b C$.

(f)   Further,

$$\frac{V_{oa}}{V_{ob}} \cong - \frac{T_2}{R_b C} \qquad\qquad (3.14)$$

provided $T_2 \ll R_b C$ and $T_1 \gg R_a C$.

(g)   The output voltage waveform approximates a rectangular wave, nearly identical to the source voltage, if any of the conditions of (d), (e), or (f) are satisfied. The d-c levels, of course, may not be the same.

These relationships of V_{oa} and V_{ob} are helpful in understanding many types of pulsing and waveshaping circuits. As one simple illustration, a clamping circuit (discussed in more detail in Chapter 4, where a circuit using diodes is described) serves the function of clamping positive or negative peak values of voltage waveforms to a desired voltage level. This means that (still referring to Figure 3.3) it is desirable to make the V_{oa}/V_{ob} ratio either small or large. The manner in which this clamping action depends on the V_{oa}/V_{ob} ratio is illustrated with a numerical example. Let us assume that a solution for the output voltage waveform gives

$$V_{oa} = - 0.01\, V_{ob}$$

Then, for a 100 volt step (E of Figure 3.3),

$$V_{oa} = 100 + V_{ob}$$

provided that the circuit parameters are such as to make the output voltage waveform approximate the rectangular wave of the source. Thus, V_{oa} is approximately equal to one volt and V_{ob} is approximately equal to 99 volts. Even with a larger step voltage of 200 volts, V_{oa} still has a small value of two volts. Consequently, the positive peaks of the source voltage are nearly clamped to zero volts for the given V_{oa}/V_{ob} ratio, independent of the d-c level of the source.

3.3 Effect of Source Output Resistance

The output resistance of a source is represented as R_o in Figure 3.4a. The circuit is rearranged in Figure 3.4b in order to represent the voltage v_o' as the sum of the voltages across R_o and R. This permits an evaluation of the voltage v_o' by the same procedure that was explained in the preceding section for a rectangular wave of source voltage. Appropriate attenuation factors are then easily applied to evaluate the desired output voltage v_o. For a linear circuit, the presence of R_o does not create any particular problem of solution for the circuit. The situation is somewhat different, however, when the circuit parameters take on different values during each cycle of the source voltage.

A rectangular wave of source voltage is again selected to explain the effect of the source resistance on the output voltage. The subscripts a and b are again used in the same manner as defined in the preceding section. To include the possibility of the source resistance having two values, R_{oa} and R_{ob} are assigned for R_o. Then defining R_a' and R_b' as,

$$R_a' = R_{oa} + R_a$$
$$R_b' = R_{ob} + R_b$$

$$(3.15)$$

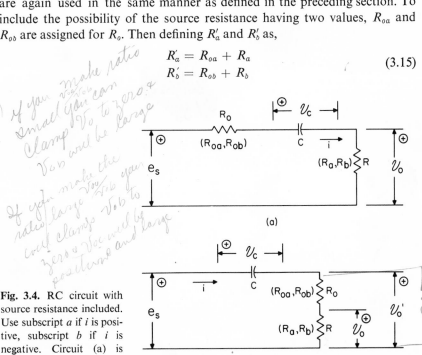

If you make ratio
small you can
clamp V_o to zero &
V_{ob} will be large

If you make the
ratio large you
will clamp V_{ob} to
zero & V_{oc} will be
positive and large

Fig. 3.4. RC circuit with source resistance included. Use subscript a if i is positive, subscript b if i is negative. Circuit (a) is rearranged in (b).

and recalling Equation (3.9), the ratio of the positive to the negative peak values of v_o' is

$$\frac{V_{oa}'}{V_{ob}'} = -\frac{1 - e^{-T_2/R_b'C}}{1 - e^{-T_1/R_a'C}} \tag{3.16}$$

The voltage v_o' is easily evaluated since the steps on v_o' (not on v_o) have the magnitude of the steps on the source voltage. To evaluate v_o, the resistance ratios applicable to the two time intervals of T_1 and T_2 will convert v_o' to v_o. For each value of v_{oa}' and v_{ob}',

$$v_{oa} = v_{oa}' \frac{R_a}{R_a'} \tag{3.17}$$

$$v_{ob} = v_{ob}' \frac{R_b}{R_b'} \tag{3.18}$$

EXAMPLE

Given: the source voltage is a square wave with the limiting voltages of 200 volts and 40 volts.

R_{oa} (when the source is at 200 volts) = 40 K.

R_{ob} (when the source is at 40 volts)   = 8 K.

R = 100 K and is constant.

C = 0.001 μfd.

The time intervals of the source T_1 and T_2 are 200 μs each. (See Figure 3.3 for definition of T_1 and T_2).

Determine: the problem is to plot a steady state cycle of the output voltage.

Solution:

$$e^{-T_1/R_a'C} = e^{-200/140} = 0.24$$

$$e^{-T_2/R_b'C} = e^{-200/108} = 0.157$$

$$\frac{V_{oa}'}{V_{ob}'} = -\frac{1 - 0.157}{1 - 0.24} = -1.11$$

$$0.24\, V_{oa}' - V_{ob}' = 200 - 40 = 160$$

$$0.24\, V_{oa}' + 0.9\, V_{oa}' = 160$$

$$V_{oa}' = 140 \text{ volts}$$

$$V_{ob}' = -0.9 \times 140 = -126 \text{ volts}$$

$$V_{oa} = 140\, \frac{100 \text{ K}}{140 \text{ K}} = 100 \text{ volts}$$

$$0.24\, V_{oa} = 24 \text{ volts}$$

$$V_{ob} = -126\, \frac{100 \text{ K}}{108 \text{ K}} = -117 \text{ volts}$$

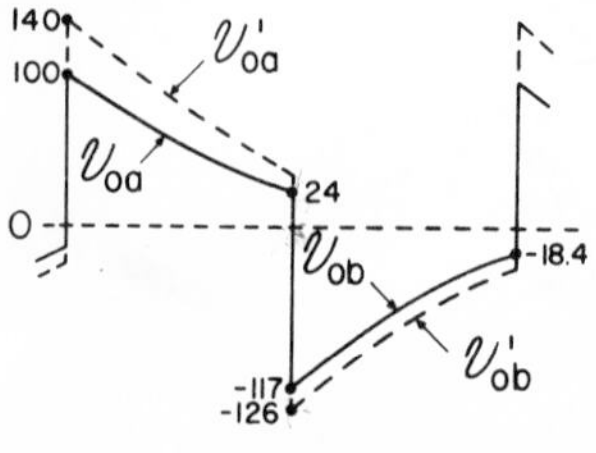

Fig. 3.5. Representation of v_o and v_o' for example in Section 3.3.

$$0.157\, V_{ob} = 0.157\,(-117) = -18.4 \text{ volts}$$

Results: The results and the last six voltages are indicated on Figure 3.5.

3.4 A Sinusoidal Source Voltage

When a sinusoidal voltage, e_s, is applied to the RC circuit in Figure 3.4, the voltage v_o' is also a sinusoidal voltage, even when the circuit is nonlinear, provided that the capacitor voltage is a constant. Why must the capacitor voltage be a constant voltage to make the preceding statement true? From Figure 3.4b, observe that $v_o' = e_s - v_c$. If v_c is a constant, the waveform for v_o' is identical, in shape, to the waveform for e_s, differing only by the d-c constant voltage on the capacitor. This is not necessarily true for the voltage across either R or R_o alone. A sinusoidal voltage for v_o', assuming a large capacitance, is represented as Figure 3.6a. The subscripts a and b for the areas, resistors, and voltages are used in the manner defined in the preceding sections.

The area ratio, A_a'/A_b', is equal to the negative of the resistance ratio R_a'/R_b'. See Equations (3.8) and (3.15). Expressions for the two areas and their ratios are now developed.

Referring to Figure 3.6a,

$$v_o' = E_m\,(\cos \omega t - \cos \theta_1) \qquad\qquad (3.19)$$

$$A_a' = E_m \int_{-\theta_1}^{\theta_1} (\cos \omega t - \cos \theta_1)\, d\omega t$$

$$= 2E_m\,(\sin \theta_1 - \theta_1 \cos \theta_1) \qquad (3.20)$$

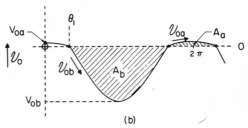

(a)

(b)

Fig. 3.6. (a) For calculating area ratios of a sinusoidal voltage. (b) Clipping effect because of R_o, Figure 3.4.

$$A_b' = E_m \int_{\theta_1}^{2\pi - \theta_1} (\cos \omega t - \cos \theta_1)\, d\omega t$$

$$= -2E_m[\sin \theta_1 + (\pi - \theta_1) \cos \theta_1] \tag{3.21}$$

$$\frac{A_a'}{A_b'} = -\frac{\sin \theta_1 - \theta_1 \cos \theta_1}{\sin \theta_1 + (\pi - \theta_1) \cos \theta_1} \tag{3.22}$$

$$= -\frac{\tan \theta_1 - \theta_1}{\tan \theta_1 - \theta_1 + \pi} \tag{3.23}$$

$$\frac{A_b'}{A_a'} = -\left(1 + \frac{\pi}{\tan \theta_1 - \theta_1}\right) \tag{3.24}$$

A graph of Equation (3.24) is given in Figure 3.7 for a range of values of θ_1 from 6° to 90°. The area ratio for selected values of θ_1 is given in Table 3.1. The graph, or the table of values, is a convenient aid in evaluating v_o' for

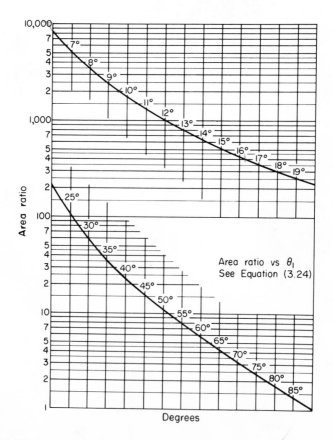

Fig. 3.7. Area ratio as a function of θ_1 for a sinusoid. See Equation (3.24) and Figure 3.6(a).

the RC circuit in Figure 3.4b when the source voltage is sinusoidal. Equation (3.24) is not too difficult to evaluate provided that θ_1 is not a small angle, for example, less than 20°.

TABLE   3.1 AREA RATIOS FOR A SINUSOIDAL FUNCTION*

θ_1 (degrees)	A_b'/A_a'	θ_1 (degrees)	A_b'/A_a'
7	5134	20	212
8	3452	30	60
9	2418	40	23.3
10	1746	50	11.2
11	1316	60	5.59
12	1008	70	3.07
13	790	80	1.74
14	632	88	1.11
15	510	90	1.00
17	349		

Note: The area ratio is approximated by $3\pi/\theta^3$, for angles less than 7°.
*See Equation (3.24) and Figure 3.6a.

To apply the information of this section to a practical problem, it is essential to know the value of θ_1 only, in order to evaluate the voltage v_o' of Equation (3.19). With reference to the circuit of Figure 3.4, if the voltage v_o' is specified, then θ_1 is known and a particular resistance ratio R_b'/R_a' must exist for the circuit to make the given condition for v_o' true. The circuit can then be designed for the desired result for v_o'. It should be understood, however, that merely determining a resistance ratio is not sufficient. The condition established for this discussion, in which the capacitor voltage is essentially constant, dictates a consideration for the magnitude of resistances in the circuit as well as a consideration for the magnitude of the capacitance.

Another type of practical problem is one in which the circuit is specified as to the magnitude of the resistances of Figure 3.4. The problem, then, is to evaluate v_o' of Equation (3.19). This is easily accomplished with the aid of the graph of Figure 3.7 or from the table of area ratios. Since the resistance ratio is known, the area ratio is also known and θ_1 is read on the graph or in the table of area ratios. The particular expression for v_o' is now known.

Now we can examine the voltage v_o of Figure 3.4, as represented in Figure 3.6b. By designating the positive going portion of v_o' as v_{oa}' and the negative going portion as v_{ob}', (that is, the subscripts a and b are used as previously defined), then the corresponding two portions of v_o are,

$$v_{oa} = \frac{v_{oa}' R_a}{R_o + R_a}$$

$$v_{ob} = \frac{v_{ob}' R_b}{R_o + R_b}$$

The possible clipping effect, because of the presence of R_o, is demonstrated in Figure 3.6b.

3.5   A Trapezoidal Source Voltage (Linear Circuit)

A trapezoidal source voltage, of the form shown in Figure 3.8a, is now considered for the circuit in Figure 3.4. A linear circuit is assumed for the discussion of this section. The problem is to evaluate the output voltage waveform for v_0. The sum of the resistance R_o and R is designated as R', as before. Also, the subscripts a and b are again used with the same singificance as in the preceding sections. The notations V'_{oa} and V'_{ob} designate the positive and negative peak values, respectively, of the voltage v'_o across R'. The source voltage is assumed symmetrical as shown in Figure 3.8a; with this assumption,

$$V'_{oa} = - V'_{ob} \qquad (3.25)$$

Two of the significant values of v'_o, at the end of the time intervals T_2 and T_3, are expressed with V'_{oa} as reference according to Equations (3.26) and (3.29). At the end of the time interval T_2,

$$v'_o = V'_{oa}\, e^{-T_2/R'C} \qquad (3.26)$$

which is also the initial voltage for the time interval T_3. Since the asymp-

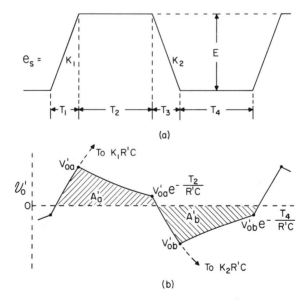

(a)

(b)

Fig. 3.8. Trapezoidal source voltage (a) and voltage v'_o (b), for the circuit in Figure 3.4 with constant parameters.

totical value for the T_3 interval is $K_2 R'C$, then at the end of the T_3 interval the value of v'_o is expressed as,

$$v'_o = V'_{ob} = K_2 R'C - (K_2 R'C - V'_{oa} e^{-T_2/R'C}) e^{-T_3/R'C} \qquad (3.27)$$

However

$$K_2 = -\frac{E}{T_3} \qquad (3.28)$$

which, when substituted in Equation (3.27), with the terms rearranged for ease of interpretation, gives

$$V'_{ob} = V'_{oa} e^{-(T_2+T_3)/R'C} - \frac{ER'C}{T_3}(1 - e^{-T_3/R'C}) \qquad (3.29)$$

Combining with Equation (3.25), the negative peak voltage for v'_o is

$$V'_{ob} = -\frac{ER'C}{T_3} \frac{1 - e^{-T_3/R'C}}{1 + e^{-(T_2+T_3)/R'C}} \qquad (3.30)$$

Sufficient information is now available to determine the graph for the voltage v'_o. To obtain the output voltage v_o (across R), multiply v'_o by the attenuation factor of $R/(R + R_o)$.

Since Equation (3.30) is developed for a linear circuit and a symmetrical source voltage ($T_1 = T_3$, and $T_2 = T_4$), then the equation reduces to the approximation

$$V'_{ob} \cong -\frac{E}{1 + e^{-(T_2+T_3)/R'C}} \qquad (3.31)$$

for small $T_3/R'C$ (also $T_1/R'C$) ratios.

Further, as the trapezoidal input voltage waveform approaches the limit of a square wave ($T_1 = T_3 = 0$), Equation (3.30) reduces exactly to

$$V'_{ob} = -\frac{E}{1 + e^{-T_2/R'C}} \qquad (3.32)$$

An output voltage waveform somewhat different than the one of Figure 3.8b, is illustrated below with a numerical example. Data for the trapezoidal source voltage is given in Figure 3.9a. With the circuit having an R_o value of 20 K, R of 80 K and the capacitance having a value of 0.001 μfd, the output voltage (v_o across R) is as indicated in Figure 3.9b. The circuit parameters and the time intervals of the source voltage, as selected, cause the output voltage to return to zero twice during each cycle to generate short positive and negative pulses. The peak values of the output voltage waveform are,

$$V_{oa} = -V_{ob} = K_1 R'C(1 - e^{-T_1/R'C})\frac{R}{R + R_o} \qquad (3.33)$$

$$= (1)(100)(1 - e^{-1})(0.8)$$

$$= 50.6 \text{ volts}$$

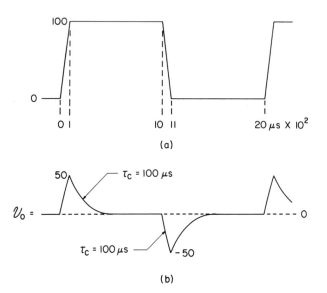

Fig. 3.9. Source voltage e_s and output voltage v_o for numerical example in Section 3.5.

With steeper leading and trailing edges for the source voltage, the output peak values are greater than 50.6 volts. The limiting value for a square wave with the same peak-to-peak voltage is 80 volts for the given circuit. This numerical example serves to illustrate the importance of the steepness of the leading and trailing edges of the trapezoidal source voltage.

3.6   A Trapezoidal Source Voltage (Resistance Switching)

For the discussion of this section, the circuit of Figure 3.4 is regarded as a nonlinear circuit in which R has either of two values, R_a (when i is positive) and R_b (when i is negative). The source resistance is regarded as a constant. The source voltage is a symmetrical trapezoidal voltage, as indicated on Figure 3.10a, with the significant time intervals of T_1, T_2, T_3, and T_4. These four time intervals are not identified in the same order as in Figure 3.8a. The reason for this particular order of identification will soon become apparent.

There are three conditions of circuit operation that need to be considered for the nonlinear circuit with a source voltage that is trapezoidal. Since the particular condition of circuit operation influences the method of analysis, each of the three conditions are stated and discussed in some detail.

(*a*)   *First condition.*   The first condition of circuit operation is one in which the capacitor voltage and the source voltage are known to have the same instantaneous values at least once in each steady state cycle of operation.

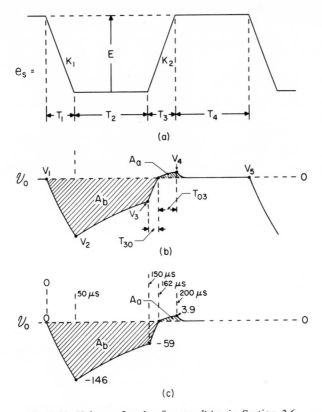

Fig. 3.10. Voltages for the *first condition* in Section 3.6.

If this happens, the output voltage is also known at this instant and the remaining evaluation for v_o is simplified considerably. To cause this first condition of circuit operation to exist, the circuit must exhibit a sufficiently small time-constant for at least one of the four significant time intervals of the source voltage. The procedure of analysis follows.

Referring to the circuit of Figure 3.4 and the source voltage representation of Figure 3.10a, it is assumed that $(R_o + R_a) C$ is much less than the time interval T_4. Thus the capacitor voltage is equal to the source voltage at the end of this time interval. This also means that the output voltage v_o is zero at the end of the time interval T_4 or at the beginning of time interval T_1. This significant point on the output voltage is designated as V_1 on Figure 3.10b. Now, since there is a known value at which to start, the voltages at other significant points on a steady state cycle of output voltage can be evaluated. These points are represented by V_2, V_3, V_4, and V_5 on Figure 3.10b. Since the output voltage will pass through zero (negative to positive) at some time during the T_3 interval of the surce voltage, the notations T_{30} and T_{03} are needed to help define the output voltage. These two time intervals are also represented on Figure 3.10b. Knowing that V_1 is zero, then

$$V_2 = K_1 R_b' C \, (1 - e^{-T_1/R_b'C}) \, R_b/R_b'$$

$$= - \frac{ER_b C}{T_1} (1 - e^{-T_1/R_b'C}) \tag{3.34}$$

where $R_b' = R_o + R_b$, and E is the peak-to-peak voltage (lower voltage to upper voltage) of the source voltage.

With V_2 evaluated, information is available for determining the next significant voltage, V_3. Thus,

$$V_3 = V_2 \, e^{-T_2/R_b'C} \tag{3.35}$$

Notice that the exponetial has the asymptotical value of zero during the T_2 interval, for the given circuit.

There are two significant exponentials during the T_3 time interval of the source voltage, one in which R_b (v_o negative) is in the circuit and one in which the circuit contains R_a (v_o positive). As previously indicated, these two time intervals are T_{30} and T_{03} respectively. The next problem, then, is to evaluate T_{30}. Thus,

$$T_{30} = R_b' C \ln \frac{K_2 R_b C - V_3}{K_2 R_b C - 0} \tag{3.36}$$

where K_2 is E/T_3. [If Equation (3.36) is not clear to you, refer to section 2.6 on the calculation of time intervals in an exponential.]

The time interval T_{03} is now known, since

$$T_{03} = T_3 - T_{30} \tag{3.37}$$

Finally,

$$V_4 = K_2 R_a C \, (1 - e^{-T_{03}/R_b'C}) \tag{3.38}$$

and the output voltage is completely identified. A little work is necessary, but the solution is not difficult. A numerical solution of a circuit problem will illustrate the procedure more clearly.

EXAMPLE 1

Given:

$R_o =$	10 K	$T_1 =$	50 μs
$R_a =$	1 K	$T_2 =$	100 μs
$R_b =$	100 K	$T_3 =$	50 μs
$C =$	0.001 μfd	$T_4 =$	100 μs

The source voltage has the limiting values of 50 and 250 volts.

Determine: significant voltages and time intervals to completely describe the output voltage.

Solution (evaluation of needed quantities):

$$K_1 = \frac{-E}{T_1} = -\frac{200}{50} = -4 \text{ volts}/\mu s$$

$$K_2 = -K_1 = 4 \text{ volts}/\mu s$$

$$K_1 R_b C = -400 \text{ volts}$$

$$K_2 R_a C = 4 \text{ volts}$$

$$K_2 R_b C = 400 \text{ volts}$$

$$R_b' C = 110 \ \mu s \qquad\qquad T_1/R_b' C = 0.454$$

$$R_a' C = 11 \ \mu s \qquad\qquad T_2/R_b' C = 0.909$$

The significant voltages and time intervals (Notice that $R_a'C$ is much less than the time interval T_4):

$$V_1 = V_5 = 0$$

$$V_2 = -400 \, (1 - e^{-0.454}) = -146 \text{ volts}$$

$$V_3 = -146 \, e^{-0.909} = -59 \text{ volts}$$

$$T_{30} = 110 \ln \frac{400 - (-59)}{400} = 12 \ \mu s$$

$$T_{03} = 50 - 12 = 38 \ \mu s$$

$$\left(\frac{T_{03}}{R_a'C} = 38/11 = 3.45 \right)$$

$$V_4 = 4 \, (1 - e^{-3.45}) = 3.9 \text{ volts}$$

Results: the results are indicated in Figure 3.10c.

(b) *Second Condition.* The second condition under which the circuit could operate is one in which the capacitor voltage is essentially constant as a function of time. The procedure of analysis, in this case, is to make use of the known area ratios. This procedure is particularly desirable here, since the voltage v_o' (see Figure 3.11b) can be assumed identical to the source voltage except for the d-c voltage level. Such an assumption is not possible for the first condition of operation.

In the preceding example, it is true that the positive area, A_a, and the negative area, A_b, have the ratio of $1/100$ since the R_a/R_b ratio is $1/100$. It would be very difficult, however, to use this information in evaluating the response of the circuit where given values satisfy the first condition as represented by that example.

However, if the capacitor voltage is essentially constant as a function

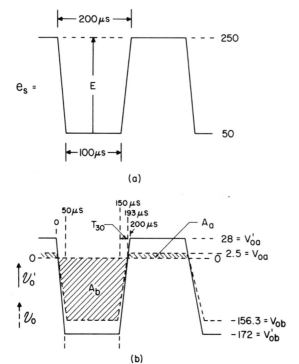

Fig. 3.11. Illustration for *second condition* in Section 3.6.

of time, the procedure of the preceding example will then become difficult. The area ratio procedure is preferred. The procedure is illustrated with numerical quantities in the example that follows.

EXAMPLE 2

Given: The given values of Example 1 are selected, except the capacitance is chosen to be sufficiently large so that its voltage is essentially constant as a function of time. According to the voltage references on the circuit of Figure 3.4,

$$v_o' = e_s - V_c \qquad (3.39)$$

With the capacitor voltage, V_c, constant, v_o' differs from e_s only by this constant voltage.

Determine: the problem is to determine the positive and negative peak values, V_{oa} and V_{ob}, of the output voltage v_o.

Solution: the procedure is somewhat simplified by first calculating

V'_{oa} and V'_{ob} of the voltage v'_o and then applying appropriate resistance ratios to convert from v'_o to v_o. (See Figure 3.11.) Now, the positive to negative area ratio for v'_o is

$$\frac{A'_a}{A'_b} = \frac{-R'_a}{R'_b} = \frac{-(R_o + R_a)}{(R_o + R_b)} = -0.1$$

To further simplify the numerics of the solution, let $100\mu s$ equal 1.0 unit of time. Then, from the geometry of Figure 3.11b and with the T_{30} and T_{03} notations the same as in Example 1, the positive area for v'_o is

$$A'_a = V'_{oa} + (0.5 - T_{30}) V'_{oa} = V'_{oa} (1.5 - T_{30})$$

The negative area for v'_o is

$$A'_b = V'_{ob} (1 + T_{30})$$

From the geometry of the graph, it is also observed that

$$\frac{V'_{oa}}{V'_{ob}} = \frac{-(0.5 - T_{30})}{T_{30}}$$

The three preceding relationships make it possible to express the area ratio in terms of the time interval T_{30}. Since the area ratio is known to be -0.1,

$$\frac{A'_a}{A'_b} = -0.1 = -\frac{(0.5 - T_{30})(1.5 - T_{30})}{T_{30}(1 + T_{30})}$$

The resulting quadratic equation yields $43\,\mu s$ for the time interval T_{30}.

Finally, the positive and negative peak voltage for v'_o and v_o are,

$$V'_{oa} = 2E(0.5 - T_{30}) = 2(200)(0.5 - 0.43) = 28 \text{ volts}$$

$$V'_{ob} = V'_{oa} - E = 28 - 200 = -172 \text{ volts}$$

$$V_{oa} = \frac{V'_{oa} R_a}{R_o + R_a} = \frac{28}{11} = 2.5 \text{ volts}$$

$$V_{ob} = \frac{V'_{ob} R_b}{R_o + R_b} = -172 \times \frac{100}{110} = -156.3 \text{ volts}$$

Results: the results are indicated on Figure 3.11b.

(c) *Third condition.* The third condition of operation, for a trapezoidal source voltage and the circuit of Figure 3.4, is one in which the capacitor voltage is not constant nor is the capacitor voltage equal to the source voltage at any instant. A circuit problem in which this third condition applies is the most difficult to solve. The circuit response is best determined by assuming a particular value of capacitor voltage at a particular instant of time and proceeding with the calculations as a function of time until steady state values are obtained for the output voltage. Any other procedure will lead to transcendental equations and a tedious graphical or iterative solution.

PROBLEMS

3.1 For the circuit of Figure 3.2 and e_s of Figure 3.3: $R_a = 10$ K, $R_b = 100$ K, $C = 0.01 \mu\text{fd}$ and $E = 100$ volts. Evaluate v_o, indicating all significant quantities, for each of the following:

(a) $T_1 = 500 \ \mu s$, $T_2 = 1000 \ \mu s$
(b) $T_1 = 100 \ \mu s$, $T_2 = 500 \ \mu s$
(c) $T_1 = 5 \ \mu s$, $T_2 = 10 \ \mu s$
(d) $T_1 = 100 \ \mu s$, $T_2 = 50 \ \mu s$
(e) $T_1 = 10 \ \mu s$, $T_2 = 5 \ \mu s$

3.2 Repeat (a), (b), (c), and (d) of Problem 3.1 with $R_a = 100$ K, and $R_b = 10$ K.

3.3 For the circuit in Figure 3.4 and e_s in Figure 3.3, $R_a = 0.1$ K, $R_b = 1$ Meg., $R_{oa} = 50$ K, $R_{ob} = 7$ K, $C = 0.001 \ \mu\text{fd}$, $E = 250$ volts, $T_1 = 300 \ \mu s$, and $T_2 = 2000 \ \mu s$. Evaluate v_o, indicating all significant quantities.

3.4 For the circuit in Figure 3.4 and e_s in Figure 3.3; $R_a = 5$ K, $R_b = 200$ K, $R_{oa} = 40$ K, $R_{ob} = 20$ K, $C = 0.001 \ \mu\text{fd}$, $E = 250$ volts, $T_1 = 20 \ \mu s$, and $T_2 = 300 \ \mu s$. Evaluate v_o, indicating all significant quantities.

3.5 Equation (3.24) is derived by starting with the cosine function of Equation (3.19). Starting with a sine function, derive an expression that corresponds to Equation (3.24).

3.6 Evaluate Equation (3.24) for different values of θ_1. Try 180°, 90°, 45°, 22.5°, 10°, and 7°.

3.7 A note with Table 2.1 suggests the use of an approximation for small angles. Verify this approximation.

3.8 The source voltage, for the circuit in Figure 3.2, is expressed by $E_m \sin \omega t$. Assuming a large value of capacitance, what is the expression for v_o if,

(a) $R_a = 10$ K, $R_b = 50$ K
(b) $R_a = 1$ K, $R_b = 500$ K
(c) $R_a = 0.1$ K, $R_b = 1$ Meg.

3.9 Exchange the values for R_a and R_b and repeat Problem 3.8.

3.10 A sinusoidal source voltage, applied to the circuit in Figure 3.2, has an internal resistance of 1000 ohms. Plot v_o for each set of (R_a, R_b) values given for Problem 3.8. Indicate all significant voltages in terms of E_m and all significant times in terms of the period. Assume a large capacitance, as before.

3.11 For the circuit of Figure 3.4 and the trapezoidal voltage e_s of Figure 3.8; $E = 160$ volts, $T_2 = T_4 = 400 \ \mu s$, $T_1 = T_3 = 40 \ \mu s$, $C = 0.001 \ \mu\text{fd}$, $R_o = 10$ K, and $R = 500$ K. Plot v_o, indicating all significant quantities.

3.12 Repeat Problem 3.11 if $R = 30$ K.

3.13 Repeat Problem 3.11 if $C = 10 \ \mu\text{fd}$.

3.14 Repeat Problem 3.11 if $R_a = 500$ ohms, and $R_b = 100$K.

3.15 Repeat Problem 3.11 if $R_a = 5$ K, $R_b = 1$ Meg, and $C = 10 \ \mu\text{fd}$.

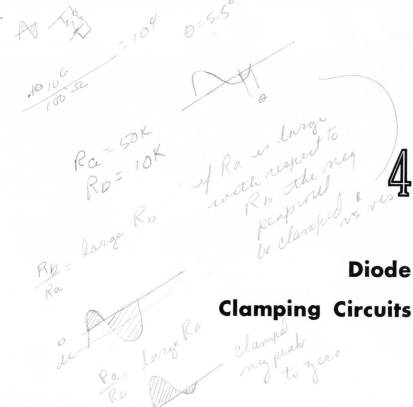

Diode

Clamping Circuits

4.1 General Discussion

The four circuits in Figure 4.1 represent the basic types of diode clamping circuits. The first circuit does not have a d-c bias voltage. The remaining three circuits are distinguished by the position of the d-c bias voltage in the circuit. These four circuits need to be studied as a group as well as separately. The remaining paragraphs of this general discussion section include some of the more important facts about the general properties of clamping circuits. Many of the statements of these paragraphs will be apparent from the studies of the preceding Chapter. Other statements will not be immediately obvious but they are included as significant items to look for during a study of clamping circuits.

The purpose of a clamping circuit is to fix either the positive or the negative peaks of the output voltage waveform at a desired d-c level. It is also desirable that the output voltage waveform shall be identical, or nearly identical, to the source voltage waveform. This places certain restrictions on the time constants of the circuit.

To properly perform a clamping action, the circuits in Figure 4.1 should satisfy five conditions: (a) The source resistance must be low; (b) the resistance, R, should have a value much greater than the resistance of the diode when the diode is conducting. This helps to establish the large area ratio required for clamping; (c) the diode should have a high resistance

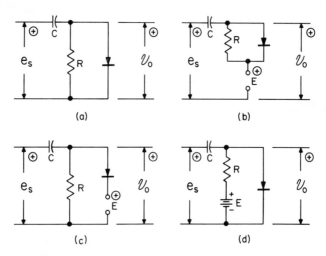

Fig. 4.1. Four basic types of clamping circuits.

ratio since this also influences the area ratio of the output voltage; (d) the capacitance, C, should have a large value to assure circuit time constants that are large in comparison to related time intervals in each cycle of the source voltage. In other words, the capacitor voltage must be essentially constant as a function of time; (e) the circuit time constant when the diode is not conducting must not be so large that the circuit cannot adjust the clamping action rapidly enough to changes in the magnitude of the source voltage. A change in magnitude of the source voltage requires the capacitor to adjust to a new voltage value. The clamping action is delayed for any change in magnitude of the source voltage that causes the diode to become nonconducting for several cycles.

The circuits as shown in Figure 4.1 will clamp the *positive* peaks of the source voltage to a particular d-c level. Ideally, the first circuit can clamp the positive peaks at approximately zero level. The second circuit can clamp the positive peaks at E, a d-c voltage that may have either positive or negative polarity. The third circuit can clamp the positive peaks at E, provided that the voltage across R, without the diode, has a positive value greater than E. The fourth circuit, (d), can clamp the positive peaks to *zero* largely independent of positive values for E. The purpose of a positive E in the fourth circuit is to cause the diode to exhibit a lower forward resistance. A negative value for E could prevent clamping. There are other circuits similar to the fourth circuit, but with functions other than clamping, that have a positive d-c voltage in series with the resistance R. These circuits will be considered later.

The circuits of Figure 4.1 can be modified to clamp the negative peaks to a particular d-c level at the output by reversing the connections to the diodes. The polarity of E in the fourth circuit should be reversed. The second and third circuits, as before, can have either polarity of E. For the fourth circuit, the clamping can be at zero volts only. A reverse d-c biasing voltage can prevent clamping, if this reverse bias is large enough to prevent the diode from conducting at all times.

4.2 Clamping Positive or Negative Peaks to Zero

The clamping of positive or negative peaks of source voltage waveforms to approximately zero at the output is illustrated with the circuit diagrams and voltage waveforms of Figure 4.2. Positive peak clamping is illustrated in the left-hand column and negative peak clamping is illustrated in the right-hand column. The clamping of a sinusoidal voltage is represented by Figure 4.2(b) and the clamping of an unsymmetrical square wave is represented by Figure 4.2(c). Notice that it is more difficult to clamp the

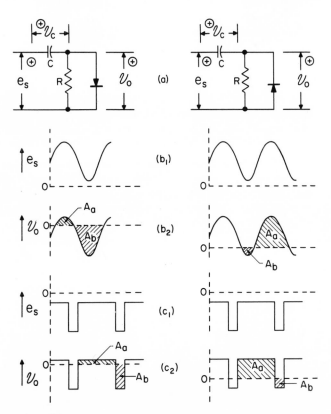

Fig. 4.2. Illustrations of positive and negative clamping assuming diodes have a constant forward resistance.

narrow negative pulses to zero than it is to clamp the wide positive pulses. The sinusoidal voltage is difficult to clamp in either case. For either type of source voltage, the area ratio A_a/A_b for the output voltage must equal the resistance ratio $-R_a/R_b$, assuming a constant forward resistance for the diode. The reverse resistance of the diode is also assumed constant but this is included in the representation of the resistor R of either circuit.

Representing the forward resistance of the diode as R_d, then for the positive peak clamping circuit, and according to the defined symbols of the preceding chapter,

$$R_a = \frac{RR_d}{R + R_d} \tag{4.1}$$

$$R_b = R \tag{4.2}$$

$$\frac{R_b}{R_a} = 1 + \frac{R}{R_d} \tag{4.3}$$

The right-hand member of Equation (4.3) is the area ratio A_b/A_a for the positive clamping circuit.

For the negative peak clamping circuit,

$$R_a = R \tag{4.4}$$

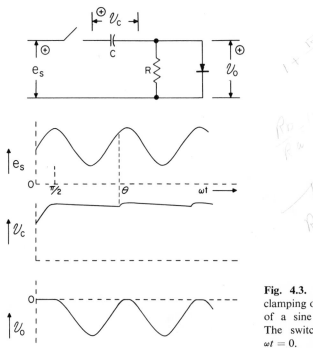

Fig. 4.3. Illustration for clamping of positive peaks of a sine wave to zero. The switch is closed at $\omega t = 0$.

$$R_b = \frac{RR_d}{R + R_d} \tag{4.5}$$

$$\frac{R_a}{R_b} = 1 + \frac{R}{R_d} \tag{4.6}$$

The right-hand member of Equation (4.6) is the area ratio A_a/A_b of the output voltage for the negative clamping circuit. The positive and negative peak values of the output voltage are determined by the procedures of Chapter 3.

A qualitative method for analyzing the clamping action of a clamping circuit is illustrated by the circuit diagram and the graphs of Figure 4.3. For this analysis, a switch is inserted in the circuit as shown in the figure, and the source resistance is neglected. If the source voltage is sinusoidal and the switch is closed when sin ωt equals zero, then the waveforms for the capacitor voltage v_c and the output voltage v_o are as indicated on the figure. For the first quarter of the sine wave, the capacitor voltage follows the source voltage exactly if R_d of the diode is negligible. As the source voltage decreases from its positive peak value, the capacitor discharges through the large resistance R until the source voltage and the capacitor voltage are again equal at θ as indicated on Figure 4.3. As a result, the clamped output voltage has the positive peaks slightly clipped during the short time interval while the capacitor recharges to the peak value of the source voltage.

When the "switch" method of analysis is applied with a rectangular wave of source voltage, the results can be the same as indicated in Figure 4.4. It is not necessary to assume R_d equal to zero in order to conveniently explain the resulting waveforms. When the switch is closed at the indicated zero time, the capacitor voltage first increases exponentially to E_1 of the source voltage. When the first positive step of the source voltage occurs at time t_1, the capacitor voltage continues to rise to E_2 of the source voltage. The preceding two changes occur for the shorter time constant state of the circuit. Now, when the negative voltage step of the source occurs at time t_2, the time constant

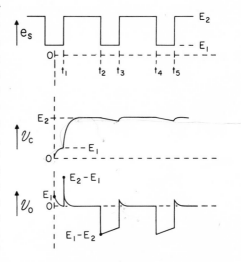

Fig. 4.4. Clamping positive peaks of a rectangular waveform to zero, showing positive spikes and overshoots.

of the circuit is large and the capacitor will discharge only a small amount
before the next positive step on the source. After the time t_2, the circuit
can perform its clamping action. The magnitude of the small positive peaks
is the magnitude of the voltage change on the capacitor.

4.3   Effect of Magnitude Changes of Source Voltage

The voltage waveforms of Figure 4.5 illustrate the response of a positive
peak clamping circuit to changes in magnitude of a sinusoidal source voltage.
The source voltage and the capacitor voltage are shown in Figure 4.5a.
Notice that the capacitor voltage will closely follow the positive peak values
of the source voltage, provided these peak magnitudes are at the same level
on each succeeding positive pulse. For a sudden increase in magnitude,
the only result is a severe clipping of the *first* large positive pulse, assuming
the three indicated large pulses are of the same magnitude. The succeeding
large pulses are only slightly clipped on the output voltage. With a decrease
in magnitude of the source voltage, there is no clipping effect whatever for

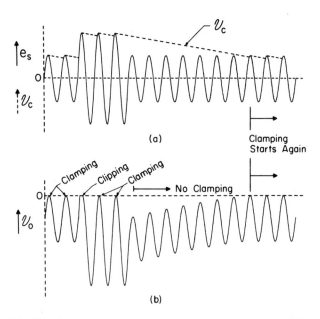

Fig. 4.5. Changing magnitudes of a sinusoidal source voltage influences
clamping action. [Contribution by Professor M. S. McVay and J. R.
Lehmann, Instructor, of the Analog Computer Laboratory, Electrical
Engineering Department, University of Illinois.]

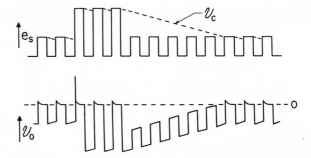

Fig. 4.6. Changing magnitudes of a rectangular source voltage influences clamping.

several cycles. As a result, the clamping action will not start again until the capacitor has discharged to the lower peak values, this discharge occuring for the larger time constant state of the circuit.

This no-clamping for several cycles is not desirable when the circuit is expected to perform the clamping action without delay. The delay time can be decreased by decreasing the RC time constant, but a decrease in time constant will increase the clipping of the positive peaks when the clamping action is re-established.

The response of a diode clamping circuit to an input waveform of rectangular pulses, that changes in magnitude, is illustrated in Figure 4.6. For normal clamping, small positive spikes (for positive clamping) may appear at the leading edge of the positive pulses. If a succeeding positive pulse has a larger magnitude, a larger positive spike appears, as indicated for the third pulse on Figure 4.6. Again (as stated before in the first paragraph), there can be a delay of the clamping action if the pulses suddenly decrease in magnitude. Any attempt to decrease this delay will increase the magnitude of the positive spikes.

The so-called disadvantages (clipping, positive spikes, delayed clamping) that can occur in diode clamping circuits are not necessarily undesirable effects. They are undesirable only if the circuit is expected to perform a clamping function. The same circuit, however, can be designed to take advantage of these effects in many applications.

4.4 Clamping to a d-c Level

The two circuits in Figure 4.7 illustrate the clamping of a source voltage to a desired d-c level at the output. In the first circuit, the positive peaks are clamped to a d-c voltage of E. In the second circuit, the negative peaks are clamped to a d-c voltage of E. The voltage E can be of either positive or negative polarity. The only difference in the two circuits is the manner of connecting the diode in the circuit. The output waveforms are shown

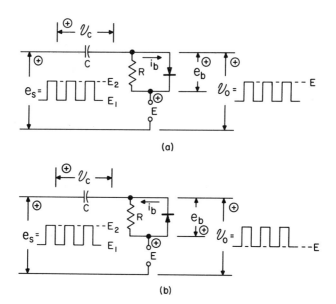

Fig. 4.7. Clamping positive peaks (a) and negative peaks (b) to the d-c voltage level of E.

clamped exactly at E. This assumes that the diode has a negligible forward resistance, the capacitance is of a large value, the source resistance is negligible, and the internal resistance of the bias voltage E is negligible.

The writing of a few voltage equations for the circuit will verify the clamping effect. In the first circuit of Figure 4.7, the capacitor has a steady state constant voltage of

$$V_c = E_2 - E$$

where E_2 is the upper limit of the input voltage. The equation for the output voltage, then, is

$$\begin{aligned} v_o &= e_s - V_c \\ &= e_s - E_2 + E \end{aligned} \tag{4.7}$$

Thus, the positive peaks of the source voltage are clamped to E, of either polarity, at the output.

The corresponding equations for the second circuit of Figure 4.7, where E_1 is the *lower* limit of the source voltage, are

$$\begin{aligned} V_c &= E_1 - E \\ v_o &= e_s - V_c \\ &= e_s - E_1 + E \end{aligned} \tag{4.8}$$

Thus, the negative peaks of the source voltage are clamped to E, of either polarity, at the output.

For the circuit in Figure 4.1c in which the resistance R is returned to ground and the diode is returned to a positive d-c voltage to produce positive peak clamping, the output voltage will have the positive peaks clamped to E only if the positive peak value of voltage across R, without the diode, is greater than E. If this positive peak value of voltage is less than E so that the diode can never conduct, there will be no clamping effect on the source voltage. Observe that the latter condition is possible only if E is positive. In the corresponding negative peak clamping circuit, the clamping action is prevented only for negative values of the bias voltage E.

4.5 Current-Biased Diode

In the circuit in Figure 4.1d, the resistance R is in series with a positive d-c voltage E. When the circuit is operating as a clamping circuit, the positive d-c voltage causes the diode to exhibit a lower resistance in the positive region of operation. The volt-ampere characteristic of a diode is nonlinear and is especially nonlinear near zero volts. The change from a state of high resistance to a state of low resistance is not abrupt. The problem is to cause the diode to conduct sufficiently past the knee of its characteristic so that it will operate in the low resistance region. A small percentage of rated diode current is sufficient bias current to establish a minimum value of diode resistance. This is important since the diode resistance influences the area ratio of the output voltage. (The circuit of Figure 4.1d is modified for clamping the negative peaks of the output voltage to near zero by reversing the diode in the circuit and by using a negative voltage for E).

There are applications, other than the clamping of waveforms, in which a circuit similar to Figure 4.1d is used. In these other applications, the positive d-c voltage for E is not used for the prime purpose of reducing the diode resistance in every case. The reasons for this are best discovered in later studies.

PROBLEMS

4.1 For the circuits (a), (b), and (c) of Figure 4.1, $R = 500$ K, $C = 0.1 \mu$fd, the forward resistance of each diode $= 200$ ohms, the source voltage is rectangular pulses as identified in Figure 3.3a ($T_1 = 100 \mu$s, $T_2 = 500 \mu$s, $E = 50$ volts). The bias voltage for circuits (b) and (c) is 10 volts. Plot a steady state cycle for v_o, indicating all significant quantities.

4.2 Repeat Problem 4.1 if the rectangular source voltage has time intervals of

$T_1 = 10$ μs, and $T_2 = 1000$ μs. Discuss the problem of clamping such a waveform.

4.3 Repeat Problem 4.1 if the rectangular source voltage has the time intervals of $T_1 = 1000$ μs, and $T_2 = 10$ μs. Compare the results with Problem 4.2.

4.4 Repeat Problem 4.1 if the diode in each circuit is inverted.

4.5 For the circuit of Figure 4.1b, the source voltage is sinusoidal, $E_m = 30$ volts, the bias voltage $= -5$ volts, the forward resistance of the diode $= 10$ ohms, $R = 1$ Meg, and C is large.
(a) Plot a steady state cycle for v_o.
(b) What is the capacitance voltage?

4.6 For the circuit and conditions of Problem 4.5, assume the source voltage is applied at an instant when the sine wave is at its negative peak value. The capacitor voltage is initially zero. Plot the capacitor voltage as a function of time. Also, plot the output voltage as a function of time through the first complete steady state cycle for v_o.

4.7 A symmetrical square wave is applied to a diode clamping circuit that will clamp the negative peaks at a zero voltage level. The freqency of the square wave is 1000 cycles per second. Design the clamping circuit such that clamping is restored after four cycles when the magnitude of the source voltage is decreased to one half its normal value.

5

Input Circuits
To Grounded-Cathode
Amplifiers

5.1 General Discussion

The studies of the preceding chapters illustrated the behavior of several circuits that have a switching mode of operation. The diode is the only electronic device incorporated in these circuits.

The vacuum tube amplifier is another electronic device that can serve as an electronic switch as well as an amplifier. It is incorporated in the circuits of this chapter for the first time. As an electronic device in switching and pulse-shaping circuits, there is a particular interest in the nonlinear properties of a complete amplifier circuit. These nonlinear properties, which we hope will be of a switching mode, can be in the tube itself, in the circuitry external to the tube, or in both. These possibilities (referring to the location of a nonlinearity) may require that a circuit be analyzed in parts rather than as a whole. The block diagram of Figure 5.1, for example, shows four blocks representing the input circuit, the output circuit, the feedback circuit and the amplifying device. Any one of the circuits of these four blocks might exhibit a switching mode of operation that is either dependent or independent of the states of operation of the circuits in the other blocks. We need to know, therefore, the influence of each external circuit (input, output and feedback) on the response of the over-all circuit for prescribed types of driving voltages.

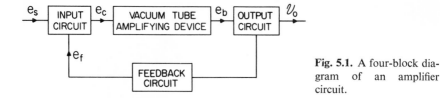

Fig. 5.1. A four-block diagram of an amplifier circuit.

   In practical vacuum tube circuits, the three external circuits are not always present. In some instances, only the input circuit is of primary importance. In other cases, the output circuit has an added significance. There are practical amplifier circuits in which feedback is also included.

   This chapter considers only input circuits to a grounded cathode amplifier where the cathode is returned directly to common ground and the plate circuit contains the resistance R_L, as illustrated in Figure 5.2a. The next chapter concentrates on the output circuits. Chapters 7 and 8 discuss semiconductor electronics and transistors that lead to a parallel treatment with tubes. Chapter 9 concentrates on the analysis of switching and pulse-shaping circuits with feedback included.

   A number of input circuits for the grounded cathode triode are shown in Figure 5.3. A sufficient number of these input circuits are discussed in this chapter to reveal a method of analysis as well as to indicate some of the important practical results that are possible. In general, the procedure of analysis is to determine the grid voltage e_c (Figure 5.2) as a function of time (The technique for doing this is no different than the procedures described in preceding chapters.) After the grid voltage is determined as a function of time, it becomes possible to evaluate the output voltage as a function of time with the aid of tube characteristics and/or tube data.

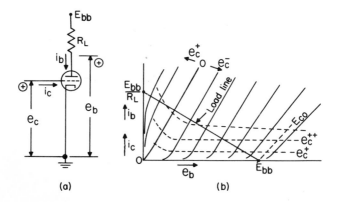

Fig. 5.2. Grounded-cathode amplifier with plate and grid characteristics.

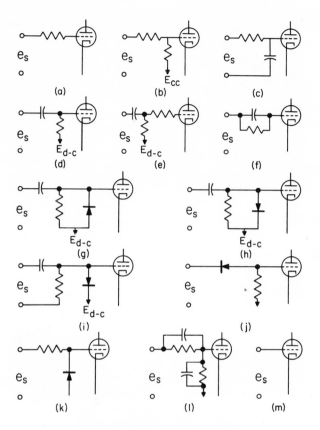

Fig. 5.3. Typical input circuits.

5.2 Series Grid Resistor

The circuit in Figure 5.4 has an input circuit containing a series resistance R and a bias voltage E_{cc}. The voltage and current notations are given on the circuit diagram.

To analyze this and other input circuits, some information is needed regarding the grid-cathode resistance. The grid cathode behaves somewhat like a diode. Its resistance for positive values of grid voltage, e_c, is identified as r_c. For negative grid voltages, the grid cathode resistance is large and is normally assumed to be infinite. Section 5.4 is devoted to a brief discussion of the grid-cathode resistance r_c. For the present discussion, r_c is assumed constant when the grid voltage is positive.

To continue with a study of the circuit of Figure 5.4, the grid current i_c is

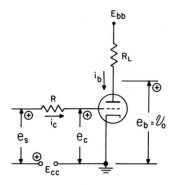

Fig. 5.4. A series resistor input circuit.

$$i_c^+ = \frac{(e_s + E_{cc})^+}{R + r_c} \qquad (5.1)$$

where the superscript $^+$ represents positive instantaneous values of current or voltage. The bias voltage E_{cc} may be either a positive or a negative d-c voltage.

The expressions for e_c, positive and negative respectively, are

$$e_c^+ = \frac{(e_s + E_{cc})^+}{1 + R/r_c} \qquad (5.2)$$

$$e_c^- = (e_s + E_{cc})^- \qquad (5.3)$$

The ratio R/r_c in Equation (5.2) is of particular interest. By making this ratio

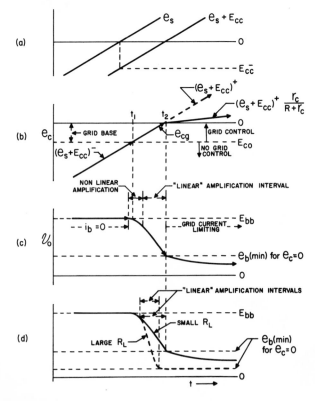

Fig. 5.5. The response of a basic amplifier with a series grid resistor: (a) input voltage, (b) grid voltage, (c) plate voltage for a triode, and (d) plate voltage for a pentode.

large, the positive excursions of grid voltage are limited to low values. Consequently, the output voltage v_o (or e_b) is also limited.

The over-all response of the circuit is illustrated with the voltage graphs of Figure 5.5. A straight line function is selected for the source voltage e_s. The bias voltage, E_{cc}, is represented as a negative voltage. The typical set of triode characteristics of Figure 5.2b should be studied along with the graphs of Figure 5.5. There are several defining terms in these two figures.

For large values of negative grid voltage, when the plate current is off, the output voltage is at E_{bb}. As the grid voltage increases from a high negative value, it eventually enters the grid control region at the indicated time t_1. As the grid voltage continues into the control region, the output voltage changes with a resulting amplification. The amplification is reasonably linear if the grid voltage is not too close to the cutoff voltage E_{cc}. This cutoff voltage is not a clearly defined value because of the nonlinearity in this region near cutoff. Some tubes have a sharper cutoff voltage than others.

A special symbol is needed to identify the grid voltage of the control region where amplification occurs. This notation is e_{cg}. The conventional symbol of e_g is not satisfactory since this implies an expression for the grid voltage with d-c components removed. There are many occasions, for switching and pulse forming circuits, in which it is essential to consider the actual instantaneous values of grid voltage. Notice on Figure 5.5, for example, that E_{cc} determines the time interval t_1 to t_2 when the grid voltage is in the negative grid control region. The subscript c of e_{cg} indicates instantaneous values, and the subscript g indicates that these instantaneous values are in the grid control region.

As the grid voltage enters the positive control region it becomes highly attenuated. [See Equation (5.2).] The change in the output voltage is, therefore, attenuated also. Notice that this does not necessarily indicate a change in the amplification. An examination of triode characteristics reveals continued linearity from the negative to the positive grid control region, provided the positive excursion of grid voltage is small.

For pentodes, the plate current is largely independent of grid voltages (positive or negative) for *low* values of plate voltage. Hence, nonlinearity of amplification with pentodes can occur for e_{cg} values near zero as well as near cutoff. Examine the plate characteristics of a pentode (refer to a tube manual) and observe that many of the grid voltage lines are a common line for a range of small values of plate voltage. The voltage graphs of Figure 5.5d are for a pentode. There are two voltage graphs, one for a small value of R_L and the other for a large value of R_L. Notice that the range of e_{cg} values for linear amplification is less for the larger R_L. Also observe the more definite limiting of plate voltage for the larger R_L, which occurs even before e_{cg} goes positive.

5.3 Determination of Output Voltage

The output voltage is determined analytically or graphically, whichever is applicable. The analytical method, in which the tube behavior is expressed in terms of its dynamic constants (μ, r_p, g_m), is applicable only if the tube is operated within the linear range of its characteristics. Otherwise, the graphical method may be necessary.

In the graphical method, a load line represented by R_L for the circuit of Figure 5.4 is drawn on a set of plate characteristics for the tube. The plate voltage (e_b) values are read from the graph for corresponding grid voltages (e_c) that are common to the load line. Knowing e_c, and e_{cg} in particular, as a function of time, then the output voltage (also e_b in this case) can be plotted as a function of time. In this way, the graphs of Figure 5.5c, or of Figure 5.5d, can be determined.

A *complete* graphical analysis is time consuming. Fortunately, a complete graphical analysis is not always necessary. In this chapter, the study of a number of amplifier input circuits is directed toward determining the various types of voltage waveforms that are possible to generate. Only a few significant voltages (usually five or less), along with significant time constants and time intervals, are sufficient to describe a particular voltage waveform. It is not sufficiently important to consdier the nonlinearity of the amplifier in the amplification region for every circuit. For the voltage graphs of Figure 5.5, for example, it is no serious problem to determine the upper and lower limits of the output voltage and the times when they occur. In Figure 5.5c, the upper limit for the output voltage is E_{bb} at time t_1 and before. The lower significant voltage, defined as e_b (min) for e_c equal to zero, occurs at time t_2. There are many instances when these two voltage limits are sufficient to indicate significant values of an output voltage waveform.

Since nonlinearity is actually present in the amplification region, it is necessary to be a little careful in any selected method of analysis. One might be tempted, for example, to find the output voltage of the circuit of Figure 5.4 by using the gain expression, $A = -\mu R_L/(r_p + R_L)$. Obviously, the use of this gain expression is limited to only a certain range of grid-voltage values e_{cg}, as indicated by the linear amplification intervals of Figure 5.5c for a triode. In the voltage graphs of Figure 5.5, the grid voltage is allowed to vary over a much wider range of values. Consequently, the gain expression gives only a portion of the output voltage change correctly, and the end values are still to be determined.

Whichever method of analysis is used, graphical or analytical, one is occasionally forced to make reasonable and necessary approximations. The method of analysis is usually dictated by the circuit problem, and perhaps by the individual doing the problem for a particular application.

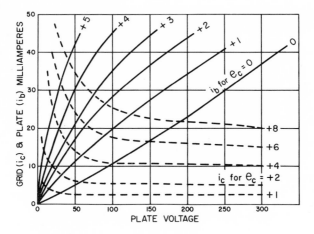

Fig. 5.6. Positive grid characteristics for a triode (dashed line).

5.4 The Grid-Cathode Resistance

The voltage and current characteristics of certain vacuum triodes include a set of curves showing positive grid current values as a function of plate voltage, for several values of positive grid voltage. A typical set of positive grid characterisitcs is shown in Figure 5.6. The grid current (i_c) curves, shown as dotted lines, are of particular interest for selecting a value of grid-cathode resistance r_c. Observe that i_c is a function of the plate voltage as well as a function of the grid voltage. To select a single value for r_c, when such a selection is permissible, it is necessary to know the operating values of plate voltage and gird voltage. According to Figure 5.6, the ratio of e_c to i_c (or r_c) is reasonably constant for a large range of values of plate voltage, especially if e_c is small. For the grid-current-limiting circuit of Figure 5.4, as one example, the grid voltage is truly limited to small values in the presence of a large series resistance R. Observe, also, that the ratio of e_c to i_c is reasonably constant as a function of e_c. This is more nearly true for high values of plate voltage than for low values of plate voltage. Even so, the plate voltage has relatively little effect on the e_c to i_c ratio, provided that the grid voltage is limited to small positive values.

If it is desired, then, to select a value of r_c for the circuit of Figure 5.4, and the set of positive grid characteristics of the tube is that of Figure 5.6, one would read the ratio of e_c to i_c from the curves for small grid voltages. The value of r_c is in the order of 400 ohms for the typical set of positive grid characteristics. This is the ratio of two volts to five milliamperes as read from the graph. This might imply that the plate voltage is 300 volts when the grid voltage is a positive 2 volts. The plate voltage, more likely, will be in the range of 50 to 100 volts. In this voltage range, the e_c to i_c ratio is more nearly equal to 380 ohms; this number should be used if it is desired to be more precise in the solution of a circuit problem. This preciseness requires an iterative method of analysis that is sometimes warranted but more often is not.

There are triodes in which the grid cathode resistance is much more nonlinear than indicated in the example of the preceding paragraph. Fortunately, the triodes that are normally used in switching and pulse forming circuits do have a reasonably constant value of r_c. No two triodes have the same value of r_c. The range is from about 200 ohms to 1000 ohms.

5.5 Series Grid Resistor (Sinusoidal Input)

The source voltage e_s of Figure 5.4 may have any one of a number of voltage waveforms, which is true for any of the other types of input circuits as well. A sinusoidal voltage is selected for the discussion of this section. Figures 5.7, 5.8 and 5.9 illustrate three possible results. The voltage graphs of Figure 5.7, indicate an attempt to generate a symmetrical square wave. The voltage plots of Figure 5.8 illustrate an attempt to generate a narrow

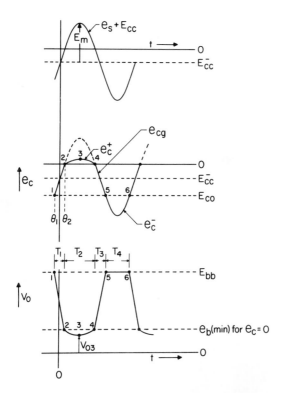

Fig. 5.7. Response of the circuit in Figure 5.4 to a sinusoidal input voltage (large signal and small bias).

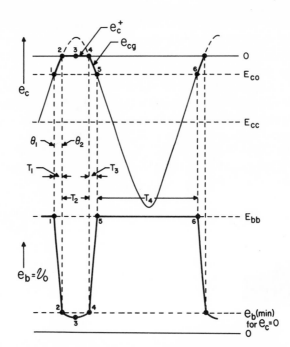

Fig. 5.8. Response of the circuit in Figure 5.4 to a sinusoidal input voltage (large signal and high negative bias).

negative pulse. Finally, Figure 5.9 illustrates operation of the amplifier within its linear range. (There are amplifier input circuits, other than that of Figure 5.4, from which similar results are attainable. This one is selected to demonstrate a procedure.) One possible disadvantage of this circuit is that the source voltage, the bias source and the output voltage cannot all have a common chassis ground. When such a circuit is used, the source voltage is probably obtained from a transformer coupled circuit.

Six significant points on the voltage graphs are required to identify the output voltage for the conditions of Figure 5.7 and for Figure 5.8. These points are numbered on the graphs as 1 though 6, reading left to right on

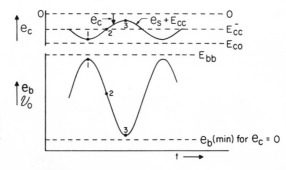

Fig. 5.9. Magnitudes of e_s and E_{cc} adjusted for best linear amplification of entire signal.

the time base. Points 6 and 1 have the same voltage values but are separated by one period of the source voltage. A complete steady state cycle, for the output voltage, is thereby described. The instantaneous voltage values, represented by these points are determined graphically. Points 1, 5 and 6 are at E_{bb} when the plate current is cut off. Points 2 and 4 are at $e_b(\text{min})$ for e_c equal to zero, where this voltage value is found from the load line on the plate characteristics for the particular triode that is used in the circuit. Determination of the lowest value (point 3) of the output voltage may create a special problem, since the interval 2 to 4 is the time interval when the grid voltage is in the positive control region.

There are three approaches that one might take with regard to the minimum value of the output voltage, identified as V_{o3} on the figures. (The o subscript has reference to the output voltage.) These three approaches are discussed in the following itemized paragraphs.

(a) The voltage V_{o3} can be determined graphically by referring to the load line on the plate characteristics for the triode and reading the value of plate voltage that corresponds to the known value of grid voltage e_{c3}, at point 3 of e_c.

(b) The voltage V_{o3} can be determined by using the gain expression for the amplifier, provided it can be assumed that the tube operates linearily in the positive grid control region. Thus,

$$V_{o3} = A e_{c3} + V_{o2} \tag{5.4}$$

where V_{o2} represents the plate voltage for e_c equal to zero.

(c) There are occasions when it is permissible to de-emphasize the importance of knowing an accurate value for V_{o3}. In the attempt to generate a square pulse, one may be more interested in the linearity and steepness of the sides of the waveform than in the value of V_{o3}. If the nonflatness of the bottom of these waveforms is objectionable, it may then become necessary to use a different circuit for generating square waves.

Inspection of the voltage waveforms of Figure 5.7 and Figure 5.8, reveals certain facts about the output voltage. The slopes of the leading and trailing edges and the dissymmetry of the output voltage are of major interest. The dissymmetry is controlled by the bias voltage E_{cc}. The slope of the leading and trailing edges depends on the magnitude and frequency of the input voltage, the amplification and the magnitude of E_{cc}. A few calculations will describe the output voltage in more detail.

For the sinusoidal source voltage, the angles θ_1 and θ_2 of Figure 5.8 (or of Figure 5.7) are expressed as,

$$\theta_1 = \sin^{-1} \frac{E_{co} - E_{cc}}{E_m} \tag{5.5}$$

$$\theta_2 = \sin^{-1} \frac{-E_{cc}}{E_m} \tag{5.6}$$

where θ_1 represents the angle when the grid voltage arrives at cutoff from a more negative value, and θ_2 represents the angle when the grid voltage arrives at zero volts from a negative value. Remember that E_{cc} is a positive or a negative real number. It is shown as a negative quantity on the diagram. The time intervals T_1 and T_3, indicated on the diagrams, have the following value:

$$T_1 = T_3 = \frac{\theta_2 - \theta_1}{2\pi} T \tag{5.7}$$

where T is the period of the source voltage. The time intervals T_2 and T_4 (see diagrams) have these values,

$$T_2 = \left(\frac{1}{2} - \frac{\theta_2}{\pi}\right) T \tag{5.8}$$

$$T_4 = \left(\frac{1}{2} + \frac{\theta_1}{\pi}\right) T \tag{5.9}$$

Note that T_2 is equal to T_4 only if θ_1 is equal to the negative of θ_2. Stated another way, referring to Equations (5.5) and (5.6), the output voltage is most symmetrical when the bias voltage is adjusted to one half the cutoff voltage. This, of course, assumes linear amplification throughout the negative grid control region.

In a situation such as that of Figure 5.7, it may be permissible to assume that the sides of the output voltage waveform are straight lines. The positive slope, point 4 to point 5, then becomes

$$K = \frac{E_{bb} - e_b \text{ (min)}}{T_3} \tag{5.10}$$

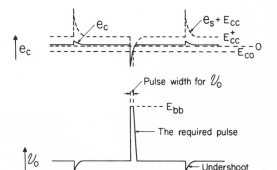

Fig. 5.10. Clipping of positive and negative spikes to generate narrow rectangular pulse. The circuit is Figure 5.4.

where e_b(min) is defined as the value of plate voltage when the grid voltage is zero as observed from the load line.

For the illustration of Figure 5.9, the bias voltage and the magnitude of the sinusoidal input voltage are adjusted to give a near linear amplification of the entire portion of the source voltage. A graphical analysis for this condition is not warranted unless one wishes to analyze the harmonic content created by the nonlinearity of the tube characteristics. The gain expression for an amplifier is normally used here.

Although this section has concentrated on a sinusoidal source voltage to a grid-current limiting circuit, it should also be understood that the source voltage may be of other forms. An example of another form is illustrated with Figure 5.10 (without a discussion) where the input voltage contains positive and negative spikes. The bias voltage is positive, resulting in narrow rectangular positive pulses for the output voltage. In any case, the first problem in the solution is to determine the grid voltage e_c as a function of time.

5.6 RC Coupling (Large Time-Constants)

The circuit of Figure 5.11 offers several possibilities for generating different types of voltage waveforms at the output. The output voltage waveform is influenced by the type and magnitude of the source voltage, the RC time constant, the magnitudes of R_g and of C, the magnitude and polarity of the bias voltage E_{cc}, the magnitude of the plate supply voltage E_{bb}, the magnitude of the plate load resistance R_L and the characteristics of the tube that is used in the circuit.

The studies of this section restrict the circuit to a large value of C and a large RC time constant, large compared to the period of the input voltage or to particular time intervals of the input voltage. The source resistance is neglected also. Since the grid-cathode behaves like a diode, the developments of Chapters 3 and 4 are applicable for calculating the grid voltage e_c. The only additional problem here is to evaluate the output voltage v_o.

The behavior of the circuit of Figure 5.11, even after detailed studies of similar circuits have been presented in the earlier chapters, often seems rather perplexing, especially for large values of C. Yet, its operation is rather simple. To fully

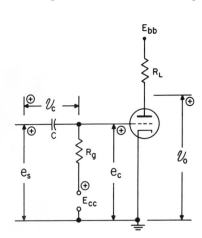

Fig. 5.11. RC input circuit.

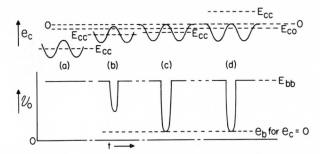

Fig. 5.12. To show how bias voltage, in circuit of Figure 5.11, influences output voltage.

understand the circuit, visualize its behavior as the peak-to-peak value of the source voltage is assigned different magnitudes and also as the bias voltage changes in magnitude or polarity. Let each new magnitude of voltage be of sufficient time duration to allow the capacitor voltage to adjust to its new steady state value, which is approximately a constant voltage when C is large. Then, also remember that any attempt to drive the grid voltage into the positive control region is limited largely by the ratio of r_c to R_g as indicated by the area ratio developments of the preceding chapters.

The RC-coupled input circuit may, or it may not, act like a diode clamping circuit. It is possible to have one condition like that represented in the graphs of Figure 5.9 in which the bias voltage is approximately one-half of the cutoff voltage and the peak-to-peak values of the grid voltage are within the limits of zero and the cutoff voltage. With this as a reference condition, let the source voltage increase in magnitude or let the bias voltage increase (negative to positive), then as the positive peaks reach the zero level, clamping begins. Continue to increase the magnitude of the signal voltage, or of E_{cc}, and the positive peaks remain essentially at zero volts, provided that r_c is much much less than R_g.

Make E_{cc} negative, and it becomes possible to cut the plate current

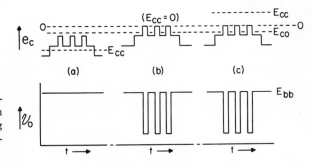

Fig. 5.13. Another illustration for the circuit in Figure 5.11. (Selecting positive pulses on a pedestal.)

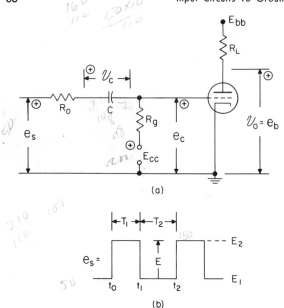

Fig. 5.14. Input circuit and source voltage for the studies of Section 5.7.

off completely, in which case the output voltage remains constant at the plate supply voltage E_{bb}.

Several possible results of grid voltage and output voltage waveforms are illustrated in Figure 5.12 and Figure 5.13. The source voltage e_s is not shown on these figures, but it will be the same as e_c in each case except for the d-c levels, if the capacitor voltage is essentially constant.

5.7   RC Coupling (Small Time Constant)

The circuit diagram of Figure 5.14 is similar to Figure 5.11, except for the addition of the source resistance R_o. The presence of R_o takes on an added significance when the circuit time constants are small compared to particular time intervals of the source voltage. A rectangular wave of source voltage is selected for an analysis of the circuit.

Some of the possible waveforms for the grid voltage and corresponding output voltages, for different values of bias voltage, are shown in Figures 5.15, 5.16, and 5.17. These waveforms are representative, only, and are not drawn with complete accuracy. Detailed analysis is given a little later, in this section, with the aid of two numerical examples of circuit problems.

It is good to observe certain generalities about the circuit with a rectangular wave of source voltage before considering a detailed circuit problem. These generalities are itemized for ease of presentation and study.

(a) The source voltage may have any d-c level, theoretically, as suggested by the absence of a zero reference in Figure 5.14b.

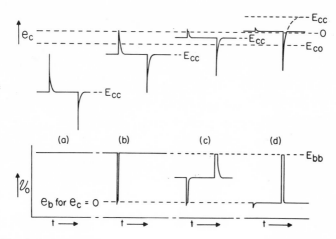

Fig. 5.15. A possible set of waveforms for the circuit in Figure 5.14, for different values of E_{cc}.

(b) With the open grid-cathode circuit, the voltage e_c has alternately positive and negative-going spikes, averaging at the bias voltage E_{cc}, as illustrated in Figure 5.15a and in Figure 5.17a. These spikes have a magnitude of $ER_g/(R_g + R_o)$, where E is the peak-to-peak value of the source voltage and R_o is regarded as a constant. For a rectangular wave of source voltage, the source resistance could switch to different values, as was explained in Chapter 3. This possibility is neglected for the present study.

(c) To keep the plate current off, the bias voltage must be

$$E_{cc} \leqq E_{co} - \frac{ER_g}{R_g + R_o} \qquad (5.11)$$

as illustrated in Figure 5.15a.

(d) As E_{cc} is increased (less negative), the positive spikes enter the grid control region. Increase E_{cc} sufficiently and the *negative* spikes enter the

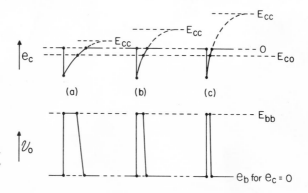

Fig. 5.16. Output pulse-width is decreased by increasing positive E_{cc}.

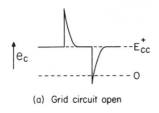

(a) Grid circuit open

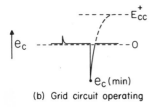

(b) Grid circuit operating

Fig. 5.17. Positive values of E_{cc} do not change minimum value of e_c, appreciably, if R_0 is small.

grid control region. Three possible grid-cathode and output voltage waveforms are illustrated in (b), (c), and (d) of Figure 5.15.

(e) The minimum value of e_c (maximum negative value) is essentially constant for positive values of E_{cc}, especially if r_c and R_0 are relatively small compared to the resistance R_g. See Figure 5.16 and Example 2 of this section. For small r_c/R_g ratios, the minimum value of E_{cc}, to prevent the grid voltage from going negative, is

$$E_{cc} = \frac{ER_g}{R_0} \quad \text{for } e_c \text{ (min)} = 0 \quad (5.12)$$

This is verified from Equation (5.13) which follows. At the instant of the negative step on the source voltage, the capacitor is charged approximately to the upper limit of the source voltage. Then immediately after the negative step, $e_s = V_c = -E$, where E is the *magnitude* of the step voltage, or as measured in a positive sense. Thus the minimum value of e_c is,

$$e_c \text{ (min)} = (-E - E_{cc})\frac{R_g}{R_g + R_0} + E_{cc} \quad (5.13)$$

Set e_c(min) equal to zero and Equation (5.12) results. This development should avoid the common error of doubting that the grid voltage can ever go negative after it is in the positive region when E_{cc} may have a large positive value.

(f) One advantage of a positive E_{cc} is that it gives a method of controlling the time duration of the output pulse, provided that the circuit time constant is sufficiently small. Again, refer to Figure 5.16 and Example 2 of this section.

Two examples, one with a negative bias voltage and the other with a positive bias voltage E_{cc}, will illustrate a method of analysis and describe the voltage waveforms in greater detail. Refer, occasionally, to the itemized paragraphs (a) through (f) just preceding.

EXAMPLE 1 (negative bias)

Given: Figure 5.14a   6j5 triode   Source voltage, Figure 5.14b

$R_g = 100$ K $r_c \cong 1$ K $E_1 = 50$ volts
$C = 0.001$ μfd $R_L = 25$ K $E_2 = 150$ volts
$R_0 = 10$ K $E_{bb} = 250$ volts $T_1 = T_2 = 600$ μs
$E_{cc} = -60$ volts

Determine: significant voltages, time constants and time intervals to describe the voltages e_c and v_o.

Solution (Including a detailed discussion of the problem): the possible circuit time constants are

$$(R_o + R_g)\, C = (10\ \text{K} + 100\ \text{K})\,(0.001\ \mu\text{fd}) = 110\ \mu\text{s}.$$

$$\left(R_o + \frac{r_c R_g}{r_c + R_g}\right) C = (10\ \text{K} + 0.99\ \text{K})\,(0.001\ \mu\text{fd}) = 11\ \mu\text{s}.$$

Both of these possible circuit time constants are sufficiently less than 600 μs to permit exponential voltages to reach asymptotical values. Thus, at the end of time interval T_1, e_c is -60 volts and V_c is 210 volts. At the end of time interval T_2, e_c is -60 volts and V_c is 110 volts. This information is sufficient to start a plot of the two voltage waveforms, e_c and v_o. Their waveforms are illustrated in Figure 5.18 with the calculated voltages and time intervals as given in Table 5.1. When doing a similar problem it may be more convenient to indicate the calculated values on the waveforms. To facilitate the explanation of this example, it is desirable to number the significant points on the waveforms and tabulate the calculated values.

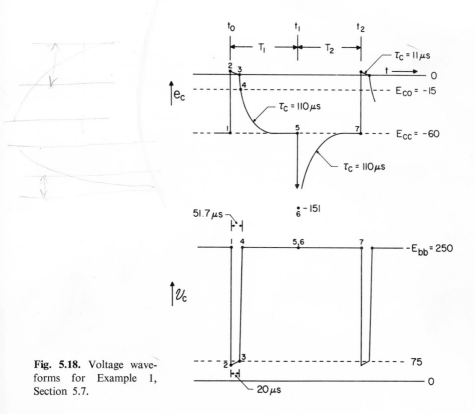

Fig. 5.18. Voltage waveforms for Example 1, Section 5.7.

With the possible exception of Point 2, the significant voltages are easily determined. There are two significant time intervals, t_{23} and t_{24}, where the double subscript is used to indicate the elapsed time from the first subscript point to the second. The time interval t_{34} presents no serious problem to evaluate but the time interval t_{23} could be deceptive. In any case, let us get the entire job done, point by point.

TABLE 5.1   VOLTAGES AND TIME INTERVALS
FOR FIGURE 5.18, EXAMPLE 1, SECTION 5.7.

PT.	e_c	v_0	TIME INTERVALS
1	-60	250	
2	3.1	27	
3	0	75	$t_{23} = 20\ \mu s$
4	-15	250	$t_{34} = 31.7\ \mu s$
5	-60	250	$t_{24} = 51.7\ \mu s$
6	-151	250	
7,1	-60	250	

At Point 1, just preceding the positive step of the source voltage, e_c is -60 volts and v_0, therefore, is at E_{bb} of 250 volts. From the plate characteristics for a 6j5 tube, the grid cathode voltage at cutoff is about -15 volts.

Now, the problem is to determine the voltages at Point 2 immediately following the positive step of the source voltage. At this instant,

$$e_s - V_c = 150 - 110 = 40 \text{ volts}$$

To make use of this 40 volts, it is helpful to sketch an equivalent circuit as shown in Figure 5.19a. In this equivalent circuit, by applying Thevenin's theorem, R_a is the parallel combination of r_c (1 K) and R_g (100 K) which is approximately equal to 1 K. The equivalent Thevenin's voltage of this parallel circuit is -0.6 volt. At Point 2, then, e_c is calculated as 3.1 volts.

The next problem is to find the time interval, t_{23}. (It is convenient to continue with a plot of the grid voltage and consider the output voltage

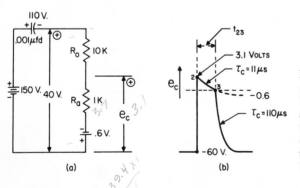

Fig. 5.19. (a) Equivalent circuit and voltages for Example 1 immediately after the positive step of the source voltage. (b) The exponential voltage for e_c from which t_{23} is calculated.

$V_0 = \dfrac{100 \times 100}{110} - \dfrac{60 \times 10}{110}$ $5.5 \, 10K$ $\dfrac{100 \times 100}{110}$ 91 $91 - 5.5$

86

$\dfrac{110|600}{500}$ $110\dfrac{100.00}{99}$

Sec. 5.7 / RC Coupling (Small Time Constant)   71

later.) From the quivalent circuit of Figure 5.19a and the grid-voltage plot
of Figure 5.19b,

$$t_{23} = (R_o + R_a)\, C \ln \frac{3.7}{0.6}$$

$$= (11\ \mu\text{s})\,(1.82) = 20\ \mu\text{s}$$

The accuracy of this time interval is dependable only to the extent that the
selected value of r_c is dependable.

Assuming that the grid-cathode resistance becomes infinite immediately
following Point 3 when the grid voltage enters the negative region, the
circuit reverts back to contain E_{cc} of -60 volts and the circuit time constant
of $(R_o + R_g)C$. For the cutoff voltage of -15 volts, the time interval t_{34}
is evaluated as

$$t_{34} = (R_o + R_g)\, C \ln \frac{60}{60 - 15}$$

$$= (110\ \mu\text{s})\,(0.288) = 31.7\ \mu\text{s}$$

The remaining plot of the grid voltage is self explanatory. At the instant
of the negative step of the source voltage, e_c drops from -60 volts (Point
5) to -151 volts (Point 6) with an exponential return to -60 volts at Point 7

The output voltage at Point 3, when e_c is zero, is 75 volts. This is determined from the plate characteristics of the tube at the point where the
load line intersects the $e_c = 0$ line. If positive grid characteristics are available, the same procedure can be used to find the output voltage at Point
2 when $e_c = 3.1$ volts. Or, the gain expression can be used (if assumed
linear amplification is permissible) to calculate the change in output voltage
that corresponds to a 3.1 volt change in the grid voltage; this change should
then be subtracted from the 75 volts for $e_b(\text{min})$ at e_c equal to zero.

EXAMPLE 2 (Positive bias)

Given: Same as Example 1 except $E_{cc} = 200$ volts and $C = .002\ \mu\text{fd}$.

Determine: Significant voltages, time constants and time intervals to
describe the voltages e_c and v_o.

Solution (Including a detailed discussion of the problem):

The possible time constants for the circuit, this time, are 220 μs and
22 μs.

Refer to Figure 5.20 for the numbered notations at the significant points
on the voltage waveforms. At Point 1, which is at the end of the time interval
when the upper limit of the supply voltage is applied, the grid voltage is
2 volts. This is apparent from the equivalent circuit of Figure 5.21a, which
corresponds to the equivalent circuit of Figure 5.19a. Certainly, the grid
voltage is 2 volts at Point 1 since the circuit time constant is only 22 μs

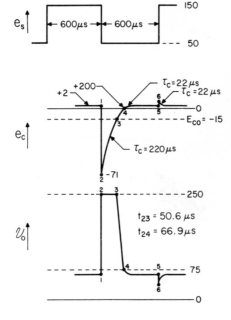

Fig. 5.20. Voltage waveforms for Example 2, Section 5.7.

which is small compared to the time interval of 600 μs when the upper limit of the source voltage is applied.

The remainder of the solution is very similar to that of Example 1. The results are tabulated in Table 5.2.

One interesting part of this problem is the fact that the bias voltage (when positve) influences the time intervals t_{23} and t_{34}. The time duration of the positive pulse at the output can be controlled, therefore, by the positive bias voltage. The time interval t_{23} is expressed as,

$$t_{23} = (R_o + R_g) C \ln \frac{200 + 71}{200 + 15}$$
$$= 50.6 \,\mu s$$

where E_{cc} is 200, $e_c(\min)$ is -71 and E_{co} is -15 volts.

Another significant part of this example is the fact that r_c is not a factor in the generation of the positive output pulse during the time interval t_{24}.

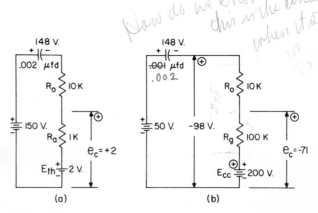

Fig. 5.21. Equivalent circuits for Example 2, Section 5.7. (a) Circuit and steady state voltages for interval when input is 150 volts. (b) Circuit and *initial* voltages for interval when input is 50 volts.

aids for writing voltage equations necessary to the analysis of the circuit. When the grid voltage is negative, the equivalent circuit in Figure 5.22b is applicable. For this state of operation,

$$e_c^- = e_s - v_c \tag{5.14}$$

When the grid voltage is positive, the equivalent circuits in Figure 5.22c and 5.22d are applicable. From the former circuit,

$$e_c^+ = (e_s - v_c)\frac{r_c}{R + r_c} \tag{5.15}$$

The equivalent circuit resistance and Thevenin's equivalent voltage are needed also. They are shown in Figure 5.22d as approximations. Actually, r_c should be included in these evaluations. It is omitted, here, until it becomes necessary to use Equation (5.15) which does include r_c.

Although the method of analysis is very similar to that of the preceding section, a particular set of conditions is selected that will reveal some interesting facts about the circuit. So, it is assumed that E_{cc} is positive, the circuit time constants are small, and the source voltage is a square wave having an upper value of E_2 volts and a lower value of E_1 volts. The difference in these two voltages is the step voltage E.

The maximum voltage on the capacitor, then becomes

$$V_c\,(\text{max}) = E_2 - \frac{E_{cc}R}{R + R_g} \tag{5.16}$$

which is the capacitor voltage at the instant of the negative step of the source voltage.

Assuming the grid voltage can be negative immediately following the negative step of the source voltage, then the minimum value of the grid voltage is

$$e_c\,(\text{min}) = e_s\,(\text{min}) - V_c\,(\text{max})$$

$$= E_1 - \left(E_2 - E_{cc}\frac{R}{R + R_g} \right)$$

$$= -E + \frac{E_{cc}R}{R + R_g} \tag{5.17}$$

The grid voltage is truly negative, then, provided that

$$E > \frac{E_{cc}R}{R + R_g} \tag{5.18}$$

Stated in another way, the maximum value of E_{cc} to prevent the grid voltage from disappearing entirely into the positive grid-control region, is

$$E_{cc} = E\left(1 + \frac{R_g}{R}\right) \tag{5.19}$$

Proceeding as in Example 2, Section 5.7, when $e_c(\text{min})$ is below the cutoff voltage for the tube, it is significant to determine the time interval for

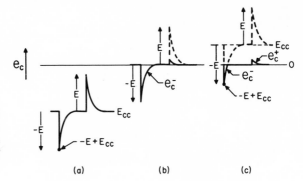

Fig. 5.23. A possible set of grid voltage waveforms for the circuit in Figure 5.22 for three values of E_{cc}. $R \gg R_g$.

(a)   (b)   (c)

the grid voltage to relax exponentially back to the cutoff voltage as well as to zero volts. The time constant for this exponential is R_gC and the asymptotical value is E_{cc}, for which a positive value is assumed. After passing zero volts, the exponential changes to a time constant, assuming negligible r_c, of

$$\tau_c = \frac{CR_gR}{R + R_g} \tag{5.20}$$

and e_c has an asymptotical value, from Figure 5.22c, of

$$E_{as} = E_{cc}\frac{r_c}{R + R_g + r_c} \tag{5.21}$$

Observe, for large values of R, that the two possible circuit time constants have approximately the same value, R_gC.

The three graphs of Figure 5.23 represent a possible set of grid voltage waveforms for the conditions specified in the preceding developments. For these graphs R is much greater than R_g in which case $e_c(\min) = -E + E_{cc}$, as noted from Equation (5.17). This means that the $(e_s - v_c)$ voltage can be raised into the positive region by an adjustment of E_{cc}. The portion of this voltage that enters the positive region is attenuated at the grid according to Equation (5.15).

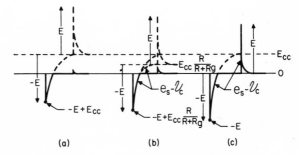

Fig. 5.24-1. Grid voltage waveforms (solid lines) for the circuit in Figure 5.22. (a) $R \gg R_g$. (b) R not much greater than R_g. (c) $R = 0$. See Figure 5.24-2.

(a)   (b)   (c)

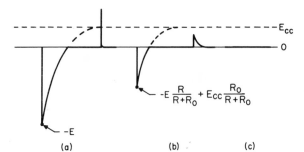

Fig. 5.24-2. Grid voltage waveforms for the circuit in Figure 5.14 for different values of R_0. (a) $R_0 = 0$. (b) R_0 is not zero. (c) R_0 is very large.

The three graphs in Figure 5.24-1 indicate the effect of the magnitude of R (series grid resistor) on the grid-voltage waveforms. Notice how the $(e_s - v_c)$ voltage waveform is changed as R is decreased. Also, observe that the positive spikes increase in magitude as R is decreased.

The three graphs in Figure 5.24-2 are shown to indicate a comparison with the circuit in Figure 5.14 which contains the source resistance, R_0. These graphs can be interpreted by reference to Equation (5.13) and Example 2 of Section 5.7. Observe that a large value of R_0 can cause the grid voltage to collapse to zero when E_{cc} is positive. For the same peak-to-peak value of the source voltage, this collapsing effect does not exist for the circuit containing the series resistance R, as in Figure 5.22.

It should be recognized that the illustrations given with this section are only examples of the behavior of the circuit. There are other possible conditions as to type of source voltage waveforms, relative magnitudes of circuit parameters and magnitude of the bias voltage. This circuit is often used, for example, to *raise* a desired portion of a sine wave into the negative grid-control region of the amplifier. Without the series R, the positive peaks of the e_c voltage would be clamped at near zero voltage.

5.9 Series Grid Resistor and a Parallel Capacitor

Either input circuit in Figure 5.25 has a capacitor in parallel with a series grid resistor. Circuit (a) includes the source resistance R_0. Circuit (b) is shown without R_0; thereby it has been assumed that the source resistance is negligible. When the resistance R is returned to the cathode, as indicated by the dotted lines on the figure, a conventional RC-coupled circuit exists. When the resistance is in series, as shown, the circuit response is similar to that of the conventional circuit in many respects. There are some differences and to account for the differences it is necessary to consider the circuit with and without R_0. To simplify the discussion, the resistor R is designated as "series" R or as "conventional" R. Some of the differences become apparent from the voltage equations that can be written for the

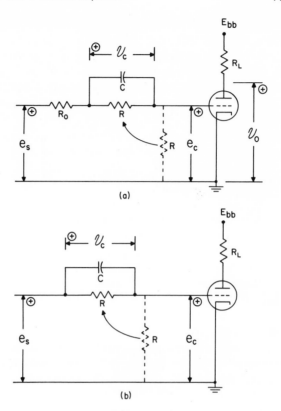

Fig. 5.25. Series grid resistor with parallel capacitor. (a) Source resistance is included. (b) Source resistance is negligible.

two circuits. For circuit (a), which includes R_o, the grid voltage for negative values is

$$e_c^- = e_s - v_c \tag{5.22}$$

for the "series" R, while for the "conventional" R, it is

$$e_c^- = \frac{(e_s - v_c)\,R}{R + R_o} \tag{5.23}$$

Thus, when the resistance is in series, the source resistance does not attenuate the negative grid voltages as it does for the "conventional" R.

The attenuation factor for positive grid voltages is essentially the same for both circuits. It is $r_c/(r_c + R_o)$ for the "series" R and $R_a/(R_a + R_o)$ for the "conventional" R, where R_a is the parallel combination of r_c and R.

Differences also exist with regard to the possible time constants for the circuits. When the grid voltage is negative, the circuit time constant is RC with the "series" R, while for the "conventional" R it is $(R + R_o)C$. For the series R, the circuit time constant is independent of the source resistance when the grid voltage is negative.

One other fact should be emphasized. The "series" R has a voltage equal to the capacitor voltage. Consequently, if the capacitor voltage is nearly constant, then the current in the resistance has, essentially, a d-c value. The "conventional" R has a component of current due to the source voltage, as well as the d-c component of current that is generated by the clamping action of the circuit. This could be important because of the different wattage ratings for the resistor in either of the two positions.

5.10 Resistance Coupling

A decision to use a particular type of input circuit is influenced by the source voltage and the type of response expected for the complete amplifier circuit. This is true for the input circuits of the preceding sections and it is also true for the resistance-coupled circuit in Figure 5.26.

The resistance-coupled circuit is desirable for three general types of applications. These are discussed in the following itemized paragraphs.

(a) It may be necessary to attenuate the source voltage sufficiently to permit linear operation of the amplifier. Many measurement systems may require this, since the voltage to be measured may have a large magnitude and must, therefore, be attenuated by a known factor. Resistance coupling can perform this function. The attenuation should not be sensitive to frequency variations within desired limits. The unavoidable presence of capacitance in the circuit may require a modification of the attenuator to make it less sensitive to frequency changes of the source voltage; this procedure is discussed later in this section. The problem of measurement, of course, is secondary to the present study, since instrumentation and measurement is a complete area of study in itself. Since this chapter restricts the amplifier to a grounded-cathode type of amplifier, there is the danger of leaving the impression that such an amplifier is the first stage of every practical system. This is far from the turth.

(b) It may be necessary to amplify a low frequency voltage. Actually, the source voltage

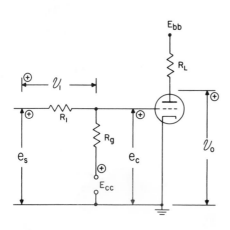

Fig. 5.26. Resistance coupled input circuit.

may be a d-c voltage. A series, or d-c blocking capacitor, cannot be used.

(c) It may be desired to turn the plate current off and hold it off with the source voltage. A resistance-coupled or direct-coupled circuit is required to perform this function.

To understand each of the three general applications of a resistance-coupled input circuit, it is helpful to study the voltage equations that apply for the circuit of Figure 5.26. Normally, the grid-cathode resistance r_c is much less than R_g. Thus, in the positive region,

$$e_c^+ \cong \frac{e_s r_c}{r_c + R_1} \qquad (5.24)$$

The bias voltage E_{cc} and the resistance R_g do not appear in this approximation and are, therefore, ineffective in a control of positive grid voltages.

In the negative grid voltage region,

$$e_c^- = \frac{e_s}{1 + (R_1/R_g)} + \frac{E_{cc}}{1 + (R_g/R_1)} \qquad (5.25)$$

which is easily written by using the superposition theorem. Notice that the R_1/R_g ratio is associated with the source voltage, while the inverse of this ratio is associated with the bias voltage term. This means that the bias voltage control is lost when R_1 is equal to zero and yet as the R_1/R_g ratio is increased, the source voltage becomes more highly attenuated at the grid.

A selection of values for R_1, R_g and E_{cc} is influenced by the magnitudes and the range of grid voltages that are desired for given magnitudes and range of voltages at the source. To study this, it is convenient to let

$$a = \frac{R_g}{R_1 + R_g} \qquad (5.26)$$

and to represent the source voltage and the grid voltage as particular instantaneous values using the symbols E_{s1} and E_{c1}, or E_{s2} and E_{c2} respectively. Then the bias voltage required to give a particular negative value of grid voltage for a particular instantaneous value of source voltage, is

$$E_{cc(1)} = \frac{E_{c1}^- - a E_{s1}}{1 - a} \qquad (5.27)$$

From Equation (5.27), it is also observed that

$$a = \frac{E_{c1}^- - E_{cc}}{E_{s1} - E_{cc}} \qquad (5.28)$$

It may seem a little strange that the bias voltage is included in Equation (5.28), especially since this ratio can also be expressed as a ratio of grid voltage change to the corresponding change of the source voltage, as

$$a = \frac{E_{c1}^- - E_{c2}^-}{E_{s1} - E_{s2}} \qquad (5.29)$$

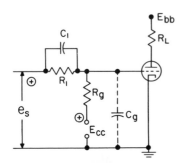

Fig. 5.27. Resistance coupled input circuit with a parallel capacitor on each resistor.

Information is now available to operate the tube as desired, either as a linear amplifier or to turn the plate current on and off with the source voltage, and hold it on or off as desired.

When the resistance-coupled circuit is used as a part of a switching circuit, it is sometimes necessary to add a capacitor in parallel with R_1 as indicated by C_1 in Figure 5.27. The capacitance C_g represents stray capacitance and interelectrode capacitance effects due to the presence of the tube. The capacitance introduced into the circuit by the tube is not fully accounted for at this time. It is more than the grid cathode capacitance, because of feedback effects, and is a topic for discussion in a later chapter. To appreciate the need for the capacitor C_1 in Figure 5.27, it is advisable to review the discussion of Section 2.9 and especially the solution of Problem 2.19. The presence of C_1 permits a step voltage to appear across C_g when the source voltage has a step voltage.

When the resistance-coupled circuit is used as an attenuator, for measurement purposes, it is sometimes necessary to include the capacitor C_1, and perhaps an additional capacitor in parallel with R_g. When the two parallel combinations have the same time constant, the attenuation is a constant as a function of frequency. The circuit is often identified, then, as a frequency compensated attenuator.

5.11   Input Circuits with Diodes

The three-circuits in Figures 5.28, 5.29 and 5.30 are examples to illustrate the use of diodes in the input circuits to grounded cathode amplifiers.

The circuit in Figure 5.28a has a diode in series with the source such that only negative values of e_c can exist. Any positive values of e_s are very higly attenuated by the high reverse resistance of the diode. The negative values are only slightly attenuated in the presence of a large R_g and a low forward resistance for the diode. This circuit with the series diode can be compared with the resistance-coupled circuit in Figure 5.26. If the series resistance R_1 is very large, then positive values of e_c are small, but the negative values of e_c are highly attenuated as well. [See Equations (5.24) and (5.25).] However, if R_1 is small, both the positive and the negative values of e_c are only slightly attenuated. The series diode, replacing R_1, has the effect of switching R_1 to a small value when a small value of series resistance is needed and to a large value when a large series resistance is needed.

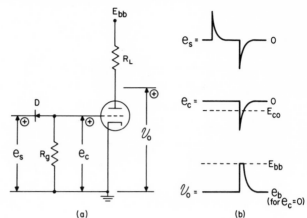

Fig. 5.28. A series diode replaces R_1 of circuit in Figure 5.26 with illustrative waveforms.

(a)   (b)

The voltage waveform in Figure 5.28b illustrate the advantage of the series diode. Here, the source voltage is represented as alternately positive and negative spikes. The grid voltage e_c contains only the negative pulses. Any positive pulses for e_c are highly attenuated. The output voltage v_o contains rectangular positive pulses of short time duration. Notice, in particular, that the output voltage is not appreciably disturbed during the time interval of the positive spike at the input. Thus, the undershoot, as at Point 6 of Figure 5.20, is reduced in magnitude considerably.

The circuit in Figure 5.29 has two diodes, D_1 and D_2. There is also a capacitor C. (The response of this circuit can be very similar to the previous example of Figure 5.28.) Here, it is assumed desirable to generate negative spikes at the grid when the source voltage is a square wave. With the $R_g C$ time constant much less than the time interval of the negative pulse at the source, the negative spike can be generated each cycle provided the capacitor can recharge to the upper limit of the source voltage during the interval

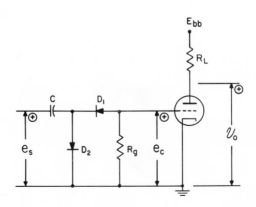

Fig. 5.29. Diode input circuit with capacitance coupling.

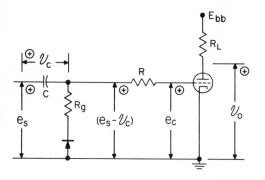

Fig. 5.30. A diode in series with R_g.

when the upper limit of the source voltage exists. The diode D_2 provides a low time constant circuit for the capacitor to fully recharge to the upper limit of the source voltage.

The circuit in Figure 5.30 is similar to the circuit in Figure 5.22, which was identified as "RC coupling with a series grid resistor". With regard to Equation (5.20), the statement was made that the two possible circuit time constants are approximately equal if R (the series resistance) is much larger than R_g. In the circuit in Figure 5.30, these two circuit time constants *are* equal when R is equal to R_g, assuming an ideal diode. When the grid voltage is positive, the diode blocks R_g out of the circuit. When the grid voltage is negative, the series resistance R is blocked out of the circuit. Thus, with R equal to R_g, the circuit resistance remains constant. This means that there is no clamping effect in the circuit. In other words, the voltage $(e_s - v_c)$ averages to zero, and the positive values of this voltage are clipped at the grid, leaving what could be a desired portion in the negative grid control region.

PROBLEMS

5.1 Positive grid voltage characteristics, typical for a triode, are represented in Figure 5.6. Evaluate and plot r_c as a function of e_b for each indicated value of e_c.

5.2 Repeat Problem 5.1 for a number of assigned triodes for which grid current characteristics are available. Suggested triodes (or twin triodes) are 12AU7, 12AT7, 6SN7, 6C4, 6J6, 6U8.

5.3 For the circuit of Figure 5.4, $R_L = 30$ K, $R = 1$ Meg, $E_{bb} = 300$ volts, $E_{cc} = 0$, $e_s = 100 \sin \omega t$, the tube is $\frac{1}{2}$ 12AT7. Neglecting interelectrode and stray capacitances, plot e_c and v_o indicating significant voltages. Also indicate significant time intervals in terms of the period.

5.4 Repeat Problem 5.3 if $E_{cc} = -90$ volts.

5.5 Repeat Problem 5.3 if $E_{cc} = 80$ volts.

5.6 For the circuit of Figure 5.14a, $R_L = 100$ K, $R_g = 100$ K, $C = .001$ µfd, $R_o = 600$ ohms, $E_{bb} = E_{cc} = 250$ volts, the tube is $\frac{1}{2}$ 12AT7 (let $r_c = 400$ ohms), e_s

is rectangular pulses as in Figure 5.14b ($T_1 = T_2 = 100\ \mu s$, $E = 200$ volts). Plot e_c and v_o, indicating all significant quantities.

5.7 Repeat Problem 5.6 if $E_{cc} = 100$ volts, and $T_1 = T_2 = 600\ \mu s$.

5.8 All quantities are given as in Problem 5.6 except for E_{cc}. What is the maximum value of E_{cc} for which the triode plate current is zero during a complete cycle of the source voltage?

5.9 Repeat Problem 5.8 if $T_1 = T_2 = 1000\ \mu s$.

5.10 Repeat Problem 5.6 if R_{oa} (for time interval T_1) $= 40$ K, R_{ob} (for the time interval T_2) $= 1$ K, and the source voltage has an upper limit of 200 volts, and $T_1 = T_2 = 200\ \mu s$.

5.11 For the circuit of Figure 5.14a, $R_L = 30$ K, $R_g = 100$ K, $R_o = 10$ K, C is large, $E_{bb} = 150$ volts, $E_{cc} = 0$, a semiconductor diode is placed in parallel with R_g (forward direction is toward ground and the forward resistance is 20 ohms), e_s is sinusoidal ($E_m = 100$ volts, $f = 1000$ c/s), the tube is $\frac{1}{2}$ 12AU7 (let $r_c = 1200$ ohms). Plot e_c and v_o, indicating all significant quantities.

5.12 Repeat Problem 5.11 if R_o is 200 ohms.

5.13 For the circuit of Figure 5.22a, $R_L = 30$ K, $R_g = 100$ K, $R = 10$ K, $C = .001\ \mu fd$, the tube is $\frac{1}{2}$ 12AU7, $E_{bb} = 210$ volts, $E_{cc} = -100$ volts, e_s is a square wave ($T_1 = T_2 = 1000\ \mu s$, $E = 250$ volts). Plot e_c and v_o, indicating all significant quantities. Neglect the source output resistance.

5.14 Repeat Problem 5.13 if $E_{cc} = 100$ volts.

5.15 Repeat Problem 5.13 if the output resistance of the source is constant at 5 K.

5.16 Repeat Problem 5.13 if $E_{cc} = 0$, C is large, and e_s is a sinusoidal voltage ($E_m = 100$ volts, $f = 1000$ c/s).

5.17 For the circuit of Figure 5.25a, $R_L = 40$ K, R (in parallel with C) $= 50$ K, $C = .005\ \mu fd$, $R_o = 5$ K, $E_{bb} = 240$ volts, the tube is 6J5 (let $r_c = 1$ K), the source voltage is a square wave ($T_1 = T_2 = 2000\ \mu s$, $E = 100$ volts with the lower limit at 10 volts). Plot e_c and v_o, indicating all significant quantities.

5.18 Repeat Problem 5.17 if R (the 50 K resistor) is returned to the cathode, rather than having it in parallel with the capacitor.

5.19 For the circuit of Figure 5.26, $R_L = 25$ K, $R_1 = 1$ Meg, $R_g = 500$ K, $E_{bb} = 250$ volts, $E_{cc} = -90$ volts, the source voltage is a square wave having an upper limit of 210 volts and a lower limit of 24 volts. The tube is $\frac{1}{2}$ 12AU7. What are the two significant voltages for e_c and for v_o?

5.20 Repeat Problem 5.19 if the upper limit of the source voltage is 168 volts rather than 210 volts.

5.21 The quantities are given as in Problem 5.19 except for E_{cc}.
(a) What is the maximum value of E_{cc} for which the plate current is zero when the source voltage is at its lower limit of 24 volts?
(b) What value of E_{cc} will make e_c exactly zero when the source voltage is at its upper limit of 210 volts?

5.22 For the circuit of Figure 5.29, $R_L = 90$ K, $R_g = 50$ K, $C = .003\ \mu fd$, $E_{bb} = 270$ volts, the tube is $\frac{1}{2}$ 12AT7, the source voltage is a square wave ($T_1 = T_2 = 200\ \mu s$, $E = 50$ volts). Assume ideal diodes and plot e_c and v_o, indicating all significant quantities.

5.23 Repeat Problem 5.22 if a bias voltage of 100 volts (positive) is inserted in series with R_g.

5.24 For the conditions of Problem 5.22, discuss the results
(a) if diode D_1 is removed.
(b) if diode D_2 is removed from the circuit (D_1 is present).

5.25 A sinusoidal voltage is applied to the circuit of Figure 5.30. The frequency is 1000 c/s, $E_m = 100$ volts, the tube is $\frac{1}{2}$ 12AU7. Design the circuit so that v_o approximates a symmetrical square wave.

6

Output Circuits
For Grounded-Cathode
Amplifiers

6.1 General Discussion

A number of amplifier output circuits are given in Figure 6.1. Although
the amplifying tube is indicated as a triode, it might also be a multigrid
tube. In order to concentrate on the output circuits, the discussions of
this chapter are largely restricted to triodes.

A sufficient number of these, or other output circuits, are studied to
develop a technique of analysis under different conditions of linear and
switching modes of operation. To do this, it is necessary to obtain an equivalent circuit that will represent the behavior of the tube in the circuit. The
manner of representing the tube is influenced by the response of the amplifier
input circuit. Some information on representation of the tube was given
in the early portion of Chapter 5. Additional information (Section 6.2)
is needed to analyze the amplifier with the many possible types of output
circuits.

The output and input circuits give a great number of possible combinations. To present an analysis and study of all possible *combinations* is
a practical impossibility. After a study of a number of output circuits,
one should be in a position to more easily understand a great number of
complete circuits.

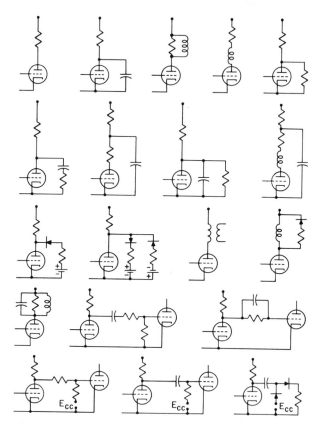

Fig. 6.1. Typical output circuits.

It was observed, from Chapter 5, that the grid voltage can have the same or a different waveform from that of the source. Only that portion of the grid voltage which is in the grid-control region is amplified.

6.2 Equivalent Circuits

The amplifier circuits of Chapter 5 were restricted to a grounded-cathode, resistive-load, type of amplifier. Several facts regarding the output characteristics of this circuit need to be considered before continuing a discussion that involves other output circuits.

To represent the response of the amplifier, it may be necessary to use either of two types of equivalent circuits illustrated in (a_1), or (a_2), and (b) of Figure 6.2. Each circuit has its limitations. The circuit (a_1), or (a_2), is the conventional equivalent circuit for representing the response of the amplifier to changing components of the grid-control voltage. It neglects quiescent values of plate voltage, grid voltage, and plate current, and applies only in the assumed linear operation region of the tube characteristics.

The circuit of Figure 6.2b is shown primarily to define r_b.

$$r_b = \frac{e_b}{i_b} \qquad (6.1)$$

Although this resistance is likely to be a variable, there are circuit problems in which r_b is constant for particular time intervals. In such problems it may be convenient and desirable to use the equivalent circuit containing r_b, since this circuit retains the plate supply voltage. Actual instantaneous values of voltage can then be calculated from the circuit.

The resistance, r_p, is usually identified as the dynamic plate resistance and r_b as the static plate resistance. Two r_b lines and one r_p line are identified on a set of triode characteristics in Figure 6.3 and on a set of pentode characteristics in Figure 6.4. For the triode characteristics, observe that r_b is approximately equal to r_p when e_c is

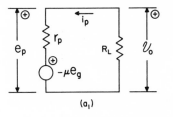

(a₁)

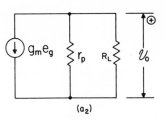

(a₂)

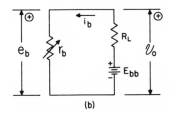

(b)

Fig. 6.2. Possible equivalent circuits for grounded-cathode amplifier.

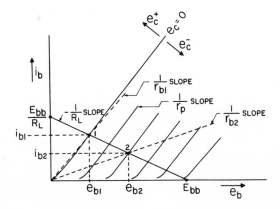

Fig. 6.3. An illustration of r_p and two values of r_b for a triode.

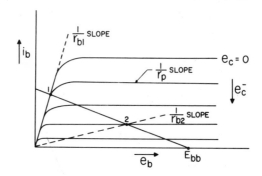

Fig. 6.4. An illustration of r_p and two values of r_b for a pentode.

zero. Several illustrations were given in Chapter 5 in which the grid voltage was zero for a large portion of the period of an input voltage. The equivalent circuit that includes the static plate resistance r_b and the plate supply voltage is applicable in such problems.

The significance of r_b cannot be fully appreciated until the output circuit is modified to include something more or different than just a load resistance R_L. It is sufficient for now to know that the d-c load line with a slope of $-1/R_L$ is the operating line provided that the plate circuit contains *only* R_L.

6.3 Output Resistance

From the equivalent circuits of Figure 6.2, the output resistance, R_o, of a grounded-cathode, resistive-load amplifier is

$$R_o = \frac{r_p R_L}{r_p + R_L} \tag{6.2}$$

when the dynamic resistance, r_p, is applicable to the solution of a circuit problem.

With circuit problems in which r_b applies for a time interval, the output resistance is

$$R_0 = \frac{r_b R_L}{r_b + R_L} \tag{6.3}$$

When the plate current is cut off, the output resistance is

$$R_o = R_L \tag{6.4}$$

The study of various output circuits, for particular circuit arrangements and voltage conditions, will dictate the value of R_o that should be used for a solution of the circuit.

6.4 Drift Voltage

Several factors can cause the output voltage of an amplifier to change. Changes in plate supply voltage, bias voltage, magnitude of circuit parameters, or tube characteristics, can produce undesirable voltage changes or "drift" of the output voltage. Drift voltages resulting from the plate supply and the bias supply are studied in this section for the grounded-cathode, resistive-load type of amplifier. The voltage gain of this amplifier,

$$A = -\frac{\mu R_L}{r_p + R_L}$$

when derived from appropriate geometric figures on the tube characteristics, provides a background of information for a study of drift voltage.

From Figure 6.5, the voltage gain can be expressed as

$$A = \frac{e_{b2} - e_{b1}}{e_{c2} - e_{c1}} \tag{6.5}$$

Referring to the triangle acd,

$$bc = e_{b2} - e_{b1}$$

$$ab + bc = -\mu\,(e_{c2} - e_{c1})$$

thus,

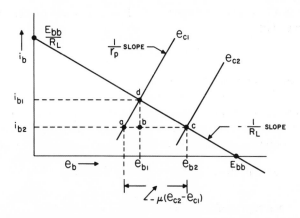

Fig. 6.5. Diagram for calculating the voltage gain of an amplifier.

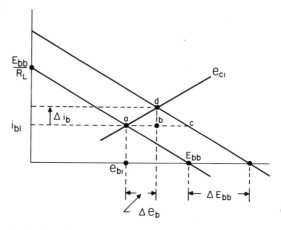

Fig. 6.6. Drift voltage caused by a change in plate supply voltage.

$$\frac{e_{b2} - e_{b1}}{-\mu\,(e_{c2} - e_{c1})} = \frac{bc}{ab + bc}$$

$$= \frac{bc/bd}{ab/bd + bc/bd}$$

$$= \frac{R_L}{r_p + R_L} \tag{6.6}$$

where the ratio bc/bd is R_L and the ratio ab/bd is r_p. Consequently,

$$A = \frac{e_{b2} - e_{b1}}{e_{c2} - e_{c1}} = -\frac{\mu\,R_L}{r_p + R_L} \tag{6.7}$$

The effect of a change in the plate supply voltage on the output (or e_b) voltage is illustrated in Figure 6.6. From a study of the triangle acd we can show that

$$\Delta e_b = \Delta E_{bb}\frac{r_p}{r_p + R_L} \tag{6.8}$$

when the grid voltage is constant at e_{c1}.

Although Equation (6.8) gives the drift in plate voltage produced by a drift of the plate supply voltage, it is more significant to compare this drift voltage with the change in plate voltage produced by the input voltage. The ratio is defined as per cent drift. From Equations (6.8) and (6.7),

$$\text{per cent drift } (E_{bb}) = \frac{\Delta E_{bb}r_p/(r_p + R_L)}{-\Delta e_c\mu R_L/(r_p + R_L)} \times 100$$

$$\text{per cent drift } (E_{bb}) = -\frac{\Delta E_{bb}}{\Delta e_c} \times \frac{1}{g_m R_L} \times 100 \tag{6.9}$$

Notice that the per cent drift is inversely proportional to $g_m R_L$.

The per cent drift for a drift in bias voltage is more critical than for a drift in the plate supply voltage. In the linear operating region of the tube characteristics a change in bias voltage, E_{cc}, will have the same effect on the output voltage as a corresponding change in the source voltage. Thus,

$$\text{per cent drift } (E_{cc}) = \frac{\Delta E_{cc}}{\Delta e_c} \times 100 \qquad (6.10)$$

where Δe_c is a change in the grid voltage produced by the source voltage.

These changes in output voltage that are not caused by the signal, suggest the importance of using regulated d-c power supplies or some other circuit that will inherently compensate for drift when drift is objectionable.

6.5 Resistance Plate Coupling

The circuits (a), (b), and (c) in Figure 6.7 are three examples of resistance-plate coupling. In (a) a single resistor is connected plate to cathode, in (b) a resistance potentiometer is in series with a d-c biasing voltage from plate to cathode, and (c) shows resistance coupling (direct-coupling)

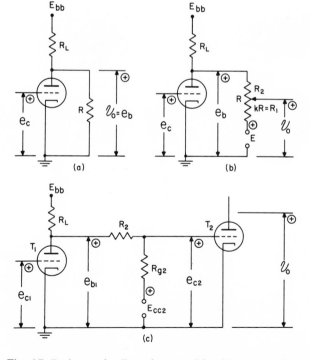

Fig. 6.7. Resistance loading of an amplifier (three examples).

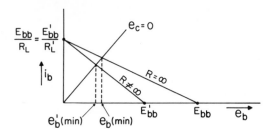

Fig. 6.8. Equivalent plate supply voltage and load line with resistance loading. See Figure 6.7a.

to provide a control voltage to a second stage amplifier. A study of these circuits will indicate their behavior and possible applications to practical problems.

(a) For the circuit in Figure 6.7a, the output voltage is equal to the plate voltage. One convenient method for analyzing this circuit is to determine an equivalent plate supply voltage, E'_{bb}, and an equivalent plate load resistance, R'_L.

$$E'_{bb} = E_{bb}\frac{R}{R + R_L} = \frac{E_{bb}}{1 + R_L/R} \tag{6.11}$$

$$R'_L = \frac{R R_L}{R + R_L} \tag{6.12}$$

Then,

$$v_o \text{ (or } e_b) = E'_{bb} - i_b R'_L \tag{6.13}$$

The d-c load lines, with and without R, can then be represented as shown in Figure 6.8. Observe that the range of controllable plate voltage is decreased as the resistance R is decreased. The maximum value of e_b is decreased from E_{bb} to E'_{bb} and the minimum value of e_b (for $e_c = 0$) is decreased from

$$e_b \text{ (min)} = E_{bb}\frac{r_b}{r_b + R_L} = \frac{E_{bb}}{1 + R_L/r_b} \tag{6.14}$$

to

$$e'_b \text{ (min)} = E'_{bb}\frac{r_b}{r_b + R'_L}$$
$$= \frac{E_{bb}}{1 + R_L[(1/r_b) + (1/R)]} \tag{6.15}$$

where it is assumed that r_b is constant for e_c equal to zero. It is interesting to observe also that a switching R (assume a switch in series with R) results in a d-c load line that pivots about a common i_b intercept for e_b equal to zero as illustrated in Figure 6.8. With R absent and R_L having different values, however, the load line pivots about the e_b interecept of E_{bb}. This suggests two methods of controlling the position of the operating load line on the tube characteristics; that is, use R in parallel with the tube or omit R and change R_L.

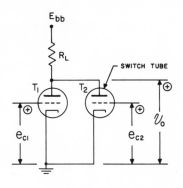

Fig. 6.9. A gating circuit.

A further study of the circuit reveals the effect of R on the gain of the amplifier. The voltage gain

$$A = -\mu \frac{R'_L}{r_p + R'_L}$$

reveals more information when rewritten as

$$A = - \frac{\mu}{1 + (r_p/R_L)\,[1 + (R_L/R)]} \tag{6.16}$$

For an R_L/R ratio much greater than unity, the voltage gain is approximately

$$A \cong - \frac{\mu}{1 + (r_p/R)} \tag{6.17}$$

which states that R becomes the controlling factor in determining the gain of the amplifier when R is much less than R_L. The voltage gain will be low if R is also much less than r_p. This suggests the possibility of switching a small resistance, R, in and out of the circuit to block amplification or to permit normal amplification, which could be done by replacing R of Figure 6.7a with a triode tube identified as a switch tube (see Figure 6.9). The r_b of the switch tube can be made to have a low value when its grid voltage is positive. Normal amplification exists when the switch tube is cut off.

(b) To evaluate e_b for the circuit of Figure 6.7b it is again convenient to determine the equivalent plate supply voltage, E'_{bb}, and the equivalent load resistance, R'_L. The voltage E is a d-c voltage. Applying Thevenin's theorem,

$$E'_{bb} = (E_{bb} - E)\frac{R}{R + R_L} + E$$
$$= \frac{E_{bb}}{1 + R_L/R} + \frac{E}{1 + R/R_L} \tag{6.18}$$

$$R'_L = \frac{R_L R}{R_L + R} \tag{6.19}$$

The voltage, e_b, and the d-c load line are then represented by

$$e_b = E'_{bb} - i_b R'_L$$

The output voltage is

$$\begin{rcases} v_o = k\,(e_b - E) + E \\ \quad = ke_b + E\,(1 - k) \end{rcases} \tag{6.20}$$

where,

$$k = \frac{R_1}{R_1 + R_2} = \frac{R_1}{R} \tag{6.21}$$

An examination of the last four equations will reveal several results that can be obtained with the circuit in Figure 6.7b.

If R is much larger than R_L the output circuit does not affect the voltage gain of the basic amplifier. Equations (6.18) and (6.19) reduce to E_{bb} and R_L which means that the voltage E will not influence the value of the plate voltage, e_b. However, for R much less than R_L, the voltage E can have a much greater influence on the value of e_b than the plate supply voltage, E_{bb}. As a matter of fact, a negative value of E might even make the amplifying tube completely inoperative. One may or may not wish this to happen.

In general, there are two types of problems to consider for the circuit of Figure 6.7b: one is where the output circuit does not load the amplifier and the other is where the output circuit does load the amplifier. Further discussion of the latter is reserved for Section 6.6.

The output circuit provides a method of controlling the magnitude and polarity of the output voltage for a particular value of plate voltage without loading the circuit. Thus, v_o can be adjusted to any desired d-c reference voltage but with the disadvantage of attenuation by the factor, k. To make v_o equal to zero, for example, we observe from Equation (6.20) that

$$E\left(1 - \frac{1}{k}\right) = e_b \tag{6.22}$$

Since k is a positive number less than unity, the voltage E must have a negative value to make v_o zero for any particular value of e_b. Observe that as k is made larger the required magnitude of E is also increased and can become prohibitively large. So voltage gain is sacrificed to obtain control of the d-c reference voltage. With R much larger than R_L, the over-all voltage gain of the circuit is

$$A = \frac{-\mu k R_L}{r_p + R_L} \tag{6.23}$$

(c) The circuit of Figure 6.7c has similarities to circuits (a) and (b). When the grid voltage of tube 2 is negative, circuit (b) is applicable. When the grid voltage of tube 2 is positive, the series resistor, R_2, is returned to the cathode through r_{c2}. Circuit (a) is then applicable.

The circuit involving R_2, R_{g2} and E_{cc2} can be regarded as the input

circuit to a second amplifier stage. (See
Section 5.10.) The response of the second
stage can then be determined for any
operating condition—as a linear amplifier,
a switch tube or as a pulse-forming circuit.

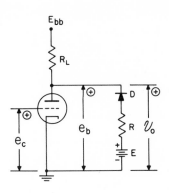

6.6 Plate Catching Diode

The circuit of Figure 6.10 has an output circuit that contains a diode to limit
the lower value of the plate voltage approximately to the d-c voltage, E. The resistance,
R, is the output resistance of the biasing
voltage and the resistance of the diode.

Fig. 6.10. Plate-catching diode.

This resistance must be small. The circuit is similar to the circuit of Figure
6.7b where k is equal to unity but with a small value of resistance R
switched in and out of the circuit by the action of the diode. When the
plate voltage is greater than E, the diode circuit is open and the amplifier
is not loaded. The diode conducts when the plate voltage falls below the
d-c biasing voltage and the amplifier is then heavily loaded by the small
resistance in the diode circuit. The response of the circuit is illustrated
with an example.

EXAMPLE

Given: $\frac{1}{2}$ 12AT7 triode

$E_{bb} = 300$ volts

$R_L = 50$ K

$R = 2$ K

Determine: a value of E equal to the plate voltage when e_c is zero and
determine v_o for a positive value of e_c, with and without the diode circuit.

Solution: from the tube characteristics e_b, for e_c equal to zero with a
50 K load line, is 58 volts. Thus, E is adjusted to 58 volts. Now, let e_c equal
one volt. The corresponding value of e_b on the 50 K load line (diode removed
from the circuit), is 25 volts. To find the corresponding value of e_b with the
diode circuit connected, it is necessary to find the equivalent load line.
From Equations (6.18) and (6.19),

$$E'_{bb} = \frac{300}{1 + 25} + \frac{58}{1 + \frac{1}{25}} = 67 \text{ volts}$$

$$R'_L = \frac{(50)(2)}{50 + 2} = 1.92 \text{ K}$$

Now, from the equivalent load line, e_b, for e_c equal to one, is 52 volts. The diode circuit limits the plate voltage change to 6 volts (58 − 52), while in the absence of the diode, the plate voltage change is 33 volts (58 − 25). Under-shoots, below 58 volts, are then highly attenuated with the diode circuit.

6.7 Parallel Capacitor

The circuit in Figure 6.11 shows a capacitance from plate to cathode, as well as the usual R_L in series with the plate supply voltage. Some of the specific reasons for using this circuit are (1) to provide a low-pass RC filter, (2) to generate a ramp voltage function or a sweep voltage, and (3) to "deaden" either the leading or trailing edge of a rectangular pulse. A linear RC series circuit will perform *some* of these functions, but a switching mode of nonlinearity for the circuit may also be required. In addition to its amplifying properties, the presence of the tube in the circuit can also provide the switching requirements.

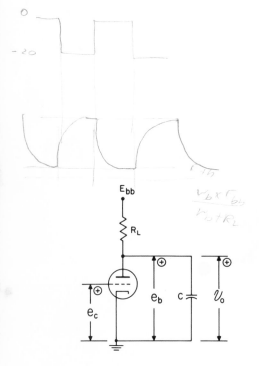

Fig. 6.11. Shunt capacitance loading.

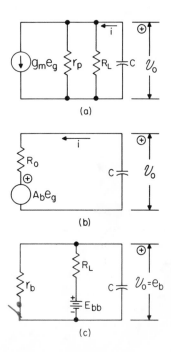

Fig. 6.12. Equivalent circuits for the circuit in Figure 6.11. (a) and (b) are for linear operation, (c) is for switching mode of operation.

Three equivalent circuits, for Figure 6.11, are shown in Figure 6.12. The first two, (a) and (b), are equivalent circuits representing linear operation. The third equivalent circuit, (c), represents a switching mode of operation. The switching mode of operation is of primary interest for this text. The linear circuits are shown to define R_o and A_b (used more extensively in later studies) and to call attention to the frequency response of the circuit. The frequency response for linear operation is not identical to the frequency response for the switching mode of operation. A comparison, for the two types of operation, is important.

(a) As a linear amplifier with a sinusoidal input, the response of the circuit is determined from the equivalent circuit, (a) or (b) in Figure 6.12. The second of these two equivalent circuits is of a form that is often convenient in simplifying and clarifying the analysis of certain circuit problems. To verify the equivalence of the two circuits, (a) and (b), we proceed by first writing the following current equation for circuit (a):

$$v_o \left(\frac{1}{R_L} + \frac{1}{r_p} \right) + g_m e_g - i = 0$$

Solving for v_o,

$$v_o = i \frac{R_L r_p}{R_L + r_p} - g_m \frac{r_p R_L}{r_p + R_L} e_g$$

or,

$$v_o = iR_o + A_b e_g$$

where R_o and A_b are respectively the output resistance and voltage gain of the amplifier, the grounded-cathode, resistance-loaded amplifier.

Taking the capacitive reactance into consideration, for rms values of sinusoidal voltages

$$v_o = A_b E_g \frac{1}{1 + j\omega R_o C} \qquad (6.25)$$

and with $R_o C$ represented by $1/\omega_2$ (ω_2 is the upper half-power frequency), the over-all voltage gain for linear operation is

$$A = A_b \frac{1}{1 + j\omega/\omega_2} \qquad (6.26)$$

(b) To generate a repeated ramp function, or sweep voltage, the grid-cathode voltage should be repetitive negative pulses. The voltage waveforms in Figure 6.13 represent the response of the circuit. The grid voltage is below cutoff during the sweep, and its upper value is zero volts. As indicated on the V_o waveform, and from Figure 6.12c, the two possible circuit time constants are

$$\tau_c = R_L C = R_{oa} C$$

and

$$\tau_c = \frac{r_b R_L}{r_b + R_L} C = R_{ob} C$$

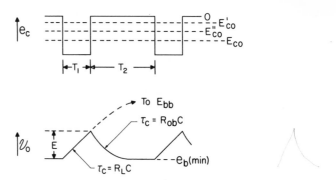

Fig. 6.13. An example of voltage waveforms for the circuit in Figure 6.11.

where r_b is the tube resistance for e_c equal to zero. Observe that the output resistance has two values, R_{oa} and R_{ob}, for this switching mode of operation. Notice, also, that the static resistance r_b is used to evaluate R_{ob}. The magnitude of the sweep voltage, E, is

$$E = (E_{bb} - e_b \,(\text{min}))\,(1 - e^{-(T_1/R_L C)}) \tag{6.27}$$

To obtain a reasonably linear sweep, T_1 should be much less than $R_L C$. Since E is a small fraction of the plate supply voltage, it may be necessary to amplify the generated sweep voltage to obtain greater magnitudes of sweep.

On completion of the sweep, the output voltage should return quickly to the steady state value of e_b (min) for e_c equal to zero. This means that R_L must be greater than r_b. The time T_2 in Figure 6.13 is the *recovery* time interval. It is possible to decrease the recovery time by allowing a positive overshoot on the grid voltage. This will force r_b to have smaller values during the time of the overshoot.

The allowable sweep and recovery time intervals, as well as difficulties in obtaining large R_L/r_b ratios, places limitations on the applications of this circuit for generating sweep voltages. Other sweep circuits are discussed in later chapters.

The path of operation on the tube characteristics is of interest. This path of operation is a loop as indicated in Figure 6.14. When the plate current is cut off by the negative step of grid voltage, the capacitor voltage is still at e_b (min) with the sweep voltage starting at this value. Observe that the cutoff voltage is less than E_{co} for a triode. It is represented as E'_{co} in Figure 6.14. On completion of the sweep the cutoff voltage is represented as E''_{co}. Immediately after the positive step of grid voltage, the plate current increases instantly to a value on the zero grid-voltage line corresponding to the plate voltage at the end of the sweep. The path of operation then continues on the zero grid-voltage line to the steady state value on the d-c

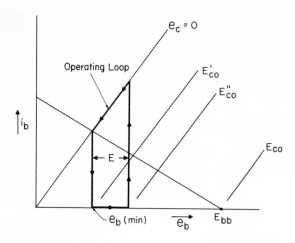

Fig. 6.14. The operating loop for a capacitance loaded amplifier.

load line. A solution of the circuit is illustrated with an example for a grid
voltage waveform in Figure 6.13.

EXAMPLE

Given: $\frac{1}{2}$ 5963 tube

$$E_{bb} = 300 \text{ volts}$$
$$R_L = 100 \text{ K}$$
$$C = 0.01 \ \mu\text{fd}$$
$$T_1 \text{ (sweep time)} = 100 \ \mu\text{s}$$
$$T_2 \text{ (recovery)} = 400 \ \mu\text{s}$$

Determine: Significant values to describe the output voltage for the
circuit in Figure 6.11.

Solution: The plate resistance for e_c equal to zero, as determined from
the plate characteristics in the probable operation range, is

$$r_b = 9 \text{ K}$$

Thus,

$$R_o = \frac{r_b R_L}{r_b + R_L} = 8.2 \text{ K}$$

The two circuit time constants that are applicable, are

$$\tau_{c1} = R_L C = 1000 \ \mu\text{s sweep time constant}$$
$$\tau_{c2} = R_{ob} C = 82 \ \mu\text{s recovery time constant}$$

The steady state value of plate voltage for e_c equal to zero is determined from the plate characteristics, from which

$$e_b \text{ (min)} = 23 \text{ volts}$$

From Equation (6.27) the magnitude of the sweep voltage is

$$E = (300 - 23)(1 - e^{-0.1})$$
$$= 26.3 \text{ volts}$$

Thus, at the end of the sweep,

$$v_o = e_b = 23 + 26.3 = 49.3 \text{ volts}$$

and the corresponding cutoff voltage is approximately -4 volts. An input voltage of this order of magnitude is sufficient to give the results of this example. It is not necessary to have a 25 volt signal which is the approximate cutoff voltage corresponding to E_{bb} of 300 volts.

The recovery time constant (82 μs) is sufficiently less than the recovery time interval (400 μs) to permit the output voltage to return to its minimum steady state value. Defining recovery time, T_{rec}, as the time for 0.9 completion of the exponential,

$$T_{rec} = R_{ob}C \ln \frac{E}{0.1E} \qquad\qquad (6.28)$$
$$= 82 \ln 10 = 189 \ \mu s$$

The solution of the problem is now completed. The plate current immediately after the sweep, when e_c is returned to zero, is of interest as a study of the operating path on the plate characteristics. At this instant, since the capacitor voltage is e_b,

$$i_b = \frac{e_b}{r_b} = \frac{49.3}{8.33 \ K} = 5.9 \text{ ma}$$

which is the largest value of plate current on the operating path.

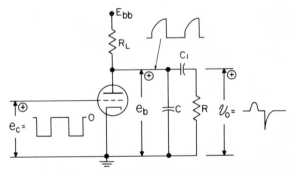

Fig. 6.15. Decreasing the magnitude of positive output pulses with a shunt capacitance.

(c) When rectangular pulses are applied to a differentiating circuit, the output voltage can be a series of alternately positive and negative spikes. Certain applications require an elimination, or near elimination of either the positive or negative spikes. One method of deemphasizing the positive pulses is shown with the circuit in Figure 6.15. If the capacitance C is omitted, the plate-voltage waveform could be approximately a square wave. By including the shunt capacitance C of proper magnitude, it is possible to "deaden" the leading edge of the e_b waveform and still retain a steep *trailing* edge. A capacitance smaller than that of the preceding example is required. The two-valued R_o is a significant factor here.

6.8 Shunt Capacitance Frequency Compensation

The circuit in Figure 6.16 is discussed in this section for two conditions of operation. One problem, (a), is to study the frequency response of the circuit for sinusoidal input voltages and assumed linear operation of the amplifier. The second problem, (b), is to study the response of the circuit for a rectangular pulse input voltage and a switching mode of operation of the amplifier. The results of these two studies can then be compared with the results obtained for the circuit of Figure 6.11 in the preceding section. The only difference in the two circuits is that in Figure 6.16 the capacitance, C, is returned to the cathode from a tap on the plate load resistance while in Figure 6.11, the capacitance shunts the tube, plate to cathode. A discussion of the second problem is reserved for Section 6.9.

For linear operation of the amplifier, the equivalent circuit of Figure

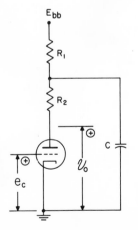

Fig. 6.16. Frequency compensation with a shunting capacitor.

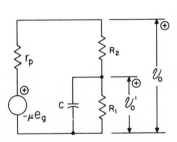

Fig. 6.17. Equivalent circuit for assumed linear operation of the circuit in Figure 6.16.

6.17 is applicable. This is an innocent looking circuit. Voltage equations are easily written for this circuit, but getting the equations into a readily understandable form does require some juggling of terms.

Before writing any general equations, let us study the circuit for certain limiting conditions of operation. These limiting conditions will suggest the desired form of a general equation. The limiting conditions are low frequency operation and high frequency operation.

At low frequencies, the capacitive reactance is high and much greater than R_1 in ohms. For this condition the voltage gain, identified as A_{LF}, is

$$A_{LF} = -\mu \frac{R_1 + R_2}{r_p + R_1 + R_2} \tag{6.29}$$

which is the voltage gain of a basic amplifier. The capacitance, C, is effectively out of the circuit. The output resistance at low frequencies, identified as $R_o(LF)$, is

$$R_o\,(LF) = \frac{r_p\,(R_1 + R_2)}{r_p + R_1 + R_2} \tag{6.30}$$

At high frequencies, the capacitive reactance and output voltage are low. The voltage gain and output resistance, then, are

$$A_{HF} = -\mu \frac{R_2}{r_p + R_2} \tag{6.31}$$

$$R_o\,(HF) = \frac{r_p R_2}{r_p + R_2} \tag{6.32}$$

Observe that the voltage gain has the lower limit of Equation (6.31). It is not zero as in the case when the tube is shunted directly with a capacitance. This means that we can "boost" the gain at low frequencies and still retain a finite voltage gain for higher frequencies. Of course, any stray capacitance shunting the output voltage will still limit the high frequency response of the amplifier. The advantage of the circuit in Figure 6.16 is to improve the low frequency response and help discount the effect of a series coupling capacitor that may be in the input circuit.

An examination of the capacitor voltage, identified as v_o' on the equivalent circuit will lead to significant quantities that will appear in the general expressions for the output voltage, v_o, and the overall gain, A, of the amplifier. Knowing v_o', then, the following can be deduced:

$$v_o = (-\mu e_g - v_o') \frac{R_2}{r_p + R_2} + v_o'$$

$$v_o = -\mu e_g \frac{R_2}{r_p + R_2} + v_o' \frac{r_p}{r_p + R_2} \tag{6.33}$$

$$= A_{HF} e_g + v_o' \frac{r_p}{r_p + R_2} \tag{6.34}$$

TABLE 5.2 VOLTAGES AMD TIME INTERVALS
FOR FIGURE 5.20, EXAMPLE 2, SECTION 5.7.

PT.	e_c	v_o	TIME INTERVALS
1	2	43	
2	-71	250	
3	-15	250	$t_{23} = 50.6\ \mu s$
4	0	75	$t_{24} = 66.9\ \mu s$
5	2	43	
6	11	(Small value)	

5.8 RC Coupling and Series Grid Resistor

The circuit in Figure 5.22a represents an input circuit with RC coupling and a series grid resistor, R. In addition to knowing the behavior and response of such a circuit, it is also of interest to compare it with the circuit in Figure 5.14 as studied in Section 5.7. The source resistance, R_o, was included in that study. The source resistance is neglected in the circuit in Figure 5.22a. This can be taken into consideration when the circuit is compared with that of the preceding section.

Equivalent circuits, for the different states of operation, are valuable

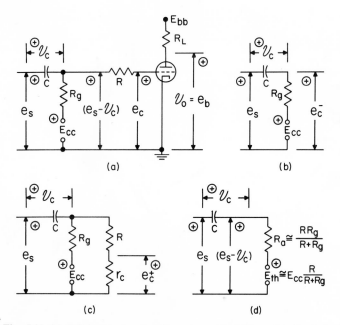

Fig. 5.22 (a) RC input circuit with series grid resistor. (b) Equivalent circuit when grid voltage is negative. (c), (d) Equivalent circuits when grid voltage is positive.

But,

$$v_o' = A_b' E_g \frac{1}{1 + j\omega R_o' C} \qquad (6.35)$$

where

$$A_b' = -\mu \frac{R_1}{r_p + R_1 + R_2} \qquad (6.36)$$

$$R_o' = \frac{R_1 (r_p + R_2)}{r_p + R_1 + R_2} \qquad (6.37)$$

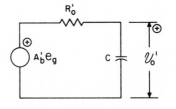

Fig. 6.18. Equivalent circuit for assumed linear operation of the circuit in Figure 6.16.

The equivalent circuit in Figure 6.18 is helpful in writing the last three equations. Note that R_o', not R_o, is a significant quantity.

However, we are primarily interested in the true output voltage. Equation (6.34) can now be written as

$$v_o = A_{\mathrm{HF}} E_g + A_b' E_g \frac{r_p}{(r_p + R_2)(1 + j\omega R_o' C)} \qquad (6.38)$$

It is easily shown that

$$A_{\mathrm{LF}} = A_{\mathrm{HF}} + A_b' \frac{r_p}{r_p + R_2} \qquad (6.39)$$

Then, the over-all circuit voltage gain from Equations (6.38) and (6.39) can be written in factored form as

$$A = A_{\mathrm{LF}} \frac{1 + j\omega \left(\dfrac{R_o' A_{\mathrm{HF}}}{A_{\mathrm{LF}}} \right) C}{1 + j\omega R_o' C} \qquad (6.40)$$

Let

$$\frac{1}{\omega_a} = R_o' C, \qquad \frac{1}{\omega_b} = \left(R_o' \frac{A_{\mathrm{HF}}}{A_{\mathrm{LF}}} \right) C \qquad (6.41)$$

The db gain can be determined by multiplying both members of Equation (6.40) by $20 \log_{10}$. Thus,

$$A_{db} = 20 \log_{10} A_{\mathrm{LF}} + 10 \log_{10} \left[1 + \left(\frac{\omega}{\omega_b} \right)^2 \right] - 10 \log_{10} \left[1 + \left(\frac{\omega}{\omega_a} \right)^2 \right] \qquad (6.42)$$

To represent A_{LF} as zero db reference, merely omit the first term of Equation (6.42). The frequency response for the circuit is represented in Figure 6.19.

The preceding developments reveal the following additional points of interest:

(a) From Equation (6.41),

$$\frac{\omega_b}{\omega_a} = \frac{A_{\mathrm{LF}}}{A_{\mathrm{HF}}} \qquad (6.43)$$

(b) The resistance, R_o' in Equation (6.37) can be written as

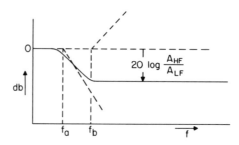

Fig. 6.19. Frequency response for the circuit in Figure 6.16.

$$R_o' = \frac{R_1}{1 + R_1/(r_p + R_2)}$$

If a pentode is used, $(r_p + R_2)$ is likely to be much greater than R_1. Then,

$$R_o' \cong R_1 \tag{6.44}$$

(c) The A_{HF}/A_{LF} ratio can be written as,

$$\frac{A_{HF}}{A_{LF}} = \frac{1}{1 + (r_p/R_2)}\left[1 + \frac{r_p}{R_1 + R_2}\right]$$

Thus, for large values of r_p, as in a pentode,

$$\frac{A_{HF}}{A_{LF}} = \frac{\omega_a}{\omega_b} \cong \frac{R_2}{R_1 + R_2} \tag{6.45}$$

(d) For large values of r_p, the parenthetical factor of Equation (6.40) becomes

$$R_o'\frac{A_{HF}}{A_{LF}} \cong \frac{R_1 R_2}{R_1 + R_2} \tag{6.46}$$

6.9 Pulse Input Voltage to Low Frequency Compensation Circuit

The voltage waveforms of Figure 6.20 illustrate the response of the circuit in Figure 6.16 when the grid voltage is rectangular pulses. This was indicated as a second type of problem in Section 6.8, and is explained here with the aid of a numerical example.

EXAMPLE

Given: 6SJ7 Pentode (see Figure 6.16)

$$E_{bb} = 200 \text{ volts}$$
$$R_1 = 20 \text{ K}$$
$$R_2 = 20 \text{ K}$$
$$C = 0.01 \text{ } \mu\text{fd}$$

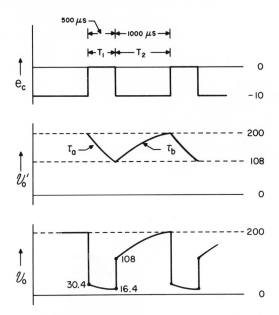

Fig. 6.20. Response of the low-frequency compensated amplifier to a pulsed-voltage input.

Determine: significant values to describe the output voltage when the grid voltage is as given in Figure 6.20.

Solution: The given grid voltage consists of rectangular pulses with an upper limit of zero volts and a lower limit of -10 volts. The latter is sufficient to cut off the plate current of the tube. The two equivalent circuits of Figure 6.21 are applicable to a solution of the problem. When the grid voltage is at zero value, the equivalent circuits (a_1) and (a_2) apply. When the grid voltage is at -10 volts, the equivalent curcuit (b) applies. Circuits (a_2) and (b) are the circuits from which basic calculations are made. To find the output voltage,

$$v_o = v_o' \frac{r_b}{r_b + R_2}$$

when the first equivalent circuit is applicable. When the second equivalent circuit is applicable,

$$v_o = v_o'$$

To proceed with the calculations, it is first necessary to determine r_b. From the plate characteristics and the 40 K d-c load line we find that,

$$r_b = 3.6 \text{ K}$$

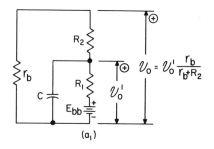

(a₁)

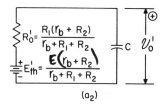

(a₂)

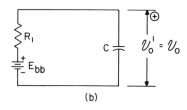

(b)

Fig. 6.21. Equivalent circuits for the example in Section 6.9.

Now, the output resistance, R_o, and Thevenin's equivalent voltage for Figure 6.21a₂ is calculated.

$$R'_o = \frac{R_1(r_b + R_2)}{r_b + R_1 + R_2}$$

$$= \frac{20\,(3.6 + 20)}{3.6 + 20 + 20}$$

$$= 10.8 \text{ K}$$

$$E'_{th} = E_{bb}\frac{r_b + R_2}{r_b + R_1 + R_2}$$

$$= 200\frac{23.6}{43.6} = 108 \text{ volts}$$

The time constants for the two equivalent circuits are,

$$\tau_a = R'_o C = 108\ \mu s$$

$$\tau_b = R_1 C = 200\ \mu s$$

Since these two time constants are sufficiently less than the respective time intervals of 500 μs and 1000 μs to permit the capacitor voltage to reach the limiting values of 200 volts and 108 volts, the plot of v'_o is as indicated in Figure 6.20.

From the equivalent circuit (a₂),

$$v_o = v'_o\frac{r_b}{r_b + R_2} = \frac{3.6}{23.6}v'_o$$

$$= 0.152\ v'_o$$

and from the equivalent circuit (b),

$$v_o = v'_o$$

Significant values for the output voltage are now easily determined. The results are indicated in the plot of v_o, Figure 6.20. This is a type of waveform in which the high frequency components of voltage are attenuated as indicated by the convex shape of the top and bottom portions of the waveform. The tilt of the waveform is a result of the phase shift that accompanies the attenuation. Thus, if an input waveform has an attenuation and leading phase shift of low frequency voltages, the circuit of Figure 6.16 can compensate for this by attenuating the higher frequency voltages.

6.10 An RC Series Circuit Paralleling the Tube

The circuit in Figure 6.22 has an RC series circuit directly paralleling the tube and the output. The eqivalent circuit for assumed *linear operation* of the tube is (a_1), or (a_2), in Figure 6.23.

Writing voltage equations with the view of determining the frequency response of the circuit we observe that,

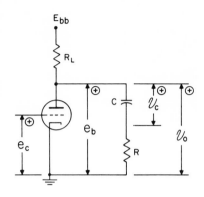

Fig. 6.22. A series RC-loading circuit.

$$v_o = A_b E_g \frac{R - j\dfrac{1}{\omega C}}{R_o + R - j\dfrac{1}{\omega C}}$$

where A_b, the gain of the basic amplifier, is

$$A_b = -\mu \frac{R_L}{r_p + R_L}$$

and R_o is defined as the output resistance of the basic amplifier, which is

$$R_o = \frac{r_p R_L}{r_p + R_L}$$

The expression for the output voltage can be written in factored form as

$$v_o = A_b E_g \frac{1 + j\omega C R}{1 + j\omega (R_o + R) C} \tag{6.47}$$

The voltage gain for the circuit is,

$$A = A_b \frac{1 + j\omega RC}{1 + j\omega (R_o + R) C} \tag{6.48}$$

Observe the similarity in the form of this expression for gain and that of Equation (6.40) which was developed in Section 6.8 for the circuit of Figure 6.16. In Equation (6.48), A_b is also the gain for low frequencies. Letting

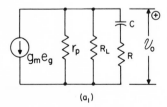

(a₁)

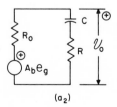

(a₂)

Fig. 6.23. Equivalent circuits for linear operation of the circuit in Figure 6.22. See Figure 6.25 for the switching mode.

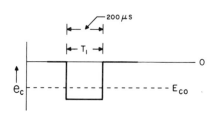

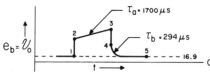

Fig. 6.24. Voltage waveforms for the example in Section 6.10. The significant voltages at points 1 through 5 are 16.9, 46.6, 72, 26.1, and 16.9.

$$\frac{1}{\omega_b} = RC$$

$$\frac{1}{\omega_a} = (R_o + R)\,C \qquad (6.49)$$

the voltage gain is

$$A = A_b \frac{1 + j\dfrac{\omega}{\omega_b}}{1 + j\dfrac{\omega}{\omega_a}} \qquad (6.50)$$

The frequency response, in db, is identical to that shown in Figure 6.19. It is of interest to again observe that

$$\frac{\omega_a}{\omega_b} = \frac{A_{\mathrm{HF}}}{A_{\mathrm{LF}}} = \frac{R}{R_o + R} \qquad (6.51)$$

The circuit is one type used as a means of generating a trapezoidal waveform needed for oscilloscopes with magnetic sweep. Typical voltage waveforms are shown in Figure 6.24. This Figure is supported with a numerical example.

EXAMPLE

Given: $E_{bb} = 270$ volts

$R_L = 150$ K

$R = 20$ K

$C = 0.01\ \mu\mathrm{fd}$

$r_b = 10$ K (for $e_c = 0$)

Determine: significant values to describe the output voltage waveform when the grid voltage is a 200 μs negative pulse with limiting voltages of zero and below cutoff as indicated in Figure 6.24.

Solution: the equivalent circuits (a) and (b) of Figure 6.25 are applicable to the solution of the problem, circuit (a) when the plate current is cut off, and circuit (b) when the grid voltage is zero. The equivalent circuit (c) of Figure 6.25 is shown to illustrate the similarity to the nonlinear circuit problem presented in Chapter 3. Here, R_{oa} is equal to 150 K and R_{ob} equals 9.4 K.

The two possible circuit time constants are

$$\tau_a = 1700\ \mu\mathrm{s}$$

$$\tau_b = 294\ \mu\mathrm{s}$$

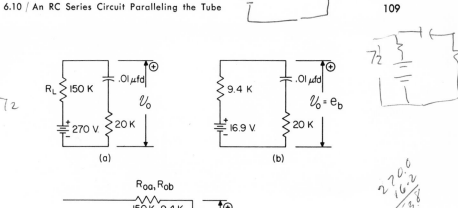

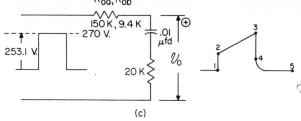

Fig. 6.25. Equivalent circuits for calculating significant voltages for example in Section 6.10.

With the grid voltage at zero for a long time, the output voltage and the capacitor voltage is 16.9 volts, which is the voltage at Point 1, or Point 5, on the plot of v_o in Figure 6.24.

From the equivalent circuit (a), the voltages at Point 2 and Point 3 are calculated as follows:

$$v_{o(2)} = (270 - 16.9)\frac{20\text{ K}}{170\text{ K}} + 16.9$$
$$= 29.7 + 16.9 = 46.6 \text{ volts}$$

$$v_{o(3)} = 270 - (270 - 46.6)\, e^{-200/1700}$$
$$= 72 \text{ volts}$$

At Point 3, the capacitor voltage is

$$v_c = 72 - (270 - 72)\frac{20\text{ K}}{150\text{ K}}$$
$$= 45.6 \text{ volts}$$

This capacitor voltage is needed to determine the voltage at Point 4 on the voltage waveform for v_o. Thus, from equivalent circuit (b),

$$v_{o(4)} = 45.6 - (45.6 - 16.9)\frac{20\text{ K}}{29.4\text{ K}}$$
$$= 26.1 \text{ volts}$$

The output voltage then continues exponentially with the initial value of

26.1 volts and an asymptotical value of 16.9 volts and a time constant (τ_b) equal to 294 μs.

6.11 More About Load Lines

In Section 6.7, it was discovered that the load line pivots about a common i_b intercept when the tube is shunted with a resistance. The problem now is to consider load line conditions when the tube is shunted with an RC series circuit as in Figure 6.22. Writing the current equation for this circuit to express the plate current as a function of plate voltage, we find that

$$i_b = \frac{E_{bb}}{R_L} + \frac{v_c}{R} - e_b\left(\frac{1}{R_L} + \frac{1}{R}\right) \qquad (6.52)$$

For high frequency operation ($\omega > 10\omega_b$), the capacitor voltage is essentially constant at the quiescent plate voltage, E_b, as defined in Figure 6.26. Thus, in this high frequency range Equation (6.52) is rewritten as

$$i_b = \frac{E_{bb}}{R_L} + \frac{E_b}{R} - e_b\left(\frac{1}{R_L} + \frac{1}{R}\right) \qquad (6.53)$$

which is an equation of a straight line with a slope of $-[(1/R_L) + (1/R)]$, an i_b intercept of $[(E_{bb}/R_L) + (E_b/R)]$ and an e_b intercept of $[E_{bb}R/(R + R_L) + E_b R_L/(R + R_L)]$. These values are indicated on the d-c load line of Figure 6.26.

The d-c load line of Figure 6.26 applies for a low frequency range of operation. This can be verified by replacing v_c of Equation (6.52) with e_b, since the capacitor voltage is essentially equal to the plate voltage at low frequencies ($\omega < \omega_a/10$). Thus,

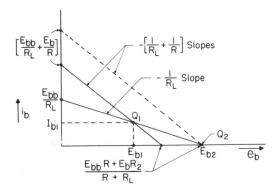

Fig. 6.26. Load lines for the circuit in Figure 6.22, with and without RC loading. Two load lines are shown with RC loading: One for a *constant* capacitor voltage equal to E_{b1} and the other for a constant capacitor voltage equal to E_{b2}.

$$i_b = \frac{E_{bb}}{R_L} + \frac{e_b}{R} - e_b\left(\frac{1}{R_L} + \frac{1}{R}\right)$$
$$= \frac{E_{bb}}{R_L} - \frac{e_b}{R_L} \tag{6.54}$$

which is the equation of a straight line with a slope and intercepts as identified on the d-c load line of Figure 6.26.

6.12   Waveshaping with RC-Coupled Amplifier

A two-stage RC-coupled amplifier circuit is shown in Figure 6.27. This
circuit can operate as a linear amplifier or as a pulse-forming amplifier.
For either type of operation an analysis of the circuit is very similar to
previous discussions on RC-coupled circuits as given in Chapter 3 and in
Sections 5.6, 5.7, and 6.10. This similarity is recognized when the input
circuit for the second tube (T_2) is represented as the $R_{g2}C$ coupling, where
the source voltage is generated by the first stage.

This section is devoted to a study of the two-stage RC-coupled circuit
when operated as a pulse-forming amplifier to obtain a narrow rectangular
pulse at the output when the input voltage is a symmetrical square wave
as illustrated in Figure 6.28. A numerical example will help to identify significant voltages and time intervals on these waveforms. Stray capacitance
and interelectrode capacitances of the tubes are neglected for now.

The example which follows illustrates only one of several possibilities.
It is given primarily to indicate a procedure of correlating the switching
times of the two tubes in the circuit. In general, previous circuit problems
have included only one amplifying tube. The example has a negative bias

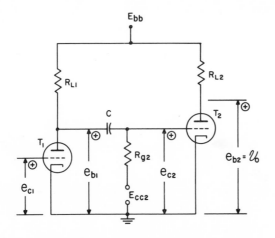

Fig. 6.27. A two-stage, RC-coupled amplifier.

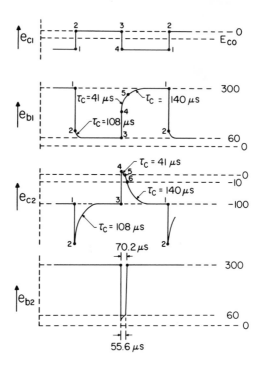

Fig. 6.28. A possible set of voltage waveforms for the RC-coupled amplifier. See Example in Section 6.12.

voltage for tube 2. Practical circuits normally use a positive bias voltage (see Problems 6.22 and 6.23). The negative bias is used here because it presents a more difficult problem.

EXAMPLE

Given: $E_{bb} = 300$ volts $r_{c2} = 1$ K

$R_{L1} = R_{L2} = 40$ K $E_{co} = -10$ volts for each tube

$C = 0.001$ μfd $R_b = 10$ K for each tube ($e_c = 0$)

$R_{g2} = 100$ K $e_{c1} =$ voltage as given in Figure 6.28

$E_{cc2} = -100$ volts

Determine: significant voltages and time intervals to describe the two plate voltages and the grid voltage of tube 2 (e_{b1}, e_{b2}, and e_{c2}).

Solution: The possible circuit time-constants are
(a)   140 μs when e_{c2} is negative and e_{c1} is below cutoff.

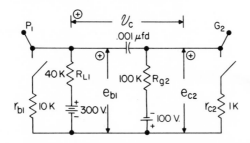

Fig. 6.29. An equivalent switching circuit for the RC-coupled amplifier.

(b) 41 μs when e_{c2} is equal to or greater than zero and e_{c1} is below cutoff.

(c) 108 μs when e_{c2} is negative and e_{c1} is at zero volts.

(d) 9 μs, when both e_{c2} and e_{c1} are equal to or greater than zero volts.

The first three time constants, only, are applicable in this problem. To obtain the above time constants and a further solution of the problem, it is convenient to refer to the equivalent circuit of Figure 6.29.

At the instant of Point 1 on the voltage waveforms of Figure 6.28, the capacitor voltage is at 400 volts and the capacitor current is zero. Thus, e_{b1} is at 300 volts and e_{c2} is at -100 volts.

Immediately after the grid of tube 1 is driven to zero volts, Point 2 on the waveforms, the capacitor voltage is 400 volts and r_b of tube 1 is switched into the equivalent circuit. From the equivalent circuit, the voltages e_{b1} and e_{c2} are calculated for this instant.

$$e_{b1} = 60 + \tfrac{8}{108}(400 - 160) = 78 \text{ volts}$$

$$e_{c2} = e_{b1} - v_c = 78 - 400 = -322 \text{ volts}$$

The left-hand portion of the equivalent circuit reduces to an equivalence of 8 K in series with a d-c voltage of 60 volts. Since the grid voltage of tube 2 is driven still further below cutoff, the plate voltage of tube 2 remains at the plate supply voltage of 300 volts.

The voltage e_{b1} and e_{c2} then continue exponentially with a time constant of 108 μs to the steady state values of 60 and -100 volts respectively. These steady state values exist since the circuit time constant of 108 μs is much less than the 1000 μs of the input pulse. At the instant of Point 3 and therefore at Point 4 (immediately before and after tube 1 is again cut off), the capacitor voltage is

$$v_c = e_{b1} - e_{c2} = 60 - (-100)$$
$$= 160 \text{ volts}$$

Thus, at Point 4 on the waveforms,

$$e_{c2} = -1 + \tfrac{1}{41}(-160 + 301) = 2.44 \text{ volts}$$

$$e_{b1} = v_c + e_{c2} = 160 + 2.44$$
$$= 162.4 \text{ volts}$$

Observe that the right-hand portion of the equivalent circuit reduces to an equivalence of a 1 K resistance (approximately) in series with a d-c voltage of -1 volt.

Since the grid voltage of tube 2 was driven to a positive value, the plate voltage of tube 2 is driven instantly to a low voltage less than 60 volts. To determine the magnitude of this undershoot, it is necessary to have some information regarding the positive grid characteristics of the tube.

[To digress from the problem for a moment, a more nearly rectangular narrow pulse can be generated at the output if a large positive bias instead of a negative bias is used for tube 2. This makes use of the negative spikes (rather than the positive spikes) at the grid to generate the narrow pulse. The output pulse becomes a narrow positive pulse rather than a narrow negative pulse. The undershoot is not, then, a part of the desired pulse. Observe also that the exponential on the negative spike has a smaller time constant than that for the positive spike—108 μs as compared to 140 μs.]

Returning to the example, the time interval from Point 4 to Point 5 on the e_{c2} waveform is, from Equation (2.15),

$$t_5 - t_4 = 41 \ln \frac{-1 - 2.44}{-1}$$
$$= 55.6 \, \mu s$$

The plate voltage, e_{b1}, at Point 5 is

$$e_{b1} = 300 - (300 - 162.4) \, e^{-55.6/41}$$
$$= 300 - 137.6 \times 0.26 = 264 \text{ volts}$$

At this same instant the output voltage is 60 volts.

Now, when e_{c2} reaches cutoff the output voltage, or e_{b2}, is 300 volts. The time required for the output voltage to increase from 60 to 300 volts is

$$t_6 - t_5 = 140 \ln \frac{-100}{-100 - (-10)}$$
$$= 140 \ln 1.11 = 14.6 \, \mu s$$

TABLE 6.1: TABULATED VALUES OF SIGNIFICANT VOLTAGES AND TIME INTERVALS FOR THE VOLTAGE WAVEFORMS OF FIGURE 6.28:

	e_{b1}	e_{c2}	e_{b2}	TIME INTERVALS
Point 1	300.0	-100.00	300	
Point 2	78.0	-322.00	300	$t_5 - t_4 = 55.6 \, \mu s$
Point 3	60.0	-100.00	300	$t_6 - t_5 = 14.6 \, \mu s$
Point 4	162.4	2.44	Less than 60	$t_6 - t_4 = 70.2 \, \mu s$
Point 5	264.0	0.00	60	
Point 6		-10.00	300	

6.13   Waveshaping with Sinusoidal Input to RC-Coupled Amplifier

For the discussion of this section it is desired to modify the two-stage RC-coupled amplifier of Figure 6.27 to include a series grid resistor as the input circuit for the first stage and apply a sinusoidal voltage of large magnitude. It is then possible to generate a reasonably good rectangular narrow pulse at the output of the second stage. If the input voltage is not of large magnitude, it may be necessary to use three stages with the first two stages serving as clippers and amplifiers in order to obtain a trapezoidal wave with steep leading and trailing edges before differentiating and clipping with the last stage. A large time constant is needed for the RC-coupled circuit between the first and second stage. A small time constant between the second and third stage is needed to perform the peaking or differentiating function.

The fact that a trapezoidal type of waveform is initially generated in the circuit suggests the need for a discussion explaining a procedure of analysis. The RC coupling, with the resulting nonlinearities depending on the trapezoidal waveform, presents certain problems of analysis.

To understand the method of analysis for a two-stage RC-coupled amplifier, it is necessary to recall the material of Section 5.5 in which a voltage waveform approximating a trapezoid was generated at the output of a basic amplifier (see Figure 5.7). What must we do, however, when this basic amplifier is RC coupled to another stage of amplification, and there is particular interest in a small time constant for the RC-coupled circuit? The plate voltage of the previous stage becomes distorted in the presence of the coupled circuit.

A suggested procedure is to consider the equivalent circuit in Figure 6.30. The input voltage to this equivalent circuit is the trapezoidal output of the basic amplifier as described in Section 5.5. The output resistance of this basic amplifier is R_o. Selecting proper values for R_o is the major problem. It is not a constant. When the plate current of the source stage is cut off the output resistance is simply R_{L1}, as in Figure 6.27; during the leading

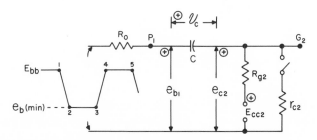

Fig. 6.30. An equivalent circuit to suggest a method of solution when RC-coupled amplifier is overdriven with a sinusoidal voltage.

and trailing edges of the trapezoidal waveform, the ouput resistance is a parallel combination of R_{L1} and the dynamic plate resistance, r_p; and when the plate voltage is at e_b (min) for e_{c1} equal to zero, the output resistance is a parallel combination of R_{L1} and r_b. In addition, one must also be careful about assuming that r_p and r_b are constants. It is necessary to know the tube characteristics and the probable path of operation on the plate characteristics in order to make reasonably accurate assumptions.

In spite of the problems for selecting a value of output resistance, R_o cannot be greater than R_{L1}. In many instances R_{L1} is much less than R_{g2}, which simplifies the problem considerably and places less importance on selecting accurate values for the output resistance. When the grid of the second stage becomes conducting, the output resistance of the first stage is significant, since r_{c2} is normally small. This condition, however, does not exist at a time interval when the desired narrow output pulse is generated, provided we make use of the negative spikes to generate this pulse by employing a positive bias at the second stage. This was explained in the preceding section.

Once values of R_o are selected, the method of analysis is very similar to the procedures explained in Section 3.6 and Section 3.7. If the circuit time constants are sufficiently small to perform the desired peaking or differentiating function, then the voltages at the instant of Point 1 on the input waveform of Figure 6.30 are determined exactly as described in the preceding section (see Figure 6.28). Now proceed from this point taking into account the slopes of the leading and trailing edges of the input voltage.

PROBLEMS

6.1 For e_c equal to zero, evaluate r_b as a function of e_b for a number of assigned triodes.

6.2 For a grounded cathode triode, $E_{bb} = 250$ volts, $R_L = 50$ K, and $e_c = -2$ volts. Evaluate r_b at this operating point for a 6J5 tube, for a 12AU7 tube, and for a 12AT7 tube.

6.3 For a grounded cathode triode, $E_{bb} = 250$ volts, $R_L = 25$ K, and the quiescent point is in the linear region. Evaluate the per cent drift for a change in plate supply voltage for a 12AU7 tube, a 12AX7 tube, and a 6SN7 tube.

6.4 For the circuit in Figure 6.7a, $E_{bb} = 250$, $R_L = 50$ K, $e_c = 0$ and the tube is $\frac{1}{2}$12AU7. Evaluate e_b (for $e_c = 0$) and show the operating load line if,
  (a) $R_1 = 500$ K
  (b) $R_1 = 50$ K
  (c) $R_1 = 5$ K

6.5 What is the cutoff voltage E'_{co} for each value of R_1 in Problem 6.4?

6.6 For the circuit in Figure 6.7b, $E_{bb} = 250$ volts, $R_L = 25$ K, $k = 0.4$, $e_c = 0$, and the tube is $\frac{1}{2}$6SN7. Evaluate v_o and show the load line if,
  (a) $R = 100$ K, $E = -100$ volts
  (b) $R = 500$ K, $E = -200$ volts

$$k = \frac{R_1}{R}$$
$$R_1 = 40 k$$

(c) $R = 1$ Meg, $E = -40$ volts

6.7 Repeat Problem 6.6 if $e_c = -30$ volts.

6.8 What is the cutoff voltage E'_{co} for each part of Problem 6.6?

6.9 For the circuit in Figure 6.7c with $E_{bb} = 250$ volts, $R_L = 50$ K, $R_2 = 200$ K, $R_{g2} = 150$ K, and a 12AU7 twin triode.

(a) For what value of E_{cc2} is $e_{c2} = -30$ volts when $e_{c1} = 0$?

(b) For the calculated value of E_{cc2}, evaluate e_{b1} and e_{c2} when e_{c1} is below cutoff.

6.10 For the circuit in Figure 6.11, $E_{bb} = 400$ volts, $R_L = 200$ K, $C = 0.01$ μfd and the tube is $\frac{1}{2}$6SN7. Plot v_o if e_c is a negative 20-volt, 200 μs pulse. Indicate all significant quantities.

6.11 What is the per cent slope deviation of v_o in Problem 6.10?

6.12 Show the operating loop on a set of tube characteristics for the results of Problem 6.10.

6.13 Repeat Problem 6.10 if $C = 0.001$ μfd.

6.14 Determine the frequency response for the circuit in Figure 6.11 with the quantities as given in Problem 6.10. Compare with the frequency response obtained when $C = 0.001$ μfd.

6.15 For the circuit in Figure 6.16, $E_{bb} = 200$ volts, $R_1 = 10$ K, $R_2 = 40$ K, $C = 0.01$ μfd, e_c is a negative 20-volt, 1000 μs pulse. The tube is $\frac{1}{2}$12AU7. Plot v_o, indicating all significant quantities.

6.16 For the results in Problem 6.15, show the operating loop on a set of tube characteristics.

6.17 Determine the frequency response for the circuit as represented by Problem 6.15.

6.18 For the circuit in Figure 6.22, $E_{bb} = 250$ volts, $R_L = 50$ K, $R = 100$ K, $C = 0.005$ μfd, e_c is a negative 12-volt, 200 μs pulse repeated with a period of 3200 μs. The tube is a 6J5. Plot v_o, indicating all significant quantities.

6.19 For the results of Problem 6.18, show the operating loop on a set of plate characteristics for the tube. Verify.

6.20 Determine the frequency response for the circuit as represented in Problem 6.18.

6.21 Repeat Problem 6.18 if $R_L = 100$ K and $R = 10$ K. Compare results.

6.22 For the circuit in Figure 6.27, $E_{bb} = 150$ volts, $R_{L1} = R_{L2} = 30$ K, $R_{g2} = 500$ K, $C = 0.001$ μfd, $E_{cc2} = 200$ volts, e_{c1} is a negative ten-volt, 1000 μs pulse. The tubes are a 12AT7 twin triode. Plot the four voltages e_{c1}, e_{b1}, e_{c2} and v_o to the same time base and indicate all significant quantities on each waveform.

6.23 Repeat Problem 6.22 if $C = 0.003$ μfd.

6.24 Insert a 1-megohm resistor in series with the grid of tube 1 for the circuit in Figure 6.27. Drive the circuit with a sinusoidal voltage having a frequency of 500 cycles per second, and E_m equal to 60 volts. The circuit quantities are as represented in Problem 6.22. Plot e_{c1}, e_{b1}, e_{c2} and v_o to the same time base and indicate all significant quantities for each waveform.

7

Semiconductor
Electronics

7.1 General Discussion

This chapter is intended to be a review of some of the principles of semiconductors as applied to diodes and transistors. It is assumed that the reader has studied semiconductors in a beginning electronics course and is familiar with the basic principles of the physics of the semiconductor. Some of these principles will be repeated here to maintain the continuity of the presentation of the material. In preparation for practical circuits which will be discussed in later chapters, special emphasis will be placed on nonlinear operation of the transistor.

7.2 Semiconductor Diodes

In addition to vacuum and gas diodes, another class of diodes which has been an outgrowth of semiconductor research is the semiconductor junction diode. A brief discussion of the theory of the semiconductor diode will be included here. While it is not feasible or necessary in a book of this kind to give a complete discussion of all the principles of physics involved in semiconductor theory, it seems desirable to cover some of the basic principles. This will give the reader a better understanding of the semiconductor diode and the transistor.

On the basis of conduction of electricity, materials are divided into the following three classes: conductors, insulators, and semiconductors. As the name implies, a semiconductor is a material whose conductivity lies between that of a conductor and an insulator. The conductivity of a material depends on the crystal structure of the material and the freedom of the outer atomic electrons. In a conductor these electrons are free to move about and are shared by all the atoms. Conduction consists of the motion of the free electrons due to an applied field. In an insulator, the electrons are bound to the atoms and move only under the influence of exceedingly strong fields and/or high temperatures.

The conductivity of a semiconductor depends on its purity and temperature. For example, a pure (intrinsic) semiconductor is an insulator at absolute zero. At temperatures above absolute zero, it has a conductivity which is a function of the temperature. There are many semiconductor materials available, but at the present time, only two, germanium and silicon, are being produced which are pure enough to be used commercially. In germanium and silicon, there are four valence electrons in each atom. These electrons with the valence electrons from neighboring atoms form covalent bonds as shown in Figure 7.1 for germanium. Here an atom and its four nearest neighbors form four covalent bonds. Since all the electrons are needed to fill the covalent bonds, there are no free electrons to move through the crystal and hence the material is a good insulator. Conductivity may be increased by raising the temperature as suggested above, or by adding certain impurities to the crystal.

As the temperature is increased above absolute zero, the valence electrons acquire energy. If the temperature is increased sufficiently, some of the valence electrons gain sufficient energy to break away from the covalent bonds and move through the crystal. When this happens, the space originally occupied by the electron loses a negative charge and the net charge of the atom is then positive. It is convenient to think of the void left in the covalent bond when the electron leaves as a "hole" having a positive charge. Thus, when an electron breaks away from its covalent bond, an electron-hole pair is formed which provides two charge carriers, one negative and one positive. These charge carriers will move through the crystal if an electric field is applied to it. It is rather easy to visualize an electron moving under the influence of a field but difficult to imagine a hole as moving.

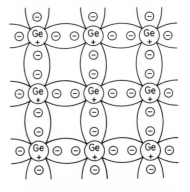

Fig. 7.1. Simplified diagram of germanium atoms showing valence electrons and covalent bonds.

Actually a given hole does not move but the effect is the same as though it did. When an atom loses an electron, the hole formed can be filled by an electron from a neighboring atom. Of course, this electron leaves a hole in a covalent bond of its atom which may be filled by an electron from one of its neighbors, and so on. The over-all effect is as though the electrons moved in one direction through the crystal and the holes moved in the opposite direction under the influence of a field.

The current which flows is given by the equation

$$I = (N\mu_n + P\mu_p)\, e\epsilon A \text{ amp} \tag{7.1}$$

where N = number of electrons per cu m, μ_n = mobility of the electrons in sq m per volt sec., P = number of holes per cu m, μ_p = mobility of holes in sq m per volt sec., e = charge on electron or hole in coulombs, ϵ = field intensity in volts per m, A = cross-sectional area in sq m.

When the electron-hole pairs are formed by increasing the temperature, there will always be as many electrons as holes, and the semiconductor is classified as intrinsic.

It is possible to change the electrical characteristics of a semiconductor by the addition of certain impurities. Impurity-type or extrinsic semi-conductors have higher conductivities than the pure type and have a surplus of free electrons or holes depending on the type of impurity added.

Suppose, for example, a small amount of pentavalent impurity, such as arsenic, antimony, or phosphorus, is added to a tetravalent semiconductor such as germanium or silicon. The atoms of the pentavalent impurity will replace some of the tetravalent atoms in the crystal. Now, since the penta-valent atom has five valence electrons, there will be enough to fill the four covalent bonds with one free electron left over which is free to move through the crystal as a negative carrier. These pentavalent atoms have been called "donor" atoms because they donate electrons to the semiconductor. An intrinsic semiconductor to which impurity atoms have been added is said to be "doped." In the example given above, where an excess of electrons over holes is produced, the resulting semiconductor is called n-type. It derives this name from the fact that the majority carrier is the electron which has a negative charge. Holes exist in the n-type semiconductor due to temperature effects, but they are in the minority and hence are called the minority carriers.

On the other hand, if a small amount of a trivalent impurity such as aluminum, boron, gallium or indium is added to germanium or silicon, atoms of the impurity will replace certain atoms of the intrinsic material. The three valence electrons of the trivalent atom will take their place in the covalent bonds with the neighboring atoms, but one covalent bond will remain unfilled.

This bond may be filled with an electron from a neighboring atom,

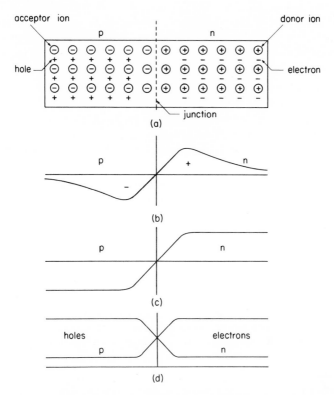

Fig. 7.2. (a) Distribution of charge in *p-n* junction diode; (b) charge concentration in diode; (c) potential barrier on each side of junction; (d) concentration of holes and electrons in diode.

thus leaving a hole in that atom and adding an electron to the trivalent atom. In this way a hole (positive charge) is produced and the trivalent atom acquires a negative charge. Trivalent atoms are called "acceptor" atoms or impurities because they accept an electron from a neighboring atom. The semiconductor which has been doped with acceptor atoms is called a *p*-type semiconductor because the majority carrier is the hole.

If an intrinsic semiconductor is doped on one end with donor atoms and on the other end with acceptor atoms, a *p-n* junction diode is formed. Figure 7.2a shows an idealized *p-n* junction diode in which a few acceptor and donor atoms are shown as well as a few electrons and holes.

Charge carriers (electrons and holes) move through the semiconductor material due to diffusion and conduction. In the absence of a field, the carriers have a random motion due to variations in the charge concentration. In general, the carriers move from regions of high concentration to regions of low concentration. Accordingly, in the junction diode shown in Figure 7.2a, holes tend to diffuse from left to right and electrons tend to diffuse from right to left. When an electron moves from the *n* region into the *p* region it leaves behind a donor atom. This diffusion electron combines with a hole near the junction in the *p* region and thus, near the junction, positive donor atoms in the *n* region and negative acceptor atoms in the *p* region are left with no carriers as shown in Figure 7.2a. This region, near the junction, is known as the *depletion layer* or *space charge region* and results in the charge density distribution shown in Figure 7.2b. It is this charge distribution which is responsible for the space charge capacitance across the junction which is so important at high frequencies. This will be discussed in more detail in Section 7.14.

In Figure 7.2c, the electrostatic potential in the diode is shown. On the *n* side of the junction a positive potential barrier exists which prevents holes from crossing the junction and on the *p* side, a negative barrier prevents electrons from crossing the junction. In the next section, the effect of a bias voltage on these potential barriers will be discussed. Figure 7.2d shows the relative concentration of the holes and electrons on each side of the junction.

7.3 Biasing and the Equation for Current in Junction Diode

The *p-n* junction diode has properties similar to the vacuum diode. The resistance in the forward direction is small while in the reverse direction it is quite large.

Suppose, for example, a biasing voltage is applied to a junction diode as shown in Figure 7.3. The electrons are attracted toward the positive terminal but no current can flow since there are no electrons in the *p* section to flow across the junction to maintain a current. Theoretically, therefore, the current is zero. Actually a small current flows due to the electron-hole pairs formed near the junction resulting from thermal agitation. The total

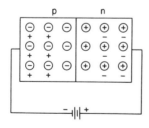

Fig. 7.3. Reverse biased diode. (+) and (−) charge carriers are stationary. No current.

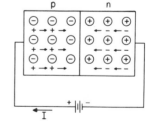

Fig. 7.4. Forward biased diode. (+) and (−) charge carriers move as shown. There is current.

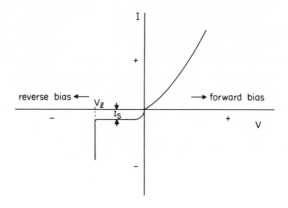

Fig. 7.5. Typical semiconductor diode volt-ampere characteristic.

occurrence is called reverse bias and corresponds to a vacuum diode in which the plate is negative and the cathode is positive.

If a forward bias is applied as shown in Figure 7.4, the situation is quite different. In this case, holes will move across the junction to the right and electrons will move across the junction to the left. Therefore, a relatively large current will flow. Referring to Figure 7.2c, the potential barriers prevent a movement of the carriers when the junction is not biased but with a forward bias applied, the barriers are partially or totally overcome and holes and electrons may move freely across the junction.

Figure 7.5 shows an idealized volt-ampere characteristic of a *p-n* junction diode for forward and reverse bias.

The reverse saturation current I_s is quite small in the typical diode. The current scale is not the same on both sides of the origin, differing by a factor of 10^3 or more; that is, when the forward biased currents are in milliamperes, the reverse biased currents are in microamperes. This accounts for the apparent discontinuity in the curve at the origin.

An equation which satisfies this curve over a limited range is

$$I = I_s \left(\epsilon^{eV/kT} - 1 \right) \tag{7.2}$$

where I = diode current, unit the same as I_s, I_s = magnitude of the reverse saturation current, ϵ = Naperian base, e = charge on carriers in coulombs, V = voltage applied to junction (the sign of V is plus for forward bias and minus for negative bias), k = Boltzman's constant, and T = temperature in degrees Kelvin.

Let $V_T = kT/e = T/11,600$ when values of k and e are substituted. For $T = 300°K$, or $27°C$, $V_T = 0.026$ volts or

$$I = I_s \left(\epsilon^{39V} - 1 \right) \tag{7.3}$$

It is obvious that as V increases in a positive direction, the current I increases. This increase is the result of overcoming the potential barrier discussed earlier. However, when the voltage is rasied to a few tenths of a volt, which is sufficient to overcome the barrier completely, Equation (7.2) no longer holds and the voltage-current relationship follows Ohm's law.

When the polarity of V is reversed so as to reverse bias the diode, the current I approaches I_s in magnitude. For $V = -0.026$, $I = -0.632\,I_s$, and for V as large as a few tenths of a volt negative, I is almost equal to $-I_s$.

7.4. Breakdown Conditions and the Zener Diode

As the reverse bias voltage on the junction diode is increased, a value is finally reached at which the diode breaks down as shown at V_z in Figure 7.5. This voltage is called the *Zener breakdown voltage;* when this value is reached, the current increases rapidly with almost no increase in voltage across the junction. Unless a current limiting resistor is in series with the diode, it will be destroyed. If the current is limited to a safe value by a series resistance, however, the diode will recover with no ill effects when the voltage is removed. There is a small increase in the diode voltage after breakdown due to the IR drop in the diode. This voltage V_z is sufficiently constant that so called Zener diodes are manufactured which are useful as voltage regulators. It is possible to build Zener diodes which have breakdown voltages from a few volts to several hundred volts depending on the degree of doping. As might be expected, the breakdown voltage is a function of temperature and special circuits have been devised to overcome the effects of temperature change.

7.5 Principle and Applications of Tunnel Diodes

If the degree of doping with donor and acceptor atoms is increased beyond that normally used for the conventional junction diodes, the conductivity of the p and n materials is increased and the p-n junction takes on unusual characteristics. This diode was first discovered by Esaki and has been called the *tunnel diode.* It gets its name from the fact that as the conductivity of the material increases, the width of the depletion layer decreases to a value where some of the electrons are able to "tunnel" through the junction in spite of the potential barrier.

Figure 7.6 shows a typical volt-ampere characteristic of a tunnel diode. At small

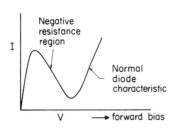

Fig. 7.6. Typical tunnel diode characteristic for forward bias.

forward bias voltages the current increases due to the tunneling of the electrons. This tunneling effect is thought to be due to the wave character of an electron which enables it to pass through a potential barrier V even though its energy is less than V. A complete understanding of this principle requires a knowledge of Quantum Mechanics. As the voltage is further increased, the current reaches a maximum value and then decreases resulting in a region of negative resistance between the peak and valley points. Beyond the minimum point, the potential barrier is sufficiently overcome so that conduction similar to that in a conventional diode is obtained. This unusual characteristic of the tunnel diode makes it especially good in switching circuits and oscillators. Experimenters have reported switching times of 2 nanoseconds (millimicroseconds) and frequencies of oscillation as high as 4 gigacycles (kilomegacycles).

The current at the maximum point on the characteristic can be controlled during the manufacture of the tunnel diode and it has been found to be relatively independent of temperature. Its value can be varied from a few microamperes to several amperes.

One important application of tunnel diodes is in switching circuits of computers. The shape of the characteristic curve makes a very simple bistable circuit possible.

7.6 Characteristics and Uses of Silicon Controlled Rectifiers

Another type of semiconductor diode which is used primarily as a controlled rectifier has a third electrode, called a gate. The purpose of the gate is to control the value of the forward voltage at which the diode switches from a small value of anode current to a large value .The action is very similar to the controlled gas rectifier such as the thyratron or ignitron. This diode has been called the silicon controlled rectifier.

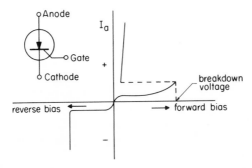

Fig. 7.7. Volt-ampere characteristic curve for silicon controlled rectifier. Insert-recommended symbol.

Figure 7.7 shows a typical volt-ampere characteristic curve for the silicon controlled rectifier with the recommended circuit symbol shown in the insert. With reverse voltage applied, the diode functions much like the ordinary semiconductor diode. As the voltage is increased in the positive direction, a small forward current flows, increasing slowly until a breakdown point is reached at which the diode shifts from a high-voltage, low-current state to a low-voltage, high current state, similar to a gas tube switching from a glow to an arc discharge. At forward voltages less than the breakdown value, the diode can be made to switch states by the application of a pulse to the gate electrode. Once the state of operation has been switched, the pulse may be removed and the diode will remain in its high current state until the current is interrupted.

The silicon controlled rectifier has many applications in special control circuits. The reader is referred to the General Electric Company Transistor Manual for a more complete discussion of its operation and uses.

7.7   The Transistor

By the combination of two p-n junction diodes, it is possible to produce a device which has very desirable characteristics. This device is called the transistor and in its simplest form is composed of either one n and two p sections or one p and two n sections. These are appropriately named p-n-p and n-p-n transistors respectively. The p-n-p transistor is shown diagrammatically in Figure 7.8. As indicated, the p-n junction on the left side is forward biased and the other junction is reverse biased. For the forward biased junction the p side is much more heavily doped than the n side. Due to the forward bias, holes are injected into the n side and because the holes are the majority carriers, the current I_E is essentially a current due to holes. The width of the n section is quite small, about 1 mil in most cases, so the holes which are injected into the n section migrate readily to the other junction. Under the influence of the reverse bias on that junction, they move on through the right hand p section to the terminal C. A small current I_B flows out at B, but most of the current I_E leaves the transistor at C as the current I_C.

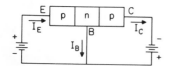

Fig. 7.8. *p-n-p* transistor showing polarity of biasing voltages and direction of emitter, collector and base currents.

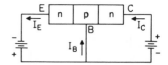

Fig. 7.9. Same as Figure 7.8 except for *n-p-n* transistor.

In the *n-p-n* type shown in Figure 7.9, the *p-n* junction on the left side is again forward biased and the other junction is reverse biased. Operation is the same as for the *p-n-p* transistor except the electron is the majority carrier in this case. The terminal marked E in each case is called the emitter because it provides the connection to the semiconductor section of the transistor which provides the carriers. The C terminal is called the collector since it connects to the section which collects the carriers which pass across the second junction. The center section B is called the base.

Since the transistor has been used to replace the vacuum tube in circuits it is desirable to compare them. The cathode, plate and grid of a vacuum tube correspond to the emitter, collector and base respectively in a transistor.

7.8 Symbols and Circuit Configurations

The symbols for transistors, as recommended by the IRE (Institute of Radio Engineers), will now be given so that the reader may immediately identify the type transistor which is used in a given circuit. Figure 7.10 shows these conventional symbols.

The arrow on the emitter line in the transistor circle shows whether the transistor is *p-n-p* or *n-p-n*. The direction of the arrow is that in which the emitter current will flow if the emitter-base junction is forward biased. The currents shown are the assumed positive direction in each case. In the *p-n-p* transistor, I_E is positive, but I_C and I_B are both negative since they flow away from the transistor. In the *n-p-n* type, the current directions are opposite to what they are in the *p-n-p* type. The polarities of the voltages shown are according to IRE standards. V_{EB} is actually the voltage drop from E to B. If E is positive with respect to B, the polarity is as shown.

Transistors are used in three different circuit arrangements or configurations. These are shown in Figure 7.11 and are called common base, common emitter, and common collector (emitter follower). These circuits have their counterparts in the three common vacuum tube circuits which

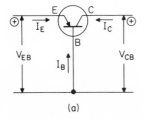
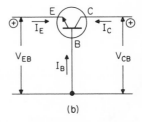

(a)   (b)

Fig. 7.10. Transistor symbols showing *assumed* direction of positive currents and positive *reference* polarity of voltages.

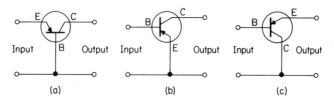

Fig. 7.11. Transistor configurations showing input and output terminals, *p-n-p* transistor shown. (a) Common base; (b) common emitter; (c) common collector.

are, the grounded-grid, grounded-cathode, and grounded-plate (cathode follower) amplifiers respectively.

The common base configuration is characterized by low input impedance, high output impedance, high voltage gain, and low current gain. The common emitter circuit has moderate input and output impedance and high voltage and current gains, while the common collector configuration has high input impedance, low output impedance, high current gain and a voltage gain of approximately unity. Of the three circuits, the common emitter is used more than the other two, although all three are used and the one chosen for a given application depends on the characteristics desired.

7.9   Common Emitter Characteristic Curves

As in the case of the vacuum tube, the transistor has certain parameters which are important in analyzing their operation in a given circuit.

In addition to the parameters, characteristic curves are helpful in the analysis of circuit operation in the linear (small signal) region and in determining particular current and voltage values in the range of operation beyond the linear region. The work which follows in later chapters is concerned primarily with circuits which operate in the nonlinear region.

Since the common emitter circuit is generally used, the common emitter static characteristic curves will be presented here and discussed in some detail. Figure 7.12a shows a family of typical common emitter characteristics with collector current versus collector to emitter voltage plotted with base current as the third parameter.

In Figure 7.12b, a circuit is shown for an amplifier using an *n-p-n* transistor. The load resistor is R_L and a load line for R_L is shown drawn on the characteristic curves. The method of drawing load lines for transistors is identical with that used for vacuum tubes. The quiescent operating point (Q point) is determined by I_B and in the case of a linear amplifier is set at or near the center of the linear region. In pulse-shaping circuits, the Q point may be at any point which fits the special requirements of the

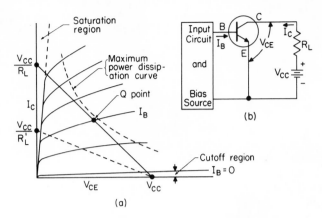

Fig. 7.12. (a) Common emitter characteristic curves; (b) circuit showing currents and voltages shown in (a).

particular circuit used. The signal is applied to the base and in linear amplifier operation, its amplitude is adjusted so that the base current swings within the linear region on both sides of the Q point. Also shown on the characteristic curves is a curve of maximum allowable power dissipation. When operating as a linear amplifier, it is important to select the Q point and load resistor so that operation is confined to the region below this maximum power dissipation curve. In pulse circuits, however, it is not always necessary to restrict operation to this region, because in many cases, the base bias current is zero or in saturation and the transition through the active region is so short that excursions into the region above the maximum allowable dissipation curve do not generate sufficient heat to damage the transistor.

7.10 Cutoff, Active, and Saturation Regions

Three regions of operation which are of particular interest in the use of transistors are cutoff, active, and saturation. In Figure 7.12a, the cutoff and saturation regions are indicated and the active region lies between them. The cutoff and saturation regions are important in switching operation while the active region is of importance in linear operation.

As the name implies, the cutoff region is where the collector current is zero. This region begins approximately where I_B is equal to zero, and extends over the region where the base current is reversed from its normal active region direction. In many switching and pulse shaping circuits the base current is zero for a certain time interval and during this time $V_{CE} \cong V_{CC}$. However, the value of V_{CE} differs from V_{CC} by an increasing amount as R_L is increased, as shown in Figure 7.12a.

In the saturation region, the voltage V_{CE} is quite small and is practically independent of I_C and I_B. Changing the value of R_L has very little effect on V_{CE} in the saturation region; however, it has a marked effect on I_C. Transistor manuals which list the electrical characteristics of transistrors, give the value of V_{CE} at a specified point in the saturation region for transistors used for switching and pulse circuits. This value of voltage is very useful to circuit designers. Reference will again be made to the saturation voltage in later chapters.

The active region, as stated earlier, lies between cutoff and saturation, and it is in this region that the linear amplifier is operated. In switching circuits, the active region is of secondary importance since the transistor is switched from cutoff to saturation, or vice versa, through the active region very quickly. Therefore, the points of greatest interest are the two end points.

7.11 h and r Transistor Parameters

Similar to the vacuum tube, the transistor has certain parameters which are required to solve equivalent circuits used to represent amplifiers and other linear applications. While it is not the intention in this discussion to elaborate on linear circuits, since this book deals primarily with switching and pulse-shaping circuits, a brief introduction *will* be made at this point.

The transistor can be considered to be a two-terminal pair network with two input terminals and two output terminals. As such, it is possible to represent the transistor internally by hybrid parameters defined in such a way as to account for the various effects present. Figure 7.13 shows an a-c equivalent circuit in which the hybrid parameters are used. The input resistance is represented by h_i and is defined as the input resistance with the output short-circuited. The ratio of output current to input current is represented by h_f and is defined as the forward short-circuit current gain. The effect of the output voltage on the input circuit is represented as h_r and is defined as the reverse voltage gain with the input open-circuited.

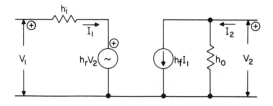

Fig. 7.13. Hybrid parameter equivalent circuit.

The output conductance is represented by h_o and is defined as the ratio of output current to output voltage with the input open-circuited.

The equations for the two-terminal pair network shown in Figure 7.13 are

$$V_1 = I_1 h_i + V_2 h_r \qquad (7.4)$$

$$I_2 = I_1 h_f + V_2 h_o \qquad (7.5)$$

With the output short-circuited, $V_2 = 0$ and Equation (7.4) reduces to

$$h_i = \frac{V_1}{I_1}$$

while Equation (7.5) reduces to

$$h_f = \frac{I_2}{I_1}$$

With the input open-circuited, $I_1 = 0$, and from Equation (7.4),

$$h_r = \frac{V_1}{V_2}$$

and from Equation (7.5),

$$h_o = \frac{I_2}{V_2}$$

In ordinary usage, these hybrid parameters have two subscripts, the second subscript being b, e, or c to designate common base, common emitter, or common collector, respectively. For example, h_{ie} is the input resistance of the common emitter configuration.

The equivalent circuit shown is perfectly general and can be used for any of the three configurations. It is only necessary to use the appropriate parameters for the configuration being used. It is also possible to represent the transistor, when operating in the linear region, by an a-c, T equivalent circuit. Since the common emitter circuit is used more than the other two, a T equivalent circuit for it will be presented as an example. Figure 7.14a shows such a circuit, in which r_e is the emitter resistance, r_b is the base resistance, r_c is the collector resistance and α_b is the common base short-circuit current gain. Figure 7.14b shows the circuit in a more convenient form with common emitter values throughout. With the input and output circuits connected, the equivalent T can be solved as a simple two-mesh network.

It is also possible to represent the transistor by a π equivalent circuit. This will not be given here because the two circuits given are sufficient to illustrate the method. The reader can easily derive the equivalent π from the equivalent T.

The h and r parameters used in Figures 7.13 and 7.14 are dynamic, or a-c parameters, and are a function of frequency, current magnitudes, and temperature. To find these parameters for a given transistor, it is customary

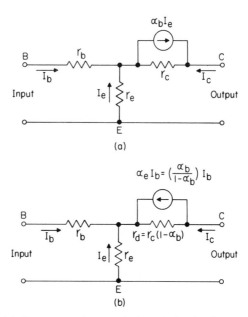

Fig. 7.14. (a) Common emitter equivalent T circuit; (b) a more convenient form of circuit in (a).

to find the h parameters by measurement with a-c and then by means of the appropriate relationships the r parameters can be caluclated. Transistor manuals usually give certain h parameters at specified currents and frequencies.

In switching applications, certain static or d-c hybrid parameters are used. These are distinguished from the a-c parameters by the use of upper case subscripts. Essential d-c parameters are published in transistor manuals for the convenience of the circuit designer. Use is made of these parameters in later chapters.

7.12 Linear and Nonlinear Operation

In the material presented so far in this chapter, two distinctly different types of operation have been emphasized. In Section 7.11 the parameters and equivalent circuits discussed were for small signal linear operation. The transistor, however, is a nonlinear device and can be considered to be linear only if the Q point is carefully set and the applied signal is small. In many circuits, such as amplifiers, distortion is undesirable and linear operation is employed. Such circuits may be readily analyzed by the linear equivalent circuit method.

On the other hand, there are many circuits used for switching and pulse shaping which do not operate in the linear region. These circuits cannot be analyzed by the linear equivalent circuit method but must be handled by some graphical, empirical or piecewise method.

The transistor can be successfully used as a switch because its resistance is relatively small when it is conducting and large in comparison when it is cut off. Referring to Figure 7.12a the *off* condition would be in the cut-off region where the collector voltage is large and the collector current is small. With a small reverse bias on the base to emitter junction, it is possible to cause I_c to approach the reverse saturation current, and this will make the collector resistance as large as several megohms. Thus an open switch condition is closely approximated. The closed switch condition is achieved by biasing the base to emitter junction so that the operating point moves to the saturation region. In this region, the collector current is large and the collector to emitter voltage is small resulting in a small collector resistance. Certain switching transistors have an *on* resistance of less than one ohm.

When a switching transistor is used in a multivibrator circuit, it switches from *on* to *off* in a very short time, but remains in the *on* or *off* condition for a relatively long time compared to the switching time. When it is *on* or *off*, the voltages and currents are d-c. To aid the designer of switching circuits, transistor manuals list several important d-c parameters in addition to the usual a-c parameters. These parameters include, collector cutoff current I_{co}, common emitter static forward current transfer ratio h_{FE} (a d-c hybrid parameter), collector to emitter saturation voltage V_{CE}^{SAT} and base input voltage V_{BE}. It is important to notice that all of the d-c parameters are characterized by having upper case letters in their subscripts and superscripts. Some of these d-c parameters will be used in the solution of switching circuits in later chapters.

The parameters given in transistor manuals are average values and aid in the design or solution of circuits. A set of characteristic curves is not required for transistors if the necessary parameters are given. In this respect, transistors differ from vacuum tubes because for tubes, the characteristic curves are practically always used to solve nonlinear circuits.

7.13 Common Emitter Input and Output Resistance

In Chapter 5, the subject of input circuits to grounded cathode vacuum tubes was discussed. The way in which the input circuit responds to a given input signal is, of course, a function of the nature and arrangement of the components in the circuit. In addition to this, the response also depends on the input impedance of the tube or transistor to which it is connected. Vacuum tube performance is covered in Chapter 5. Transistor performance will be introduced here and discussed in greater detail in Chapter 8.

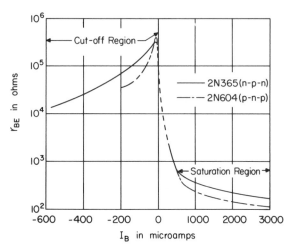

Fig. 7.15. Curves of static input resistance *vs* base current.

In order to obtain a better knowledge of how the static input resistance varies with base bias in a transistor, data were taken on a common emitter transistor circuit by varying I_B and reading V_{BE}. Figure 7.15 shows the results of such tests made on two switching transistors, one a *p-n-p* and the other an *n-p-n*. The curves are plots of r_{BE} versus I_B, where r_{BE} is the ratio of V_{BE} to I_B. At collector current cutoff, the resistance is as high as 250 to 300 K while in the saturation region it drops to less than 200 ohms. An expanded scale for I_B is used in the region beyond cutoff to show the variation in resistance to better advantage. It should be kept in mind that these curves are for d-c or static resistance and do not represent the input resistance of the common emitter circuit when an a-c signal is applied. To obtain the a-c input resistance, it is necessary to use the a-c *h* or *r* parameters and solve the appropriate equivalent circuit for input resistance. It is obvious from the results shown in Figure 7.15 that the loading effect of the transistor is much greater at saturation than it is at cutoff and in the saturation region the loading effect is relatively constant. In Chapter 8, this effect is discussed for several different input circuits.

The output resistance of a transistor is an important parameter. In the common emitter circuit it is the ratio of collector-to-emitter voltage to collector current. In switching operations the d-c resistance values at cutoff and saturation are quite useful. In the ideal case, the cutoff resistance is infinite (switch *off*) and the saturation resistance is zero (switch *on*). Actually, however, these ideal values are never realized but values sufficiently close to ideal are obtained to make the operation satisfactory. Transistor manuals provide d-c and cutoff characteristics from which the output resistance can be calculated. For example, the collector to emitter saturation voltage V_{CE}^{SAT} is given for a certain collector current. From these values, a value of d-c saturation resistance can be calculated. Typical values of saturation resistance range from 1 to 25 ohms. For certain types, the saturation resistance is given along with the other d-c parameters.

The d-c cutoff resistance is quite high but of course is never equal to infinity. The so-called cutoff current is not zero but ranges from a fraction of a microampere to several microamperes depending on the collector-to-emitter voltages. Values of resistance are as high as several megohms.

The a-c output resistance is used for linear operation in the active region. It is calculated by means of one of the a-c or incremental equivalent circuits and is assumed to be constant. The well known procedure for finding a-c output impedance is followed and involves the solution of a circuit by mesh or nodal methods.

7.14   High Frequency Operation (Cutoff Frequency)

The linear, small signal, equivalent circuits discussed in Section 7.11 are for low frequencies. They do not take into account inductive and capacitive effects present in the wiring and internally in the transistor. As the frequency of operation is increased, however, it becomes necessary to consider these reactive components in analyzing the transistor a-c equivalent circuit.

Within the transistor, capacitance exists at the two junctions. In a reverse biased junction, the depletion layer or space charge region is as shown in Figure 7.2a. The bound donor atoms on the n side are positive and the bound acceptor atoms on the p side are negative. They are separated by germanium or silicon semiconductor material at the junction. This combination forms a capacitor with the bound ions acting as the plates and the material between as the dielectric. This capacitance, known as the depletion-layer, space charge, or transition capacitance, is a function of the bias voltage, the dielectric constant of the semiconductor material, and the area of the junction. As the reverse voltage is increased, the effective thickness of the dielectric increases and the capacitance decreases. Figure 7.16a is a copy of Figure 7.14a in which the capacitances have been added. The collector capacitance C_c is considered to be in parallel with r_c as shown.

The so called diffusion capacitance of a transistor is across the forward biased junction. The forward bias lowers the potential barrier so that holes from the p side enter the n side and electrons from the n side move across the junction to the p side. The holes upon entering the n side diffuse away from the junction and combine with electrons. The hole density decreases with distance from the junction on the n side and the electron density decreases with distance from the junction on the p side. This charge distri-

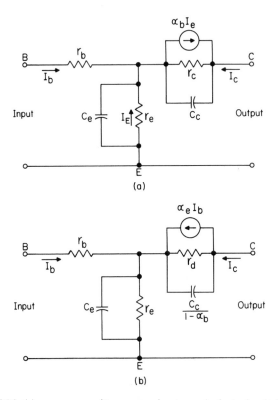

Fig. 7.16. (a) common emitter approximate equivalent circuit for high frequencies; (b) a more convenient form.

bution results in an emitter to base capacitance C_e which is a function of the applied voltage. Actually, across a forward biased junction, both transition and diffusion capacitances exist. The diffusion capacitance predominates. However, its effect on the circuit is reduced since it is considered to be in parallel with the forward dynamic resistance of the emitter to base junction. This resistance is small so that the RC time constant is small and the effect of C_e may be neglected in many cases.

It should be pointed out that the circuit shown in Figure 7.16a is not strictly correct and should be considered to be an approximation. The circuit parameters are not lumped as shown but are distributed. To represent exactly a circuit with distributed constants is impossible. It is, therefore, necessary to make approximations. The more approximations that are made, the easier it becomes to solve the circuit, but the farther the final results are from the correct value. The circuit shown is a compromise. It will give fair accuracy and is simple to solve.

Figure 7.16b shows Figure 7.14b modified for high frequency operation. As mentioned above, r_e is quite small and C_e is frequently neglected.

A transistor characteristic important in high frequency operation is the common base cutoff frequency. It is defined as that frequency at which the common base current gain of a transistor drops to a value which is 0.707 of its value at 1 KC. Among the other high frequency characteristics given in manuals, the common base Alpha cutoff frequency (f_{hfb}) is also given. In the subscript, the letters hf denote high frequency and b denotes common base. This value of cutoff frequency is useful in predicting the upper frequency limit of a transistor.

In the equivalent circuit for a transistor, the h and r parameters vary with the frequency. The common base short-circuit current gain, α_b, is a function of frequency and its variation can be shown to be

$$\frac{\alpha_{bf}}{\alpha_{bo}} = \frac{1}{1 + j(f/f_{hfb})} \tag{7.6}$$

where α_{bf} = common base short-circuit current gain at frequency f, α_{bo} = common base short-circuit current gain at low frequencies, f_{hfb} = common base cutoff frequency. Equation (7.6) indicates that as f increases, α_{bf} decreases, and when $f = f_{hfb}$, $\alpha_{bf} = 0.707 \, \alpha_{bo}$.

The common emitter alpha cutoff frequency can be calculated by the expression

$$f_{hfe} = f_{hfb}(1 - \alpha_{bo}) \tag{7.7}$$

where f_{hfe} is equal to the common emitter alpha cutoff frequency.

It was not intended in the foregoing discussion of high frequency operation of transistors to present a rigorous analysis. The equivalent circuits presented are only approximate as are the equations given. It is felt, however, that if the reader's interest is aroused, he will seek a more complete discussion in sources devoted exclusively to the transistor.

7.15 Unijunction Transistor Principles and Operation

The unijunction transistor is a device which exhibits a negative resistance characteristic over a portion of its operating range. Like the tunnel diode, it is used in oscillator and switching circuits.

This transistor consists of a bar of n-type semiconductor material with an electrical connection at each end. A p-n junction is situated between the two end connections and on the opposite side of the bar. Figure 7.17a shows the recommended symbol for the transistor with the terminals indicated and biasing voltages shown. With the emitter unbiased, the semiconductor bar between terminals $B1$ and $B2$ acts as a voltage divider as shown in Figure 7.17b. If the emitter bias voltage is less than the voltage across R_1, the p-n junction will actually be reverse biased and the junction

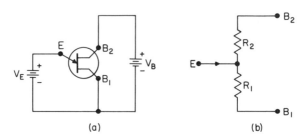

Fig. 7.17. (a) Circuit of unijunction transistor showing symbol and biasing voltages. (b) simplified circuit.

current will be the reverse saturation current. If V_E is now increased so that the *p-n* junction is forward biased, a forward current consisting primarily of holes will flow from E into the bar. The holes move toward the terminal $B1$ resulting in a decrease in resistance between E and $B1$ with a decrease in voltage. Hence, as the current increases, the voltage decreases and a negative resistance characteristic is obtained between the two terminals.

The unijunction transistor exhibits a very stable negative resistance characteristic. Because of this property, it is used in many circuits alone or in conjunction with ordinary transistors. To cite a few examples, the unijunction transistor is used in multivibrators, relaxation oscillators, timing and switching circuits. Further reference will be made to this special type transistor in Chapter 13.

PROBLEMS

7.1 A silicon *p-n* junction diode has a reverse saturation current of 20 μ amperes at 350°K. When 0.3 volts bias is impressed on the diode, find the dynamic resistance at 350°K
    (a) in the forward direction.
    (b) in the reverse direction. The dynamic resistance is defined as $r = \partial V/\partial I$.

7.2 A *p-n* junction diode has a reverse saturation current I_s of 10 μ amperes and a zener breakdown voltage of 25 volts at 300°K. Bias voltage is applied to the diode through a resistor R.
    (a) Find the value of R so that the forward current is limited to 30 ma when a forward bias of 50 volts is applied.
    (b) What reverse current flows when the 50 volts bias is reversed and the value of R is 10,000 ohms?

7.3 In the circuit shown, for diode 1, $I_s = 20$ μa., and $V_z = 19.8$ volts. For diode 2, $I_s = 10$ μa., and $V_z = 50$ volts. The temperature of operation is 400°K.
    (a) Find the voltage across each diode when a voltage of 20 volts is applied as shown.
    (b) Repeat Part (a) with the polarity of the voltage reversed.

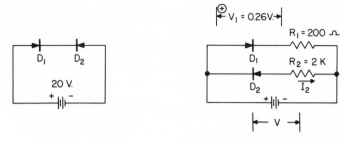

Fig. P7.3.   Fig. P7.4.

(c)   Find the dynamic resistance of diode No. 2 at 400°K with a reverse bias of 0.2 volts applied.

7.4 Two semiconductor diodes are connected as shown: for diode 1, $I_s = 10$ μa., and $V_z = 50$ volts. For diode 2, $I_s = 20$ μa., and $V_z = 20$ volts. The operating temperature is 300°K. Find V and I_2.

8

Input
and Output Circuits
for Grounded-Emitter
Transistors

8.1 General Discussion

This chapter is restricted to a study of single transistor circuits applicable to switching and pulse-forming circuits. The general objectives are to determine methods by which some of the more important voltage waveforms are generated with single transistor circuits and to consider problems of analysis that are unique to transistors.

One of the features of transistors, of course, is the possibility of using either the *n-p-n* or the *p-n-p* type of transistor. Either of these two types is represented for the detailed study of each particular circuit. A general explanation is included for the type not represented in a circuit.

The early sections of the chapter are chiefly concerned with equivalent circuits to represent the transistor behavior for conditions of switching. Once an equivalent circuit is established, the analysis of a transistor switching or pulse-forming circuit is simplified.

8.2 Square Wave Testing

The circuit in Figure 8.1 shows a common-emitter transistor circuit with a resistor in series with the base. When positive pulses are applied to this *n-p-n* transistor circuit, the collector-to-emitter voltage is of the form shown in Figure 8.2, provided the positive pulses are sufficiently small to permit the transistor to operate in the active region only. The leading and trailing edges of the output pulses have appreciable fall and rise times, respectively. The resulting voltage waveform at the collector suggests that the transistor circuit has the properties of a low-pass filter. The first of the equivalent circuits, presented in Section 8.3, will make use of this property.

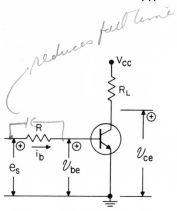

reduces fall time

Fig. 8.1. Series base resistance with common emitter (*n-p-n*) circuit.

It is of interest, at this point, to realize that the cutoff frequency of the transistor circuit could be determined experimentally by this method of square wave testing. Assuming the leading and trailing edges of the collector voltage are true exponentials, with a time constant τ_c, the cutoff frequency is represented with reasonable accuracy by

$$f_{ae} = \frac{1}{2\pi\tau_c} \qquad (8.1)$$

The time constant τ_c is $t_r/2.2$, where t_r is the measured rise or fall time. The number 2.2 is the natural logarithm of a 0.9/0.1 ratio. Rise time is defined as the time from 0.1 of total voltage change to 0.9 of total voltage change.

Operation of the transistor entirely within the active region, as illustrated here, is necessary only when linear response is required. As an electronic switch, it becomes desirable to drive the transistor through the active region

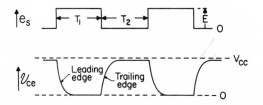

Fig. 8.2. Square wave testing for the circuit in Figure 8.1.

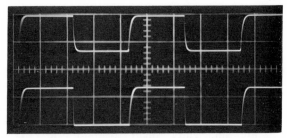

Fig. 8.3. Improvement of leading edge with large driving voltage. Top trace is collector voltage for a small signal. Bottom trace is for a large signal. (*n-p-n* transistor).

as quickly as possible. Fortunately, the cutoff frequency of the transistor can be made to take on less significance in switching and pulse-forming circuits. The driving voltages and the circuitry external to the transistor become the controlling factors.

8.3 Improving the Leading Edge with a Large Driving Voltage

The waveforms of Figure 8.3 show the collector-to-emitter voltage v_{ce} for two conditions of signal magnitude. The circuit is the *n-p-n* transistor circuit in Figure 8.1. The upper trace is the collector voltage when the positive pulses of the source voltage have a magnitude, depending on the series

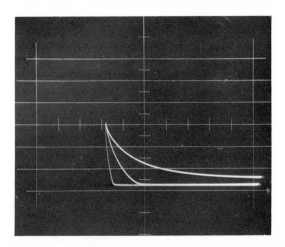

Fig. 8.4. Same as in Figure 8.3 with the leading edge on an expanded time scale, superimposed for three values of driving voltage. The lower limit is zero voltage. The time and voltage scales are $1\,\mu s$/div. and 5 volts/div. (2N365 transistor)

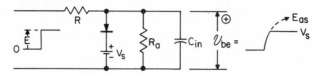

Fig. 8.5. An equivalent input circuit to explain improvement of leading edge.

base resistance R, to allow the transistor to operate entirely within the active region. The lower trace shows the collector voltage when the positive pulses are increased in magnitude to drive the transistor into saturation. Observe the increased steepness of the leading edge, when the collector voltage drops from its upper limit (near V_{cc}) to its lower limit (near zero) for the n-p-n type of transistor.

The three superimposed traces of Figure 8.4, drawn on an expanded time scale so that the leading edge may be observed more clearly, are for three different magnitudes of positive pulses at the source. Notice that the fall time is reduced to a fraction of a microsecond with the largest of the three driving pulses. Excessive driving voltages are not required to produce this result, provided the series R is not large. The lowest limit of these traces is approximately zero volts.

The behavior of the leading edge as controlled by the magnitude of the source voltage is simulated by the circuit of Figure 8.5. This circuit permits an examination of the base-to-emitter voltage, not the collector-to-emitter voltage. Here, R_a and C_{in} represent average input resistance and capacitance that are applicable over the active region of the transistor. The diode branch of the base voltage v_{be} is sufficient to produce saturation, represented by V_s. Recalling the studies of Chapters 2 and 3, this circuit reveals that the rise time to reach the saturation voltage is decreased as the positive step of the source is increased. The exponential that precedes the limiting value of V_s has an E_{as} value of $ER_a/(R_a + R)$, where E is the magnitude of the positive step. Refer to the v_{be} plot of Figure 8.5.

To observe the same results with a p-n-p type of transistor in the circuit, it is only necessary to invert all voltages and waveforms. The "saturating" diode of Figure 8.5 is also inverted.

8.4 Equivalent Circuits to Represent the Switching of Transistors.

The circuit of Figure 8.6a is shown to illustrate the three regions of operation for a transistor, and specifically for an n-p-n type of transistor. The three resistance branches of this circuit represent the saturation (s) region, the active (a) region and the *off* region when the base-emitter junction has a reverse (r) voltage, as identified by the subscripts s, a and r.

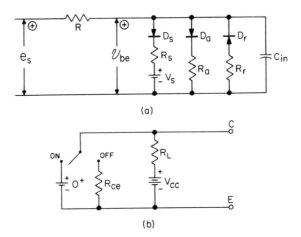

(a)

(b)

Fig. 8.6. (a) Equivalent input circuit to illustrate the three regions of operation. (b) Equivalent output circuit for *on—off* switching.

Let us examine this circuit without too much concern as to whether it is a true representation of a transistor. If the source voltage is negative, then the R_r branch is in the circuit, and the diodes D_s and D_a are open. As the source voltage becomes positive, diode D_a is the first to conduct. Diode D_s conducts for a sufficiently positive source voltage to overcome the voltage V_s. The correct sequence of operation from the *off* state, through the active region and finally to the saturation region, is simulated by this circuit. The manner of using this circuit is made more clear in later sections of this chapter, when methods of generating voltage waveforms are presented.

The two regions of saturation and *off* are of special interest when analyzing transistor switching circuits, as illustrated by the circuit of Figure 8.6b, neglecting the transition time through the active region. When the transistor is in saturation, the collector voltage is only a fraction of a volt as suggested by the 0^+ notation. When the transistor is *off*, the collector voltage is nearly equal to V_{CC} provided R_L is much less than the collector-to-emitter resistance R_{ce}, which is more nearly true if the base-to-emitter has a reverse voltage (negative for the *n-p-n*, positive for the *p-n-p*).

If the circuit of Figure 8.6b is applicable, it is only necessary to know when the transistor is *on* and when it is *off*, which must be determined by an evaluation of an input circuit. Perhaps the circuit in Figure 8.6a will give some assistance.

8.5 Improving the Trailing Edge

The circuits in Figures 8.5 and 8.6a suggest additional methods of controlling the response of a transistor. The leading edge, as illustrated in Figure 8.4 and referred to in Section 8.3, was made to fall more rapidly by increasing the magnitude of a positive pulse at the source. Referring again to the *n-p-n* transistor circuit of Figure 8.1, the trailing edge of the collector-to-emitter voltage will rise more rapidly if the source voltage has a negative value as well as a positive value. This is true since the trailing edge exponential for v_{be} is now headed for a negative E_{as} value, thereby reducing the transition time from saturation to the *off* state.

The equivalent circuits also suggest the possibility of reducing both the rise and fall times by inserting a capacitor in parallel with the series base resistor R in Figure 8.1. The reason for this improvement is quickly understood by recalling Problem 2.19 of Chapter 2. In this problem, the circuit contained two resistors in series and a capacitor in parallel with each resistor. The voltage across either parallel combination is independent of frequency provided the RC time constants of the two parallel combinations are equal. The relationship is not exactly realizable for the transistor circuit, however, since the $R_a C_{in}$ product of the equivalent circuits is not a constant. Nevertheless, considerable improvement is possible by the addition of the capacitor.

8.6 A Collector Catching Diode

The circuit of Figure 8.7a is an *n-p-n* transistor circuit that is similar to that of Figure 8.1 except for the addition of the diode circuit. With the diode returned to a normally desired value of V_{CC}, the results illustrated

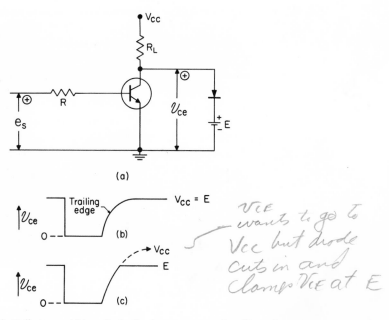

VCE wants to go to Vcc but diode cuts in and clamps VCE at E

Fig. 8.7. (a) Collector catching diode for improvement of trailing edge. (b) $V_{CC} = E$. (c) $V_{CC} > E$.

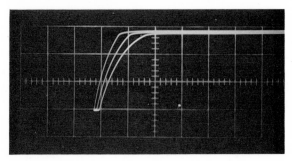

Fig. 8.8. Laboratory results with collector catching diode (*n-p-n*) circuit. Three values of V_{CC}. *E*, unchanged, is the upper limit. The time and voltage scales are 2μs/div. and 5 volts/div. (Observe that the transistor comes out of saturation more quickly with large values of V_{CC}).

by the collector voltage waveforms of Figure 8.7 are possible. With V_{CC} greater than *E*, the trailing edge of the collector voltage will rise more rapidly to the *E* value limited by the diode. Laboratory results are demonstrated by the three superimposed traces of Figure 8.8. The source voltage consists of purely positive pulses.

For the *p-n-p* counterpart, the diode is inverted as are all voltages and waveforms.

8.7   Overdriving with a Sinusoidal Voltage

A sinusoidal voltage applied to the transistor circuit of Figure 8.1 can give the results shown by the waveforms of Figure 8.9. The upper trace is

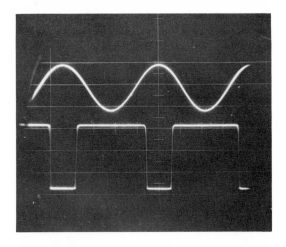

Fig. 8.9. Laboratory results with sinusoidal source voltage for circuit in Figure 8.1. (*n-p-n* transistor).

the source voltage, and the lower trace is the collector-to-emitter voltage v_{ce}. The nearly symmetrical square wave, thus generated, has sufficiently steep edges for some applications requiring rectangular pulses.

There are two significant voltage levels of the source voltage. One level is zero and the other level is that voltage required to establish saturation of the collector current. The time elapsed for the source voltage to traverse between these two voltage levels is an approximate measure of the rise and fall times of the collector voltage. The limiting values of the collector voltage are V_{CC} and zero. If one is willing to disregard the rise and fall times, then the only significant point on the source voltage is zero volts.

8.8   A Series Diode in the Base Circuit

The overdriving of transistors for the purpose of shaping waveforms may result in a reverse voltage breakdown of either or both junctions of the transistor. The collector-base junction is the more vulnerable because of the d-c component of reverse voltage established by V_{CC} on this junction.

The effect of a reverse voltage breakdown of the collector junction is illustrated by the waveforms of Figure 8.10. The circuit conditions are the same as for the voltage waveforms of Figure 8.9 except for a large driving voltage. Notice that the top portion of v_{ce} does not remain flat at a value near V_{CC} as before. The dip suggests that the circuit is behaving like a clipping circuit during the time of the dip, rather than as an amplifier and phase inverter. This is what could happen if there was a reverse voltage

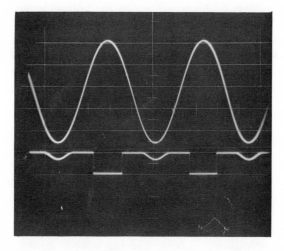

Fig. 8.10. Oscillogram to illustrate breakdown of collector junction with a sinusoidal driving voltage. Lower trace is collector voltage for an *n-p-n* transistor.

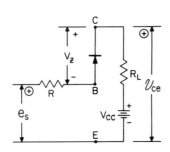

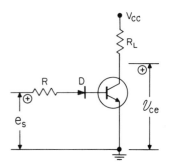

Fig. 8.11. Equivalent circuit to represent reverse voltage breakdown of collector junction (*n-p-n* transistor).

Fig. 8.12. A diode in series with the base.

breakdown of the collector-base junction. An equivalent circuit for examining this voltage breakdown is represented in Figure 8.11.

In this circuit, derived from the *n-p-n* transistor circuit in Figure 8.1, let V_Z represent the reverse voltage or the Zener breakdown voltage of the collector junction. Consider only negative values of e_s, since this is the only condition for which the circuit is represented. In accordance with the voltage reference notations on the circuit diagram, the critical value for the source voltage is $e_s = V_{CC} - V_Z$. The voltage v_{ce} is less than V_{CC} if e_s is less (more negative) than its critical value. The two resistors then cause an attenuation of course. This is clearly evident in the voltage waveforms in Figure 8.10.

The pupose of the diode in series with the base is now apparent, and is shown in Figure 8.12. The presence of this diode will eliminate the dip in the collector voltage waveform when the reverse voltage is excessive. Again, the *p-n-p* counterpart will have all voltages, waveforms, and diodes inverted.

8.9　RC Input Circuit

The *n-p-n* transistor circuit of Figure 8.13 has an RC input circuit. The behavior of the transistor and the response of the circuit are most easily understood when the source voltage is a square wave and the circuit time constants are small.

The voltage waveforms of Figure 8.14 are for a particular condition when the bias voltage V_{BB} is zero. The top trace is e_s, the middle trace is v_{be}, and the bottom trace is v_{ce}. It is most important to study the collector voltage waveforms, observing, in particular, that the collector voltage will hold at either limiting value of V_{CC} or zero. Since the circuit time constants are small, the base voltage relaxes to zero after each step of the source voltage. Consequently, the base current relaxes to zero causing the collector voltage to relax to a value that corresponds to zero base current. It is convenient to regard the collector voltage as having the three significant values of V_{cc}, zero, and v_{ce} for I_b equal to zero. As explained in Chapter 7, the collector voltage for I_b equal to zero is more nearly equal to V_{cc}, for smaller values of R_L.

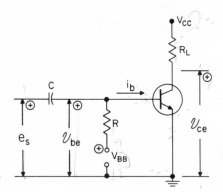

Fig. 8.13. RC input circuit.

if R_L is larger V_{ce} will differ more

The resulting waveforms, with the RC input circuit, suggest the need of avoiding a quiescent value of zero volts at the base. This is especially important when the transistor is used as an electronic switch or as a means of generating pulses of controllable time duration.

The bottom trace in Figure 8.15 shows a positive pulse of controllable time duration for an *n-p-n* transistor. The factors which influence the time duration are pointed out as we continue with the study of the RC input curcuit. The bottom trace in Figure 8.16 is a negative pulse of controllable time duration for a *p-n-p* transistor. All of the voltage waveforms of these two figures are collector-to-emitter voltages when the circuit is driven by

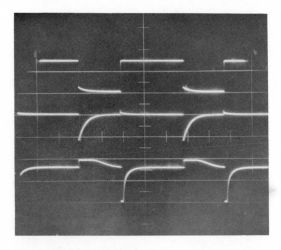

Fig. 8.14. Laboratory results for the *n-p-n* circuit in Figure 8.13 with $V_{BB} = 0$. The traces (top to bottom) are e_s, v_{be} and v_{ce}.

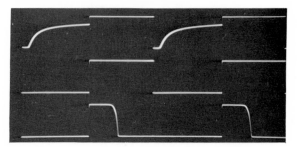

Fig. 8.15. The collector (*n-p-n*) voltage for the RC input circuit with three values for V_{BB}. See text for identification.

a square wave of source voltage. The three traces, on each figure, are for three different values of bias voltage V_{BB}. The magnitude of V_{BB} is one of the factors that influence the time duration of the pulses.

In the top trace in Figure 8.15 (*n-p-n*), or in Figure 8.16 (*p-n-p*), the bias voltage is zero. This waveform of the collector voltage differs from the collector voltage waveform of Figure 8.14 because of a larger time constant of the RC input circuit. Notice that the collector voltage is held at V_{cc}, without a break, up to the instant when the transistor is driven into saturation by the source voltage. The RC time constant of the input circuit is large enough to just insure that the base-emitter voltage will not relax back to zero during the desired *off* time of the transistor, as it did in the middle trace of Figure 8.14.

The middle trace of Figure 8.15, or of Figure 8.16, is the waveform for the collector voltage when V_{BB} (positive for *n-p-n*, negative for *p-n-p*) is of sufficient magnitude to just hold the collector current in saturation up

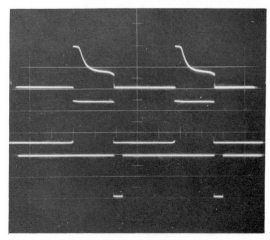

Fig. 8.16. Same as Figure 8.15 for a *p-n-p* transistor.

to the instant when the transistor is driven *off* by the source voltage. The collector voltage is now a square wave with time durations as influenced by the source voltage only.

Any further increase in the magnitude of V_{BB}, of proper polarity, will reduce the time duration of the positive pulse, or of the negative pulse, for the *n-p-n* or the *p-n-p* respectively. These pulses of controllable time duration are illustrated by the lower trace of Figure 8.15 and of Figure 8.16.

A calculation of the pulse width requires some information as to the magnitude of R_r, the input resistance (base-to-emitter), when the transistor is in the *off* state. This information is required in order to determine the more exact value of the time constant for the input circuit and to determine the asymptotical values for any exponential voltages. When the transistor is switched *off*, the base-to-emitter voltage relaxes toward an E_{as} value of $V_{bb}R_r/(R + R_r)$. The time constant of this exponential is the product of the capacitance C and the parallel combination of R and R_r. When this voltage reaches zero, or just slightly before, the transistor enters the active region. The equivalent input circuit then changes and the transistor is driven into saturation where the equivalent circuit again changes, as suggested by the circuit of Figure 8.6a in Section 8.4.

The time for the voltage v_{be} to relax to zero, from the *off* condition, can be regarded as the most significant time, since this is a measure of a significant time duration on the output pulse.

8.10 Pulse Forming with a Clamped Sinusoidal Voltage

The *p-n-p* transistor circuit of Figure 8.17 has a capacitor in series with the base. If the capacitance is large, the base voltage waveform is identical to the source voltage except for the d-c levels. The voltage v_{be} will have its negative peaks clamped to *near* zero. The waveforms for v_{be} and v_{ce} are

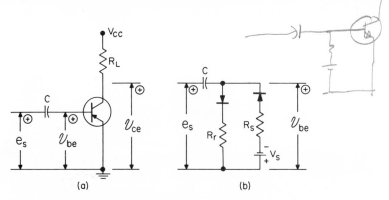

Fig. 8.17. (a) Capacitor input circuit and (b) equivalent switching circuit for *p-n-p* transistor.

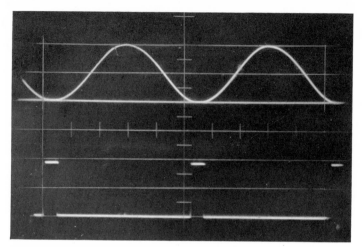

Fig. 8.18. Pulse-forming with a clamped sine wave for the circuit in Figure 8.17.

shown in Figure 8.18 for a sinusoidal source voltage. The positive pulses for the collector voltage are of special interest.

The clamped voltage at the base and the resulting rectangular pulses for the collector voltage are dependent on the input characteristics of the transistor. The equivalent input circuit, omitting the active region, is represented in Figure 8.17b, and is a modification of the input circuit in Figure 8.6a. As before, the input resistance is represented by R_r when the transistor is *off*, and by R_s when the collector current is in saturation. The term V_s is the voltage required, base-to-emitter, to establish saturation. The clamped sine wave at the base will have V_s as reference and an area ratio equal to the R_r/R_s ratio. This resistance ratio and the output resistance of the signal generator account for the flat top of the positive pulses at the collector.

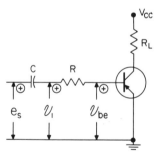

Fig. 8.19. Series RC input circuit.

The width of the positive pulses at the collector can be increased by inserting a resistance in series with the base as shown in Figure 8.19. The area ratio of the sine wave at v_1 is then changed so as to decrease the degree of clamping. The clipping is then more pronounced at the base and the positive pulses for the collector voltage are of a longer time duration.

The presence of, or an increase of the series resistance R, will require a greater change in the source voltage to drive the

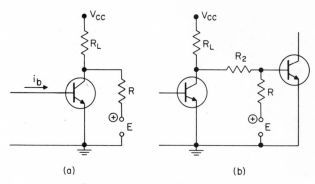

Fig. 8.20. Two examples of resistive loading.

transistor through the active region, and the result is greater rise and fall times for the positive pulses.

Except for inverted waveforms, the results are identical for an *n-p-n* transistor with corresponding characteristics.

8.11 Resistive Loading

Resistive loading in vacuum tube circuits was described in Section 6.5, and the three circuits of Figure 6.7 were used to illustrate possible situations. The two circuits of Figure 8.20 illustrate two possible resistive loading situations for transistors. The first circuit suggests constant resistive loading, and the second circuit suggests that the resistive loading is dependent on the state of operation of the coupled transistor. Whatever the circuit may be, these are the conditions that need to be emphasized. The resistive loading circuit may or may not be constant. In switching circuits the resistive loading can exhibit two or more sets of values during a complete cycle of operation. Each set of values includes a resistance value and a voltage value. The behavior of the loaded transistor is determined by taking the possible R and E combinations into account during the applicable time intervals. This is done by reducing the circuit to equivalent values of supply voltage and load resistance, obtaining equivalent values V'_{cc} and R'_L respectively. This corresponds to E'_{bb} and R'_L as determined by using Thevenin's theorem with vacuum tubes, as in Chapter 6.

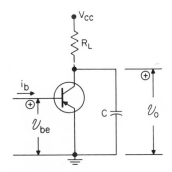

Fig. 8.21. Capacitive loading.

8.12 Capacitive Loading

The circuit of Figure 8.21 is one example of capacitive loading of a transistor. Perhaps

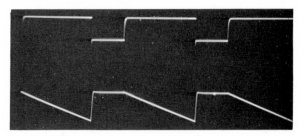

Fig. 8.22. Laboratory results with a capacitive loaded *p-n-p* circuit. Top trace is the source voltage. Bottom trace is v_0.

the circuit is intended to generate a sweep voltage when the transistor is triggered *off*.

A sweep voltage, as generated with this circuit, is illustrated by the lower trace in Figure 8.22 for a *p-n-p* transistor. Observe that the recovery time is the result of a low collector-to-emitter resistance when the transistor is driven back to saturation at the end of the sweep time.

By sketching the operating loop on a set of transistor characteristics, similar to Figure 6.14 with the vacuum tube circuit, one readily recognizes the possibility of excessive collector current during the recovery time. This could be detrimental to the life of the transistor, especially if the sweep voltage is more than a small percentage of the supply voltage. The circuit of Figure 8.23 shows a resistance R in series with the collector, inserted (when required) for the purpose of limiting the collector current to safe values. The resistance R could also be inserted in series with the capacitance, either internally or externally to the output voltage v_o. The circuit time constants and voltage values, however, are dependent on the position of R in the circuit.

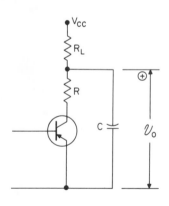

Fig. 8.23. Capacitive loading with a resistance R inserted in the collector circuit.

The circuit in Figure 8.24 illustrates a two-stage RC-coupled transistor circuit that could be used for the forming of pulses. The resistance R, from the base of the second transistor, is significantly returned to V_{cc}. The corresponding RC-coupled circuit for vacuum tubes was discussed in the last two sections of Chapter 6. The two circuits are evaluated in very much the same manner, but the solution of the transistor circuit is somewhat more simplified because of the normally small values of resistance and voltage, collector-to-emitter, when a transistor is in saturation.

The waveforms in Figure 8.25 illustrate a result for the output voltage of the RC-

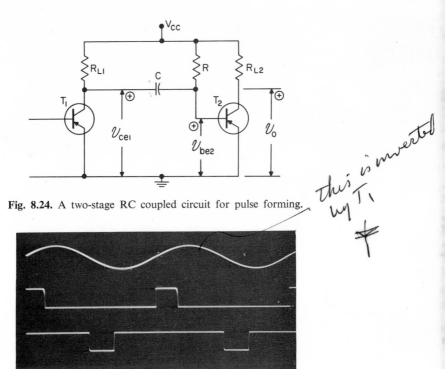

Fig. 8.24. A two-stage RC coupled circuit for pulse forming.

this is inverted by T_1

Fig. 8.25. Pulse-forming with two-stage RC coupled circuit, with a sinusoidal source voltage. See text for identification.

coupled circuit when the driving voltage is sinusoidal and the input circuit is a series resistance as in Figure 8.1. The middle trace is with *n-p-n* transistors. The lower trace is with *p-n-p* transistors in the circuit. Compare the results with the two types of transistors and observe the phase difference and inversion of the narrow output pulses.

8.13 Inductive Loading

The *n-p-n* circuit in Figure 8.26 shows an inductive load in the collector circuit, and a collector catching diode is also shown. Without the diode, the collector voltage will peak to approximately twice the supply voltage when the transistor is switched *off*. The diode prevents this overshoot and a possible reverse voltage breakdown of

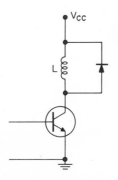

Fig. 8.26. Inductive loading with collector-catching diode.

the collector junction. The diode is inverted for a *p-n-p* transistor. Although the diode is in parallel with the inductor, it is convenient to regard it as a collector-catching diode as demonstrated in Figure 8.7.

PROBLEMS

8.1 For the circuit and driving voltage of Figure 8.5, $R = 2$ K, $R_a = 4$ K, $C_{in} = 300$ pfd, $V_s = 0.4$ volts, E = 1 volt. Plot v_{be}, indicating all significant quantities.

8.2 Repeat Problem 8.1 if $E = 5$ volts.

8.3 For the circuit of Figure 8.6a, $R = 2$ K, $R_s = 400$ ohms, $R_a = 4$ K, $R_r = 100$ K, $C_{in} = 100$ pfd, $v_s = 0.2$ volts. The source voltage is a symmetrical square wave having a period of 100 μs, an upper voltage limit of 0.3 volts and a lower limit of zero. Plot v_{be}, indicating all significant quantities.

8.4 Repeat Problem 8.3 if the source voltage has upper and lower limits of 5 and -5 volts, respectively.

8.5 For the circuit of Figure 8.1: $R = 5$ K, $R_L = 3$ K, $V_{CC} = 12$ volts. The transistor is an *n-p-n* type and the reverse breakdown voltage for the collector junction is 25 volts. Plot v_{ce} if e_s is a sinusoidal voltage having a peak value of 20 volts. Neglect the time intervals of transition through the active region of the transistor.

8.6 For the circuit of Figure 8.13, $V_{CC} = V_{BB} = 12$ volts, $R_L = 3$ K, $R = 100$ K, $C = 0.001$ μfd. The source voltage is rectangular pulses as represented by e_s in Figure 8.2 where $T_1 = T_2 = 200$ μs and $E = 20$ volts. Plot v_{be} and v_{ce} to the same time base, indicating the significant quantities on each waveform. Make the necessary assumptions for an unknown *n-p-n* transistor.

8.7 Repeat Problem 8.6 for a *p-n-p* transistor in the circuit. Make the necessary changes in the given quantities for this change from *n-p-n* to *p-n-p*.

8.8 Repeat Problem 8.6 if the reverse input resistance for the transistor is assumed constant at 500 K.

8.9 For the *p-n-p* transistor circuit in Figure 8.17, $V_{CC} = -15$ volts, $R_L = 5$ K, R_r (of the equivalent circuit) = 1 Meg, $R_s = 500$ ohms, $V_s = -0.3$ volts. Plot v_{be} and v_{ce}, indicating the significant quantities on each waveform if $e_s = -10 + 10 \sin \omega t$.
Assume that C is large. Neglect the small value of collector voltage when the transistor is in saturation.

8.10 Repeat Problem 8.9 if the reverse input resistance R_r is assumed infinite but a resistance of 200 K is connected from the base to the emitter.

8.11 Repeat Problem 8.9 for an *n-p-n* transistor in the circuit. Assume the necessary changes in the given quantities to convert from the *p-n-p* to the *n-p-n* transistor.

8.12 For the *p-n-p* transistor circuit of Figure 8.19, $V_{CC} = -20$ volts, $R_L = 4$ K, $R = 20$ K, C is large, the reverse input resistance of the transistor is 2 Meg, and $e_s = 30 \sin \omega t$. Plot v_1, v_{be} and v_{ce}, indicating the significant quantities

$$\frac{2 \times 4}{6} \qquad \frac{8}{6} \qquad \frac{4}{3} \times \frac{300}{1200}$$

on each. Neglect the small values of base voltage and collector voltage when the transistor is in saturation.

8.13 Repeat Problem 8.12 for an *n-p-n* transistor in the circuit. Assume the necessary changes in the given quantities.

8.14 Repeat Problem 8.12 with the following changes: The reverse input resistance is assumed infinite; a resistance of 200 K is placed in the position indicated by the voltage v_1.

8.15 Repeat Problem 8.14 for an *n-p-n* transistor in the circuit.

.3

9

Effects of
Feedback in
Switching Circuits

9.1 General Discussion

In addition to learning some of the effects that can be produced with feedback, we should be interested in methods of analysis for switching operation as well as for linear operation. These studies will be made largely with the aid of specific circuits. Most of the circuits of this chapter are restricted to single-tube circuits, while representative transistor circuits are illustrated near the close of the chapter.

Preliminary to a study of specific circuits, let us consider some general relationships and problems of analysis peculiar to feedback circuits. As stated above, we are confronted with two major problems: (a) linear circuit operation and (b) switching operation.

For assumed *linear circuit operation* in which circuit parameters are assumed constant and voltages are continuous, there is a general equation that is convenient for analysis of feedback circuits. It is,

$$A = \frac{A_b}{1 - \beta A_b} \qquad (9.1)$$

where A is the gain of the actual circuit with feedback, A_b is the gain with no feedback, and β is the feedback factor. Quite often the gain represents a

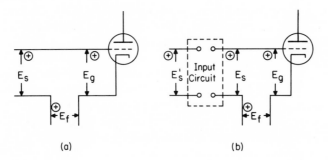

Fig. 9.1. Symbolic representation to include a feedback voltage.

voltage ratio of the output voltage to the input voltage. This is not essential, however. The gain could be a voltage versus current, current versus current, or current versus voltage. To include all these possibilities it is sometimes convenient to refer to the transfer function of the circuit. In this chapter, we are concerned only with voltage gain.

The general relationship of Equation (9.1) is easily derived. First, as represented by the diagrams of Figure 9.1 it must be true that

$$E_g = E_s + E_f \tag{9.2}$$

by selecting the reference voltage polarities as indicated. The feedback voltage E_f is the product of the output voltage and the feedback factor.

$$E_f = \beta V_o \tag{9.3}$$

To be more exact, β is defined as the ratio of the feedback voltage to the output voltage. It could be a complex number. Care must be taken with regard to E_s since it is the source voltage E_s, as shown is diagrams of Figure 9.1, that makes Equation (9.2) true; not the source voltage E'_s ahead of an input circuit.

To continue with the derivation of the general gain expression, Equation (9.1), the output voltage is

$$V_o = A_b E_g \tag{9.4}$$

The voltage, E_g, must be modified to account for the presence of a feedback voltage in addition to the source voltage. Thus,

$$V_o = A_b (E_s + \beta V_o) \tag{9.5}$$

Then the over-all voltage gain, defined as the V_o/E_s ratio, becomes

$$A = \frac{V_o}{E_s} = \frac{A_b}{1 - \beta A_b}$$

For now, we should consider this equation as a possible convenient means of calculating the voltage gain when feedback is present in a circuit. If you are anxious to draw further conclusions, remember that both β and A_b can be complex numbers and that it is not sufficient to know the magnitude of β only. The general equation has considerable significance and any further discussion is more appropriately presented in later sections.

(b) For the switching operation of amplifiers with feedback, it is usually impossible to establish a general mathematical relationship applicable to a number of feedback circuits, and it is often necessary to know the specific circuit before a detailed method of analysis can be established. The reason for this is that such circuits require frequent use of a graphical method of solution by reference to tube characteristics at certain points in the solution of a circuit problem. By comparison, once feedback circuits are adjusted for the nearly linear operation we may forget about the tube characteristics and load lines. This we cannot always do for a switching operation.

9.2 The Cathode Follower (Linear Operation)

The cathode follower, or grounded-plate amplifier, is a type of feedback amplifier that is frequently used. It is represented by either of the two circuits in Figure 9.2, distinguished by the location of the bias voltage.

For assumed linear operation the equivalent circuit in Figure 9.3 is applicable.

The voltage gain

$$A = \frac{\mu R_K}{r_p + (1 + \mu) R_K} \tag{9.6}$$

and the output resistance

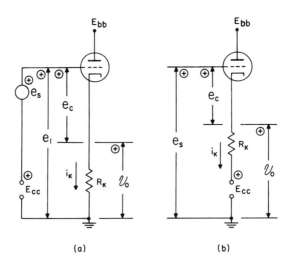

(a)   (b)

Fig. 9.2. Cathode follower circuits.

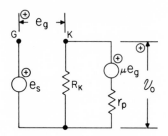

Fig. 9.3. Equivalent circuit for linear operation of a cathode follower.

$$R_o = \frac{r_p R_K}{r_p + (1 + \mu) R_K} \tag{9.7}$$

are easily derived from the equivalent circuit.

To derive the gain expression, write the voltage equation

$$v_o = e_g \frac{\mu R_K}{r_p + R_K} \tag{9.8}$$

then replace e_g with its equivalent,

$$e_g = e_s - v_o \tag{9.9}$$

and obtain

$$v_o = \mu (e_s - v_o) \frac{R_K}{r_p + R_K} \tag{9.10}$$

The voltage gain, $\dfrac{dv_o}{de_s}$ of this equation, is then expressed as indicated by Equation (9.6).

To derive the expression for the output resistance, it is convenient to modify the equivalent circuit to that in Figure 9.4 where the source voltage is set equal to zero. The output resistance is the V_o/I_o ratio, regarding V_o as an applied voltage. Noting that

$$E_g = -V_o \tag{9.11}$$

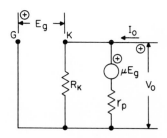

Fig. 9.4. Equivalent circuit for calculation of output resistance of a cathode follower.

and solving the circuit for the V_o/I_o ratio, Equation (9.7) is obtained for the output resistance.

Several interesting facts are revealed with a further study of the expression for the output resistance and the voltage gain of a cathode follower.

(a) The output resistance is an effective parallel combination of R_K and $r_p/(1 + \mu)$. Observe that Equation (9.7) can also be written as

$$R_o = \frac{(r_p/1 + \mu) R_K}{(r_p/1 + \mu) + R_K} \tag{9.12}$$

(b) The output admittance, or reciprocal of R_o, can be expressed as

$$
\begin{aligned}
Y_o &= \frac{1}{R_K} + \frac{1}{r_p} + \frac{\mu}{r_p} \\
&= \frac{1}{R_K} + \frac{1}{r_p} + g_m
\end{aligned}
\tag{9.13}
$$

The third admittance term, g_m, is present because of feedback. This feedback admittance term has considerable significance and is discussed in more detail in later sections of this chapter.

(c) The cathode follower has a low output resistance. For increasing values of R_K, R_o approaches the upper limit

$$
\begin{aligned}
R_o \,(\text{max}) &= \frac{r_p}{1 + \mu} \\
&= \frac{1}{g_p + g_m}
\end{aligned}
\tag{9.14}
$$

This maximum value of R_o is only a few hundred ohms for many tubes. The cathode follower, then, is a means of obtaining a source voltage with low internal resistance. This permits impedance matching to a low impedance load, and aids in reducing distortion or improving frequency response in cathode coupled circuits. The effect of the source resistance was discussed several times in preceding chapters.

(d) If g_p is much less than g_m, as it is for pentodes and some triodes, then the maximum value of R_o is

$$R_o \,(\text{max}) = \frac{1}{g_m} \tag{9.15}$$

(e) The voltage gain of a cathode follower can also be expressed as

$$A = g_m R_o = \frac{g_m}{Y_o} \tag{9.16}$$

which is apparent by replacing μ with its equivalent $g_m r_p$, in Equation (9.6).

(f) The maximum voltage gain of a cathode follower, recalling Equation (9.14), is

$$A \,(\text{max}) = \frac{g_m r_p}{1 + \mu} = \frac{\mu}{1 + \mu} \tag{9.17}$$

This states that the voltage gain is always less than unity and approaches unity for large values of μ.

(g) The general feedback expression

$$A = \frac{A_b}{1 - \beta A_b}$$

is applicable to a cathode follower, where $\beta = -1$ and

$$A_b = \frac{\mu R_K}{r_p + R_K} \tag{9.18}$$

To verify this, divide the numerator and denominator of Equation (9.6) by $(1 + \mu)$.

(h) For $\beta = -1$, $\qquad 1 - A = \dfrac{1}{1 + A_b} \tag{9.19}$

9.3 The Cathode Follower (Instantaneous Voltages and Load Lines)

The behavior of a cathode follower is more fully appreciated through a study of instantaneous voltages for the circuit. Such a study is also a preparation for the analysis of other circuits that employ a cathode resistance, or perhaps cathode coupling to another amplifier stage or circuit.

In the circuit of Figure 9.2a, let the source voltage be zero for the moment. Then, the grid-circuit voltage equation is

$$e_c = E_{cc} - i_k R_K \tag{9.20}$$

or

$$i_k = \frac{E_{cc} - e_c}{R_K} \tag{9.21}$$

But, from the plate circuit we observe that,

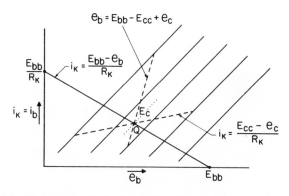

Fig. 9.5. The two methods for finding the Q point with a cathode follower.

$$i_k = \frac{E_{bb} - e_b}{R_K} \tag{9.22}$$

which is the equation that specifies the path of operation on the plate characteristic of the tube (see Figure 9.5). From the preceding two equations we have

$$e_b = E_{bb} - E_{cc} + e_c \tag{9.23}$$

Either Equation, (9.21) or (9.23), can be used to determine the actual point on the load line as indicated in Figure 9.5. If the circuit is adjusted for linear operation about this point, then it is often referred to as the quiescent or Q point, in which case no further graphical analysis is necessary. In certain nonlinear problems, however, we find that we cannot be restricted to this one graphical solution.

The two Equations (9.21) and (9.23) have certain merits as an aid in determining the point of operation on the plate characteristics. When a resistance R_L is added in the plate circuit, Equation (9.21) is independent of this resistance while Equation (9.23) is not. For this reason one might prefer to use the former equation. However, we will be confronted with circuit problems in which it is particularly important to determine e_b with reasonable accuracy. This is more easily done with the second equation when the load line has a small slope, which happens when R_K (or R_L plus R_K) is large. The diagram in Figure 9.6 illustrates the problem. The i_b scale is much more difficult to read than the e_b scale. The plate current (or i_K) can always be calculated once e_b is known.

With further regard to instantaneous voltages in a cathode follower, it is of interest to determine the range of E_{cc} values that will cause the grid voltage to vary between zero volts and cutoff voltage. As a hypothetical problem, let E_{bb} equal 300 volts, e_b (for $e_c = 0$) equal 100 volts, and let the cutoff voltage equal -10 volts. Note that only the 100 volt value is determined from the load line.

Rewriting Equation (9.23),

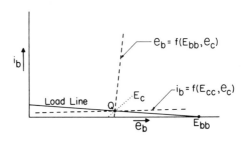

Fig. 9.6. The two test lines when R_K, or $(R_L + R_K)$, is large.

$$E_{cc} = E_{bb} - e_b + e_c$$

and inserting the given values when $e_c = -10$,

$$E_{cc} = 300 - 300 - 10 = -10 \text{ volts}$$

or for $e_c = 0$,

$$E_{cc} = 300 - 100 + 0 = 200 \text{ volts}$$

Thus, E_{cc} could vary between the limits of -10 volts and 200 volts for a grid voltage change of 10 volts in the negative control region. The corresponding change in cathode voltage, or output voltage, is zero to 200 volts. This is a 200 volt change in the output voltage as compared to a 210 volt change in the input voltage, a voltage gain of 0.952. Another interesting fact is that the response will be very linear over this wide range of operation. To test for this linearity, it is suggested that you consider an actual circuit with some type of tube and plot several points, v_o versus e_s, using the procedure outlined in the example and the discussion preceding.

At the beginning of this section we let e_s equal zero. There are several possible situations for the source voltage. It could vary over wide limits just as for E_{cc} changes, or it could have its own d-c component, in which case the bias voltage may not be required. The source voltage could be of small magnitude, thereby requiring a bias voltage if linear operation is desired. If it is desired to ground the source when a bias voltage is dictated, it is also possible to insert the bias in the cathode circuit as in Figure 9.2b in order to permit the grounding of the source. It is also sometimes desirable to insert the bias in the cathode circuit in order to establish a disired d-c level for the output voltage. Finally it may even be desired to turn the tube *on* and *off* with the source voltage.

9.4 Amplifier with Both Anode and Cathode Resistors

The amplifier circuit in Figure 9.7 contains a resistance, R_L, in the anode circuit as well as a resistance, R_K, in the cathode circuit. Although a d-c voltage, E, is shown in series with the source voltage, this d-c voltage is omitted when the d-c voltage developed across R_K is of proper magnitude to give the desired biasing voltage.

This circuit has a number of applications and is used in different ways. The output voltage can be taken from the plate, from the cathode, or from both. When the output is taken from the plate, the circuit approximates the conventional anode-follower type of amplifier. When the output voltage is taken from the cathode, the circuit behaves somewhat like an ordinary cathode follower amplifier. By using both output voltages, the circuit provides a convenient method for obtaining two voltages displaced in time phase by 180°. Finally, the circuit can be used as a nonlinear amplifier as well as a

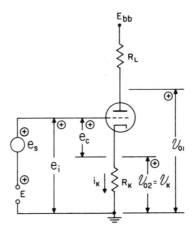

Fig. 9.7. R_L-R_K amplifier.

linear amplifier. As a nonlinear circuit, it is often used as a switching circuit
or as a part of a switching system. It is in these switching circuits that the
d-c voltage, E, is likely to be required.

Problems of analysis are considered for this circuit in sections immediately
following, keeping in mind the possible uses for the circuit. Following these
studies, the circuit can be modified to include other arrangements. The
circuit which contains both an anode resistor and a cathode resistor is a circuit
basic to a study of other circuits in this and later chapters.

One of the important studies for the circuit is a determination of instantaneous voltages and currents for possible conditions of operation. This
study follows in Section 9.5.

9.5 Instantaneous Voltages of $R_L - R_K$ Amplifier

A study of instantaneous voltages and currents for the circuit of Figure
9.7, requires that we write equations applicable to the circuit. The symbol,
e_i, is employed to represent the input voltage. For the given circuit,

$$e_i = e_s + E \qquad (9.24)$$

Now, we must write the equations for the grid circuit and for the plate circuit.
In the grid circuit,

$$e_c = e_i - v_K \qquad (9.25)$$

or

$$i_K = \frac{e_i - e_c}{R_K} = \frac{v_K}{R_K} \qquad (9.26)$$

In the plate circuit,

$$i_K = i_b = \frac{E_{bb} - e_b}{R_K + R_L} \qquad (9.27)$$

which gives the path of operation (load line) on the plate characteristics of the tube. This is true since the equation expresses i_b as a function of e_b which agrees with the coordinates of the plate characteristics.

By combining Equations (9.26) and (9.27), it follows that

$$e_b = E_{bb} - (e_i - e_c)\left(1 + \frac{R_L}{R_K}\right) \tag{9.28}$$

or

$$e_b = E_{bb} - v_K\left(1 + \frac{R_L}{R_K}\right) \tag{9.29}$$

Assigning some particular value to e_i, which we might identify as e_{i1}, it is now no problem to determine the desired quiescent voltages and currents for this one value of input voltage. The procedure of Section 9.3 applies. In this case, Equation (9.27) is the load line and either Equation (9.26) or Equation (9.28) can be used as the "test lines" to determine the operating point on the load line, as illustrated in Figure 9.8.

Specific problems associated with the $R_L R_K$ amplifiers deserve further consideration in order to further clarify the possible uses for the circuit and to indicate short cuts of analysis in some instances.

(a) One problem is to determine the particular value of input voltage e_{i1}, that will result in particular and required instantaneous value of cathode voltage, v_{K1}. A simple procedure is to calculate e_{b1} from Equation (9.29) and then read the grid voltage on the load line of the tube characteristics. Next the input voltage is calculated from Equation (9.25). It is not necessary to sketch a "test line."

(b) Another problem is to evaluate a particular value of input voltage that will give a particular value of grid voltage. Again, with e_{c1} known, the procedure is simply to read i_{b1}, or e_{b1}, from the graph and to calculate the input voltage from Equation (9.26), or Equation (9.28), respectively.

(c) If a particular value of input voltage is given, then one of the two "test lines" must be drawn in order to evaluate instantaneous values elsewhere in the circuit.

(d) When the circuit is used as a linear amplifier, with the cathode voltage

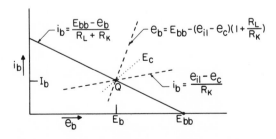

Fig. 9.8. The two test lines for locating Q point of R_L-R_K amplifier.

providing the required biasing voltage, we have the problem of selecting a value for R_K. This could require a trial-and-error solution. However, R_K is likely to be much less than R_L in which case R_K could be omitted from the load line equation, Equation (9.27). Then select a desired quiescent operating point and knowing E_c and I_b, calculate R_K from Equation (9.26) for zero input voltage.

(e) It is sometimes worthwhile to recognize from Equation (9.29) that

$$e_b = E_{bb} - v_K \qquad (9.30)$$

when R_K is much greater than R_L. The approximation becomes an identity for R_L equal to zero, which represents an ordinary cathode follower. Further, for R_L much greater than R_K

$$e_b = E_{bb} - v_K \frac{R_L}{R_K} \qquad (9.31)$$

This approximation becomes indeterminant for R_K equal to zero and represents a basic anode follower amplifier.

9.6 Voltage Gain and Output Resistance of $R_L R_K$ Amplifier

The equivalent circuit for linear operation of the $R_L R_K$ amplifier is shown in Figure 9.9. This circuit is analyzed for two conditions of operation: one with the output voltage taken from the plate, and the other with the output voltage taken from the cathode. These two voltages are identified as V_{o1} and V_{o2} respectively. Similarly, the voltage gains are specified as A_1 and A_2.

(a) With the output voltage taken from the plate, the voltage gain is conveniently determined from the general feedback equation

$$A_1 = \frac{A_b}{1 - \beta A_b} \qquad (9.32)$$

where

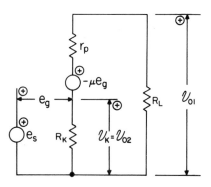

Fig. 9.9. Equivalent circuit for linear operation of R_L-R_K amplifier.

$$A_b = -\frac{\mu R_L}{r_p + R_L + R_K} \tag{9.33}$$

and

$$\beta = \frac{E_f}{V_{o1}} = \frac{R_K}{R_L} \tag{9.34}$$

The voltage gain, A_1, then becomes

$$A_1 = -\frac{\mu R_L}{r_p + R_L + (1 + \mu) R_K} \tag{9.35}$$

The same result can be obtained by writing either the voltage equation, or the current equation, for the equivalent circuit.

The output resistance is determined by considering V_{o1} as a source with e_s equal to zero. Observe, for this condition, that

$$E_g = -V_K$$
$$= -V_{o1} \frac{R_K}{r_p + (1 + \mu) R_K} \tag{9.36}$$

Making use of this relationship in writing the current equation,

$$I_o = V_{o1} \left[\frac{1}{R_L} + \frac{1}{r_p + R_K} \right] + \frac{\mu}{r_p + R_K} \left[-V_{o1} \frac{R_K}{r_p + (1 + \mu) R_K} \right]$$

we find that the output admittance, the coefficient of V_{o1}, is

$$Y_{o1} = \frac{1}{R_L} + \frac{1}{r_p + R_K} \left[1 - \frac{\mu R_K}{r_p + (1 + \mu) R_K} \right] \tag{9.37}$$

It is significant that the output admittance can also be expressed as

$$Y_{o1} = \frac{1}{R_L} + \frac{1}{r_p + R_K} (1 - A_K) \tag{9.38}$$

where A_K is a voltage gain, considering the circuit as a cathode follower, with R_L removed. Notice that the effect of feedback in this type of circuit is to decrease the admittance of the branch containing the feedback voltage by the factor of $(1 - A_K)$. This is a characteristic of amplifier circuits having *current feedback*. Voltage feedback has the effect of increasing the output admittance.

For the particular circuit under study, the output admittance and the output resistance can be simplified from Equation (9.37), to

$$Y_{o1} = \frac{1}{R_L} + \frac{1}{r_p + (1 + \mu) R_K}$$
$$R_{o1} = \frac{R_L [r_p + (1 + \mu) R_K]}{R_L + r_p + (1 + \mu) R_K} \tag{9.39}$$

(b) When the output voltage is taken from the cathode, Figure 9.9, the procedure for analyzing the circuit is similar to the preceding development. One of the chief differences is the presence of voltage feedback rather than of current feedback. For other comparisons let us examine the voltage gain and output admittance characteristics of the amplifier. Since

$$E_g = E_s - V_{o2} \tag{9.40}$$

the current equation in terms of V_{o2} and E_s is

$$V_{o2}\left(\frac{1}{R_K} + \frac{1}{r_p + R_L}\right) - \frac{\mu}{r_p + R_K}(E_s - V_{o2}) = 0 \tag{9.41}$$

For this voltage feedback amplifier both the output admittance and the voltage gain are easily determined from this one expression. To find the output admittance, we should consider V_{o2} as a source with E_s set to zero, and the result thus obtained is identical to the coefficient of V_{o2} in Equation (9.41). Therefore,

$$Y_{o2} = \frac{1}{R_K} + \frac{1}{r_p + R_L} + \frac{\mu}{r_p + R_L} \tag{9.42}$$

The presence of voltage feedback is responsible for the third admittance term. The output resistance is

$$R_{o2} = \frac{(r_p + R_L) R_K}{r_p + R_L + (1 + \mu) R_K} \tag{9.43}$$

Notice that the presence of the voltage feedback has the effect of increasing the admittance, or of decreasing the output resistance. The voltage gain from Equation (9.41) is

$$A_2 = \frac{\mu R_K}{r_p + R_L + (1 + \mu) R_K} \tag{9.44}$$

Comparing the two voltage gains, A_1 and A_2, we find that

$$\frac{A_1}{A_2} = -\frac{R_L}{R_K} \tag{9.45}$$

which means that the two output voltages can be made equal, and of exact phase opposition, if R_K and R_L are equal. In other words,

$$V_{o1} = -V_{o2} \quad \text{if} \quad R_K = R_L \tag{9.46}$$

9.7 A Capacitor Paralleling R_K

The circuit of Figure 9.10 is similar to the $R_L R_K$ amplifier but with a capacitance, C, in parallel with R_K. If C is large, the cathode voltage will be essentially constant except for a low frequency range of operation, which means that the circuit can be used as a part of a low frequency compensation circuit when required. Also, the circuit provides a self bias without feedback above a certain range of low frequencies.

A study of the frequency response reveals that the voltage gain for the circuit, with the output voltage taken from the plate, can be expressed as

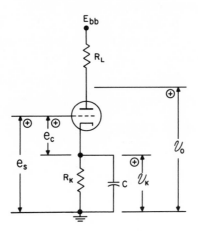

Fig. 9.10. A capacitor in parallel with R_K.

$$A = A_1 \frac{1 + j\omega R_K C}{1 + j\omega R_{o2} C} \tag{9.47}$$

where

$$A_1 = -\frac{\mu R_L}{r_p + R_L + (1 + \mu) R_K}$$

which is Equation (9.35) and

$$R_{o2} = \frac{(r_p + R_L) R_K}{r_p + R_L + (1 + \mu) R_K}$$

which is Equation (9.43).

The gain expression, Equation (9.47), is conveniently derived by replacing R_K of Equation (9.35) with Z_K where

$$Z_K = \frac{R_K / j\omega C}{R_K + (1/j\omega C)} \tag{9.48}$$

The frequency response for the circuit is shown in Figure 9.11 where f_a

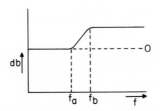

Fig. 9.11. Frequency response for the circuit in Figure 9.10.

represents the lower corner frequency and f_b represents the upper corner frequency. From Equation (9.47),

$$\frac{1}{\omega_a} = R_K C$$

$$\frac{1}{\omega_b} = R_{o2} C \tag{9.49}$$

In the low frequency range (below f_a), the voltage gain from Equation (9.47) is

$$A_{\mathrm{LF}} = A_1 \tag{9.50}$$

For the high frequency range (above f_b), the voltage gain is

$$A_{\mathrm{HF}} = A_1 \frac{R_K}{R_{o2}} \tag{9.51}$$

or

$$\frac{A_{\mathrm{HF}}}{A_{\mathrm{LF}}} = \frac{R_K}{R_{o2}} = \frac{\omega_b}{\omega_a} \tag{9.52}$$

At this point it is suggested that you review Section 6.8 and Section 6.10 for the purpose of comparing the results developed in those sections with the results developed here. Observe that the output resistance looking back from the capacitor is a significant factor in each case. Also, observe the frequency response graphs. Here the frequency response rises from f_a to f_b, while the frequency response falls for the circuits of Section 6.8 and Section 6.10 (see Figure 6.19). This suggests that it might be desirable to combine two circuits into one circuit to take advantage of the opposing frequency response characteristics, as suggested by the circuit of Figure 9.12.

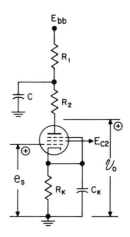

Fig. 9.12. A frequency compensated circuit.

How does the circuit provide self-bias as suggested in the first paragraph of this section? Equation (9.51) gives an answer by replacing A_1 and R_{o2} with their respective equivalence as given in support of Equation (9.47). With these substitutions we find that

$$A_{\text{HF}} = -\frac{\mu R_L}{r_p + R_L} \tag{9.53}$$

which means that the cathode voltage is a constant in the high frequency range above f_b. Self-bias, without feedback, will exist provided that

$$\omega_b > \frac{10}{R_{o2} C} \tag{9.54}$$

Selection of a quiescent operating point on the plate characteristics of the tube is identical to that given in Section 9.5 for an ordinary $R_L R_K$ amplifier, since the circuit of this section becomes an $R_L R_K$ amplifier in the low frequency range. The presence of the parallel capacitance does not change the quiescent operating point but it does affect the slope of the operating path. For the ordinary $R_L R_K$ amplifier, recall that the load line is given by

$$i_b = \frac{E_{bb} - e_b}{R_K + R_L}$$

while in the high frequency range with the capacitor added, the load line is given by

$$i_b = \frac{(E_{bb} - V_K) - e_b}{R_L} \tag{9.55}$$

where V_K is the constant bias voltage. The parenthetical term $(E_{bb} - V_K)$ is an equivalent plate supply voltage and is the load line intercept on the e_b axis of the plate characteristics.

9.8 Square Wave Input to $R_K - C_K$ Amplifier

The circuit in Figure 9.13 is no different than the circuit in Figure 9.10. It is repeated to draw attention to a square wave input and the particular problems of analysis that must be considered for such an input. The capacitance, C_K, may be present for reasons explained in the preceding section or it may be present because of the input capacitance of a coupling circuit.

In an explanation of the circuit for a square wave, or triggering input voltage, it is only necessary to recall that the capacitor voltage, and consequently, the cathode voltage, cannot change instantaneously. This means that the grid voltage must exactly follow the input voltage for instantaneous changes of the source voltage, disregarding any other capacitance in the circuit.

In the absence of C_K, the grid voltage will remain within the negative grid control region for a large change of input voltage, as explained in

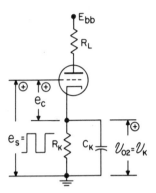

Fig. 9.13. R_K-C_K circuit with square wave input.

Sections 9.3 and 9.5 This is not true when C_K is present if the input voltage changes too rapidly.

There is another factor to consider, also. For example, what is the grid cutoff voltage? It is not always the grid voltage corresponding to the E_{bb} intercept on the e_b axis of the plate characteristics. It is the grid voltage corresponding to the $(E_{bb} - V_K)$ intercept, for intervals when the cathode voltage is constant. Thus, if V_K is large the cutoff voltage could be a very low negative voltage.

For example, the grid cutoff voltage might be -4 volts at the $(E_{bb} - V_K)$ intercept and -10 volts at the E_{bb} intercept. Therefore, for a particular steady state conditon an input voltage of 40 volts might be required to make the grid voltage -1 volt. With these hypothetical numbers, the input voltage would only need to drop instantaneously from 40 to 37 volts in order to cut the tube *off* momentarily. To keep the plate current cut off, however, the input voltage must drop from 40 to -10 volts; only the first three-volt change must be instantaneous. The required rate of change the rest of the way is largely determined by the time constant of the circuit. The circuit may have either of two time constants, as suggested in Section 9.7. They are

$$\tau_c = R_K C_K$$
$$\tau_c = R_{o2} C_K$$

(9.56)

9.9 Plate-to-Grid Coupling

The next few sections are devoted to a study of circuits in which the feedback voltage is produced as a result of coupling from the plate to the control grid of an amplifier circuit.

There are several methods of attack that can be employed for the solution of such circuits. To be certain of a correct solution, however, voltage or current equations must be written for the circuit as it stands. Any other method of solution must be derived from these equations. We use another method of analysis because it would be easy to overlook some of the important properties of the circuit by always analyzing the circuit from its given arrangement of circuit parameters. In additon, a revision of the circuit that has an equivalent to the original may permit a more rapid solution.

The procedure of obtaining one particular type of equivalent circuit is suggested by the two diagrams in Figure 9.14. The actual circuit has a coupling circuit, identified as Z_c, from the plate to the control grid; the modified equivalent circuit, Figure 9.14b, does not have this coupling. Observe that it is only necessary to revise the input circuit in order to account for the effects of feedback. This equivalent circuit, with some reservations, is then evaluated as though feedback did not exist.

The three circuits in Figure 9.15 are a sequence of diagrams illustrating the steps in obtaining the equivalent circuit that is apparently without feed-

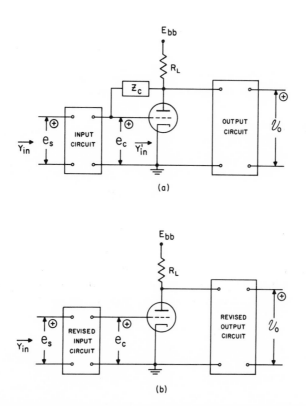

Fig. 9.14. Plate-to-grid coupling can be represented by revised input and output circuits.

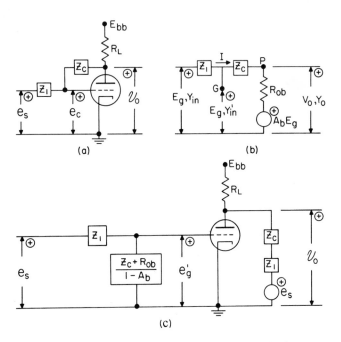

Fig. 9.15. Plate-to-grid coupling and equivalent circuits.

back. The circuit in Figure 9.15a represents the actual circuit with plate-to-grid coupling. By representing the voltage gain of the basic amplifier as

$$A_b = -\frac{\mu R_L}{r_p + R_L} = -g_m R_{ob}$$

where the output resistance of the basic amplifier is

$$R_{ob} = \frac{r_p R_L}{r_p + R_L}$$

then, the a-c equivalent circuit in Figure 9.15b results.

The equivalent circuit that we are looking for is given in Figure 9.15c which is obtained by writing appropriate equations for the a-c equivalent circuit. Writing the current equation at node G, we have

$$\frac{E_g}{R_{ob} + Z_c} - \frac{A_b E_g}{R_{ob} + Z_c} = I$$

or

$$E_g \frac{1 - A_b}{R_{ob} + Z_c} = I \tag{9.57}$$

The coefficient of E_g is the input admittance looking into the grid-cathode of the actual circuit. Thus,

$$Y'_{in} = \frac{1 - A_b}{R_{ob} + Z_c} \tag{9.58}$$

or

$$Z'_{in} = \frac{R_{ob} + Z_c}{1 - A_b} \tag{9.59}$$

The equivalent input impedance is shown on the equivalent circuit in Figure 9.15c. Notice that the output circuit retains the parallel branch of (Z_1, Z_c, e_s). This branch is often omitted because of a low loading effect on the output voltage. A solution of the equivalent circuit, Figure 9.15c, will give the correct values of the output voltage and the input impedance. The equivalent circuit does not reveal the correct values of output impedance and grid voltage. We can trust only the a-c equivalent circuit to provide a completely correct solution. Yet, the equivalent circuit, Figure 9.15c, has considerable merit as an aid in the evaluation of certain circuit problems. The circuit problems of the next section are examples.

The voltage gain can be derived from either equivalent circuit. First, by reference to Figure 9.15c, we can write the voltage equation from its a-c equivalent circuit (not shown) as

$$V_o = (A_b E'_g - E_s) \frac{Z_1 + Z_c}{R_{ob} + Z_1 + Z_c} + E_s$$

or

$$V_o = A_b E'_g \frac{Z_1 + Z_c}{R_{ob} + Z_1 + Z_c} + E_s \frac{R_{ob}}{R_{ob} + Z_1 + Z_c} \tag{9.60}$$

From the simple voltage divider action of the input circuit, the modified grid voltage can be expressed as

$$E'_g = E_s \frac{Z_c + R_{ob}}{Z_1 (1 - A_b) + Z_c + R_{ob}} \tag{9.61}$$

The voltage gain expression is found by combining the last two equations. In simplified form

$$A = \frac{A_b Z_c + R_{ob}}{Z_1 (1 - A_b) + Z_c + R_{ob}} \tag{9.62}$$

By writing a *current* equation at node P of Figure 9.15b, we will have an expression from which the output admittance (true value) can be determined, as well as the expression for voltage gain. The current equation is

$$V_o \left(\frac{1}{R_{ob}} + \frac{1}{Z_1 + Z_c} \right) - \frac{A_b E_g}{R_{ob}} - \frac{E_s}{Z_1 + Z_c} = 0 \tag{9.63}$$

The true value of grid voltage, in terms of V_o and E_s, is

$$E_g = E_s \frac{Z_c}{Z_1 + Z_c} + V_o \frac{Z_1}{Z_1 + Z_c} \tag{9.64}$$

$$= \text{Voltage from source} + \text{Feedback voltage}$$

The grid voltage Equation (9.64) is written in a form that has been used several times in previous discussions. It is probably recognized more easily in the form

$$E_g = E_s + (V_o - E_s)\frac{Z_1}{Z_1 + Z_c}$$

The grid voltage equation also has added significance when expressed with regard to the feedback factor, β.

$$E_g = (1 - \beta)E_s + \beta V_o \qquad (9.65)$$

since

$$\beta = \frac{Z_1}{Z_1 + Z_c} \qquad (9.66)$$

Making the substitution for grid voltage, Equation (9.64), the current expression, Equation (9.63), becomes

$$V_o\left[\frac{1}{R_{ob}} + \frac{1}{Z_1 + Z_c} - \frac{A_b Z_1}{R_{ob}(Z_1 + Z_c)}\right]$$
$$- E_s\left[\frac{A_b Z_c}{R_{ob}(Z_1 + Z_c)} + \frac{1}{Z_1 + Z_c}\right] = 0 \qquad (9.67)$$

Solving for the voltage gain, this expression gives the same result as previously given in Equation (9.62). The two circuits, (b) and (c), in Figure 9.15 are therefore equivalent for calculations of output voltage and voltage gain. The output admittance is the coefficient of V_o in Equation (9.67).

$$Y_o = \frac{1}{R_{ob}} + \frac{1}{Z_1 + Z_c} - \frac{A_b \beta}{R_{ob}} \qquad (9.68)$$

where the third admittance term is present because of feedback. It is interesting to recall that the feedback admittance term of preceding feedback circuits can also be expressed as

$$Y_{fb} = -\frac{\beta A_b}{R_{ob}} \qquad (9.69)$$

provided A_b and R_{ob} are properly defined for the particular circuit. Since

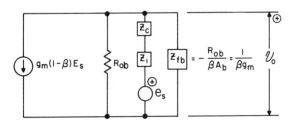

Fig. 9.16. Equivalent circuit represented by Equation (9.67).

$A_b = -g_m R_{ob}$ for the circuit under discussion, the feedback admittance term in this case is also

$$Y_{fb} = \beta g_m \qquad (9.70)$$

The equivalent circuit as defined by Equation (9.67) and shown in Figure 9.16, does not reveal the grid voltage and the input impedance of the given circuit.

9.10 Plate-to-Grid Capacitive Coupling: "Miller" Effect

The circuit in Figure 9.17a shows a capacitor that couples the plate to the control grid of an amplifier. The value of the coupling capacitance includes the interelectrode capacitance, C_{pg}. Thus, a coupling capacitance is always present even in the absence of an external capacitor.

The equivalent circuit, in agreement with Figure 9.15c, is shown in Figure 9.17b. Observe that the grid-cathode is paralleled with $C(1 - A_b)$ in series with $R_{ob}/(1 - A_b)$, while the plate-cathode retains the parallel branch of C

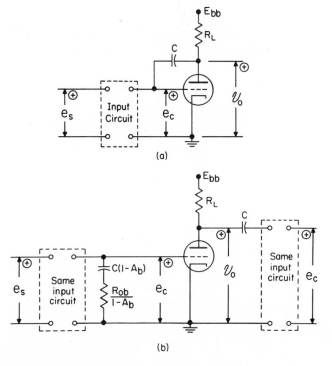

(a)

(b)

Fig. 9.17. Plate-to-grid capacitance coupling. (a) The given circuit. (b) Equivalent circuit.

in series with the given input circuit. The latter branch can be omitted provided it produces negligible affect on the output voltage.

It is important to consider a circuit having capacitive coupling from the plate to the grid, as represented in the next section.

9.11 An Integrating Amplifier

The circuit in Figure 9.18a can be used to generate an output voltage that approximates a ramp function, or a linear sweep voltage. A method of analysis is suggested by the approximate equivalent circuit shown in Figure 9.18b. Static values are determined with reference to circuit (a) and dynamic values are determined with reference to equivalent circuit (b).

The sweep time is the time interval that the switch remains open. The switch represents any one of a number of possible electronic circuits which, when properly triggered, will perform the switching function electrically.

In the process of analyzing the circuit we first of all observe that the initial grid voltage is E_{cc}, a negative voltage near cutoff for the amplifier. For the time interval that the switch is open, the grid voltage as a function of time is

$$e_c = E_{bb} - (E_{bb} - E_{cc})\, e^{-t/RC(1-A_b)} \tag{9.71}$$

The allowable sweep time is limited since the grid voltage, as calculated from Equation (9.71), must remain within the grid-control region for the tube. Designating the sweep time as T_s, the change in grid voltage, Δe_c, is represented in Equation (9.71) by replacing the time variable with T_s. The change in plate voltage, or output voltage is then

$$\begin{aligned} \Delta e_b &= A_b \Delta e_c \\ &= A_b\left[E_{bb} - (E_{bb} - E_{cc})\, e^{-T_s/RC(1-A_b)}\right] \end{aligned} \tag{9.72}$$

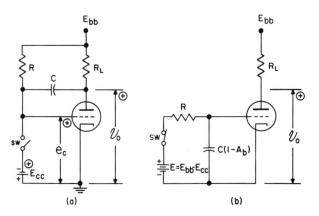

Fig. 9.18. (a) An integrating amplifier, (b) An approximate equivalent circuit.

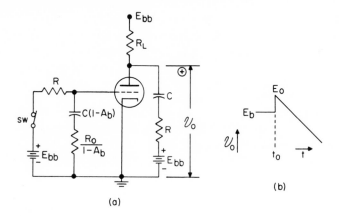

Fig. 9.19. (a) A complete equivalent circuit for calculating v_0 of circuit in Figure 9.18a. (b) Sweep voltage starts when switch of Figure 9.18a is opened.

Thus, knowing the initial quiescent plate voltage (load line on plate characteristics) and the change in plate voltage from Equation (9.72), the output voltage is completely described according to the circuits in Figure 9.18.

The equivalent circuit of Figure 9.19a will give a more nearly correct solution. An analysis of this circuit reveals a small positive step in plate voltage at the start of the sweep. Except for identifying the presence and magnitude of this step, the procedure of analysis is exactly the same as for the approximate equivalent circuit (see Figure 9.18b).

Remembering that E_{cc} is a negative quantity with the reference polarity on the grid side, the magnitude of the voltage step at the grid is found by writing a voltage equation on the input circuit at the instant the sweep starts. Since the grid is really coupled to the plate by a capacitor, any instantaneous change in grid voltage will also appear at the plate. Identifying the step in plate voltage as $E_o - E_b$ (Figure 9.19b), we then write

$$E_o - E_b = (E_{bb} - E_{cc}) \frac{R_o/(1 - A_b)}{R + R_o/(1 - A_b)}$$

which, by replacing A_b with its equivalent of $- g_m R_o$, can be rewritten in simplified form as

$$E_o - E_b = \frac{E_{bb} - E_{cc}}{1 + g_m R + R/R_o} \tag{9.73}$$

With a normally large value of R, the magnitude of the step is small.

This step in voltage can be eliminated by adding a resistance, R_c, in series with the capacitance as shown in Figure 9.20a. What magnitude of resistance is needed for R_c? We can obtain the answer from the equivalent circuit without apparently disregarding any part.

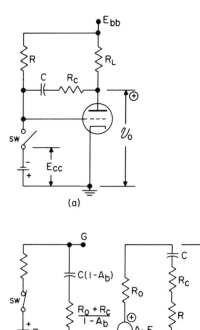

Fig. 9.20. (a) $R_c C$ coupling, plate-to-grid. (b) The equivalent circuit.

The d-c voltage E_s represents the sum of E_{bb} and $-E_{cc}$. Defining Δe_c and Δe_b as the instantaneous changes of the grid voltage and the plate voltage at the instant the sweep begins, we can proceed with the solution of the circuit for this instant. From the equivalent plate circuit, Figure 9.20b, the instantaneous change in plate voltage is

$$\Delta e_b = A_b \Delta e_c - (A_b \Delta e_c - E_s)\frac{R_o}{R_o + R_c + R}$$

or

$$\Delta e_b = A_b \Delta e_c \frac{R_c + R}{R_o + R_c + R} + E_s \frac{R_o}{R_o + R_c + R} \qquad (9.74)$$

Replacing A_b and Δe_c with their equivalence of

$$A_b = -g_m R_o$$

$$\Delta e_c = \frac{E_s}{1 + g_m R R_o/(R_o + R_c) + R/(R_o + R_c)} \qquad (9.75)$$

where Equation (9.75) is derived in the same manner as Equation (9.73) Δe_b can be expressed in simplified form as

$$\Delta e_b = E_s \frac{1 - g_m R_c}{1 + g_m R + (R + R_c)/R_o} \qquad (9.76)$$

We observe that the presence of R_c can make the step in plate voltage positive, zero, or negative. The step is eliminated provided

$$R_c = \frac{1}{g_m} \qquad (9.77)$$

9.12   Cathode-to-Grid Coupling with a Cathode Follower

The circuit in Figure 9.21a shows a cathode follower with a coupling impedance from the cathode to the grid; circuit (b) is an equivalent circuit. Applying Thevenin's theorem to a portion of the equivalent circuit, the circuit in Figure 9.21c results. It is desirable to refer to this latter circuit containing the significant quantities R_{ob} and A_b. With the reference voltage polarities as indicated on the diagram, we have

$$R_{ob} = \frac{r_p R_K}{r_p + R_K}$$

$$A_b = g_m R_{ob}$$

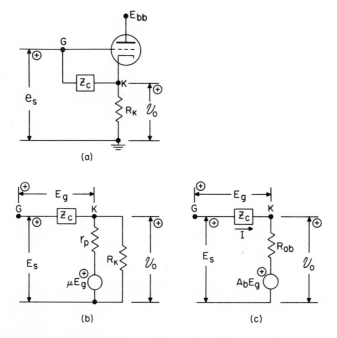

(a)

(b)   (c)

Fig. 9.21. (a) Circuit with grid-to-cathode coupling. (b) and (c) Equivalent circuits.

Except for the sign of A_b, these two quantities are identical to the corresponding expressions for the plate-to-grid coupled circuit in Figure 9.15, Section 9.9. Observe also that the only significant difference in the two equivalent circuits is the points of measurement for E_g. It is of interest to compare the two circuits for several reasons. A comparison of input impedances is particularly important. In addition, it is possible that we can have another type of integrating amplifier, or sweep circuit (see Section 9.14).

First, let us determine the input impedance of the cathode follower with cathode-to-grid coupling by writing a current equation for the equivalent circuit (Figure 9.21c).

$$I = \frac{E_s - A_b E_g}{R_{ob} + Z_c}$$

But E_g is a function of E_s. It is

$$E_g = E_s \frac{Z_c}{R_{ob} + Z_c (1 + A_b)} \tag{9.78}$$

Therefore, in simplified form

$$I = \frac{E_s}{R_{ob} + Z_c (1 + A_b)} \tag{9.79}$$

Replacing A_b with its equivalent of $g_m R_{ob}$, the input impedance form Equation (9.79) becomes

$$Z_{\text{in}} = R_{ob} + Z_c (1 + g_m R_{ob}) \tag{9.80}$$

This input impedance is large compared to the input impedance for the plate-to-grid coupled circuit. Refer to Equation (9.59) and observe that the input impedance for that circuit is $(R_{ob} + Z_c)/(1 + g_m R_{ob})$. The two expressions have identical definitions for R_{ob} except for the exchange of R_L and R_K, therefore a direct comparison is permitted. For example, the interelectrode capacitances will have much less effect in reducing the input impedance of a cathode follower than for an anode follower.

The input impedance, Equation (9.80), can also be expressed as a function

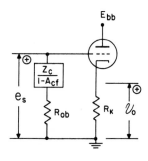

Fig. 9.22. Equivalent circuit showing input impedance for circuit in Figure 9.21a.

of the gain of a cathode follower rather than as a function of A_b. Since A_b is the voltage gain without feedback, then

$$A_b = \frac{A_{cf}}{1 + \beta A_{cf}} \tag{9.81}$$

where A_{cf} denotes the voltage gain of an ordinary cathode follower. With β equal to -1, the input impedance becomes

$$Z_{\text{in}} = R_{ob} + \frac{Z_c}{1 - A_{cf}} \tag{9.82}$$

The equivalent circuit in Figure 9.22 shows the input impedance of a cathode follower.

9.13   Another Integrating Circuit: Bootstrap Circuit

The circuit in Figure 9.23 illustrates one form of a sweep voltage generator that employs a cathode follower with RC coupling from cathode to grid. A circuit of this type is commonly identified as a bootstrap circuit. The switch represents an electronic gate which is triggered at a desired repetition rate.

With the switch closed, the steady state value of cathode voltage is determined from the plate characteristics and load line for an ordinary cathode follower. For the zero input voltage, the cathode voltage is a low value. The corresponding grid-cathode voltage is within the grid-control region but near the cutoff voltage for the amplifier (see Section 9.3). The capacitor voltage, V_2, is approximately equal to E. (This approximation neglects the small cathode voltage and the forward resistance of the diode.)

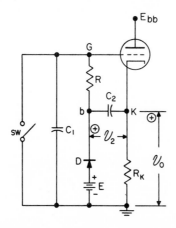

Fig. 9.23. A "bootstrap" sweep circuit.

The d-c voltage, E, is shown to simplify the analysis. The diode can be returned to E_{bb}.

The switch is opened to start the sweep voltage and remains open during the sweep interval. While the switch is open, the potentials at the three indicated points (G, K, and b) will rise. Since the voltage gain of a cathode follower is near unity, the potentials at K and G (ground reference) will increase by nearly equal amounts. The potential at b will also increase (turning diode *off*) by nearly the same value, provided that C_2 is a large capacitance. All of these nearly equal voltage increases result in a nearly constant voltage V_{bG}, the voltage across the resistance R. Consequently, the charging current is nearly constant for the working capacitor, C_1, and the sweep voltage is nearly linear.

$$v_c = \frac{1}{C} \int I \, dt$$
$$= \frac{I}{C} t + \text{constant} \tag{9.83}$$

The bootstrap circuit can be analyzed in greater detail by reference to either of the two equivalent circuits in Figure 9.24. The factor $(1 + A_b)$ is used to permit further comparison with the "Miller" circuit. Another equivalent circuit could also be shown in which $(1 + A_b)$ is replaced by $1/(1 - A_{cf})$. From the development of Section 9.12, recall that

$$1 + A_b = \frac{1}{1 - A_{cf}} \tag{9.84}$$

for a cathode follower, with A_b and A_{cf} as defined in that section. The equivalent circuit, Figure 9.24a, is in agreement with the development of the preceding section.

A study of the input circuit time constant will help to verify the equivalent circuit in Figure 9.24b. Since R_{ob} is normally much less than $R(1 + A_b)$, the time constant of the input circuit is

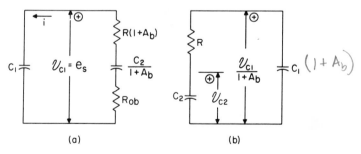

(a)   (b)

Fig. 9.24. Equivalent circuits for "bootstrap" circuit (applicable during sweep interval).

$$\tau_c = R(1 + A_b)\frac{C_1 C_2/(1 + A_b)}{C_1 + C_2/(1 + A_b)} \qquad (9.85)$$

which can be written as

$$\tau_c = R\frac{C_2 C_1 (1 + A_b)}{C_2 + (1 + A_b) C_1} = RC' \qquad (9.86)$$

The equivalent RC' circuit represents a series combination of R, C_2 and $C_1(1 + A_b)$ as indicated in Figure 9.24b. Compare this equivalent circuit with Figure 9.19 for the Miller circuit and observe the similarities of the two circuits. The capacitance is $C_1(1 + g_m R_{ob})$ in each circuit. Each circuit has the series resistance R, and C_2 of the bootstrap circuit takes the place of E_{bb} in the Miller circuit. However, C_2 is large and is charged to a d-c voltage of E that can be E_{bb}. So the two input circuits are essentially identical, especially if C_2 is much greater than $C_1(1 + A_b)$.

What then is the difference between two circuits? The triode, or pentode, will amplify the sweep voltage many times while the cathode follower has a voltage gain less than, but near, unity. However, the sweep voltage at the input of the cathode follower has a much greater allowable voltage swing to keep the grid voltage within the grid-control region. In addition, the cathode follower has a low dynamic output resistance. To give similar degrees of sweep linearity, C_2 of the bootstrap circuit would have to be charged to a voltage greater than E_{bb} of the Miller integrator.

For the bootstrap circuit, the sweep voltage is expressed as

$$v_{c1} = E_{bb}\frac{C'}{C_1}(1 - e^{-t/RC'}) \qquad (9.87)$$

where C' is as defined in Equation (9.86).

The C'/C_1 ratio in Equation (9.87) is understandable from a study of the initial and final steady state values of voltage on the two series capacitors in Figure 9.24b. Initially, V_2 is equal to E, and $V_{c1}/(1 + A_b)$ is zero. A steady state voltage for the two series capacitors then becomes

$$\frac{V_{c1}}{1 + A_b} \text{ (steady state)} = E\frac{C_2}{C_2 + (1 + A_b) C_1}$$

For the true input voltage,

$$V_{c1} \text{ (steady state)} = E\frac{C_2(1 + A_b)}{C_2 + (1 + A_b) C_1} \qquad (9.88)$$

$$= EC'/C_1 \qquad (9.89)$$

9.14 Blocking Oscillator

The circuit in Figure 9.25 illustrates a basic form for a blocking oscillator using a vacuum triode. The circuit necessarily contains a pulse transformer and an RC input circuit to the triode amplifier.

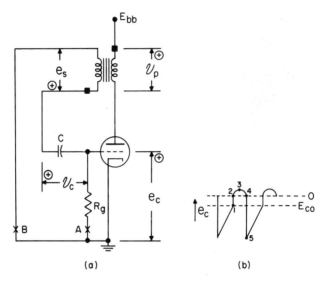

Fig. 9.25. (a) A blocking oscillator circuit. (b) Grid voltage waveform with expended time scale from points 1 to 5.

A bias voltage can be inserted in the circuit at point A. If used, the bias voltage, which should be a positive voltage, is intended to adjust the frequency of the blocking oscillator.

Synchronizing pulses can also be inserted at point A. Positive pulses are required. Negative synchronizing pulses can also be inserted in the circuit at point B, as indicated on the circuit diagram.

Calculations for the circuit are difficult in the presence of the pulse transformer. The pulse transformer is close-coupled, yet it does have some leakage inductance that is not constant under switching conditions. There is also the presence of distributed capacitance of the windings that influence the behavior of the blocking oscillator. The behavior of the circuit may be understood, however, by assuming an ideal pulse transformer.

The waveform as shown for e_c in Figure 9.25b is needed for an explanation of the circuit. There are five significant voltage points on this waveform. As the grid voltage relaxes into the active region (at point 1), the plate current starts to increase. The increasing current induces a positive going voltage for e_s, for the indicated reference polarity, and a regenerative action is established. The grid is quickly driven into the positive voltage region. Then the comparatively small grid-cathode resistance r_c is established (at point 2), and the time constant of the input circuit is now small. Consequently, the capacitor quickly charges to the peak value of e_s, which cannot be greater than E_{bb} multiplied by the turns ratio of the transformer.

Since the plate current is limited and cannot continue to increase at a rapid rate, the induced voltages in the transformer windings must soon start to decrease after the grid voltage is driven positive. The grid voltage becomes negative (at point 4) when e_s starts to decrease. It actually started to decrease (at point 3) at a previous time. This is true since the time constant of the circuit is small, when the grid voltage is positive and the capacitor voltage closely follows that of e_s. Once the induced voltages start to decrease, a regenerative action is again established after point 4. This removes the small input resistance and the time constant for the input circuit is now much larger and is equal to $R_g C$. The resulting negative voltage generated at e_s and the previously established voltage on the capacitor will drive the grid to a negative value (at point 5) to completely cut off the plate current. The grid voltage then relaxes back to the active region of the triode and the cycle is complete. The time interval that the plate current is cut off is a significant time interval and constitutes the major time of one cycle. Increasing R_g, C, E_{bb} or the secondary-to-primary turns ratio, will decrease the frequency of the blocking oscillator. The increase of a positive bias voltage, if used, will increase the frequency. The output voltage can be taken from the plate, from the grid or from a third winding on the transformer.

9.15 Transistor Sweep Circuit

The circuit in Figure 9.26 represents a "Miller" type sweep circuit in which a capacitor is connected from the collector to the base of transistor 2. Transistor 1 serves as the electronic switch that is switched *off* during the time of the sweep. A possible set of voltage waveforms is shown in Figure 9.27 The driving voltage for the switching transistor is a rectangular waveform. The $R_1 C_1$ input circuit is chosen to clamp the positive pulses to a slightly positive voltage at the base of transistor 1. The base current of transistor 1

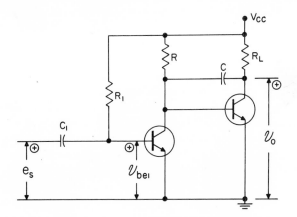

Fig. 9.26. A transistor sweep circuit.

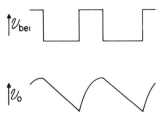

Fig. 9.27. Generation of a sweep voltage (lower trace) with the circuit in Figure 9.26, using *n-p-n* transistors.

must be sufficient to hold the *n-p-n* transistor in saturation during the time of the positive pulse. This current is V_{cc}/R_1.

While transistor 1 is in saturation, the base voltage of the second transistor is sufficiently small to hold transistor 2 nearly *off* under quiescent conditions. The sweep voltage, as observed for v_o, is initiated the instant transistor 1 is switched *off* by the negative pulse of the driving voltage. The sweep voltage continues for the duration of the negative input pulse provided that the second transistor has not entered the saturation region in the meantime. In any event, the sweep voltage has a lower limit of zero and an upper limit of V_{cc} for the *n-p-n* transistor. When transistor 1 is switched *on*, following the allowable sweep time, the output voltage starts its recovery toward its upper limit. The positive pulse of the driving voltage should be of sufficient time duration to allow complete recovery.

9.16 Transistor Blocking Oscillator

The circuit in Figure 9.28 represents one possible arrangment for a blocking oscillator using a *p-n-p* transistor. The arrangement is identical for *n-p-n* transistors.

For the *p-n-p* transistor, V_{cc} and V_{BB} are negative quantities. The biasing voltage can be used to control the frequency of the blocking oscillator as in the vacuum tube circuit. The frequency is also dependent on V_{cc}, the RC time constant, and the transformer turns ratio.

Synchronizing pulses can be inserted at point *B*, indicated on the circuit diagram. Synchronizing pulses inserted at this point must be positive pulses for the *p-n-p* transistor, or negative pulses for *n-p-n* transistors. Synchronizing pulses can also be inserted in place of the bias voltage but of the opposite polarity indicated for point *B*. The problems of synchronizing various types of circuits are discussed in considerable detail in Chapters 12 and 13.

The behavior of a transistor blocking oscillator is very similar to that for vacuum tubes. The major difference is concerned with the significant times

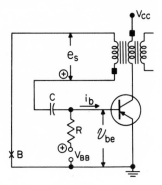

Fig. 9.28. Transistor blocking oscillator.

when the time constant of the RC input circuit becomes small. For transistors, this happens when the base voltage relaxes into the active region; for tubes, when the grid voltage is positive.

PROBLEMS

9.1 For the circuit in Figure 9.2a, $R_K = 50$ K, $E_{bb} = 250$ volts, and the tube is a 6J5. Plot a graph of v_o as a function of e_1. Plot this graph as a point-by-point analysis using the plate charateristics for the tube. *Suggestion:* first, evaluate v_o as a function of e_c then use the relationship $e_1 = e_c + v_o$.

9.2 The graph of Problem 9.1 approximates a straight line. Write the equation that expresses v_o as a function of e_s.
   (a) Write this equation in terms of the numerical values obtained for Problem 9.1.
   (b) Also, write the general equation in terms of circuit parameters and tube constants.

9.3 The cathode follower circuit in Figure 9.2a has three possible values of output resistance for the corresponding three conditions of operation. Two of these conditions are for static operation (plate current is zero or the tube is operating in the active region) and the remaining condition is for dynamic operation. For the given quantities of Problem 9.1, determine the output resistance.
   (a) when the plate current is zero
   (b) when the tube is operating at a quiescent grid voltage of -2 volts
   (c) when the tube is operating under dynamic conditions for changing signals.

9.4 Use the two methods suggested by Figure 9.5 to determine the quiescent operating points for an assigned cathode follower circuit. Discuss the merits of these two methods.

9.5 Use the two methods suggested by Figure 9.8 to determine the quiescent operating point for an assigned $R_L - R_K$ amplifier. Discuss the merits of the two methods.

9.6 For the circuit in Figure 9.10, $R_L = 20$ K, $R_K = 5$ K, $C = 1$ μfd; r_p (for the tube) $= 8$ K and $\mu = 40$. Determine the frequency response for the circuit.

9.7 For the circuit in Figure 9.10, $E_{bb} = 250$ volts, $R_L = 5$ K, $R_K = 20$ K, $C = 0.1$ μfd, and the tube is a 6J5. Plot v_K and v_o, indicating all significant quantities on these waveforms if e_s is a positive step voltage of 100 volts. Before the step e_s is -20 volts for a long time.

9.8 Continue the voltage plots for Problem 9.7 if e_s is at $+80$ volts for a long time and is then followed by a step of -100 volts.

9.9 Determine the frequency response for the circuit of Problem 9.7.

9.10 For the circuit in Figure 9.18a, $E_{bb} = 300$ volts, $R_L = 30$ K, $R = 100$ K, $C = .01$ μfd, $E_{cc} = -16$ volts and the tube is $\frac{1}{2}$ 12AU7.
   (a) Evaluate v_o if the switch has been closed for a long time.
   (b) Evaluate v_o the instant after the switch is opened.
   (c) The sweep voltage that is generated at v_o can be regarded as a portion of an exponential. What is the E_{as} value of this exponential?
   (d) What is the sweep time if the sweep voltage is allowed to continue until $v_o = 120$ volts before the switch is again closed?

9.11 Repeat Problem 9.10 with the following changes: $E_{cc} = -8$ volts, and the tube is $\frac{1}{2}$ 12AT7.

9.12 Repeat Problem 9.10 with the following changes: $E_{cc} = -4$ volts, and the tube is $\frac{1}{2}$ 12AX7.

9.13 Refer to the circuit in Figure 9.20a. What value of R_c is required in each of the preceding three problems to eliminate the step at the beginning of the of the sweep voltage?

9.14 For the circuit in Figure 9.23, $E_{bb} = 300$ volts, $R_K = 30$ K, $R = 100$ K, $C_1 = .01$ μfd, $C_2 = 1$ μfd, $E = 300$ volts, and the tube is $\frac{1}{2}$ 12AU7.
   (a) Evaluate v_o if the switch has been closed for a long time.
   (b) The switch is opened to initiate the sweep. What is the E_{as} value for the exponential that represents the sweep voltage at v_o?

9.15 Repeat Problem 9.14 for a 12AU7 tube in the circuit.

9.16 Repeat Problem 9.14 for a 12AX7 tube in the circuit.

10

Dual-Tube Switching and Pulse Forming Circuits

10.1 General Discussion

Several sections of this chapter are devoted to a study of dual-tube circuits that will generate nearly rectangular waveforms with controlled time durations and repetition rates. (Chapter 11 is a corresponding study with transistors.) Some of these dual-tube circuits are oscillators that generate the rectangular pulses without the need of an external signal or trigger pulse. Other circuits must be triggered in order to generate the rectangular voltage waveform. Of the circuits that must be triggered, the trigger pulse initiates the rectangular waveform. The time duration of the generated pulse is terminated by the circuit in some instances, while in other circuits, the pulse is terminated by a second trigger pulse.

Dual-tube circuits that generate rectangular waveforms repetitively, without the necessity of external trigger pulses, are identified as "free-running" multivibrators, astable multivibrators, or relaxation oscillators. Dual amplifier circuits in which the rectangular pulse is initiated by an external trigger voltage but terminated by the circuit itself is identified as a monostable multivibrator. Dual amplifier circuits in which the rectangular pulse is both initiated and terminated by external trigger pulses is a bistable multivibrator. This latter type of circuit also provides a controllable *on* and *off* condition needed for digital computers and binary counting systems. In a sense, each of the three types of multivibrators are *on* or *off* circuits in that where one of the two amplifying tubes is conducting, the other, for ideal operation, is not conducting. Only the bistable multivibrator can remain in a stable state for either the *on* or the *off* condition.

Several dual-amplifier circuits employ cathode coupling with a common cathode resistor for the two amplifying tubes. In addition to providing a self-bias voltage for the two tubes, this type of coupling permits circuit responses of considerable value.

10.2 A "Free-Running" (Astable) Multivibrator: Qualitative Analysis

The circuit diagram of Figure 10.1 represents a free-running, or astable type of multivibrator. The circuit will oscillate and the voltage waveform at the plate of either tube approximates a square wave for a proper selection of circuit parameters. A method of calculating significant voltages and time intervals is given in the next section. The switch symbol is shown in the plate circuit of tube 2 to assist in giving a qualitative explanation of the circuit. It is not required to start oscillations.

The capacitor currents, i_1 and i_2, with references as indicated on the circuit diagram, provide a key to an understanding of the circuit operation. A grid voltage is positive, zero, or negative depending on whether the corresponding capacitor current is respectively positive, zero, or negative.

Now let us try to observe what might happen in the circuit of Figure 10.1; first with the plate circuit of tube 2 open for a long time and then after the plate circuit is closed. With the plate circuit open each capacitor will charge to some steady state value of voltage. The capacitor currents are then zero and the two grid voltages are also zero. This means that tube 1 is conducting, and since its grid voltage is zero the plate voltage is at some low

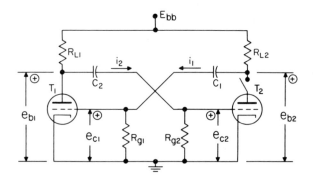

Fig. 10.1. A free-running (astable) multivibrator.

value, for example 60 volts. The grid voltage of tube 2 is also at zero, consequently tube 2 is ready to conduct when its plate circuit is closed. Before considering the effect of closing this circuit, observe that C_2 is charged to the low voltage of 60 volts while C_1 is charged to the full plate supply voltage of 300 volts.

Closing the plate circuit allows plate current of tube 2 to exist causing e_{b2} to drop from 300 volts to a much lower voltage (not necessarily 60 volts). As a consequence, i_1 of capacitor C_1 becomes negative causing the grid voltage of tube 1 to drop to a highly negative voltage which cuts off the plate current in tube 1. Thus, e_{b1} rises to a voltage greater than 60 volts (not 300 volts) which drives the grid of tube 2 into the positive grid voltage region, causing tube 2 to have a greater plate current than initially assumed. Tube 1 is now *off* and tube 2 is *on*, but this is not a stable state. The grid voltage of the *off* tube will relax back *toward* zero volts with the next switching action taking place when its grid voltage re-enters the grid control region. In the meantime, the capacitor voltage of C_2 has probably reached 300 volts and that of C_1 has approached but never will reach the steady state low voltage of 60 volts as initially assumed for C_2. The whole process keeps repeating with the two tubes alternately exchanging *on* and *off* conditions. The next few sections are devoted to a more detailed analysis and study of free-running multivibrators.

10.3 Quantitative Analysis of an Astable Multivibrator

The equivalent circuits (a) and (b) of Figure 10.2 suggest a method of analysis for the astable multivibrators of Figure 10.1. Each of these two circuits represents a two-stage, RC-coupled amplifier. The input voltage to circuit (a) is e_{c1} as calculated from circuit (b); the input voltage to circuit (b) is e_{c2} as calculated from circuit (a). Observe that e_{b1} and e_{c2} are calculated from the first circuit while e_{b2} and e_{c1} are calculated from the second circuit. Both circuits contain tube 1 and tube 2. With the assumption that tube 1 is *on* when tube 2 is *off* and vice versa, each circuit is analyzed for corresponding time intervals. This gives two conditions for each circuit or a total of four circuits to be evaluated. The four equivalent circuit conditions are shown in Figure 10.3. Circuits (a1) and (b1) apply when tube 1 is *on* and tube 2 is *off*. Circuits (a2) and (b2) apply when tube 1 is *off*, and tube 2 is *on*. The symbol r_{b1}, or r_{b2}, represents the static plate-to-cathode resistance when e_{c1}, or e_{c2}, is at zero volts. Since the grid voltages are driven positive for short time intervals, these values of r_{b1} and r_{b2} do not give calculated circuit voltages in agreement with experimental values of voltage. Nevertheless, r_b values are selected for zero grid voltage. There is a good reason for doing this, as will be explained later.

For simplicity of analysis let us define R_{o1}, R_{o2}, E_{b1}, and E_{b2} as

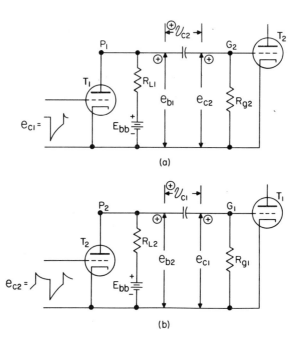

Fig. 10.2. The two equivalent circuits for the astable multivibrator.

$$R_{o1} = \frac{r_{b1} R_{L1}}{r_{b1} + R_{L1}} \tag{10.1}$$

$$R_{o2} = \frac{r_{b2} R_{L2}}{r_{b2} + R_{L2}} \tag{10.2}$$

$$E_{b1} = E_{bb} \frac{r_{b1}}{r_{b1} + R_{L1}} \tag{10.3}$$

$$E_{b2} = E_{bb} \frac{r_{b2}}{r_{b2} + R_{L2}} \tag{10.4}$$

Also, define R_1 and R_2 as

$$R_1 = \frac{r_{c1} R_{g1}}{r_{c1} + R_{g1}} \tag{10.5}$$

$$R_2 = \frac{r_{c2} R_{g2}}{r_{c2} + R_{g2}} \tag{10.6}$$

which are approximately equal to r_{c1} and r_{c2}, respectively, if R_g is much greater than r_c. The grid cutoff voltages, E_{co1} and E_{co2}, are also required in an analysis of the multivibrator.

The problem is to plot e_{b1}, e_{c2}, e_{b2}, and e_{c1} as a function of time as represented in Figure 10.4. Significant points are numbered on these waveforms.

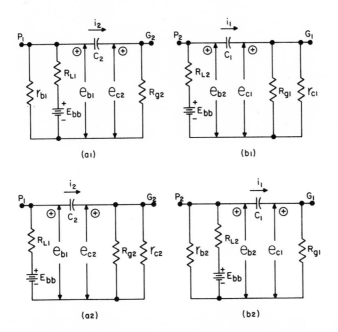

Fig. 10.3. The four equivalent circuits for the astable multivibrator; (a_1) and (b_1) are for tube 1 *on* and tube 2 *off*, (a_2) and (b_2) are for tube 1 *off* and tube 2 *on*.

Point 1 represents an instant of time when tube 2 is *off*, tube 1 is *on*, and when switching action is ready to take place since e_{c2} has relaxed from a negative voltage to cutoff, E_{co2}. The four voltages for Point 1 are obtained from circuits (a1) and (b1) of Figure 10.3.

Normally, the voltages of circuit (b1) attain steady state quiescent values, in which case e_{c1} is zero, e_{b2} is at E_{bb}, and C_1 is charged to E_{bb}.

The voltages of circuit (a1) at the instant of Point 1 are more difficult to determine. The key to representing the circuit voltages lies in the fact that e_{c2} is at cutoff at this instant. For the plate voltage, at any instant of time when circuit (al) is applicable, we have

$$e_{b1} = E_{b1} - e_{c2}\frac{R_{o1}}{R_{g2}} \qquad (10.7)$$

Thus at Point 1 of the voltage waveform,

(Point 1) $\qquad\qquad e_{b1} = E_{b1} - E_{co2}\frac{R_{o1}}{R_{g2}} \qquad (10.8)$

Further, e_{b1} at this instant is very nearly equal to E_{b1} and is so indicated in Figure 10.4. This is true not only because R_{g2} is normally much greater

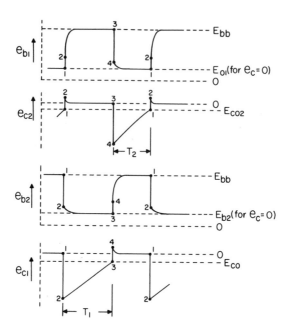

Fig. 10.4. Voltage waveforms for the astable circuit.

than R_{o1} but also because of the normally low value of E_{co2}. The voltage on C_2 at this instant is now known. At Point 1 the capacitor voltage is

(Point 1) $V_{C_2} \cong E_{b1} - E_{co2}$ (10.9)

Utilizing this equation for an example, if E_{b1} is 70 volts and E_{co2} is -10 volts, then C_2 has a voltage of 80 volts at Point 1.

Now we can proceed to determine the four voltages at Point 2 on the waveforms (see Figure 10.4); this (Point 2) is immediately after switching action has taken place. The circuits (a2) and (b2) are now applicable. The initial capacitor voltages for this circuit are the final values that existed just before the switching action. With this information on initial capacitor voltages, the four voltages at Point 2 are easily determined. Each of the parenthetical terms of the following equations represent the initial voltage on the capacitor.

(Point 2) $e_{b1} = E_{bb} - [E_{bb} - (E_{b1} - E_{co2})]\dfrac{R_{L1}}{R_{L1} + R_2}$

$$= E_{bb}\dfrac{R_2}{R_{L1} + R_2} + (E_{b1} - E_{co2})\dfrac{R_{L1}}{R_{L1} + R_2} \qquad (10.10)$$

(Point 2) $e_{c2} = [E_{bb} - (E_{b1} - E_{co2})]\dfrac{R_2}{R_{L1} + R_2}$ (10.11)

(Point 2) $\qquad e_{b2} = E_{b2} + [(E_{bb}) - E_{b2}]\dfrac{R_{o2}}{R_{o2} + R_{g1}}$ $\qquad$ (10.12)

(Point 2) $\qquad e_{c1} = -[(E_{bb}) - E_{b2}]\dfrac{R_{g1}}{R_{o2} + R_{g1}}$ $\qquad$ (10.13)

The instantaneous voltage changes from Point 1 to Point 2 must be equal for e_{b1} and e_{c2} and also for e_{b2} and e_{c1}.

The next significant point on the voltage waveforms of Figure 10.4 is at the instant when e_{c1} (grid voltage of the *off* tube) enters the grid-control region at E_{co1}, designated as Point 3. Observe that Point 3 corresponds to Point 1, except that tube 1 is *off* at Point 3 whereas tube 2 is *off* at Point 1. Calculations to determine the waveforms for the next half-cycle are similar to the calculations for the first half-cycle; equations (10.10) through (10.13) are applicable. To determine the voltages at Point 4, merely exchange the subscripts 1 and 2 in these four equations.

The time intervals T_1 and T_2 when tube 1 and tube 2 are alternatelty *off* are

$$T_1 = (R_{g1} + R_{o2})\, C_1 \ln \frac{e_{c1}\ (\text{at point 2})}{E_{co1}} \qquad (10.14)$$

$$T_2 = (R_{g2} + R_{o1})\, C_2 \ln \frac{e_{c2}\ (\text{at point 4})}{E_{co2}} \qquad (10.15)$$

These time intervals reduce to the approximations of

$$T_1 \cong R_{g1} C_1 \ln \frac{E_{b2} - E_{bb}}{E_{co1}} \qquad (10.16)$$

$$T_2 \cong R_{g2} C_2 \ln \frac{E_{b1} - E_{bb}}{E_{co2}} \qquad (10.17)$$

when R_{o1} is much less than R_{g2} and R_{o2} is much less than R_{g1}.

The frequency of the free-running multivibrator is

$$f = \frac{1}{T_1 + T_2} \ \text{cycles/second} \qquad (10.18)$$

10.4 Undershoots in an Astable Multivibrator

The voltage waveforms and the equations of the preceding section were developed on the assumption of a constant plate-cathode resistance, r_b, when either of the two tubes was on. Actually each grid is driven positive as indicated by Points 2 and 4 on the grid-voltage waveforms of Figure 10.4. This causes the plate voltage to drop to a lower value than the calculated value. Likewise, this additional drop in plate voltage is transferred to the grid of the other tube because of the RC coupling. The waveforms of Figure 10.5 show these voltage undershoots. The undershoot 2–2' on e_{b2} is a result

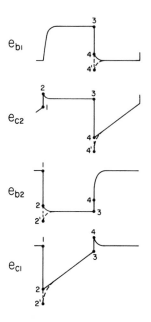

Fig. 10.5. Undershoots in astable multivibrators.

of the positive voltage spike at its grid. The undershoot 2–2' at e_{c1} must correspond to that at e_{b2} because of the RC coupling.

The voltage at Point 2' for e_{b2} is determined with reasonable accuracy by referring to the point on the load line corresponding to the positive peak of grid voltage, e_{c2}. This assumes that the output resistance of tube 2 is much less than R_{g1}.

The voltage undershoots are of relatively short time duration and do not appreciably affect the frequency of the multivibrator. Diode clipping circuits can be used to eliminate the plate voltage undershoots in the event these undershoots are objectionable for a particular application. Also, Equation (10.11), which gives the positive overshoot of a grid voltage, suggests methods of minimizing the positive voltage excursion. The use of a tube having a low value of r_c is required for this purpose.

10.5 Astable Multivibrators with Positive Bias

Except for the addition of the positive bias voltages, E_1 and E_2, the multivibrator circuit of Figure 10.6 is similar to the circuit of Figure 10.1. In many instances $E_1 = E_2 = E_{bb}$, in which case, R_{g1} and R_{g2} are returned directly to E_{bb} as shown in Figure 10.7. The discussion of this section is with

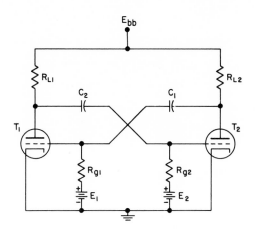

Fig. 10.6. Biased astable multivibrator.

reference to the circuit (Figure 10.6) where a separate bias voltage for each tube is indicated.

The most important effect of positive bias voltages is illustrated by a plot of e_{c1} in Figure 10.8. A plot of e_{c1} from Figure 10.4, for zero bias voltage, is superimposed for comparison. Observe that the positive bias voltage has the effect of reducing the *off* time of tube 1. Similarly, the *off* time of tube 2 is decreased by the presence of E_2. The negative peak value of grid voltage (Point 2) is not appreciably altered by the addition of the positive bias voltage, provided that R_g is much greater than the output resistance of the amplifier to which the grid is coupled.

Let us determine an expression for the peak negative value of e_{c1} in the presence of a positive bias voltage, E_1 which is Point 2 on the graph of e_{c1}.

At Point 1, just before tube 1 is turned *off*, the voltage on C_1 is

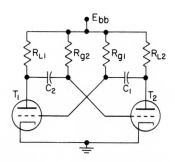

Fig. 10.7. Each grid is biased to E_{bb}.

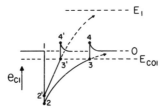

Fig. 10.8. A positive bias voltage decreases *off* time.

(Point 1) $$V_{C_1} = E_{bb} - e_{c1} \tag{10.19}$$

At this instant, however, e_{c1} is

(Point 1) $$e_{c1} = E_1 \frac{r_{c1}}{r_{c1} + R_{g1}} \tag{10.20}$$

which becomes a very low value, if R_{g1} is much greater than r_{c1}. Thus,

(Point 1) $$V_{C_1} \cong E_{bb} \tag{10.21}$$

The negative peak value of e_{c1}, at Point 2, then becomes

(Point 2) $$e_{c1} = -[(E_{bb}) + E_1 - E_{b2}] \frac{R_{g1}}{R_{o2} + R_{g1}} + E_1$$

$$= -[(E_{bb}) - E_{b2}] \frac{R_{g1}}{R_{o2} + R_{g1}} + E_1 \frac{R_{o2}}{R_{o2} + R_{g1}} \tag{10.22}$$

Except for the approximation of Equation (10.21), the negative peak value of e_{c1} is accurately given by Equation (10.22). Observe, however, that the equation reduces to Equation (10.13) if R_{o2} is much less than R_{g1}. Consequently, the negative excursion of a grid voltage is not appreciably affected by the addition of a positive bias voltage.

The *off* times for each tube are then determined by modifying Equation (10.14) and Equation (10.15) to

$$T_1 = (R_{g1} + R_{o2}) C_1 \ln \frac{E_1 - (e_{c1} \text{ at point 2})}{E_1 - E_{co1}} \tag{10.23}$$

$$T_2 = (R_{g2} + R_{o1}) C_1 \ln \frac{E_2 - (e_{c2} \text{ at point 4})}{E_2 - E_{co2}} \tag{10.24}$$

Corresponding to Equation (10.16) and Equation (10.17), the above time intervals are represented by the approximations

$$T_1 \cong R_{g1} C_1 \ln \frac{E_1 + E_{bb} - E_{b2}}{E_1 - E_{co1}} \tag{10.25}$$

$$T_2 \cong R_{g2} C_2 \ln \frac{E_2 + E_{bb} - E_{b1}}{E_2 - E_{co2}} \tag{10.26}$$

when R_{o2} is much less than R_{g1} and R_{o1} is much less than R_{g2}.

In the event that the grid resistors are returned to E_{bb}, as in Figure 10.7, then E_1 and E_2 in the preceding equations of this section are replaced with E_{bb}.

10.6 Cathode Coupling: Common Cathode Resistor

The circuit of Figure 10.9 can be used in a number of ways. Three of the most important uses are: (a) as a compensated direct-coupled amplifier with $v_{o1} - v_{o2}$ as the output voltage when e_{s2} is replaced with a fixed bias; (b) as a voltage difference amplifier, or voltage comparator, where v_{o2} is proportional to $e_{s1} - e_{s2}$; and (c) as a dual-tube clipper and amplifier with v_{o2} as the output voltage and e_{s2} replaced by a fixed bias.

The discussion of this section is restricted to a study of the circuit as a dual-tube clipper and amplifier. In addition to revealing a particular type of clipping circuit, this study will also provide background information for the analysis of multivibrator circuits having a common cathode resistor. This is the reason for interrupting the study of multivibrator circuits. We shall return to the circuit of Figure 10.9 in the closing sections of this chapter.

As a clipping circuit the plate of tube 1 is connected directly to the plate supply voltage as indicated in Figure 10.10. A possible voltage waveform for the output voltage when the input voltage is sinusoidal, is illustrated in Figure 10.11. The upper limit of the output voltage is E_{bb} and exists when tube 2 is *off.* The lower limit of output voltage exists when tube 1 is *off.* The

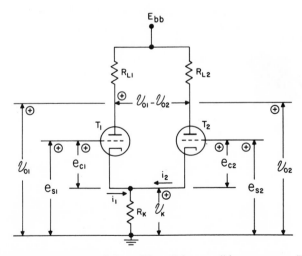

Fig. 10.9. Cathode coupled amplifier. Other possible names are: Difference amplifier, comparator, gating circuit and compensated d-c amplifier.

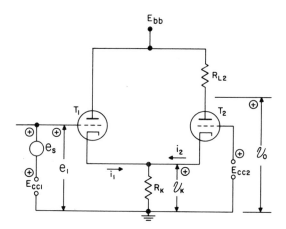

Fig. 10.10. Dual triode clipper amplifier.

objective is to make both the upper and lower limits of voltage dependent on the plate current cutoff and not dependent on grid clipping. This gives a flat bottom to the waveform as well as a flat top.

The problem is to determine the upper and lower limits of e_1 (the sum of e_s and E_{cc1}) to produce the upper and lower limits of v_o, the output voltage. This is done by assuming tube 2 is *off* and solving for the lowest value of e_1 for which tube 2 is *off*; tube 2 will then be *off* for any higher value of e_1. The same procedure is then used for the condition that tube 1 is *off*. In this case, we are finding the *highest* value of e_1 for which tube 1 is *off*. Tube 1 is *off* for any *lower* value of e_1.

The cutoff voltage, E_{co}, for one tube operating by itself is identical to the cutoff voltage for the other tube operating by itself. This cutoff voltage is dependent on E_{bb}. For a triode, the cutoff voltage is essentially proportional to E_{bb}.

Thus, when tube 2 is *off* and tube 1 is *on*, the adjusted cutoff voltage E'_{co2} for tube 2 is decreased to

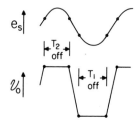

Fig. 10.11. Double clipping action with the circuit in Figure 10.10.

$$E'_{co2} = E_{co} \frac{E'_{bb}}{E_{bb}} = E_{co} \frac{E_{bb} - V_{K1}}{E_{bb}} \tag{10.27}$$

where V_{K1} is result of plate current in tube 1. If we can find the minimum value of V_{K1} required to keep tube 2 *off*, then we can find the lowest value of e_1 to make this true. Since

$$e_{c2} = E_{cc2} - V_{K1} \tag{10.28}$$

and for e_{c2} at E'_{co2} we have that

$$E_{cc2} - V_{K1} = E_{co} \frac{E_{bb} - V_{K1}}{E_{bb}} \tag{10.29}$$

Solving for V_{K1} we obtain

$$V_{K1} = (E_{cc2} - E_{co}) \frac{E_{bb}}{E_{bb} - E_{co}} \tag{10.30}$$

as the minimum value of V_{K1} to keep tube 2 *off*. With tube 1 operating as an ordinary cathode follower, the value of e_1 for the predetermined value of V_{K1} is easily determined by reference to the tube characteristics.

When tube 1 is *off* its cutoff voltage is

$$E'_{co1} = E_{co} \frac{E_{bb} - V_{K2}}{E_{bb}} \tag{10.31}$$

where V_{K2} is a result of plate current in tube 2. Considering tube 2 operating as an $R_L R_K$ amplifier, we now determine V_{K2} for a given value of E_{cc2} by reference to the tube characteristics. (The procedure was explained in Chapter 9.) Continuing with the solution, observe that

$$e_{c1} = e_1 - V_{K2} \tag{10.32}$$

and with e_{c1} at cutoff, E'_{co1}, we have

$$e_1 - V_{K2} = E_{co} \frac{E_{bb} - V_{K2}}{E_{bb}} \tag{10.33}$$

Solving for e_1 (V_{K2} is now known), we obtain

$$e_1 = V_{K2} \left(1 - \frac{E_{co}}{E_{bb}}\right) + E_{co} \tag{10.34}$$

as the *highest* value of e_1 for which tube 1 is *off*. (Tube 1 is *off* for all *lower* values of e_1.) Remember that E_{co} is a negative quantity.

10.7   A Bistable Multivibrator

A bistable multivibrator circuit has two stable states. The dual-tube circuit of Figure 10.12 can be such a circuit, with a proper selection of circuit parameters and d-c voltages (E_{bb} and E_{cc}). It is the purpose of this section to determine the requirements that will make the circuit bistable; that is, if tube 1 is *on*, then tube 2 must be *off* and the circuit will *remain* in this condition

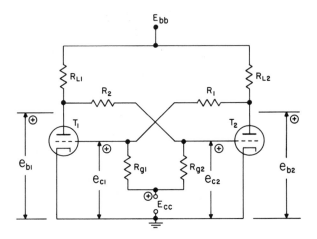

Fig. 10.12. A bistable multivibrator with fixed bias.

unless triggered by some means from an external source. When triggered, the two tubes exchange *on* and *off* conditions and the circuit remains in either state until the next trigger pulse. Methods of triggering this and other types of circuits are discussed in a later chapter.

Actually, the circuit as shown in Figure 10.12 requires a finite transition time because of the presence of interelectrode and stray capacitances. The transition time can be decreased by placing "commutating" capacitors (about 50 pf each) in parallel with R_1 and R_2, as in Figure 10.13.

Self-bias, employing a common cathode resistor, can be used as well. A method of analysis for such a circuit is presented in Section 10.8.

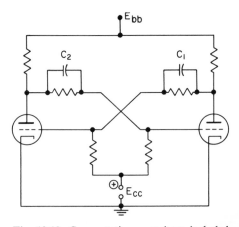

Fig. 10.13. Commutating capacitors included.

If the circuit of Figure 10.12 is to have two stable states, then the grid voltage of either tube must have either of two values to insure stability for each state. These two values of grid voltage are normally 0^+ and well below cutoff, E_{co}. For example, e_{c2} should be at 0^+ when tube 1 is *off*, and e_{c2} should be well below cutoff when tube 1 is *on*.

Voltage equations that can be written for e_{c2} will reveal the design requirements for the circuit. Similar equations can be written for e_{c1}. The first and general equation disregards the possibility of grid current. Thus,

$$e_{c2} = (e_{b1} - E_{cc}) \frac{R_{g2}}{R_2 + R_{g2}} + E_{cc}$$
$$= e_{b1} \frac{R_{g2}}{R_2 + R_{g2}} + E_{cc} \frac{R_2}{R_2 + R_{g2}} \tag{10.35}$$

From this general equation we observe that E_{cc} must be a negative value to satisfy the negative voltage requirements for e_{c2} when tube 1 is *on*. The plate voltage of tube 1 for this condition is at a low value, identified as E_{b1} when e_{c1} is 0^+.

For e_{c2} less than E_{co} we have the inequality

$$E_{b1} \frac{R_{g2}}{R_2 + R_{g2}} + E_{cc} \frac{R_2}{R_2 + R_{g2}} < E_{co} \tag{10.36}$$

from which

$$E_{cc} < E_{co} \frac{R_2 + R_{g2}}{R_2} - E_{b1} \frac{R_{g2}}{R_2} \tag{10.37}$$

For the particular condition of R_2 equal to R_{g2} (a frequent choice),

$$E_{cc} < 2E_{co} - E_{b1} \tag{10.38}$$

As a numerical example, E_{cc} should be more negative than -70 volts if E_{b1} is 50 volts and E_{co} is -10 volts.

The second desired value for e_{c2} is 0^+ when tube 1 is *off*. The plate voltage of tube 1 is then at a high value, slightly less than E_{bb}. This upper plate voltage is identified as E'_{bb} (often assumed equal to E_{bb} when R_2 is much greater than R_{L1}).

Thus, for e_{c2} greater than 0 volts we have the inequality

$$E'_{bb} \frac{R_{g2}}{R_g + R_{g2}} + E_{cc} \frac{R_2}{R_2 + R_{g2}} > 0 \tag{10.39}$$

or

$$E_{cc} > -E'_{bb} \frac{R_{g2}}{R_2} \tag{10.40}$$

In order for R_2 and R_{g2} to be equal, then E_{cc} must be greater, or less negative, than $-E'_{bb}$. A value of E_{cc} should be selected well within its limits to insure complete transitions.

The possibility of grid current was disregarded in all of the preceding developments of this section. Once E_{cc} and the circuit parameters are selected, Equation (10.35) is applicable when tube 2 is *off*. When tube 2 is *on*, however, its grid voltage is slightly positive and Equation (10.35) is no longer strictly true since the grid is essentially returned to ground potential through r_{c2}. For this condition, the grid voltage is

$$e_{c2} = E_{bb} \frac{r_{c2}}{r_{c2} + R_2 + R_{L1}} \tag{10.41}$$

which is normally a very low positive voltage and can be indicated as 0^+ volts. Nevertheless, Equation (10.41) should not be assumed true unless preceded by a check with Equation (10.35) or Equation (10.39).

10.8 The Flip-Flop Circuit with Self-Bias

The circuit of Figure 10.14 can be a bistable multivibrator since it has a common cathode resistor for the two tubes rather than a fixed bias voltage as in Figure 10.13. An analysis of the circuit is somewhat more involved than that encountered in the preceding section. In this case the self-bias voltage across the common cathode resistor is dependent on all other parameters of the circuit, the tube characteristics, and the plate supply voltage E_{bb}. Even so, the equations required for an analysis of the circuit are not burdensome to evaluate.

The major problem of analysis is to examine the two grid voltages, e_{c1} and e_{c2}, in order to determine the existence of two steady states for the circuit. In accordance with the notations on Figure 10.14,

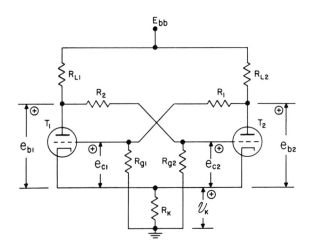

Fig. 10.14. A cathode coupled bistable multivibrator.

$$e_{c2} = (e_{b1} + v_K) \frac{R_{g2}}{R_2 + R_{g2}} - v_K$$

$$= e_{b1} \frac{R_{g2}}{R_2 + R_{g2}} - v_K \frac{R_2}{R_2 + R_{g2}} \qquad (10.42)$$

This equation disregards the possibility of grid current. If the equation does give a positive value of grid voltage, then the correct expression (R_{g2} large) becomes

$$e_{c2} = e_{b1} \frac{r_c}{r_c + R_2} \qquad (10.43)$$

which can be indicated as 0^+ volts for large values of R_2. A grid voltage of 0^+ volts should not be assumed unless verified from Equation (10.42) that the grid voltage is truly positive. How is Equation (10.42) used, however, to make this test?

A condition of particular interest is to have the grid voltage of tube 1 below cutoff when the grid voltage of tube 2 is at 0^+ volts. This is one stable state that is desirable to have for the circuit. It can be assumed that tube 1 is *off* and a check can be made later to determine if it truly is *off*.

With tube 1 *off*, the first form of Equation (10.42) becomes

$$e_{c2} = E_{bb} \frac{R_{g2}}{R_2 + R_{g2}} - V_{K2} \qquad (10.44)$$

where V_{K2} is a result of current in tube 2 only and assuming that the direct-coupling circuit has negligible loading on R_{L1}. Now, if e_{c2} is to be at 0^+ volts, then

$$E_{bb} \frac{R_{g2}}{R_2 + R_{g2}} - V_{K2} > 0 \qquad (10.45)$$

which cannot be answered unless V_{K2} is known. This is determined by considering tube 2 as an $R_L R_K$ amplifier with an input voltage of $E_{bb} R_{g2}/(R_2 + R_{g2})$, remembering that e_{c2} can be only slightly positive. Equation (10.44) is only a test to determine that tube 2 is *on*. Normally, e_{c2} should be at 0^+ volts although this is not absolutely essential to cause the circuit to have two stable states.

If tube 2 is *on*, there must be a check to determine if tube 1 is truly *off* as initially assumed. With tube 2 *on*,

$$e_{c1} = E_{b2} \frac{R_{g1}}{R_1 + R_{g1}} - V_{K2} \frac{R_1}{R_1 + R_{g1}} \qquad (10.46)$$

where E_{b2} and V_{K2} are particular quiescent values as determined from the preceding test.

If it is found that tube 1 is truly *off*, there is no need to check for the second stable state (tube 1 *on* and tube 2 *off*) when the circuit is symmetrical.

There is one other fact of some significance. The cutoff voltage for the *off* tube is less than that for an ordinary $R_L R_K$ amplifier, since the cut-

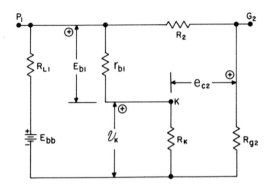

Fig. 10.15. Equivalent circuit for Figure 10.14 with tube 1 *on* and tube 2 *off*. (To write equation for e_{c2}).

off voltage is essentially proportional to E_{bb}, or an equivalent E'_{bb} for triodes. For tube 1 *off*, when tube 2 is *on*, its true cutoff voltage is

$$E'_{co1} = E_{co}\frac{E_{bb} - V_{K2}}{E_{bb}} \tag{10.47}$$

The preceding equations and procedures are satisfactory when the circuit parameters and plate supply voltage are known values. The procedure of analysis takes on a slightly different aspect when the problem becomes one of design. The equivalent circuit of Figure 10.15, with the presence of r_{b1} (static plate resistance), suggests the tube 1 is *on*. It may now be desirable to determine a range of values for the circuit parameters, or of E_{bb}, that will keep tube 2 *off* while tube 1 is *on*.

If it is specified that e_{c1} must remain at 0^+ volts, then r_{b1}, for $e_{c1} = 0$, is essentially a constant and independent of R_{L1}, R_K, and E_{bb} for a triode. The fact that r_{b1} (for $e_{c1} = 0$) can be assumed as reasonably constant, permits a synthesis of the circuit without using a trial-and-error method of analysis. Assuming $R_2 + R_{g2}$ is sufficiently large to produce negligible loading effects, the equation for e_{c2} becomes

$$e_{c2} = E_{bb}\left[\frac{(r_b + R_K)(R_{g2})}{(R_L + r_b + R_K)(R_2 + R_{g2})} - \frac{R_K}{R_L + r_b + R_K}\right] \tag{10.48}$$

But, it is required that e_{c2} shall be below the cutoff voltage, E'_{co2}, for tube 2. At cutoff,

$$e_{c2} = E'_{co2} = E_{co}\frac{E_{bb} - V_{K1}}{E_{bb}}$$

$$= E_{co}\frac{E_{bb} - E_{bb}R_K/(R_L + r_b + R_K)}{E_{bb}}$$

$$= E_{co}\frac{R_L + r_b}{R_L + r_b + R_K} \tag{10.49}$$

Combining Equation (10.48) and Equation (10.49), we have

$$E_{bb}\left[(r_b + R_K)\frac{R_{g2}}{R_2 + R_{g2}} - R_K\right] = E_{co}(r_b + R_L) \qquad (10.50)$$

Recalling that r_b and E_{bb}/E_{co} are essentially constants, then the possible variables are R_K, R_L and the $R_{g2}/(R_2 + R_{g2})$ ratio. Equation (10.50) can then be solved for any one of these as the variable to determine the critical value to hold tube 2 just at cutoff. The grid voltage e_{c2} is less than E'_{co2} for all values of R_K greater than its critical value, or for all values of $R_{g2}/(R_2 + R_{g2})$ less than its critical value, or for all values of R_L less than its critical value.

How much of an excursion from these critical values is permissible in order to keep the grid voltage of the *on* tube (tube 1 in this case) at 0^+ volts? With tube 2 *off*, a test for the 0^+ volts is determined by writing the equation for e_{c1} (disregarding the possibility of grid current) and setting it equal to zero. Thus, referring to Figure 10.16,

$$e_{c1} = E_{bb}\left[\frac{R_{g1}}{R_L + R_1 + R_{g1}} - \frac{R_K}{R_L + r_b + R_K}\right] = 0 \qquad (10.51)$$

For a completely symmetrical circuit, R_1 and R_{g1} can be replaced with R_2 and R_{g2}. Assuming these coupling resistances are much greater than R_L, Equation (10.51) can be written as

$$\frac{R_{g2}}{R_2 + R_{g2}} - \frac{R_K}{R_L + r_b + R_K} = 0 \qquad (10.52)$$

A *second* limiting and critical value for any one of the three possible variables is now determined. The grid voltage of the *on* tube is at 0^+ volts for all values of R_K less than its second critical value, or for all values of R_L greater than its second critical value, or for all values of $R_g/(R + R_g)$ greater than its second critical value where R represents either R_1 or R_2, and R_g represents either R_{g1} or R_{g2}.

The circuit parameters are not selected at random. The necessity of

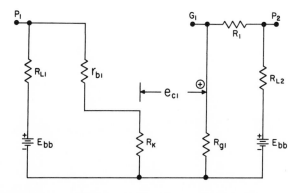

Fig. 10.16. Same conditions as Figure 10.15. (To write equation for e_{c1}).

commutating capacitors and the presence of interelectrode and stray capacities influences the transition time. For fast response, all resistances in the circuit must be of low values. Yet, they cannot be too low because of current limitations, or because of a particular type of response required of the circuit. Its applications are many and the practical problem requiring a use of the flip-flop circuit will influence its design.

10.9 A Monostable Multivibrator

The dual-tube circuit of Figure 10.17 can be a monostable multivibrator. Under quiescent conditions the grid of tube 2 is at zero volts while the grid of tube 1 can be held below the cutoff voltage with proper values of R_1, R_{g1}, and E_{cc}. Thus, tube 2 *is* normally *on* and tube 1 can be normally *off*.

The circuit can be triggered to produce the results represented by the voltage waveforms of Figure 10.18. These waveforms are shown for positive trigger pulses in the grid circuit of tube 1, the normally *off* tube. The circuit can also be triggered with negative pulses at the grid of tube 2, the normally *on* tube. (Problems of triggering are reserved for a later chapter.) The nearly rectangular pulses at the plate of either tube are initiated by the trigger pulses and have a time duration dependent on the time interval that the grid of tube 2 is below cutoff. This cutoff time is determined in the same manner as given in Section 10.3 for an astable multivibrator [see Equations (10.15) and (10.17)].

The grid resistor, R_{g2} of Figure 10.17, can also be returned to a high positive voltage. In this case, the *off* time of tube 2 is calculated in accordance with the procedure outlined in Section 10.5 for astable multivibrators

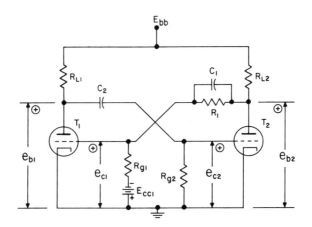

Fig. 10.17. A monostable multivibrator with fixed bias.

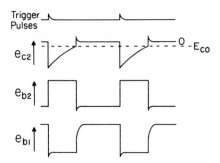

Fig. 10.18. Typical waveforms for the circuit in Figure 10.17.

with high positive bias voltages. [Refer in particular to Equations (10.24) and (10.26)].

In the circuit of Figure 10.17, C_1 can be considered as a commutating capacitor with R_1 and R_{g1} representing direct coupling to the grid of tube 1, the normally *off* tube. This direct coupling is needed to hold tube 1 *on* while tube 2 is *off*. In other words, if R_1 is removed (retaining C_1) the grid voltage of tube 1 could relax back toward and perhaps to the cutoff voltage before the desired gating pulse has been completed.

10.10 Monostable Multivibrators with Cathode Bias

The circuit of Figure 10.19 can be a monostable multivibrator. The grid voltage of tube 2 is normally zero since its grid is returned directly to the cathode through R_{g2}. With tube 2 normally *on*, tube 1 can be normally *off* because of V_{K2}. In many instances it is desirable to add a bias voltage, indicated by E_{cc} on the circuit diagram, to permit a smaller positive pulse to trigger the circuit and also to control the magnitude of e_{b1} when tube 1 is *on*. The negative voltage to which e_{c2} is driven is equal in magnitude to the drop in voltage of e_{b1} at the instant of triggering. Thus, the *off* time of tube 2 can be controlled by E_{cc} as well as by the circuit time constant involving C_2 and R_{g2}.

The limiting values of E_{cc} are E_{co} and $(E'_{co1} + V_{K2})$, where E_{co} is the cutoff voltage of an $R_L R_K$ amplifier and where E'_{co1} is the adjusted cutoff voltage of tube 1 when tube 2 is *on* and tube 1 is *off*; that is, for a triode,

$$E'_{co1} = E_{co} \frac{E_{bb} - V_{K2}}{E_{bb}}$$

Thus,

$$E_{cc} \text{ (upper limit)} = E_{co} \frac{E_{bb} - V_{K2}}{E_{bb}} + V_{K2} \qquad (10.53)$$

which can also be expressed as

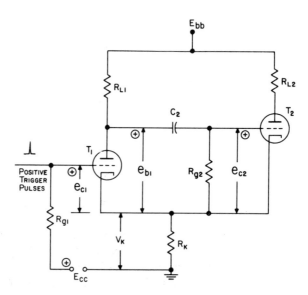

Fig. 10.19. A cathode-coupled monostable circuit.

$$E_{cc} \text{ (upper limit)} = E_{co} + V_{K2}\left(1 - \frac{E_{co}}{E_{bb}}\right) \tag{10.54}$$

The E_{co}/E_{bb} ratio is essentially a constant for a triode. This constant is the inverse of the amplification factor, μ.

It is interesting to observe that Equation (10.54) gives the lower limit of $E_{cc} = E_{co}$ when V_{K2} is zero, or when tube 2 is *off*. This means that tube 1 will not stay *on* after the triggering pulse is removed. In another sense, the minimum value of E_{cc} must be slightly greater than E_{co} in order to drop the plate voltage of tube 1 sufficiently to turn tube 2 *off*. Normally, a value of E_{cc} is selected well above its minimum value.

If the upper limit of E_{cc} is greater than zero, as determined from Equation (10.54), then R_{g1} of Figure 10.19 can be returned directly to chassis ground if desired.

The circuit is analyzed with reasonable accuracy by assuming that R_{g2} is much greater than R_{L1}. For this assumption, the method of analysis is itemized as follows:

(a) Find V_{K2} (from tube curves) when tube 1 is *off* with $e_{c2} = 0$.

(b) Find E_{b1} and V_{K1} (from tube curves) for the selected value of E_{cc} when tube 2 is *off*. Since R_{g2} is much greater than R_{L1}, the values of E_{b1} and V_{K1} are determined as though C_2 is decoupled from the plate of tube 1.

(c) Calculate the change in the plate-cathode voltage of tube 1 at the

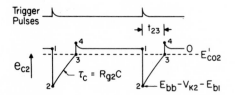

Fig. 10.20. Trigger pulses and e_{c2} waveforms for circuit in Figure 10.19.

instant of triggering. This is also the change in grid-cathode voltage for tube 2. Thus,

$$\Delta e_{c2} = \Delta e_{b1} = - [(E_{bb} - V_{K2}) - E_{b1}] \qquad (10.55)$$

(d) Calculate the *off* time of tube 2. This is indicated as t_{23} in Figure 10.20.

$$t_{23} = R_{g2} C_2 \ln \frac{E_{b1} + V_{K2} - E_{bb}}{E'_{co2}} \qquad (10.56)$$

where, for a triode,

$$E'_{co2} = E_{co} \frac{E_{bb} - V_{K1}}{E_{bb}}$$

The gated pulse can then be taken from plate to ground of either tube or from grid to ground of tube 2—preferably from plate to ground of tube 2.

Two variations for the circuit of Figure 10.19 are shown in Figures 10.21 and 10.22. In Figure 10.21 the grid of the normally *on* tube is returned to

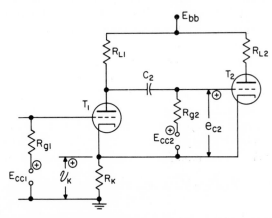

Fig. 10.21. A monostable multivibrator with R_{g2} returned to cathode through a d-c bias voltage (positive).

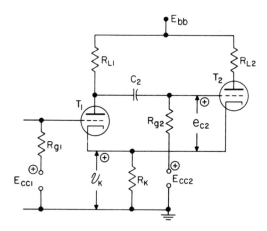

Fig. 10.22. Similar to Figure 10.21 R_{g2} returned to *ground* through a d-c bias voltage (high positive).

the cathode through a positive bias voltage. Since e_{c2}, while below cutoff, is now relaxing toward the positive voltage of E_{cc2}, then Equation (10.56) is modified to give the *off* time for tube 2. The time, t_{23}, becomes

$$t_{23} = R_{g2} C_2 \ln \frac{E_{cc2} - (E_{b1} + V_{K2} - E_{bb})}{E_{cc2} - E'_{co2}} \qquad (10.57)$$

recalling that E'_{co2} is a negative quantity.

In the circuit of Figure 10.22, R_{g2} is returned to chassis ground through a high positive voltage. Actually, R_{g2} is often returned to E_{bb} in which case E_{cc2} is equal to E_{bb}. This circuit arrangement makes e_{c2} dependent on the voltage across R_K. If e_{c2} is to be at 0 or 0^+ volts, then E_{cc2} must be equal to or greater than V_{K2} when tube 2 is normally *on* and tube 1 is normally *off*. With certain modifications, the method of analysis is similar to that given for Figure 10.19. (For example, Equation 10.55 is still applicable.) In other words, e_{c2} has the same negative peak value as before, provided that e_{c2} is at zero just before triggering. While in the negative region, e_{c2} is now relaxing toward $E_{cc2} - V_{K1}$ where V_{K1} is the cathode voltage when tube 1 is *on* and tube 2 is *off*. This assumes, as before, that R_{g2} is large and much greater than the output resistance of tube 1. Equation (10.56), or Equation (10.57), is then modified to give the *off* time for tube 2. Thus,

$$t_{23} = R_{g2} C_2 \ln \frac{(E_{cc2} - V_{K1}) - (E_{b1} + V_{K2} - E_{bb})}{(E_{cc2} - V_{K1}) - E'_{co2}} \qquad (10.58)$$

For the case that E_{cc2} is equal to E_{bb},

$$t_{23} = R_{g2} C_2 \ln \frac{2E_{bb} - (E_{b1} + V_{K1} + V_{K2})}{E_{bb} - V_{K1} - E'_{co2}} \qquad (10.59)$$

10.11   A Monostable, Bistable Multivibrator

The title heading for this section has reference to the circuit of Figure 10.23, there identified as the *Schmitt trigger circuit* (named for its inventor).

There are reasons for the confusion as to the proper label for this circuit since it represents an apparently slight modification of a number of circuits. In some respects, it resembles a modification of the monostable multivibrator of Figure 10.22, with E_{cc2} reduced to zero and R_2 paralleling or replacing C_2; yet, it behaves quite differently. It also resembles the cathode-coupled, bistable multivibrator of Figure 10.14, with one pair of coupling resistors (R_1 and R_{g1}) removed. Also, it resembles the dual-tube clipper-amplifier of Figure 10.10, with R_{L1} reinserted and with the addition of direct-coupling from the plate of one tube to the grid of the other. The only common factor in these circuits, however, is the presence of R_K.

The resemblance to other circuits is given because the circuit of Figure 10.23 can be regarded as monostable with tube 2 normally *on* provided e_1 is small enough to keep tube 1 *off*. Also, the circuit can be regarded as bistable since the circuit will flip (tube 1 *on*) provided e_1 is and *remains* sufficiently large. Finally, the circuit can generate a square wave at the output when the input is sinusoidal (or any other type of alternating voltage, periodic or nonperiodic). The circuit is a voltage-level discriminator and is often so identified. An analysis of the circuit is similar to the procedures given for the other cathode-coupled circuits of the preceding sections.

Normally the circuit is adjusted such that e_{c2} is negative but near zero

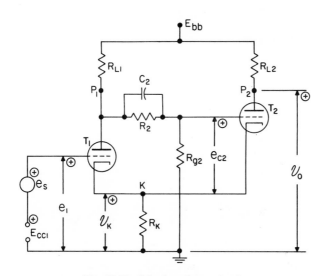

Fig. 10.23. Schmitt trigger circuit.

when tube 1 is *off*. This sets tube 2 in readiness to function as an amplifier, the instant tube 1 becomes conducting. The circuit can then be studied according to the following itemized steps of analysis.

(a) With tube 1 *off*, find V_{K2}. Note that tube 2 is now a part of an $R_L R_K$ amplifier, where the input voltage is E_{bb} attenuated by the coupling network of R_{L1}, R_2 and R_{g2}.

(b) Find the value of e_1 required to bring tube 1 into conduction. This is $(E'_{co1} + V_{K2})$ where E'_{co1} is the adjusted cutoff voltage for tube 1 when tube 2 is *on*. For this value of e_1, the circuit will "flip" and v_o goes to E_{bb}.

(c) Find the value to which e_1 must be decreased to cause the circuit to "flop" back to its original state. This is the condition for bringing tube 2 back into conduction at E'_{co2}, the adjusted cutoff voltage for tube 2 when tube 1 is *on*. A little work is required to determine the required value of e_1. The equivalent circuit of Figure 10.24 is helpful.

Referring to the equivalent circuit, e_{b1} can be regarded as the only unknown in the circuit. If we can evaluate e_{b1}, then v_{K1} is also known and e_{c1} can be identified from the tube curves. Finally, the required value of e_1 is $e_{c1} + v_{K1}$. So let us proceed in the evaluation of e_{b1}, neglecting any loading effects of R_2 and R_{g2}.

From the equivalent circuit of Figure 10.24, using capitalized symbols to represent particular values, we have

$$E_{c2} = E_{co2} = E_{b1} \frac{R_{g2}}{R_2 + R_{g2}} - V_{K1} \frac{R_2}{R_2 + R_{g2}} \qquad (10.60)$$

But

$$V_{K1} = \frac{(E_{bb} - E_{b1}) R_K}{R_L + R_K} \qquad (10.61)$$

Solving these two equations for E_{b1},

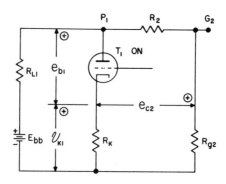

Fig. 10.24. An equivalent circuit leading to a solution of input voltage that will return e_{c2} (Figure 10.23) to cutoff when tube 1 is *on*.

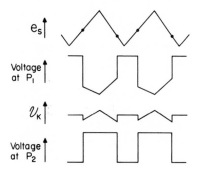

Fig. 10.25. Representative waveforms for the circuit in Figure 10.23.

$$E_{b1} = \frac{E'_{co2} + [E_{bb} R_K R_2 / (R_L + R_K)(R_2 + R_{g2})]}{R_{g2}/(R_2 + R_{g2}) + [R_2 R_K / (R_L + R_K)(R_2 + R_{g2})]} \qquad (10.62)$$

The only unknown in the right-hand side of Equation (10.62) is E'_{co2}. This can be assumed to be equal to E'_{co1}, previously determined, without an appreciable error. E_{b1} is then calculated from Equation (10.62).

Rather than considering E_{b1} as the only unknown in the circuit, we can consider r_{b1} as the unknown as in Equation (10.50) for the equivalent circuit of Figure 10.15. The advantage of Equation (10.50) is that it includes the adjusted cutoff voltage, E'_{co2} [see Equation (10.49)].

From either Equation (10.50), or Equation (10.62), we have information for evaluating E_{b1} and V_{K1}. Then we can determine E_{c1} from the tube curves and finally evaluate the value to which e_1 must be decreased to bring tube 2 back into conduction, observing that

$$E_1 = E_{c1} + V_{K1} \qquad (10.63)$$

A representative set of voltage waveforms for the circuit is shown in Figure 10.25, for a triangular input voltage.

10.12   Parallel Compensated Direct-Coupled Amplifiers

The problem of "drift" in output voltage of direct-coupled amplifiers was discussed in Section 6.4. The circuits of Figures 10.26, 10.27, and 10.28 illustrate three parallel circuit arrangements that compensate for drift.

In each circuit the output voltage is plate-to-plate. Thus, the output voltage is not influenced by a change in the d-c plate-supply voltage, provided that the two parallel circuits are symmetrical in every respect. The common cathode resistor of Figure 10.27, or Figure 10.28, will partially compensate for an unbalance of tube characteristics. In Figure 10.27, R_K is only of sufficient magnitude to provide a desirable self-bias for the two tubes. The circuit of Figure 10.28 has the grids returned to a fixed positive

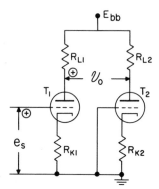

Fig. 10.26. A parallel compensated d-c (direct-coupled) amplifier.

voltage. Here, R_K is selected as a large value to better compensate for an unbalance in tube characteristics. Consequently, the fixed positive bias voltage must be added to insure linear operation of the amplifier. A potentiometer can be added to the circuit to permit zero adjustment of the amplifier, as illustrated in Figure 10.29.

The voltage gain of a cathode-coupled, parallel compensated d-c amplifier (Figure 10.27, or Figure 10.28) is independent of R_K. This is verified from the equivalent circuit of Figure 10.30, which is sketched to suggest a bridge circuit with source voltages in two arms of the bridge. For a symmetrical circuit,

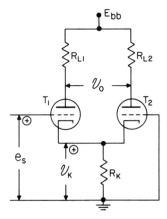

Fig. 10.27. Cathode coupled parallel compensated d-c amplifier. (R_K small).

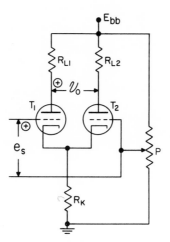

Fig. 10.28. Similar to Figure 10.27 (R_K large).

$$v_o = \frac{(v_K - \mu e_{g1})\, R_L}{r_p + R_L} - \frac{(v_K - \mu e_{g2})\, R_L}{r_p + R_L}$$
$$= \frac{\mu R_L}{r_p + R_L}\,(e_{g2} - e_{g1}) \tag{10.64}$$

With the reference polarities as indicated on the equivalent circuit and Figure 10.27,

$$e_{g2} = -v_K$$
$$e_{g1} = e_s - v_K \tag{10.65}$$

We find, therefore, that the voltage gain is

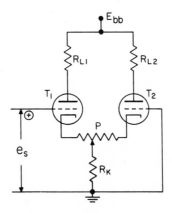

Fig. 10.29. The potentiometer permits zero balancing of d-c amplifier.

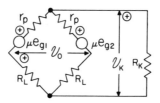

Fig. 10.30. Equivalent circuit for Figure 10.27 (or Figure 10.28) for assumed linear operation.

$$A = -\frac{\mu R_L}{r_p + R_L} \tag{10.66}$$

which is identical to the voltage gain for a basic, single-stage, R_L amplifier with fixed bias.

In addition to the "drift" compensating affects, the cathode-coupled amplifiers avoid fixed bias voltages (a possible cause of drift voltages) without a loss in voltage gain. The disadvantage is that the two points in the circuit (plate-to-plate), from which the output voltage must be taken, are completely isolated from the chassis ground.

The fact that the voltage gain is independent of R_K does not imply a constant voltage for v_K. Regarding v_K as an output voltage, the voltage gain A_K from the equivalent circuit of Figure 10.30 is

$$A_K = \frac{\mu R_K}{r_p + R_L + 2(1 + \mu) R_K} \tag{10.67}$$

This equation is easily verified by writing a node equation with v_K as the reference voltage and replacing e_{g1} and e_{g2} with their equivalent values from Equation (10.65). It is of interest to observe that A_K, Equation (10.67), has an upper limit of 0.5 for increasing values of μR_K.

10.13 A Difference Amplifier

The presence of $(e_{g2} - e_{g1})$ in Equation (10.64) suggests the use of a cathode-coupled amplifier as an amplifier that responds to the difference of two input voltages. This was previously suggested in Section 10.6 with reference to Figure 10.9 where

$$
\begin{aligned}
e_{g2} &= e_{s2} - v_K \\
e_{g1} &= e_{s1} - v_K
\end{aligned}
\tag{10.68}
$$

Therefore, Equation (10.64) becomes

$$v_o = \frac{\mu R_L}{r_p + R_L}(e_{s2} - e_{s1}) \tag{10.69}$$

Consequently, a cathode-coupled amplifier (Figure 10.9, Figure 10.27, or Figure 10.28), where the output voltage is plate-to-plate, can be used as a difference amplifier.

10.14 Cathode-Coupled Linear Amplifier

The cathode-coupled circuit of Figure 10.10 (refer to Section 10.6) can be operated as a linear amplifier. As such, the equivalent circuit of Figure 10.31 is applicable. To determine the expression for voltage gain of the circuit, it is convenient to write two current equations, one with v_K as reference and the other with v_o as reference. Thus, for identical tube characteristics,

$$v_K (G_K + 2g_p) - v_o g_p - g_m (e_{g1} + e_{g2}) = 0 \qquad (10.70)$$

and with v_o as reference

$$v_o (G_L + g_p) - v_K g_p + g_m e_{g2} = 0 \qquad (10.71)$$

Since $e_{g1} = e_{s1} - v_K$, and $e_{g2} = -v_K$, an evaluation of the preceding two equations results in the voltage gain expression

$$A = \frac{g_m}{2 (G_L + g_p)\left(1 + G_K/2 (g_p + g_m)\right) - g_p} \qquad (10.72)$$

For the particular condition of $2 (g_p + g_m) \gg G_K$, which can also be stated as $2R_K (1 + \mu) \gg r_p$, Equation (10.72) reduces to the approximation

$$A \simeq \frac{g_m}{2G_L + g_p} \qquad (10.73)$$

or

$$A \simeq \frac{\mu R_L}{2r_p + R_L} \qquad (10.74)$$

The circuit amplifies without phase inversion and has a voltage gain approaching that of an ordinary anode follower. A number of practical control and measurement systems require an amplifier in which the output

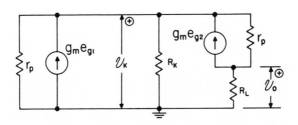

Fig. 10.31. Equivalent circuit for linear operation of the cathode coupled circuit in Figure 10.10.

voltage varies in the same sense as, or in phase with, the input voltage. This cathode-coupled circuit is, in certain instances, more desirable than a two-stage, plate-coupled amplifier. A cathode follower, of course, has no phase inversion but its amplification is less than unity.

PROBLEMS

10.1 Table 10.1 gives a variety of circuit quantities for the astable multivibrator circuit of Figure 10.6. For the given quantities of Table 10.1(a) and a 6SN7 twin triode, plot the grid voltage and the plate voltage waveforms indicating all significant quantities.

TABLE 10.1   CIRCUIT QUANTITIES FOR THE ASTABLE MULTIVIBRATOR
CIRCUIT OF FIGURE 10.6.
(The capacitances are in microfarads and the d-c supplies are in volts)

	R_{L1}	R_{L2}	R_{g1}	R_{g2}	C_1	C_2	E_1	E_2	E_{bb}
(a)	25 K	25 K	1 Meg	1 Meg	0.001	0.001	0	0	250
(b)	50 K	50 K	1 Meg	1 Meg	0.001	0.001	0	0	250
(c)	25 K	25 K	1 Meg	1 Meg	0.001	0.001	250	250	250
(d)	25 K	25 K	1 Meg	1 Meg	0.001	0.001	150	150	150
(e)	25 K	25 K	1 Meg	1 Meg	0.001	0.001	250	100	250
(f)	25 K	25 K	5 Meg	5 Meg	10	10	20	20	250
(g)	25 K	25 K	200 K	200 K	0.001	0.003	100	250	250
(h)	50 K	50 K	500 K	500 K	.1	0.001	250	250	250
(i)	25 K	25 K	500 K	500 K	0.003	0.003	250	20	250

10.2 Determine the multivibrator frequency for each set of given quantities in Table 10.1. The tube is a 6SN7 in each case. It is not necessary to plot any waveforms. Neglect the output resistance of an *on* tube.

10.3 Discuss the effects of making the successive changes, as given in Table 10.1.

10.4 What are the advantages and disadvantages of using a 12AT7 tube, rather than a 6SN7 tube, in the astable multivibrator circuit.

10.5 Inserting a common cathode resistance R_K in an astable multivibrator circuit will reduce the magnitude of the overshoots on the voltage waveforms. Why is this true? Write an equation from which the positive peak value of a grid voltage can be calculated.

10.6 The circuit of Figure 10.9 is used as a difference amplifier. Derive the gain expression for the circuit.

10.7 The cathode-coupled circuit of Figure 10.10 is to be used as a linear amplifier. Derive the voltage gain expression for the circuit.

10.8 For the circuit of Figure 10.10, $E_{bb} = 250$ volts, $R_{L2} = 20$ K, $R_K = 10$ K and the tube is a 12AU7 twin triode.
   (a) What is the maximum value of E_{cc2} for which e_{c2} is not positive when tube 1 is *off*?

(b) Let $E_{cc2} = 40$ volts. What is the maximum value of e_1 for which tube 1 is *off*?

(c) Let $E_{cc2} = 40$ volts, $E_{cc1} = 20$ volts and $e_s = 50 \sin \omega t$. Plot v_o, indicating all significant quantities on this waveform. Express time intervals in terms of the period.

10.9 The bistable circuit of Figure 10.12 is symmetrical with $E_{bb} = 300$ volts, $R_{L1} = 30$ K, $R_1 = 1$ Meg, $R_{g1} = 500$ K (the remaining resistors have corresponding values) and the tube is a 6SN7 twin triode. Determine the two limiting values for E_{cc} such that the grid voltage of an *on* tube is exactly zero (for one limit) and the grid voltage of an *off* tube is exactly at cutoff (for the other limit).

10.10 For the given quantities of Problem 10.9, $E_{cc} = -100$ volts. Assume that it is possible to replace tube 1 with any desired voltage. What must be the magnitude of this voltage to make e_{c2} exactly zero?

10.11 What is the purpose of the commutating capacitors as in Figure 10.13?

10.12 The cathode coupled bistable circuit of Figure 10.14 is a symmetrical circuit with $E_{bb} = 250$ volts, $R_{L1} = 20$ K, $R_1 = 1$ Meg, $R_{g1} = 500$ K and the tube is a 6SN7 twin triode.

(a) For what value of R_K is the grid-cathode voltage of the *on* tube exactly zero?

(b) For what value of R_K is the plate current of the *off* tube exactly zero?

10.13 In addition to the given quantities of Problem 10.12, let $R_K = 15$ K. Evaluate all of the significant voltages in the circuit.

10.14 For the monostable circuit of Figure 10.17, $E_{bb} = 250$ volts, $R_{L1} = R_{L2} = 25$ K, $R_{g1} = 500$ K, $R_{g2} = 1$ Meg, $R_1 = 1$ Meg, $C_2 = 0.001$ μfd., and the tube is a 12AU7 twin triode.

(a) For what value of E_{cc1} is tube 1 just *off*?

(b) For what value of E_{cc1} is e_{c1} exactly zero when tube 2 is *off*?

10.15 In addition to the given quantities of Problem 10.14, $E_{cc1} = -90$ volts. Determine the time interval that tube 2 will remain *off* after it has been triggered *off* by any practical method.

10.16 For the monostable circuit of Figure 10.19, $E_{bb} = 250$ volts, $R_{L1} = 40$ K, $R_{L2} = 10$ K, $R_{g2} = 1$ Meg, $C_2 = 0.005$ μfd, and the tube is a 12AT7 twin triode. and $R_K = 10$K.*

(a) For what value of E_{cc} is tube 1 just *off* in the absence of a trigger voltage?

(b) For what value of E_{cc} is tube 2 just *off* immediately following a trigger voltage?

10.17 In addition to the given quantities of Problem 10.16, let $E_{cc} = 50$ volts. Plot e_{c2}, from the instant the circuit is triggered, indicating all significant quantities.

10.18 For the monostable circuit of Figure 10.22, $E_{bb} = E_{cc2} = 270$ volts, $R_{L1} = 100$ K, $R_{L2} = 20$ K, $R_{g2} = 5$ Meg, $R_K = 10$ K, $C_2 = 0.001$ μfd, and the tube is a 12AU7 twin triode.

(a) For what value of E_{cc1} is tube 1 just *off* in the absence of a trigger voltage?

(b) For what value of E_{cc1} is tube 2 just *off* immediately after the circuit is triggered?

10.19 In addition to the given quantities of Problem 10.18, let $E_{cc1} = 25$ volts. Plot e_{c2}, from the instant the circuit is triggered, indicating all significant quantities.

10.20 For the Schmitt trigger circuit of Figure 10.23, $E_{bb} = 240$ volts, $R_{L1} = 70$ K, $R_{L2} = 30$ K, $R_2 = 1$ Meg, $R_K = 10$ K and the tube is a 6SN7 twin triode.

(a) For what value of R_{g2} is $e_{c2} = -2$ volts when tube 1 is *off*? Use this value in the circuit.

(b) For what value of e_1 is the plate current of tube 1 exactly zero (tube 1 just *off*)?

(c) Assume the circuit triggers for this value of e_1, from part (b). Evaluate all voltages in the circuit, for this value of e_1, with tube 1 *on*.

(d) With tube 1 *on*, what value of e_1 will cause the circuit to again trigger and return to the original state?

10.21 In addition to the given quantities of Problem 10.20 and R_{g2} as calculated in part (a), let $E_{cc1} = 30$ volts and $e_s = 50 \sin \omega t$. Plot v_K and v_o indicating all significant quantities on these waveforms.

11

Dual-Transistor

Switching Circuits

11.1   General Discussion

The dual-transistor circuits of this chapter are the transistor counterparts of the dual tube switching circuits of the preceding chapter. These transistor circuits, in some respects, are more easily analyzed than the corresponding tube circuits. This is due to a low collector-to-emitter voltage, nearly zero, when a transistor is in saturation or near saturation. In tubes, the plate voltage of an *on* tube is not near zero and must be determined for every circuit.

The dual transistor curcuits, as presented here, are represented in their most basic form. There are several possible variations to these circuits that are not shown nor discussed beyond this introductory section.

One variation is to not return any portion of the circuit directly to chassis ground, or zero potential. By returning the emitter circuit, the collector circuit, or both, to a d-c potential, it becomes possible to establish a desired d-c level for an output voltage waveform. This is particularly desirable when one transistor circuit is directly coupled to another transistor circuit.

Another variation in the basic transistor circuits is the need to insert diodes for reasons beyond those for tube circuits. Any diodes that are used in tube circuits are usually required to control the behavior of the circuitry external to the tube. In transistor switching circuits, diodes may be required to help control the behavior of the transistor itself. There are two major problems with transistors when used in switching circuits. One is the possibility of a reverse voltage breakdown of either or both junctions. The other problem is concerned with avoiding excessive base current when a transistor is in saturation, or even to avoid saturation and the inherent time delay in switching a transistor out of saturation.

The magnitude of the reverse input voltage required to break down the emitter junction can be increased if one or more diodes are inserted in series with the emitter. This, however, would make it more difficult to switch a transistor *off* completely.

To prevent saturation, diodes are sometimes connected from the base to the collector to divert excessive base currents to the collector. This can prevent the collector junction from becoming forward biased and thereby prevent a storage effect that could result in the delayed switching.

11.2 Astable Multivibrator

An astable multivibrator circuit is shown in Figure 11.1. Although *p-n-p* transistors are represented, the circuit is identical for *n-p-n* transistors. The supply voltage V_{cc} is negative for *p-n-p*, positive for *n-p-n*.

A typical set of voltage waveforms, with *p-n-p* transistors in the circuit, is illustrated in Figure 11.2. The two base-to-emitter voltages and the two collector-to-emitter voltages are shown in this figure. Either collector voltage waveform has the voltage limits of V_{ce}(sat) and V_{cc}. Since V_{ce}(sat) is only a fraction of a volt, the collector voltage is identified as being at zero when a transistor is in saturation.

One equivalent circuit for calculating the base voltage of one transistor and the collector voltage of the other transistor is represented in Figure 11.3. The circuit specifically identifies the collector voltage of transistor 1 and the base voltage for transistor 2. There is a corresponding equivalent

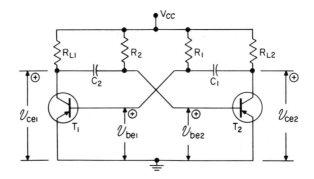

Fig. 11.1. Astable multivibrator.

circuit for the other pair of voltages, obtained simply by exchanging the subscripts 1 and 2. In this equivalent circuit, the base biasing voltage is identified as V_{BB}. It is equal to V_{CC} when R_2 is returned to V_{CC}, as shown in the astable circuit of Figure 11.1.

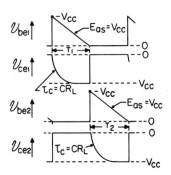

Fig. 11.2. Voltage waveforms for Figure 11.1.

When transistor 1 switches from *off* to *on*, its collector voltage has a positive step from V_{CC} to V_{ce}(sat). This positive step is transferred to the base of transistor 2. Neglecting V_{ce}(sat), the step is identified as $-V_{cc}$ on the base voltage waveforms. The circuit is then evaluated in the usual manner as specifically described in Chapter 8. The time for the base voltage V_{be2} to relax into the active region is $R_2C_2 \ln 2$, provided that the reverse resistance R_r is much greater than R_2. If R_r is not much greater than R_2, then the circuit time constant is the product of C_2 and the parallel combination of R_2 and R_r. The initial value of the reverse base voltage exponential is $-V_{cc}$, as before. The asymptotical value of this exponential is $V_{BB}R_r/(R_r + R_2)$. Solving for the time required for the reverse voltage exponential to relax to zero volts,

$$T_2 = C_2 \frac{R_2 R_r}{R_2 + R_r} \ln \frac{R_2 + 2R_r}{R_2 + R_r} \tag{11.1}$$

The time T_2 is the *off* time for transistor 2. The equation is applicable only when V_{BB} is equal to V_{CC} and assuming R_r (the reverse resistance) is a constant.

The remaining solution for the equivalent circuit is for the time interval when transistor 1 is *off* and transistor 2 is *on*. The time constant for the equivalent circuit is now C_2R_{L1}. It is represented as CR_L on the collector voltage waveforms in Figure 11.2. The small pip on the base voltage waveforms is the result of a small base to emitter input resistance when a tran-

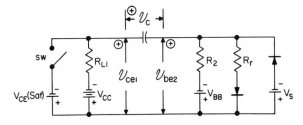

Fig. 11.3. Equivalent circuit for evaluating waveforms of Figure 11.2.

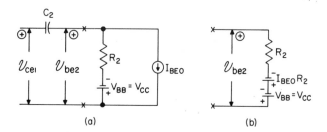

Fig. 11.4. Equivalent circuits with I_{BEO} replacing R_r.

sistor is in saturation. This resistance is not shown on the equivalent circuit, but in any case, it is much less than R_L.

A second possibility for an equivalent circuit is shown in Figure 11.4. Essentially, this circuit replaces the R_r branch of the previous circuit with a constant current branch I_{BEO}. Again, the circuit represents a *p-n-p* transistor and is applicable during the *off* time of transistor 2. From the Thevenin's equivalent circuit, Figure 11.4b, the *off* time for transistor 2 is recognized as

$$T_2 = R_2 C_2 \ln \frac{2|V_{CC}| + |I_{BEO}|R_2}{|V_{CC}| + |I_{BEO}|R_2} \qquad (11.2)$$

The voltage and current are each expressed as absolute values. The equation is applicable for either *p-n-p* or *n-p-n* transistors in the astable circuit. If I_{BEO} is neglected and assumed equal to zero, the *off* time reduces to

$$T_2 = R_2 C_2 \ln 2 \qquad (11.3)$$

as suggested for the first equivalent circuit when R_r is much greater than R_2.

11.3 Astable Multivibrator with Zero Bias

The astable circuit of Figure 11.5 has the resistors R_1 and R_2 returned directly to the common emitters. The *n-p-n* transistors are represented in this circuit. In the preceding section, the biasing voltage V_{BB} was made equal to the supply voltage V_{CC}. In this section, V_{BB} is zero.

The usefulness of this circuit, with V_{BB} equal to zero, is questionable since neither transistor will remain in saturation for the desired time interval. This problem with transistors was described in Chapter 8. A study of the circuit and the resulting waveforms is worthwhile for the information that is revealed about transistor behavior in such a circuit. The voltage waveforms for the circuit are shown in Figure 11.6. Reading from top to bottom, they are v_{be1}, v_{ce1}, v_{be2} and v_{ce2}.

The waveforms suggest a certain sequence of events in the circuit. Let us identify the sequence of events before attempting any calculations for

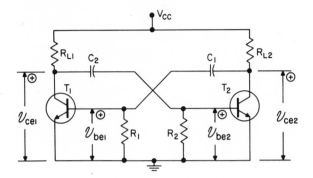

Fig. 11.5. Astable circuit with zero bias.

the circuit. When the base voltage of an *off* transistor relaxes into the active region, the circuit becomes regenerative and the *off* transistor is switched *on*. This drives the previously *on* transistor to the *off* state as normally expected in an astable multivibrator. However, the transistor that is switched *on* and into the saturation region will not remain in saturation since its base current is relaxing toward zero. When the collector current of the presumably *on* transistor falls out of saturation, its collector voltage rises toward V_{CC}. The rise of this collector voltage causes the base voltage of the other transistor (presumably *off*) to relax more rapidly toward the active

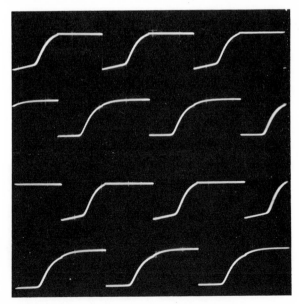

Fig. 11.6. Waveforms for Figure 11.5. Top to bottom: v_{be1}, v_{ce1}, v_{be2}, and v_{ce2}.

region. Observe the break in either base voltage waveform that occurs for one transistor when the other transistor falls out of saturation.

What is the time interval in which a transistor will remain in saturation for the astable circuit under consideration? The time interval of saturation is easily determined if the base current required to establish saturation is known. Identify this base current as I_{BS}, for now. Let $T(\text{sat})$ represent the time in saturation. Further, let the use of subscripts 1 and 2 denote parameters and quantities associated with the appropriate transistor. The base current, while a transistor is in saturation, is an exponential having an initial value of V_{CC}/R_L. The asymptotical value is zero. The time constant of the exponential current is $R_L C$. The input resistance of the transistor is assumed equal to zero during the saturation interval. Specifically, the time interval that transistor 1 is in saturation is expressed by

$$T_1(\text{sat}) = R_{L2} C_1 \ln \frac{0 - V_{cc}/R_{L2}}{0 - I_{B_1 S}} \qquad (11.4)$$

The equation is applicable for either type of transistor.

An equivalent circuit could be shown to represent the condition of saturation. It is believed, however, that the equation is sufficiently explanatory and less confusing than referring to an equivalent circuit. The particular subscripts of Equation (11.4) indicate that transistor 2 is *off* and transistor 1 is in saturation. Exchange the subscripts 1 and 2 and the equation gives the time interval that transistor 2 is in saturation. The two time intervals are equal, of course, if the circuit is symmetrical.

A study of the saturation time has a greater significance when the biasing voltage V_{BB} is not zero. The base current exponential, during the saturation interval, now has the asymptotical value of V_{BB}/R_1. Consequently,

$$T_1(\text{sat}) = R_{L2} C_1 \ln \frac{V_{BB}/R_1 - V_{cc}/R_{L2}}{V_{BB}/R_1 - I_{B_1 S}} \qquad (11.5)$$

Transistor 1 will fall out of saturation and into the active region only if V_{BB}/R_1 is less than $I_{B_1 S}$. The voltage waveforms of Figure 11.7 illustrate the condition when the base current relaxes into the active region. The quantity

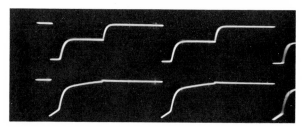

Fig. 11.7. Waveforms for astable circuit when transistors (*n-p-n*) are biased in the active region.

V_{BB}/R_1 is not large enough to hold a transistor in saturation.

Transistor specifications do not identify the base current to establish saturation, as I_{BS}. This current is sometimes indicated, but in magnitude only, along with the information for $V_{ce}(\text{sat})$.

It is also possible to make use of a transistor parameter identified as h_{FE}. This parameter is the d-c forward current transfer ratio of I_c/I_B. The minimum specified value of h_{FE} should be used. Equation (11.4) can be written in terms of this parameter.

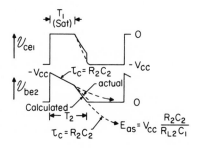

Fig. 11.8. A method for estimating *off* time for zero-biased astable circuit. Waveforms are for *p-n-p* transistors.

$$T_1(\text{sat}) = R_{L2}C_1 \ln h_{FE} \qquad (11.6)$$

The equation is true since $V_{cc}/R_{L2} = I_c$ and $h_{FE} = I_c/I_B$. With these two relationships, Equation (11.4) reduces to Equation (11.6).

The waveform plots of Figure 11.8 suggest a procedure for *estimating* the complete *off* time of a transistor in the zero-biased astable circuit. The waveforms represent the collector voltage of the *on* transistor and the base voltage for the *off* transistor. Assume that $T_1(\text{sat})$ has been determined for transistor 1; the problem is to estimate the remaining *off* time for transistor 2. Identify this remaining *off* time as $T_2 - T_1(\text{sat})$. Notice the asymptotical value that is identified on the figure as $V_{cc}R_2C_2/R_{L2}C_1$. This is the most significant quantity to observe. It comes about by assuming a ramp voltage during the first falling portion of v_{ce1}. The initial slope of the ramp voltage is $V_{cc}/R_{L2}C_1$, assuming a linear amplification of the driving current for transistor 1 and still disregarding the input resistance while the transistor is in the active region. This ramp voltage is the driving voltage for transistor 2, through the R_2C_2 coupling.

Recalling a similar problem described in Chapter 3, for a ramp driving voltage, the time interval in question is then easily calculated. First, calculate the initial voltage knowing $T_1(\text{sat})$. The asymptotical value for v_{be2} is the product of the slope of the driving voltage and the R_2C_2 time constant. Thus,

$$T_2 - T_1(\text{sat}) = R_2C_2 \ln \frac{(V_{cc}R_2C_2/R_{L2}C_1) + V_{cc}\,e^{-T_1(\text{sat})/R_2C_2}}{V_{cc}R_2C_2/R_{L2}C_1}$$

$$= R_2C_2 \ln [1 + \frac{R_{L2}C_1}{R_2C_2}e^{-T_1(\text{sat})/R_2C_2}] \qquad (11.7)$$

The portion of the *off* time estimated by this equation is a comparatively small time interval when $R_{L2}C_1$ is much less than R_2C_2, in which case the equation gives a most correct time interval. The complete *off* time, therefore, is largely dependent on the magnitude of the collector load resistors, R_L.

11.4 A Bistable Multivibrator

A bistable circuit, in a most simplified form, is shown in Figure 11.9. The circuit is represented with *n-p-n* transistors. It is important, however, to think in terms of either type of transistor. In any equations that are written, current and voltage terms are positive and negative real numbers. Merely apply the correct sign for the type of transistor when inserting numerical values.

If the circuit is to be bistable, it must remain in one of two possible states with one transistor *on* and the other transistor *off*, or nearly so. Trigger pulses are then required to cause the circuit to change its state. The specific problems and methods of triggering are reserved for the studies of Chapter 13.

Relationships discovered about the behavior of this circuit are of considerable value for the understanding of other bistable circuits. An analysis of the circuit is relatively simple. Assuming transistor 1 is *off* (the collector current is zero), then the base current of transistor 2 is

$$I_{B2} = V_{CC}/(R_{L1} + R_2) \tag{11.8}$$

Transistor 2 is then *on* and in saturation provided that I_{B2} is sufficient to saturate the collector current. With transistor 2 in saturation, its collector voltage is only a fraction of a volt. Specifically, it is equal to $V_{ce}(\text{sat})$, determined from the specifications for the transistor. This small voltage is the driving voltage for establishing a base current for transistor 1. This base current is then very small and transistor 1 is nearly *off*.

Actually, the circuit is bistable even when the coupling resistances R_1 and R_2 are reduced to zero. For such a condition $v_{ce1} = v_{be2}$ and $v_{ce2} =$

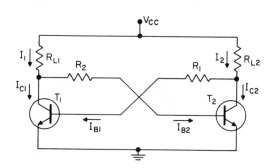

Fig. 11.9. A bistable circuit.

v_{be1}. With transistor 2 in saturation, as it could be, then its collector voltage is small. For the small collector voltage at transistor 2, the base current of transistor 1 is small and the collector current of transistor 1 is also small. The approximate relationships of the various currents as identified on the circuit diagram, assuming collector and base voltages equal to zero, are

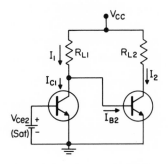

$$I_1 = I_{B2} = I_2 = I_{c2} = V_{CC}/R_L \quad (11.9)$$

$$I_{c1} = I_{B1} = 0 \quad (11.10)$$

Fig. 11.10. An equivalent circuit for Equations (11.9) and (11.10).

These current relationships are a little more convincing if one considers the circuit of Figure 11.10 that shows only one of the direct couplings. The base of transistor 1 is returned to the emitter, with a biasing voltage of $V_{ce}(\text{sat})$, rather than to the collector of transistor 2. Actually, a slightly positive voltage (n-p-n) is required at the base before the collector current can change appreciably.

11.5 A Bistable Circuit With Fixed Bias

Better stability for a bistable circuit is ensured if the *off* transistor has a reverse base to emitter voltage. One method of establishing the reverse voltage for either transistor, when it is *off*, is shown in Figure 11.11. The circuit differs from the preceding bistable circuit by the addition of the two resistors identified as R_2 and by the addition of the fixed bias voltage

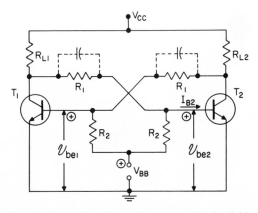

Fig. 11.11. A bistable multivibrator with fixed bias.

V_{BB}. The voltage V_{BB} is numerically negative with *n-p-n* transistors; it is positive with *p-n-p* transistors.

Assuming transistor 2 is *on* and transistor 1 is *off*, the problem is to evaluate the two quantities of I_{B2} and V_{be1}. With transistor 2 in saturation, its collector voltage is V_{ce}(sat). The base voltage of transistor 1, assuming a large input resistance for an *off* transistor, is

$$V_{be1} = \frac{V_{BB}R_1}{R_1 + R_2} = \frac{V_{ce}(\text{sat})\,R_2}{R_1 + R_2} \tag{11.11}$$

The base current I_{B2} of transistor 2, assuming zero input resistance for an *on* transistor, is

$$I_{B2} = \frac{V_{CC}}{R_{L1} + R_1} + \frac{V_{BB}}{R_2} \tag{11.12}$$

Equation (11.12) is recognized by referring to the equivalent input circuits of Figure 11.12. The first equivalent circuit (a) represents the input circuit for transistor 2 when transistor 1 is *off*. Equivalent circuit (b) shows a short circuit branch *BE* for the base current I_{B2}. Equation (11.12) is a current equation for the latter equivalent circuit.

In comparing Equation (11.12) with Equation (11.8), the added current term of V_{BB}/R_2 is observed. This added current term has the effect of decreasing the magnitude of I_{B2} since V_{CC} and V_{BB} are of opposite polarities when numerical values are inserted. The two preceding equations are equally applicable to either the *n-p-n* or the *p-n-p* transistors. A consistent choice of voltage *reference* polarities and current *reference* direction make this possible.

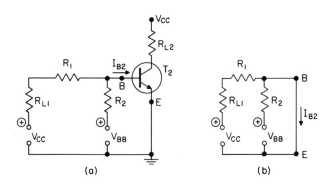

Fig. 11.12. Equivalent input circuits for transistor 2 when transistor 1 is *off*.

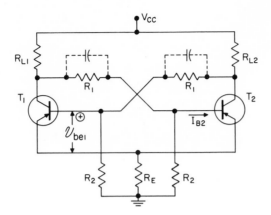

Fig. 11.13. A self-biased bistable multivibrator.

11.6 A Bistable Circuit With Self Bias

The circuit of Figure 11.13 has a common-emitter resistance identified as R_E. The circuit is a self-biased, bistable multivibrator.

With transistor 2 *on* and transistor 1 *off*, the expression for V_{be1} is

$$V_{be1} = V_{CE2}(\text{sat}) \frac{R_2}{R_1 + R_2} - V_{E2} \frac{R_1}{R_1 + R_2} \qquad (11.13)$$

The voltage V_{E2} is $(I_{B2} + I_{c2})R_E$; it is approximated by $I_{c2}R_E$ when I_{B2} is much less than I_{c2}. For this approximation,

$$V_{E2} = [V_{CC} - V_{CE2}(\text{sat})] \frac{R_E}{R_{L2} + R_E} \qquad (11.14)$$

Further, since $V_{CE}(\text{sat})$ is only a fraction of a volt and much less than V_{CC}, this term in Equation (11.14) could be set equal to zero with reasonable accuracy. Neglecting the effects of both I_{B2} and $V_{CE}(\text{sat})$ are errors of opposition. The two errors are not additive. Neglecting $V_{CE}(\text{sat})$,

$$V_{be1} = -V_{CC} \frac{R_E R_1}{(R_{L2} + R_E)(R_1 + R_2)} \qquad (11.15)$$

Again, this equation is applicable to either type of transistor. The only problem is to have circuit parameters, for a given V_{CC}, to obtain a desired level of reverse input voltage for the *off* transistor.

The equivalent circuits of Figure 11.14 suggest a method for calculating the base current of the *on* transistor. Circuit (b) represents the Thevenin's equivalent for the input circuit (a). With transistor 2 *on*, and in saturation, its base current is conveniently expressed as

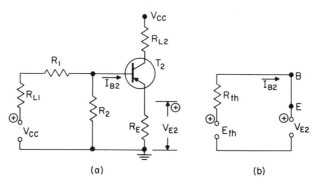

Fig. 11.14. Equivalent input circuits for calculating the base current of an *on* transistor (reference to Figure 11.13).

$$I_{B2} = \frac{E_{th} - V_{E2}}{R_{th}} \tag{11.16}$$

The subscript 'th' represents the Thevenin's equivalent voltage or resistance. Notice that R_E is not shown in the Thevenin equivalent circuit; only V_{E2}, which is known from Equation (11.14), is shown.

11.7   The Schmitt Trigger Circuit

The circuit of Figure 11.15 is a Schmitt trigger circuit. It might also be identified as a voltage level discriminator, or as a bistable circuit since it has either of two states depending on the voltage level of the source voltage for a given circuit.

The circuitry arrangment is identical to the dual-tube circuit of Figure 10.23. A possible set of voltage waveforms for the transistor circuit is represented in Figure 11.16. Taking into account the respective signal voltages, as represented, these voltage waveforms are comparable to those of Figure 10.25 for the dual-tube circuit.

When transistor 1 is *off*, transistor 2 is *on* but not in saturation. When transistor 2 is *off*, transistor 1 is *on* but not in saturation. The circuit parameters must be chosen to satisfy these conditions. These are the required conditions if the circuit is to become regenerative and self-triggering when the signal voltage is greater than, or less than, the two respectively significant values of signal voltage required to start the regenerative actions.

One of the significant values of signal voltage is that value that will cause transition of the circuit when transistor 1 is *off*. The other significant value will cause transition of the circuit when transistor 2 is *off*.

Consider the voltage e_1, represented on the circuit diagram, which is the sum of a signal voltage and any value of bias voltage that may be required.

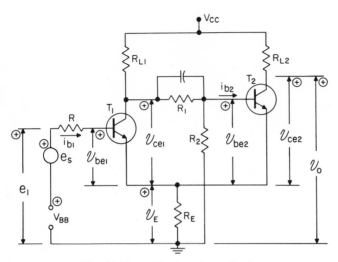

Fig. 11.15. A Schmitt trigger circuit.

(The signal voltage and bias voltage are shown in series. In practice this summation is established by some coupling circuit). With the first transistor *off*, transition is to occur when the base current is sufficient to bring this transistor into the active region. This transition starts a regenerative action, since the second transistor is initially in the active region, and the circuit changes its state such that transistor 2 is now *off*.

What value of e_1 is required to produce this first transition? If transitor 2 is *on* by a known amount, then V_{E2} is also known. (The known amount by which transistor 2 is *on* is discussed in a later paragraph of this section). For *n-p-n* transistors, transistor 1 enters the active region when e_1 is greater than V_{E2}. For *p-n-p* transistors, e_1 must be less (more negative) than V_{E2}.

For the first critical value of the source voltage, transistor 1 must go on

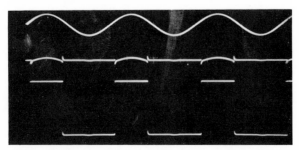

Fig. 11.16. A possible set of voltage waveform for the circuit in Figure 11.15. From top to bottom: e_s, v_E, and v_o.

sufficiently to drop its collector voltage enough to turn transistor 2 *off.*
In other words, v_{be2} must be a reverse voltage (negative for *n-p-n*, positive
for *p-n-p* transistors). The resistance R_2 has its most important purpose
in the circuit in helping to establish this required reverse voltage. This
reverse voltage for v_{be2} is evaluated by assuming zero base current for transistor 2. The circuit for this evaluation involves v_{ce1}, V_{E1}(transistor 1 *on*),
R_1 and R_2. If the calculation results in a reverse voltage for v_{be2}, then it is
correct to assume that transistor 2 has been triggered *off.*

To cause the reverse transition back to the original state, the driving
voltage must decrease to a level that will cause the base current of transistor 2 to re-enter the active region.

The degree to which transistor 2 is *on* is largely determined by R_1. The
resistance R_2 is of little importance since it is normally much larger than
the input resistance of an *on* trasistor. With transistor 2 well *on*, but not
in saturation, its base current is approximately $(V_{cc} - V_{E2})/(R_{L1} + R_1)$.
From the given data for a given transistor, the desired value of base current
is known. The voltage V_{E2} is determined by assuming some small value for
v_{ce2}, but greater than the value at saturation. Neglecting the comparatively
small contribution of the base current, the collector and emitter currents
are known. Consequently V_{E2} is known to close approximation.

11.8   Monostable Multivibrator With Fixed Bias

The circuit of Figure 11.17 is a monostable circuit with fixed bias for
the normally *off* transistor. Transistor 2, with the RC-coupled input circuit,
is normally *on.*

The circuit must be triggered from an external source. (Specific methods
for triggering are reserved for Chapter 13.) Regardless of how the circuit

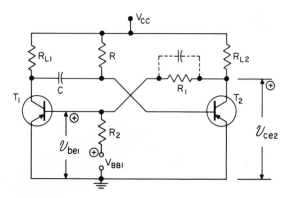

Fig. 11.17. A monostable circuit with fixed bias for the normally *off*
transistor.

is triggered, a negative trigger pulse (for the *p-n-p*) appears at the base of the normally *off* transistor and a positive pulse appears at the base of the normally *on* transistor. When a trigger pulse is injected, the circuit changes its state but will return to the original state.

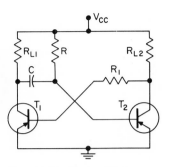

Fig. 11.18. A simplified monostable circuit.

With reference to the figure, transistor 2 remains *off* for a time interval that is calculated by exactly the same procedure described for the astable multivibrator. [See Equation (11.1), (11.2), or (11.3).] The bias voltage V_{BB1} is normally required to ensure that transistor 1 will be held *off*. Transistor 1 must remain *on*, however, during the time interval when transistor 2 is *off*, following a trigger pulse. The direct-coupled portion of the circuit is evaluated exactly as in the bistable circuit with fixed bias. The reverse voltage for v_{be1}, when transistor 1 is *off*, is determined from Equation (11.11). When transistor 1 is *on*, its base current is determined in accordance with Equation (11.12) by changing R_{L1} in that equation to R_{L2}.

If the circuit is not subjected to spurious signals that might trigger the circuit at undesirable times, then R_2 and V_{BB} could be omitted. The circuit is represented in Figure 11.18. The direct coupling with R_1 only is identical to one of the direct couplings in the bistable circuit of Figure 11.9.

11.9 A Monostable Circuit With Self Bias

The circuit of Figure 11.19 is a monostable circuit with self bias. The emitters are returned to a common resistance R_E. Transistor 1 is normally *off* and transistor 2 is normally *on*. The bias voltage V_{BB} is required to hold transistor 1 *on* during the time interval when transistor 2 is *off*. A positive trigger pulse is required, as shown, for the *n-p-n* transistors.

When a transistor is *on*, either transistor 1 or transistor 2, its collector current may or may not be in saturation. As a first condition, assume the collector current of transistor 1 is in saturation when this transistor is *on*. The circuit requirements to make this true are considered later in this section.

One of the major problems is to determine the *off* time for transistor 2 when the circuit is triggered. The voltage waveform for v_{be2} is shown in Figure 11.20. Accepting the information given on this waveform, for a moment, the *off* time T_2 is

$$T_2 = R_2 C_2 \ln \frac{(V_{CC} - V_{E1}) - (-V_{CC} + V_{E2})}{V_{CC} - V_{E1}} \qquad (11.17)$$

Let us consider Equation (11.17) to determine why it is true and the

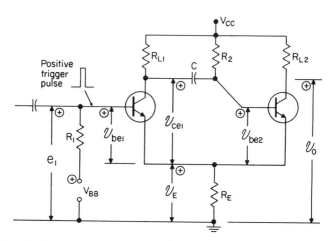

Fig. 11.19. A monostable circuit with a common emitter resistor, R_E.

conditions for which it is true. The equation is easily written, of course, if the significant quantities for v_{be2} are known, as indicated on the waveform in Figure 11.20. The initial value on the exponential for v_{be2} is indicated as $-V_{cc} + V_{E2}$. The time constant is R_2C_2 and the asymptotical value of the reverse voltage exponential is indicated as $V_{cc} - V_{E1}$. The circuit is self-triggered when v_{be2} relaxes to zero. The circuit then returns to the normal state and remains there until the next external trigger pulse. The voltage V_{E1} denotes that only transistor 1 is *on;* voltage V_{E2} denotes that only transistor 2 is *on.*

The asymptotical value of $V_{cc} - V_{E1}$ is recognized if I_{BEO}, for transistor 2, is assumed equal to zero. This is a reasonable assumption provided R_2 is not excessively large.

The initial value of $-V_{cc} + V_{E2}$, on the exponential, is more difficult to recognize immediately. Before the trigger pulse, v_{ce1} is equal to $V_{cc} - V_{E2}$. Immediately after the trigger pulse v_{ce1} is approximately zero provided that transistor 1 is driven to saturation. The step thus generated at v_{ce1} is transferred to v_{be2}. This step is negative for *n-p-n* transistors and positive for *p-n-p* transistors. For either type of transistor, it is $-(V_{cc} - V_{E2})$. Notice, therefore, that Equation (11.17) is correct only if transistor 1 is driven to saturation. Remember, also, that the equation is written on the assumption that only one transistor can be *on,* not both. The equation does not require that transistor 2 shall be in saturation before the trigger.

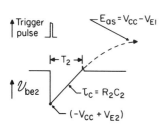

Fig. 11.20. Evaluation of the *off* time for transistor 2 in Figure 11.19. See Equation (11.17).

Since Equation (11.17) is correct whether transistor 2 is in saturation or not, let us assume that it *is* in saturation. In that event, $V_{E2} = V_{CC}R_E/(R_{L1} + R_E)$. Also, since transistor 1 is assumed to be in saturation, when *on*, then $V_{E1} = V_{CC}R_E/(R_{L1} + R_E)$. With these relationships for V_{E2} and V_{E1}, Equation (11.17) can be written as

$$T_2 = R_2 C_2 \ln \left[2\left(1 + \frac{R_E}{R_{L1}}\right) - \frac{R_E}{R_{L1}}\left(1 + \frac{R_{L1} + R_E}{R_{L2} + R_E}\right) \right] \quad (11.18)$$

Equation (11.18) is correct only if each of the two transistors is in saturation, or nearly so, when a transistor is *on*. This is one condition, not a necessary condition, for the circuit to be monostable. Equation (11.18) can be simplified considerably, if desired.

Now, how is it determined whether a transistor is *on* or *off*? Further, when a transistor is *on*, is it in saturation or is it in the active region? Let us concentrate on transistor 1, the normally *off* transistor. First, a particular value for V_{E2} is established when transistor 2 is *on*. Then V_{BB} must be less (for *n-p-n*) than V_{E2} if transistor 1 is ever to be *off*. This establishes a limiting value for V_{BB} and it is independent of R_1 since the base current of transistor 1 is zero. When a trigger pulse causes the circuit to change its state, for a time interval T_2, transistor 1 will be in saturation if $I_{c1} = V_{CC}/(R_{L1} + R_E)$. For this value of $I_{c1}(\text{sat})$, the minimum value of base current is

$$I_{B1}(\text{min}) = \frac{I_{c1}(\text{sat})}{h_{FE}} \quad (11.19)$$

The value of I_{B1} is therefore known. The base current can also be expressed, with good approximation, as

$$I_{B1} = \frac{V_{BB} - V_{E1}}{R_1} \quad (11.20)$$

Sufficient information is now available to select V_{BB} and R_1 to give the required value of base current for transistor 1, provided the difference of the two voltage terms of Equation (11.20) has the correct polarity. For the *n-p-n* transistors, V_{BB} must be greater than V_{E1}. But, as stated previously, V_{BB} must be less than V_{E2}. Therefore, V_{E1} must be less than V_{E2}.

The fact that V_{E1} must be less than V_{E2}, when either transistor goes to saturation, suggests a number of design possibilities for the self-biased monostable multivibrator. Some of these are now itemized.

(a) Select an R_{L1} greater than R_{L2}.

(b) Current-bias transistor 1 into the active region when it is *on*, and transistor 2 is *off*. Equations (11.17) and (11.18) are no longer applicable, but the circuit can be monostable; however, the time T_2 will be decreased.

(c) The permissible biasing levels for transistor 1 are dependent on the bias level for transistor 2. V_{BB} must be less than (*n-p-n*) V_{E2} in any case.

PROBLEMS

11.1 The astable circuit of Figure 11.1 uses *n-p-n* transistors. The circuit is symmetrical and has a frequency of 5000 c/s; $V_{CC} = 20$ volts, $R_L = 4$ K. Assume a transistor will hold in saturation during the *on* interval. A collector voltage has the limits of zero and 20 volts and has a rise time to $0.9 V_{CC}$ of 10 μs. Determine the values for C_1 and R_1.

11.2 The astable circuit of Figure 11.1 uses *p-n-p* transistors, as shown. The circuit is symmetrical and has a frequency of 5000 c/s. The biasing resistors are returned to a separate supply V_{BB}, rather than to V_{CC}; $V_{CC} = -20$ volts, $R_L = 4$ K. $C_1 = C_2 = .002$ μfd. The base currents have a quiescent value of 200 μa, which is sufficient to hold a transistor in saturation during the *on* interval. Determine the values for V_{BB} and the biasing resistors R_1 and R_2.

11.3 Refer to Problem 11.1 and discuss the frequency response of the astable circuit as a function of V_{BB}. Illustrate with voltage waveforms.

11.4 For the bistable circuit of Figure 11.9, $V_{CC} = 15$ volts. $R_{L1} = R_{L2} = 3$ K. The *on* transistor is in saturation and has a base current of 300 μa. Determine R_1 and R_2.

11.5 For the bistable circuit of Figure 11.11, $V_{CC} = 12$ volts. $R_{L1} = R_{L2} = 2.5$ K. The *on* transistor is in saturation and its base current is 200 μa. $V_{BB} = -6$ volts. The base voltage of the *off* transistor is -2 volts. Assume the reverse input resistance is large. Determine the values for R_1 and R_2.

11.6 Replace the fixed-bias voltage of Problem 11.5 with a common-emitter resistance R_E as in the bistable circuit of Figure 11.13. The given quantities and conditions to be satisfied are the same as in Problem 11.5. Determine the values for R_1, R_2 and R_E.

11.7 For the monostable circuit of Figure 11.17, $V_{CC} = -12$ volts. $V_{BB} = 4$ volts. The reverse base voltage when transistor 1 is *off*, is 1 volt. $R_{L1} = R_{L2} = 3$ K. $C = 0.003$ μfd. $R = 100$ K. When transistor 1 is *on*, the base current is 300 μa., and the transistor is in saturation.
(a) Determine R_1 and R_2.
(b) Assume the circuit is triggered at some instant t_0. Plot the base voltage and the collector voltage at transistor 2, indicating all significant quantities.

11.8 Refer to the Schmitt trigger circuit of Figure 11.15. Assume the circuit has been designed for satisfactory triggering action. Keeping in mind that the two values of e_1 at which the circuit will trigger are of primary interest, discuss the effect of
(a) Increasing the value of R.
(b) Increasing the value of R_{L1}.
(c) Variation in the value for R_{L2}.
(d) Decreasing the value of R_1.
(e) Variation in the value of R_2.
(f) Decreasing the value of R_E.

12

Triggering, Gating, Synchronizing
Part 1, Tubes

12.1 General Discussion

An early emphasis of two significant facts regarding the material of this chapter is important. The first point to be emphasized is that triggering, gating, synchronizing, etc., are operations performed on *familiar circuits*. With this viewpoint, it is not necessary to consider the problems of triggering, the problems of gating, the problems of synchronizing or any other similar operation on a circuit as entirely separate types of problems. The operation to be performed on a circuit is dictated by the circuit itself and by the application in which the circuit is used.

The second point to emphasize is that the triggering, gating or synchronizing of circuits includes the general problem of *injecting* a voltage, or voltages, into a familiar type of circuit for the purpose of controlling its behavior. The circuit, as used in a particular application, influences the specifications of the injected voltages; specifications regarding magnitude, waveshape, repetition rate, recovery time, polarity, and perhaps other special requirements.

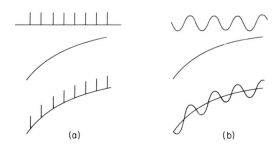

Fig. 12.1. (a) Addition of pulses and an exponential. (b) Addition of
a sine wave and an exponential.

The idea of inserting a voltage into a circuit to control its operation is
simple enough. It implies the need for a summation of voltages. The addition of two voltages is illustrated in (a) and (b) of Figure 12.1. One of the
two voltages could represent the inserted voltage and the other could represent a voltage already existing in a circuit. Unfortunately, no practical circuit involving the addition of voltages is as simple as suggested by these
illustrations. What kind of voltage must be injected in a given circuit?
What is the coupling circuit by which the voltage is injected? How does
this coupling circuit affect the circuit to be controlled? What is the behavior
of the controlled circuit after the control voltage is injected? There are no
general answers to these questions. Each controlled circuit must be examined
separately.

The subject of triggering, along with all the possible circuitry and related
problems of triggering, could be an extensive study in itself. The same is
true of gating, synchronizing or any other type of operation on a circuit.
The purpose of this chapter is to give some of the most commonly used
techniques. It is also the objective of this chapter to provide sufficient information to permit an easier understanding of practical circuits not included in this discussion.

Normally, the triggering of a circuit implies the requirement of causing
a circuit to change its state from one condition to a second condition as
rapidly as possible. Bistable multivibrators and monostable multivibrators
are particular examples of circuits that must be triggered. Sweep circuits
that are not free-running must be triggered also. Free-running sweep circuits
can be triggered but usually are only triggered for the purpose of synchronizing the sweep. Gating in electronic circuits implies the need of blocking
a signal, or of passing a signal, for prescribed time intervals.

Synchronization in electronic circuits implies the need of coordinating
the desired behavior of the various circuits of a system to a fixed time reference. Each particular application has an influence on the desired behavior

of the circuitry. Synchronization can include any one or more of a number of problems. Among these problems are: frequency stability, timing or phasing of a voltage waveform, controlled delay, correction for phase errors, allowance for recovery time of a waveform, and frequency division.

The control of electronic switching circuits, then, can involve more than triggering, gating or synchronizing. These terms mean little unless the complete circuit for a particular application is taken into consideration. For this reason, apparently similar circuits do not consistently carry the same identifying name in all applications.

12.2 Thyratron Scale-of-Two Counter

The circuit of Figure 12.2 is a thyratron circuit that can be used as a scale-of-two counter. The output voltage from cathode to cathode, or from either cathode to ground, has a frequency equal to one half the frequency of the input trigger pulses. The various voltages in the circuit are illustrated by the waveforms of Figure 12.3, neglecting the tube voltage when either tube is conducting.

The behavior of the circuit is quickly understood by considering tube T_2 conducting and T_1 not conducting at an instant just before a trigger pulse is applied. At this instant, V_{K2} is at B^+(neglecting the voltage across T_2). Also at this instant, the capacitor voltage V_c is $-B^+$. Now, when the positive trigger pulse is applied, T_1 is made to conduct. The capacitive coupling between cathodes then causes the cathode of T_2 to be raised to approximately twice B^+, thereby making T_2 nonconducting. This is true since $V_{K2} = -V_c + V_{K1}$. It is important to realize that the trigger pulse must be removed before the plate-cathode voltage of the *off* tube increases to a value that might cause the *off* tube to return to a conducting state during the time of this same trigger pulse. The time required for deionization of the gas

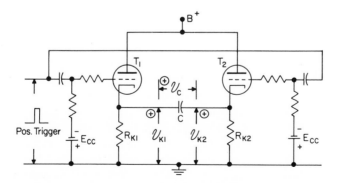

Fig. 12.2. A bistable circuit using thyratrons (cathode extinguishing).

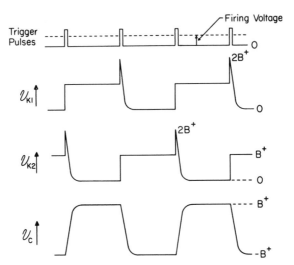

Fig. 12.3. Voltage waveforms for the circuit of Figure 12.2.

in thyratrons is a significant factor in limiting the upper frequency at which this circuit can operate satisfactorily.

A modification for the circuit in Figure 12.2 is one in which the cathode resistors are removed and inserted in the plate circuit, and with the capacitor connected from plate to plate rather than from cathode to cathode. The circuit can then be identified as an anode extinguishing circuit.

As an additional use for this circuit, the circuit in Figure 12.2 can be regarded as an inverter circuit in which the output voltage is regarded as an alternating voltage. There are applications in which information represented by the trigger pulses must be transmitted to a remote location. The thyratron inverter circuit is sometimes desirable to make this transmission of information possible.

12.3   A Rotating Electronic Switch

The circuit diagram of Figure 12.4 represents a rotating electronic switch employing thyratrons. For any one time interval between successive trigger pulses, only one of the tubes in the chain is conducting. At the instant of a trigger pulse, the next tube in the chain is made conducting, turning off the preceding tube which was *on* and presetting the following tube so that it will go *on* when the next trigger pulse is applied.

The capacitors C_1, C_2, C_3,..., etc., are respectively coupled from cathode-to cathode of adjacent tubes, thereby giving a cathode extinguishing circuit as in Figure 12.2. The preset action is accomplished by the voltage divider action of resistors R_1 and R_2, with R_2 returned to a negative bias voltage E_{cc}. The direct coupling, provided from the cathode of one tube to the grid

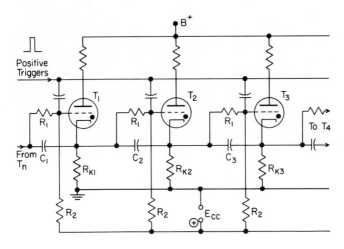

Fig. 12.4. Rotating electronic switch.

of the next tube, gives the preset voltage action required. In general, the grid voltage of tube T_2, for example, is

$$e_{c2} = (V_{K1} - E_{cc}) \frac{R_2}{R_1 + R_2} + (E_{cc} - V_{K2}) \qquad (12.1)$$

If tube T_1 and tube T_2 are not conducting, Equation (12.1) becomes

$$e_{c2} = E_{cc} \frac{R_1}{R_1 + R_2} \qquad (12.2)$$

However, with T_1 *on* and T_2 *off*, the preset voltage for T_2 is

$$e_{c2} = E_{cc} \frac{R_1}{R_1 + R_2} + V_{K1} \frac{R_2}{R_1 + R_2} \qquad (12.3)$$

By selecting a proper negative value for E_{cc}, along with the resistance ratio and the magnitude of the trigger pulses, it is possible to trigger tube T_2 *on* provided T_1 is already *on*. The same results apply to T_3 and T_2 respectively and so forth down the chain (closed chain) of tubes.

The rotating electronic switch can be used in a number of different ways depending on a particular application that requires a sequencing operation. The plate circuit of each tube, for example, might contain relays that need to be operated in a particular sequence that is repetitive. Or, the output voltage from the respective stages might be employed as trigger pulses to operate other electronic circuits in sequence.

12.4 Triggering of Bistable Multivibrators

Four methods of triggering bistable multivibrators (with vacuum tubes) are shown by the circuit diagrams in Figures 12.5 through 12.8. In each case the trigger voltage is obtained by differentiating a rectangular pulse through

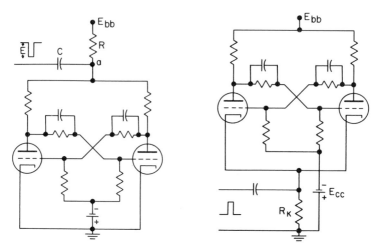

Fig. 12.5. Common anode triggering.

Fig. 12.6. Common cathode triggering.

an RC-coupling circuit. The last two circuits, Figures 12.7 and 12.8, show the use of diodes to prevent the positive spikes (a result of differentiation) from retriggering the circuit. The first two circuits do not require the diodes. In these first two circuits, the trigger voltage is injected at a point in the circuit that is symmetrical to both sides of the bistable multivibrator. In Figure 12.5, the trigger pulse is injected at a point where the plate circuits are returned to a *common* plate-load resistor. In Figure 12.6, the trigger pulse is injected at a point where the *cathodes* are returned to a common cathode resistor.

Let us analyze the possible behavior of each of these circuits. The nega-

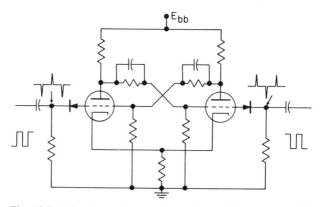

Fig. 12.7. Triggering with negative voltage spikes at the grids.

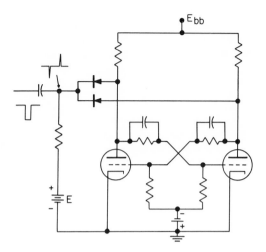

Fig. 12.8. Triggering with negative voltage spikes at the plates.

tive-going trigger voltage of Figure 12.5 can cause the circuit to change its state, provided this trigger pulse is sufficiently large to turn the *on* tube *off*. In the presence of the commutating capacitors, almost the full magnitude of the negative trigger pulse is transferred to the grid of the *on* tube by way of the coupling circuit to the plate of the *off* tube. At the instant the *on* tube is triggered *off*, its plate voltage may or may not change. The direction and magnitude of this change depends on the magnitude of the trigger pulse for a given circuit. More specifically,

$$\Delta e_b \ (on \ to \ off) = V_a - E - E_b \ (on) \tag{12.4}$$

where V_a is the voltage at the triggering point before the trigger voltage is applied, E is the magnitude of the trigger voltage, and E_b (*on*) is the plate voltage (to ground) before the trigger. Thus Equation (12.4), which neglects the plate loading of the coupling circuits, indicates that the change in plate voltage can be positive, negative, or even zero. This change, whatever it may be, is transferred through the commutating capacitor to the grid of the originally *off* tube. The result desired immediately following the trigger is to have the grid of the originally *off* tube at a higher potential (less negative) than the grid voltage of the originally *on* tube, thereby allowing the circuit to change its state. Notice that it is possible for both tubes to be *off* for a time, but the originally *off* tube must be the first to return to a conducting state. The positive-going portion of the trigger voltage will not cause the circuit to change its state since this only drives the *on* tube further into conduction.

An analysis of the cathode-triggered circuit of Figure 12.6 is somewhat similar to the anode-triggered circuit in Figure 12.5. Briefly, the positive-going trigger increases the cathode voltage of both tubes by the same amount.

In so doing, the *on* tube is triggered *off*, causing its plate voltage to ground to increase. The grid-to-ground voltage of the originally *off* tube also increases by the same amount in the presence of the commutating capacitor. Consequently, the grid-cathode voltage of the originally *on* tube can be more negative than the grid-cathode voltage of the originally *off* tube and the circuit is in a position to change its state. The fixed-bias voltage is sometimes needed whenever a smaller R_K is desired in order to decrease the transition time.

In the circuit of Figure 12.7, negative trigger pulses are applied directly to the two grids of the bistable multivibrator. If a tube is conducting before the negative trigger pulse is applied to its grid, then the tube is cut off and the circuit changes its state after the trigger pulse. There is no change of state when a negative trigger pulse is applied to a tube that is already non-conducting. For this type of triggering, the tow trigger pulses are normally derived from the output of two separate channels. With such an arrangement, the bistable multivibrator serves as one method often used to measure the time interval between significant instants of time represented by the trigger pulses (as discussed further in the next section). The diodes are included in the input circuits to prevent the positive spikes from triggering the circuit. Normally the circuit can be triggered more effectively with a smaller negative trigger than with a positive trigger. If the circuit is designed to make this true, the diodes are not then absolutely essential.

In the circuit of Figure 12.8, the circuit is triggered from a single source by way of two diodes connected respectively to the plates of the two tubes. Selecting the proper value for the bias voltage E, only the diode connected to the plate of the *off* tube will conduct when a negative trigger pulse is applied. In the presence of the commutating capacitor, the negative trigger pulse appearing at the plate of the *off* tube is also present at the grid of the *on* tube. The *on* tube is thereby triggered *off* and the circuit changes its state. The frequency of the bistable multivibrator is one half the frequency of the triggering signal.

A fifth general method (not shown) for triggering a bistable multivibrator is to inject the trigger pulse at a point where the grid resistors are returned to a common resistor. This circuit will change its state on each succeeding pulse. Clipping diodes are not absolutely essential for the same reasons given for Figure 12.7.

12.5   General Comments on the Uses of Bistable Multivibrators

The bistable multivibrator is frequently an essential part of an electronic circuit of industrial applications. Each particular application, requiring bistable circuits, has its own reasons for this requirement. The binary system of digital computers, for one example, requires bistable multivibrators. Other applications cannot be given here without going into considerable

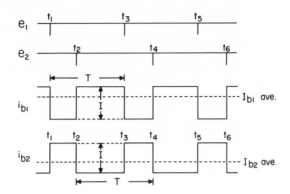

Fig. 12.9. Time interval between trigger pulses.

detail and study of a specific application. It is strongly recommended that the student make a brief survey of technical literature for the purpose of observing the frequent use of bistable multivibrators for reasons other than as a scale-of-two counter. In many instances it serves merely as a switch, or to generate a gating pulse, or as a timing reference, or perhaps even as a pulse stretcher.

One particular use of a bistable multivibrator that can be explained briefly is that of measuring the time interval between successive trigger pulses with the two-signal triggering circuit of Figure 12.7. The procedure is illustrated by the waveforms of Figure 12.9 where e_1 is one of the trigger pulses, e_2 is the second series of trigger pulses, i_{b1} is the plate current in one tube, and i_{b2} is the plate current in the other tube. The average values of these current pulses is a direct measure of a time interval between successive trigger pulses, provided both series of trigger pulses have the same period and differing only in phase, and also with the provision that the current pulses are of uniform magnitude. For the conditions shown in Figure 12.9, the average value of i_{b2} is proportional to the time interval from t_1 to t_2, for a fixed repetition rate. More specifically

$$I_{b2} \text{ (ave)} = \frac{I}{T}(t_2 - t_1) = K(t_2 - t_1) \tag{12.5}$$

Similarly, the average value of i_b is proportional to the time interval from t_2 to t_3. A d-c ammeter placed in either cathode circuit can be calibrated, for a given circuit, to read these time intervals directly. The reason for making such a measurement, of course, must come from the application.

12.6 Frequency Division with Astable Multivibrators

The diagram of Figure 12.10 illustrates four trigger pulses superimposed on a grid voltage waveform of the *off* tube for an astable multivibrator

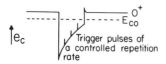

Fig. 12.10. An illustration for frequency division with astable multivibrator.

Since a transition is indicated on the fourth trigger pulse, the frequency of the astable multivibrator is exactly one fourth of the frequency of the trigger source provided the other half of the circuit is triggered at the instant of the eighth pulse. In other words, each tube is *off* for exactly four cycles of the trigger input.

Several methods of injecting these trigger pulses into the circuit are possible. Regardless of the method, however, the problem is to bring the *off* tube out of the *off* state, not to cause the *on* tube to go *off* with the trigger pulse directly. True, negative pulses applied to the grid of the *on* tube can result in a controlled transition, but only if the inverted amplification of these negative pulses have appropriate positive values to trigger the *off* tube *on* by way of the RC plate-to-grid coupling.

Reference to the RC plate-to-grid coupling suggests the possibility of controlling the transitions with positive trigger pulses applied directly to the plates. This method is seldom used, however, because of the loading on the circuit by the source or vice versa. The most acceptable methods are to inject the trigger pulses across a common cathode resistor or across a common grid resistor. In this latter method, the two main grid resistors are returned to the common grid resistor.

The magnitude of the trigger pulses, relative to the free-rise magnitude of the grid voltage, is important in order to provide controlled transitions. If the pulses are too small the circuit could be self-triggering during a time interval between pulses, perhaps some time between the fourth and fifth pulse of Figure 12.10 as an example. If the pulses are too large, the transition might occur too early, perhaps at the third pulse of Figure 12.10 This third pulse, in the illustration, must not drive the grid too close to the cut-off voltage level when the fourth pulse is required to do the triggering.

12.7 Addition of Voltages with RC Coupling

The expression *voltage injected* was used frequently in the discussions of the preceding sections. Normally, the voltage was "injected" into the circuit by RC coupling. The end result in each case was the addition of the injected voltage to a voltage already existing within the circuit. In some instances, the injected voltage was identical, or nearly identical, to the source voltage. In other instances, the injected voltage was not identical, nor even nearly identical, to the source voltage because of strong differentiation by the RC coupling.

The point of emphasis here is that a source voltage, even though it may have all the prerequisites for injection purposes, is seldom connected directly in series with the existing circuit voltage even where it might be possible to do so. The RC coupling is one method of addition that will permit a common chassis ground connection for the two voltages, thereby preventing noise disturbances by taking advantage of the shielding and the common voltage reference provided by the chassis. Remember that one terminal of the d-c power supplies is also at chassis ground. This point of emphasis is made at this late stage in the text because of the usual need to remind the student of the practical prob-

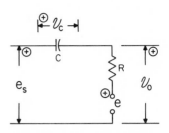

Fig. 12.11. Addition of voltages with RC coupling. $v_o = e_s + e$, if $v_c = -e$.

lem of avoiding pickup from the 60-cycle source that feeds the d-c power supplies. This pickup becomes increasingly more disturbing as the circuitry becomes more involved.

An earlier chapter (Chapter 3) was devoted entirely to RC-coupled circuits. In the presentations of that chapter, we were not particularly concerned with an RC circuit as a means of adding voltages. With the trigger injection problems of the preceding sections of this chapter, this method of addition is now of greater concern. Referring to the illustrative circuit of Figure 12.11, it is correct to state that $v_o = e_s + e$ only if the capacitor voltage v_c is equal to the negative of voltage e. Of course, this condition cannot be truly attained but can only be approached. The various problems involved are recalled by reference to the contents of Chapter 3.

An example of the voltage requirement of a coupling capacitor is illustrated by reference to Figure 12.10, which is a representation of frequency division with astable multivibrators. Here, the trigger pulses are shown as riding on the free-rising exponential of the *off* tube. This free-rising grid voltage can be represented by the voltage e of Figure 12.11. The coupling capacitor must follow this voltage, and this voltage only, if the trigger pulses are to have a free ride. This creates conflicting equivalent-circuit time constants associated with the coupling capacitor. The capacitor must be small enough to allow it to follow the voltage e, yet large enough to prevent it from following the voltage of the trigger pulses.

12.8   Addition of Voltages with Resistance Coupling

The addition of voltages with resistance coupling (Figure 12.12), as discussed in this section, has no reference to the triggering problems of earlier sections of this chapter. Specific examples for using this direct-coupled method are not given here. Its use depends on the requirements of a complete electrical system of a particular application: In general it is

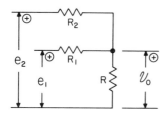

Fig. 12.12. Voltage addition with resistance coupling.

$$v_o = R_o\left(\frac{e_1}{R_1} + \frac{e_2}{R_2}\right)$$

used in any direct-coupled circuit where the output voltage must be dependent on the sum of two or more input voltages.

A resistance-coupled addition circuit with two input voltages is shown in Figure 12.12. Writing the node equation with v_o as reference,

$$\frac{v_o}{R_o} = \frac{e_1}{R_1} + \frac{e_2}{R_2} \tag{12.6}$$

where R_o is the output resistance of the circuit and is the parallel combination of R, R_1 and R_2 (also R_3, R_4, ... for additional input voltages). Thus

$$v_o = R_o\left(\frac{e_1}{R_1} + \frac{e_2}{R_2} + \cdots\right) \tag{12.7}$$

Observe that the input voltages are attenuated at the output by the respective resistance ratios of R_o/R_1, R_o/R_2, etc. Depending on the requirements of a particular application, the input voltages can be attenuated by equal or unequal amounts. The voltage magnitudes are in the inverse order of the series resistance values. Each of the series resistances should include the source resistance of their respective sources.

The resistance loading on any one source is equal to its series resistor, plus the parallel combination of the remaining resistors, including the resistance across which the output voltage is taken.

12.9   Transformer Coupling for Direct Series Addition

It is not necessary to present an extended discussion, but it is important not to disregard the possible use of transformers in addition circuits. As illustrated in Figure 12.13, the transformer output voltage e_1 is added directly in series with a second voltage e_2. This second voltage may be a d-c biasing voltage for the circuit which follows, or it may be a second signal voltage. Additional voltages are added in this same manner by using additional isolation transformers, with the various secondary windings connected in series. The transformers, with their secondaries isolated from their primaries, permit the direct series addition of voltages. Another advantage is the convenience of impedance matching—especially, matching to a low impedance source. The resistance R across the secondary

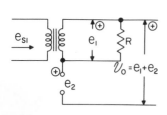

Fig. 12.13. Transformer coupling for addition of voltages.

of the transformer in Figure 12.13 provides the loading in addition to having a damping effect on oscillations that could exist because of winding capacitance. Still another advantage of series addition with transformers is the avoidance of the overloading of other sources, as could occur in parallel methods of addition. The chief disadvantages are cost, nonlinearity, and poor response at high frequencies.

12.10 Dual-Grid Control of Pentodes

For some control systems it is convenient, economical or essential to incorporate a pentode that is controlled with separate signals applied to two of the grids. In addition to applying a signal to the control grid, a second signal is applied in some instances to the screen grid or in other instances to the suppressor grid. In control problems this arrangement is usually used for the purpose of controlling the instants, or intervals, or time when the pentode shall be in a full conducting state. There are pentodes designed especially for this type of operation.

For normal operation, the suppressor grid of a pentode is returned directly to its cathode. If, however, the suppressor grid is returned to a small negative voltage, the g_m of the tube is greatly reduced. The tube can be made completely inoperative (no plate current) with a small negative voltage on the suppressor grid. All this, assuming the screen grid is at the fixed positive voltage recommended for the pentode.

The screen grid voltage also influences the g_m of the tube but much less than the suppressor grid voltage for corresponding voltage changes.

Some of the possible results attainable with dual-grid control are illustrated graphically. The two diagrams of Figure 12.14 illustrate a pentode amplifier with dual grid control. In (a), the first and third grids are controlled, while in (b), the first and second grids are controlled. Bias voltages are not indicated. The arrangement for this is influenced by the particular system

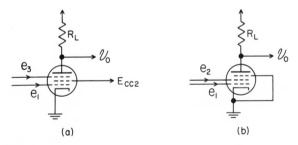

Fig. 12.14. Dual grid control of a pentode. Control voltages (a) at grids 1 and 3, (b) at grids 1 and 2.

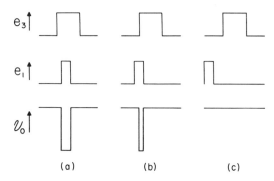

Fig. 12.15. (a) Coincidence. (b) Partial coincidence. (c) Anti-coincidence illustrations for dual-grid controlled pentode.

in which a particular dual grid controlled pentode is employed. The accompanying illustrations are represented without regard to a reference voltage level and relative voltage magnitudes.

The three sets of waveforms of Figure 12.15 are largely self explanatory. In (a), a positive-going pulse on the control grid occurs within the time interval during which a positive-going pulse on the suppressor grid has the pentode in a state to amplify the pulse on the control grid. In (b), only the last portion of the grid pulse is coincident with the suppressor pulse, while the waveforms of (c) illustrate anticoincidence. Although it is not advisable to indicate specific applications of the effects observed in Figure 12.15, there are two reasons for desiring this type of response. Either it is desired that the next circuit in a system becomes operative only for full (or partial) coincidence of the two pulses, or it is desired to detect a transition from full to partial coincidence for the purpose of initiating a correction signal in applications where coincidence represents the correct operation of a control system.

It is essential to have rectangular pulses, as illustrated in Figure 12.15, only in applications that demand this. Perhaps the problem is to distinguish between zero and 180 degrees phase relationship of two signals of identical frequencies, giving an output only if the two signals are in phase. Perhaps the problem is to amplify and pass a control-grid signal (much higher frequency than the suppressor-grid signal) within prescribed time limits. Perhaps the problem is to have a sweep voltage output, provided that the sweep voltage input coincides with the gate-opening pulse on the suppressor grid. Perhaps the problem is to establish a time delay that is influenced by either or both input signals. For this requirement the signal, or signals, may be taken from RC integrating input circuits where the time delays are easily adjusted with the time constants of the input circuits, or with the bias voltages associated with the input circuits.

Although the above problems are discussed with reference to Figure 12.14a, these problems are sometimes solved with screen-grid control rather than with suppressor-grid control. In some instances even triple-grid control is used, to satisfy triple coincidence requirements.

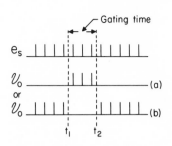

12.11   Gating

The possibility that certain control systems may require the gating of a signal was suggested in the discussions of the preceding section. The function of gating is illustrated

Fig. 12.16. Illustration of signal gating. (a) The gate is open during gating time. (b) The gate is closed during gating time.

in Figure 12.16, where it is indicated that the gate is opened to pass the signal or the gate is closed to block the signal for a prescribed time interval from time t_1 to time t_2. True, the signal is blocked in either case. In (a) of Figure 12.16, the signal is blocked from appearing at the output *external* to the time interval from t_1 to t_2, while in (b) the signal is blocked during the time interval from t_1 to t_2. Nevertheless, there are applications where it is required to pass a signal during a significant time interval that may or may not be periodically repetitive. In other applications, it may be required to block the signal during significant time intervals. Usually, the gate is initiated at a well defined instant of time. Sometimes the gate is terminated at a well defined instant of time also, although this is frequently not a rigid requirement. In any case, the permissible tolerances of the gating time are influenced by the particular application in which gating action is required.

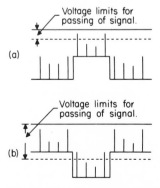

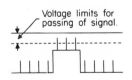

Fig. 12.17. Gating a signal with a pedestal.

Fig. 12.18. (a) Selecting large signals only. (b) Blocking small signals only.

The illustrations of Figure 12.16 show signal pulses superimposed on continuous and constant reference voltages for both the source and the output. Electronic circuits with which this is possible are included in the next section. In many instances, the source signal is superimposed on a voltage pedestal to permit the gating action. The illustration of Figure 12.17 shows three pulses of a signal on a pedestal. These three pulses are within the voltage limits for passing the signal. The gating time is represented by the time duration of the pedestal.

A third illustration for a gating action is shown in Figure 12.18. The problem as indicated here is to select the large signals only, as in (a), or to block the small signals during a gating time interval, as in (b).

It is important to emphasize that a signal is not necessarily of the pulse type as used in these illustrations. Pulses are convenient for the representation of gating action.

12.12   Gating Circuits

The two types of gating circuits of this section, Figures 12.19 and 12.20, are samples only to illustrate the principle of gating. One of these circuits illustrates amplifier gating and the other illustrates diode gating. These are the two general types of gating; that is, a gated output is obtained by either the blocking and unblocking of an amplifier or by clipping with diodes. The dual-grid control of a pentode must be included, of course, as a frequently preferred method of amplifier gating.

The two circuits of this section suggest that gating circuits are not necessarily new and special types of circuits. They are, more likely, old familiar circuits used for the particular function of gating.

The circuit of Figure 12.19a is an $R_L R_K$ amplifier. Here the signal voltage

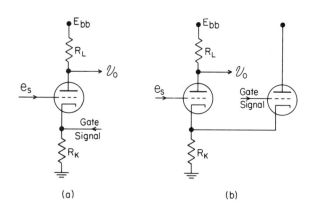

Fig. 12.19. Gating with $R_L R_K$ amplifier.

e_s is gated at the output v_o by applying a gate voltage at the cathode as indicated. A positive gate voltage of sufficient magnitude will drive the grid-cathode voltage below the cutoff voltage, thereby causing the output voltage to have a constant value equal to the d-c plate supply voltage for the time interval that the plate current is blocked. Circuit (b) of this figure shows a common method of transferring the gate signal through another amplifier that is

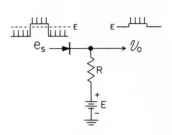

Fig. 12.20. Diode gating circuit.

cathode-coupled to the gated amplifier. The type of gate signal waveform is dependent on the requirements of the particular application. Some possible sources for gate voltages are discussed in the next section.

A diode type of gating circuit is shown in Figure 12.20. Here the signal is placed on a pedestal during the required time of gating. A positive pedestal is shown on the illustration. A negative pedestal could be represented as well. The diode clipping circuit will pass the signal to the output for time intervals when the input voltage is greater than the reference voltage E.

12.13   Gate Voltage Generators and Control

The existence of a gating circuit in an electronic control system suggests the need of additional circuitry, just to control the response of the gating circuit. The two circuits of the preceding section, as well as the discussion of Section 12.11, oversimplify the problem of gating a signal. Extensive circuitry is sometimes required.

Consider a set of hypothetical applications where the gating must be accomplished with triggered rectangular pulses of gate voltage. It is simple enough to recall familiar types of circuits that will generate rectangular pulses. The pulse generator, however, cannot be of the free-running type. It must be triggered in order to obtain the correct timing of the gate pulse, in accordance with the demands of the hypothetical application. The necessity of obtaining trigger pulses to operate the pulse generator (monostable multivibrator, bistable multivibrator, Schmitt trigger circuit, thyratron triggered circuit and others), along with the various restrictions placed on the gate voltage waveform itself, can add a number of other problems that are solved only with additional circuitry. Some of the reasons for the requirement of additional circuitry are now discussed in the following itemized paragraphs.

(a) The time duration, initiation and termination of the required gate-voltage pulse can be controlled with the design and triggering of the pulse generator. The output of the pulse generator, however, may not have the desired d-c level and magnitude of pulse. Additional circuitry is then required to restore the d-c level, and perhaps limiters to reduce the pulse magnitude to the required value. In addition it may be necessary to remove disturbing undershoots and overshoots that could exist on the output of the pulse generator.

(b) If the application requires a gate voltage of fixed time duration then perhaps a monostable, multivibrator type of circuit is satisfactory as the pulse generator. In this case, only one trigger pulse is needed to initiate the gate voltage pulse. On the other hand, there are applications that require a bistable, multivibrator type of circuit in order to provide control, with a second trigger pulse, to terminate the gate voltage pulse. The point being emphasized here is that the application dictates the method of gating to a large degree. In some instances there is a choice of methods but the choice is certainly not independent of the application. Consequently, if trigger pulses are needed, then these trigger pulses must be generated, and generated at correct instants of time.

(c) The trigger pulses must be derived from existing signals in the system. To convert an existing signal to a trigger pulse may require the use of over-driven amplifiers, differentiating circuits, clippers, limiters, or whatever is necessary to obtain the conversion. Perhaps the timing of a trigger pulse is dependent on more than one existing signal of the system. This would require still more extensive circuitry.

12.14   Recovery Time of a Circuit

The practical problems of triggering, gating, synchronizing, pulse generation, generation of sweep voltages and other types of nonlinear circuit functions often include the problem of getting a circuit to return, or recover to its original or desired state. The circuit must recover in order that the trigger pulse, or the gate voltage, or the sweep voltage, or the synchronizing pulses, or whatever nonlinear response is required, can be consistently repeated within prescribed time intervals.

In this and the next two sections, the problem of recovery is discussed with reference to circuits containing RC coupling. With this type of coupling the capacitor has a certain initial voltage when the desired pulse or voltage waveform is initiated. Immediately after the desired portion of a voltage waveform is terminated, the capacitor must recover to the initial voltage before the desired portion of the waveform can be repeated.

Recalling the requirements for the generation of a sweep voltage provides one good example to illustrate the problem of recovery. When a sweep voltage is terminated, the capacitor voltage of an RC circuit must recover to its initial voltage at the beginning of the sweep just completed. Otherwise, the next sweep will not correspond to the preceding one and, under steady state operation, the magnitude of the sweeps will be too small.

The generation of a sweep voltage is not the only example; there are many others. To understand the general methods available for reducing recovery time, it is not advisable to be too concerned with practical types of circuits for the generation of particular waveforms. In any given practical circuit, involving RC coupling, there are essentially only two things that can be done to reduce the recovery time. One is to reduce the time constant of the circuits during the recovery time and the other is to insert an extra voltage in the circuit that will have the effect of causing the capacitor voltage to overshoot its mark. This overshoot must not be permitted to exist, however. Clipping or limiting circuits can prevent the overshoots.

In any practical circuit, the small time constant for the recovery time is inherent within the design of the circuit. There is no need for any "fancy" modifications of the circuit, provided the allowable recovery time is not too short. This also precludes the possibility of a high repetition rate.

The next section, Section 12.15, includes a discussion on the use of diodes for decreasing the time constant of a circuit. The following section, Section 12.16, discusses the use of cathode followers for decreasing the recovery time of a circuit. Finally, Section 12.17 indicates the use of diodes to prevent overshoots of the capacitor voltage when this method is employed to decrease the recovery time.

12.15   Reducing Recovery Time by Decreasing the Circuit Time Constant with Diodes

One of the reasons for using diodes in certain practical circuits is to improve the required fast response of a circuit by reducing the recovery time. As stated in the preceding section, the recovery time for a circuit with RC coupling is decreased by either of two general methods: decreasing the RC time constant, or having an applied voltage that will tend to cause the capacitor voltage to overshoot the required level of recovery.

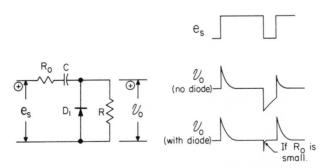

Fig. 12.21. The diode decreases recovery time.

The circuit of Figure 12.21 is a familiar circuit, from Chapters 3 and 4, so there is no need to give a detailed analysis of this or any other RC circuit with diodes that could be shown here. The circuit and the voltage waveforms of Figure 12.21 are shown to illustrate a situation where the positive peaks are the required portion of the output voltage when the input has negative pulses of comparatively short time duration. Everything about these positive peaks, including their magnitudes, is important. The illustration shows that the diode permits the positive peaks to have the maximum magnitude. In the absence of the diode the time constant of the circuit may be too large to permit the capacitor voltage to recover to the lower voltage of the negative input pulse before the next positive pulse arrives. Consequently, the magnitude of the output positive peak is too small. Imagine the difficulties that could exist if all negative pulses are not of the same time duration, thereby resulting in different magnitudes of output positive peaks in the absence of the restoring diode. Without the diode, perhaps the difficulty could be removed by adding amplifiers, clippers, or whatever is needed to obtain the required positive spike. The importance of the diode in the circuit is apparent.

Still referring to the same circuit, Figure 12.21, the output voltage is shown with the diode, assuming that the resistance of the source is zero. Since this does not hold true in practice, the negative peaks are actually highly attenuated if the diode forward resistance is much less than the source resistance. This does not mean that the diode is included in the circuit for the sole purpose of removing the negative peaks from the output. True, in some instances the negative spikes are harmful and must be removed, but in other instances their presence is not harmful. Yet, the diode is still required for the primary purpose of decreasing the recovery time in applications that require this to be done.

The absolute necessity for the diode D_1 in a circuit, such as that in Figure 12.22, is readily recognized. Assuming that the capacitor voltage is zero just before a particular positive pulse, then only a single positive spike can appear at the output. By inserting the diode D_1, the capacitor voltage can recover to the lower limit (zero volts in the illustration) of the input voltage. Consequently, the positive spikes are repetitive at the output.

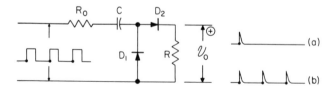

Fig. 12.22. Diode D_1 permits capacitor voltage to recover to lower limit of the input voltage. A single pulse out (a) if D_1 is omitted (assuming ideal diodes). Repeated pulses (b) if D_1 is in the circuit.

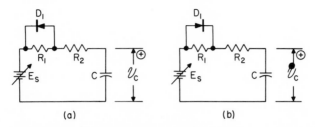

Fig. 12.23. The diode permits the capacitor voltage to follow (a) decreasing signals more closely than increasing signals, or (b) increasing signals more closely than decreasing signals.

The two circuits of Figure 12.23 give another illustration for controlling the recovery time of an RC circuit with diodes. In these circuits, the source voltage is shown as a variable d-c voltage. In circuit (a) the diode permits the capacitor voltage to follow the source voltage more closely for decreasing magnitudes than for increasing magnitudes. The inverse is true for circuit (b).

Although this section is primarily concerned with the problem of decreasing the time constant of a circuit with diodes, it must be understood that there are applications that require the inverse to be true. Remember, there are applications (past, present or future) for "anything that can be made to happen," almost without reservations. It could be a requirement, for example, in circuit (a) of Figure 12.23 that the circuit shall respond more slowly to increasing signals than to decreasing signals. The inverse is true for circuit (b). In other words, the requirement can be the inverse as well.

12.16 Reducing Recovery Time With a Cathode Follower

The partial block diagram representations of Figure 12.24 illustrate a method of reducing an RC-circuit time constant by using a cathode follower. The first diagram (a) shows two unidentified circuits that are capacitance coupled. The second diagram (b) shows a cathode follower inserted in the coupling circuit. Effectively, the RC time constant of the circuit is now changed by the replacement of the output resistance R_o of the driving circuit with the output resistance of the cathode follower. This is taking advantage of the low output resistance property of a cathode follower, for the purpose of reducing an RC time constant. For the problem under discussion, a reduced time constant for the recovery time of a circuit is of particular concern.

To illustrate one possible application, the two unidentified circuits could be the two halves of an astable multivibrator where difficulty with recovery is encountered for unsymmetrical operation of the multivibrator; that is, when one half of the multivibrator is off much longer than the other half

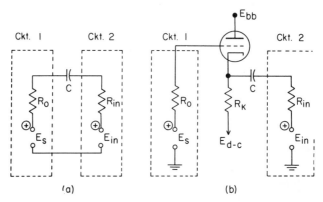

Fig. 12.24. Decreasing recovery time with a cathode follower when R_o of the source is greater than the output resistance of a cathode follower.

of the circuit. The problem of recovery is especially encountered with the capacitor that is coupled from the plate of the short-time *off* tube to the grid of the short-time *on* tube. Unfortunately, this capacitor is necessarily in the coupling circuit having the larger time constant and is very likely the larger of the two capacitors. The recovery time constant is $C(R_L + r_c)$ where R_L is the plate circuit resistor of the *off* tube and r_c is the grid-cathode resistance of the *on* tube. The output resistance R_o (see Figure 12.24) of the short-time *off* tube is R_L, the parameter chiefly responsible for a time constant too large for rapid recovery. Inserting a cathode follower, as indicated in Figure 12.24b, can improve this situation. Note that the cathode resistor is returned to a d-c biasing voltage which is probably necessary to obtain the proper operating range of the cathode follower. The cathode follower should operate as a linear circuit as nearly as possible. If its voltage gain is nearly unity, connecting one terminal of the capacitor to the cathode of the cathode follower is essentially the same as a connection to the output terminal *a* of the driving circuit.

The representations in Figure 12.24 can be misleading with regard to the notations R_o and R_{in}. These are not singular quantities in circuits that permit a circuit modification effective during recovery time only. Either or both may have dual values, one set of values during the time of the desired portion of a waveform and another set of values during the recovery time.

12.17 Reducing Recovery Time with an Excess Voltage and a Diode

The illustration of Figure 12.25 shows the basic method of reducing the recovery time of an RC circuit by applying a voltage in excess of that required of the capacitor voltage for complete recovery. A diode plays a significant role to prevent an overshoot of the capacitor voltage.

For the purpose of this discussion, the input voltage is represented as rectangular pulses. The capacitor voltage is required to recover to the upper value of E_2. The lower voltage to which the capacitor voltage goes is of no concern here; this voltage change depends on the particular circuit and its application. The subscript 2 on the resistors designate the resistances that apply during the recovery time. The

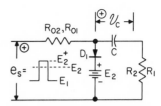

Fig. 12.25. Reducing recovery time with an overshoot, E_2^+, and a diode D_1.

voltage E_2^+ is in excess of the required limiting voltage E_2. This causes the capacitor voltage to rise more rapidly than it would without the excess voltage. In addition, the diode becomes conducting after a short time delay in the presence of R_{o2}. With the diode *on* and an assumed zero resistance in the diode branch of the circuit, the source effectively has zero resistance and the required limiting voltage of E_2. Thus the excess voltage causes the capacitor voltage to rise more rapidly before the diode goes on, and the circuit time constant decreases after the diode goes on. This latter effect is an advantage in the event the capacitor voltage has not yet completely recovered to E_2 when the diode goes on.

PROBLEMS

12.1 For the bistable thyratron circuit of Figure 12.2, $C = 0.01$ μfd., $R_{K1} = R_{K2} = 5$ K, the plate supply voltage is 200 volts, the thyratrons have a plate-cathode voltage of 20 volts when conducting, and the circuit is triggered at a rate of 100 pulses per second. Plot the two cathode voltages and the capacitor voltage, indicating all significant quantities.

12.2 Refer to the circuit of Figure 12.2, insert a plate load resistor of 5 K in each tube circuit. Remove the existing capacitor and insert a capacitance of 0.005 μfd., connected from plate-to-plate. Return the cathodes directly to ground. A conducting tube voltage is 10 volts and the plate-supply voltage is 200 volts. Plot each plate voltage and the capacitor voltage for a triggering rate of 100 pulses per second.

12.3 The rotating electronic switch of Figure 12.4 requires positive trigger pulses that are greater than 10 volts but less than 30 volts. The pulses must have a minimum time duration of 20 μs. A symmetrical square wave of source voltage with amplitude and period of 100 volts and 200 μs., respectively, is available. Design a trigger circuit to provide the required trigger pulses.

12.4 Describe the triggering behavior of a bistable multivibrator when common anode triggering is used.

12.5 Describe the triggering behavior of a bistable multivibrator with common cathode triggering.

12.6 A bistable circuit is tested in the laboratory and it is found to be truly bistable with manual triggering. Automatic plate triggering, as in Figure 12.8, is now attempted but the circuit will not trigger. State some possible reasons for this difficulty in getting the circuit to trigger.

12.7 A bistable circuit is used to measure the time interval, or the phase relationship, between two trigger pulses applied separately to the two tubes. Either plate current has the limiting values of zero and ten milliamperes. A d-c meter in one of the plate circuits gives a reading of four milliamperes.
   (a)   What is the phase relationship of the two trigger sources?
   (b)   What are the difficulties of interpretation, and how are these avoided, if it is desired to mark the meter to read degrees correctly, through the complete 360° range?

12.8 For the resistance summing circuit of Figure 12.12, $R_1 = R_2 = 5$ K, $e_1 = e_2 = 10$-volt positive pulses. Determine the magnitude of the output pulse if
   (a) $R = 1$ K
   (b) $R = 100$ K

12.9 For the RC summing circuit of Figure 12.11, $C = 0.1$ μfd., $R = 1$ Meg, the voltage e is a d-c voltage of 40 volts, and e_s is a positive 10-volt, 50 μs pulse. Plot the output voltage v_o.

13

Triggering,
Gating,
Synchronizing
Part II, Semiconductor Devices

13.1 General Discussion

This chapter is devoted to the problems of triggering, gating, or synchronizing certain circuits that contain semiconductor devices. As such, attention is directed to monostable, astable and bistable circuits, to some basic types of logic circuitry, and to modes of operation for unijunction transistor circuits as well as to tunnel diode circuits.

As stated for the preceding chapter, the general problem is concerned with the techniques and problems for controlling the mode of operation of circuits that are required to have more than one operating state.

13.2 Possible Places to Insert Trigger Pulses in a Bistable Circuit

The bistable circuit of Figure 13.1 is shown merely to illustrate the circuit junctions at which trigger pulses can be inserted to cause the circuit to change its state. These circuit junctions are labeled A, B_1 and B_2, C_1

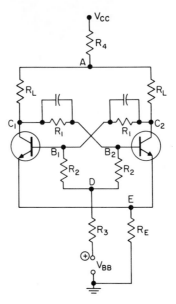

Fig. 13.1. A bistable circuit, with an excess of components, to illustrate points where trigger pulses can be inserted.

and C_2, D and E. Portions of the circuit can be omitted depending on the place chosen for triggering.

The subscripts '1' and '2' suggest the need for triggering at both of these junctions. For example, a trigger pulse applied directly to the base, or the collector, of transistor 1 is not sufficient. A trigger pulse must also be applied at the base, or the collector, of transistor 2. The trigger pulses applied directly to the base terminals, or directly to the collector terminals, can be from the same trigger source or from two separate trigger sources. It is necessary, however, to maintain isolation between the two base terminals and between the two collector terminals. Trigger pulses inserted at A, D or E are necessarily from a single trigger source.

If the trigger pulses are from a single source, applied at any of the indicated junctions, the circuit is usually regarded as a frequency divider. In computer language it is a binary. The symmetrical square pulses at the collectors, or the bases, have a frequency that is one-half the frequency of the trigger pulses.

Sometimes, however, it is required to have the circuit set to a particular state by one trigger source and then reset by a second trigger source. For this requirement, the trigger pulses must be inserted at the base junctions or at the collector junctions. Used in this way, the circuit stores information for a time interval depending on the time lapse between the trigger pulses from the two sources. This time interval is sometimes regarded as a gating time for making measurements or for observing certain phenomena.

Base triggering and collector triggering are two of the most common methods of triggering. The next two sections are devoted to triggering at the base terminals. Section 13.5 is devoted to triggering at the collector terminals.

13.3 Triggering at the Base Terminals (One Trigger Source)

Circuit techniques are now illustrated for triggering a bistable circuit at the base terminals from a single trigger source. Triggering from a single source is sometimes identified as symmetrical triggering.

The fixed-bias bistable circuit of Figure 13.2 has the resistors R_3 and R_4 connected from base-to-base of the two *n-p-n* transistors. The circuit arrangement is identical with *p-n-p* transistors in the circuit. The time constants of the significant circuits involving the capacitor, C, are sufficiently small to produce positive and negative voltage spikes at the junction of R_3 and R_4, as indicated on the figure.

To examine the triggering behavior of the bistable circuit, with *n-p-n* transistors, initially assume that transistor 1 is *off* and transistor 2 is *on* and in saturation. The positive voltage spikes (negative spikes for *p-n-p*'s) are the pulses that will trigger the circuit.

A positive pulse at base B_1, assuming this transistor is initially *off*, will

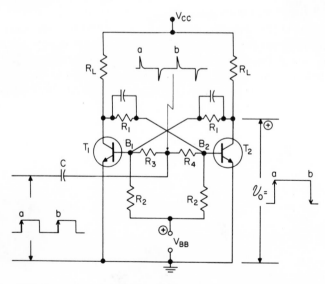

Fig. 13.2. Base triggering from a single source, with resistance coupling R_3 and R_4.

bring this transistor into the active region, lowering its collector voltage. The circuit becomes regenerative and transistor 1 goes *on* and the transistor 2 goes *off*. The negative step, which is the next step at the trigger source, could reset the circuit if the magnitude of the source pulses is too great. Assuming this undesirable reset did not occur, then the next positive voltage spike will retrigger the circuit to the initial state. The frequency of the output voltage is one half the frequency of the trigger source voltage.

When the triggering circuit consists of resistance coupling, the resistances R_3 and R_4 have equal magnitudes in ohms. The presence of these resistors has the effect of attenuating the step voltages. The attenuation is greater at the base of the *on* transistor than at the base of the *off* transistor. This is true since the input resistance of the *on* transistor, even through the active region, is small, while the reverse input resistance of the *off* transistor is large. It would be an advantage if each of the two resistors could be two-valued, alternately small and large as the circuit is triggered from one state to the other. The resistance to the transistor on which the trigger pulse is initially effective should be small. A diode can approximate this two-valued property.

Two diode-coupled triggering circuits are shown in Figure 13.3. The diodes replace the resistors R_3 and R_4. The resistance R_5 can be omitted if the reverse resistance of the diodes will permit a desired recovery time in the presence of a capacitance coupling to the trigger source. The two circuits, with diodes D_1 and D_2 and resistance R_5, are equally applicable to *n-p-n* and *p-n-p* transistors. With circuit (a), only negative pulses can appear at the bases B_1 and B_2. With *n-p-n* transistors, the *on* transistor is initially affected by the negative pulses to cause the transition. For *p-n-p* transistors, the *off* transistor is initially affected. The inverse conditions are true for circuit (b), where the positive pulses initiate the triggering.

The diode D_3, shown as a possibility in Figure 13.3, can be used in place of the resistance R_5 to decrease the recovery time of the trigger-driving

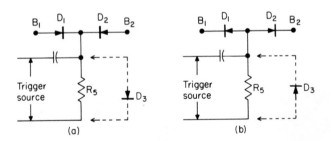

Fig. 13.3. Diodes replace R_3 and R_4 in Figure 13.3. (a) For negative triggering only. (b) For positive triggering only. See text for use of diode D_3.

circuit to a minimum. The presence of this diode, however, restricts the use of the two trigger circuits to one type of transistor. Circuit (a) is then applicable to only *p-n-p* transistors, and circuit (b) is applicable to *n-p-n* transistors only. The diode D_3, or a small value of R_5, could prevent the opposite type of transistor from entering the active region and continuing on into saturation. Why? Because with this circuit (a), using diode D_3, the base-to-emitter voltage cannot be appreciably positive and this could prevent an *n-p-n* transistor from going to the saturated *on* state. With circuit (b), the base-to-emitter voltage cannot be negative and this could prevent a *p-n-p* transistor from going to the saturated *on* state.

13.4   Triggering at the Base Terminals (Two Trigger Sources)

The two triggering circuits of Figure 13.4 illustrate one method of triggering a bistable circuit when two trigger source voltages are required. The terminals B_1 and B_2 identify the two base terminals as previously indicated in Figure 13.2.

The first triggering circuit (a) suggests, by the orientation of the diodes, that the *negative* voltage spikes are effective in triggering the bistable circuit. The second circuit (b) suggests, by the orientation of the diodes, that the *positive* voltage spikes are effective in triggering the circuit. (Although the present discussion has reference to the triggering of bistable circuits, some of these triggering techniques are applicable to other switching circuits as well). The two circuits of Figure 13.4 are equally applicable to *n-p-n* and *p-n-p* transistorized bistable circuits. Recall the discussion in the closing paragraph of the preceding section.

Observe that the circuits of Figure 13.4 are not too much different than the triggering circuits represented in the preceding section. The resistors R_3 and R_4 are positioned in the circuit exactly as in Figure 13.2. Here, the two diodes are added and the junction of the two resistors is returned to common ground. One important problem with two trigger sources is the necessity of isolating the two trigger sources. This is required to permit

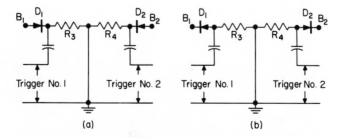

Fig. 13.4. Triggering at base terminals using two trigger sources.

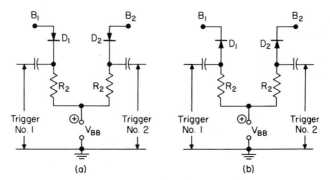

Fig. 13.5. Two-source base triggering by inserting diodes in series with resistors R_2 in Fig. 13.2. (a) For *n-p-n*'s only. (b) For *p-n-p*'s only.

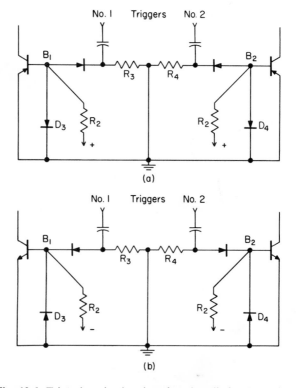

Fig. 13.6. Triggering circuit using clamping diodes D_3 and D_4.

each trigger source to perform its function independently and without undue loading from the other source. The grounded junction completely isolates the two trigger sources.

Rather than adding the resistors R_3 and R_4, it is possible to obtain satisfactory triggering with the diodes in series with the two existing resistors, identified as R_2 in the bistable circuit in Figure 13.2. Such an arrangement is illustrated by the two circuits in Figure 13.5. Normally, the first circuit (a) is for use with n-p-n transistors only while the second circuit (b) is for use with p-n-p transistors only. Inverting the diodes, or using either circuit for the opposite type of transistors, would prevent the bias voltage V_{BB} from performing its function to hold an *off* transitor firmly *off*.

Another method for triggering at the base terminals is illustrated by the two circuits of Figure 13.6. These two circuits are very similar to the two circuits of Figure 13.4, except for the addition of the diodes D_3 and D_4. Circuit (a) is for use with *n-p-n* transistors only. Circuit (b) is for use with *p-n-p* transistors only. The complete bistable circuit, except for the existing resistors R_2, is not shown for these two triggering circuits. The diodes D_3 and D_4 serve the function of clamping the base voltage of an *off* transistor to zero. Negative trigger pulses, with circuit (a), are effective in triggering the bistable circuit using p-n-p transistors. Positive trigger pulses, with circuit (b), are effective in triggering the bistable circuit that uses n-p-n transistors.

13.5 Triggering at the Collector Terminals

The circuits in Figure 13.7 illustrate a method for the triggering of a bistable circuit by applying the trigger pulses at the collector terminals. The bistable circuit is self-biased through common-emitter resistance R_E. The circuit is represented with n-p-n transistors. Two diodes are connected back-to-back from the collector of one transistor to the collector of the other transistor. The diodes are oriented so that negative pulses can be effective in triggering the n-p-n transistor circuit. With p-n-p transistors, the diodes should be inverted to allow positive pulses to trigger the circuit.

The diagram in Figure 13.7b shows the triggering circuit only. The d-c biasing voltage of this circuit may, or may not be required. It is not necessary, if R is much larger than R_L. The resistance R has the effect of lowering the collector voltage of the *off* transistor. This effect is negligible if R is large. However, a larger value of R has the effect of increasing the recovery time of the triggering circuit. It may be necessary, therefore, to select a value of R that is sufficiently small to require the use of the d-c biasing voltage E. This d-c voltage could be equal to or slightly less than V_{CC} in magnitude.

On examining the triggering operation of the bistable circuit, the negative trigger pulses are transferred to the collector of the *off* transistor by way

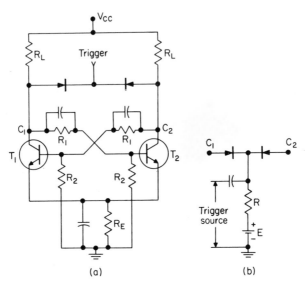

Fig. 13.7. Triggering at the collector terminals. (a) The general circuit. (b) The triggering circuit.

of the diode connected to this collector. This negative pulse at the collector of the *off* transistor is transmitted to the base of the *on* transistor. The triggering and regenerative actions are then possible. The commutating capacitors are essential for two important reasons. First, the coupling resistance R_1, without the capacitor, will have the effect of attenuating the possible step in voltage at the base. Secondly, the input capacitance of the *on* transistor will prevent a step in voltage at the base, if the commutating capacitor is not present. These effects must be avoided if the transition time is to be kept at a minimum.

It is not necessary, of course, for the trigger pulse to switch an *on* transistor completely *off*. The first requirement is to get both transistors into the active region so the circuit can become regenerative and thereby become self-triggering. However, a trigger pulse that is larger than the minimum pulse required will assist in decreasing the transition time. Recall the discussions in the early sections of Chapter 8 where it is explained that large signals will decrease the transition time of a transistor switching circuit.

13.6 Triggering of Monostable Circuits

The monostable transistor circuit of Figure 11.19 suggested that a positive trigger pulse be inserted at the base of the normally *off* n-p-n transistor. It is also possible to trigger this monostable circuit by inserting negative trigger pulses at the collector of the normally *off* transistor.

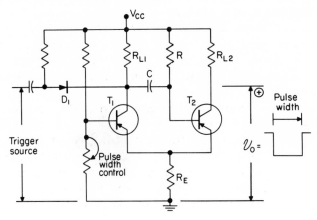

Fig. 13.8. Collector triggering of a monostable circuit.

A complete monostable circuit, with *p-n-p* transistors and with collector triggering, is shown in Figure 13.8. This circuit shows an adjustable voltage divider as the voltage and current biasing arrangement for the normally *off* transistor. The adjustable voltage is needed to help control the pulse width of the output pulse. The adjustable current is needed to control the degree at which the *off* transistor will go *on*. A positive pulse applied at the collector of the normally *off* transistor will initiate the output square pulse. The positive trigger pulse is transmitted to the base of transistor 2, through capacitor *C*, to complete the transition.

13.7 Decreasing On to Off Transition by Preventing Saturation

When a transistor is in saturation, its collector junction is forward biased. As a result, the charge density of minority carriers in the base region is greater than it would be for a nonsaturated transistor. This increase in charge density is held to a low value in the design and manufacture of modern switching transistors and only in very fast switching requirements is it a significant factor to consider.

If it is desired to avoid switching delays because of saturation, then some circuitry technique must be used to prevent the collector junction from becoming forward biased. One method of accomplishing this is illustrated in Figure 13.9. This incomplete circuit can be regarded, for this discussion, as a part of the monostable circuit of Figure

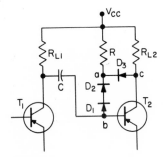

Fig. 13.9. One method of preventing saturation of an *on* transistor.

13.8, except for the addition of the three diodes. Observing the three junctions identified as *a*, *b*, and *c* we see that $v_{ca} = v_{cb} + v_{ba}$. The collector-base voltage v_{cb} is of particular interest. To avoid saturation, v_{cb} (for *p-n-p*) must not be positive. This will be true so long as v_{ba} is greater than v_{ca}. The purpose of the diodes is now obvious, since it is possible to select a set of diodes to make this condition satisfied. The three diodes should be inverted with *n-p-n* transistors.

Thinking of the circuit as the indicated part of the monostable circuit of Figure 13.8, observe that the capacitor is returned to the resistor *R* through the two diodes D_1 and D_2. The positive voltage step generated at the collector of transistor 1 is thereby transmitted directly to the base of transistor 2, and the diodes permit the circuit to function properly. An excellent treatment comparing saturated and nonsaturated transistors is found in a paper that is referenced at the bottom of this page.*

13.8   Synchronizing of Astable Transistor Circuits

The synchronizing of an astable circuit with triodes was discussed in Section 12.6. The techniques are similar for synchronizing astable circuits with transistors. One circuit method is shown in Figure 13.10. Notice that the trigger pulses are injected at a point D, which corresponds to one of the possible junctions recommended in the bistable circuit of Figure 13.1.

Since the astable circuit, Figure 13.10, is illustrated with *p-n-p* transistors, then negative trigger pulses are required to synchronize the circuit.

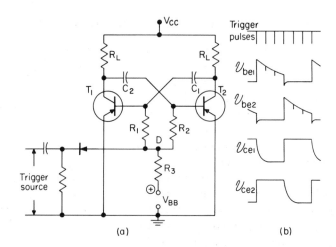

(a)   (b)

Fig. 13.10. Synchronizing an astable circuit.

---

*G. H. Goldstick, "Comparison of Saturated and Nonsaturated Switching Circuit Techniques," *IRE Transactions on Electronic Computers*, **EC-9**, Number 2 (June 1960) 161-175.

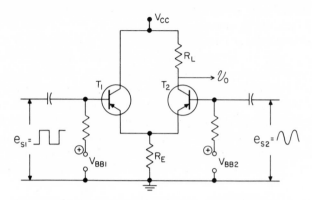

Fig. 13.11. A circuit that can serve as a gating circuit.

The voltage waveforms are shown in Figure 13.10b. Triggering is shown to occur on every third negative pulse. The frequency of the astable circuit is, therefore, one third the frequency of the synchronizing voltage. The natural frequency of the astable circuit, in this case, must be less than one third the frequency of the synchronizing voltage.

For best results, the quiescent value of base current should be sufficient to prevent saturation fallout.

The diode in the synchronizing circuit is not always necessary. The diode can be omitted if the *on* transistor is well into saturation, or the magnitude of the synchronizing source voltage is not so great as to cause the *on* transistor to amplify the positive (for *p-n-p*) base current pulses that occur with a positive voltage step at the source.

13.9 A Transistor Gating Circuit

The circuit of Figure 13.11 can serve as a gating circuit. That is, it is possible to cause a signal waveform at e_{s2} to appear, or not to appear, at the output v_o. Forcing the first transistor to be *on* with e_{s1} could hold the second transistor *off* and block e_{s2}. The second transistor and its circuit could then behave as a linear amplifier, with the first transistor *off*. This transistor gating circuit is very similar to the vacuum tube gating circuit described in Chapter 12. Refer to Figure 12.19.

13.10 About Logic Circuitry

To prepare for the logic circuitry that follows in the next few sections, a review of Chapter 1 and a review of techniques for adding voltages as presented in Chapter 12 is recommended.

The language of logic circuitry uses such identifying terms as AND, OR, NOT, NOR, and INHIBITOR.

The AND circuit has two or more input signals. There *is* an output only if *all* of these input signals are present. It is analogous to two or more switches connected in series.

The OR circuit also has two or more input signals. There *is* an output if any *one* of these input signals is present. It is analogous to two or more normally open switches connected in parallel.

The NOT circuit has one input signal. There *is* an output only if the input signal is *not* present. It is analogous to a normally closed switch.

The NOR circuit has two or more input signals. There is *not* an output if any one of the input signals is present. A clear distinction between OR and NOR circuits does not always exist. It is necessary to know the area of application and whether the output is a voltage or a current that is of primary interest.

The INHIBITOR circuit is a combination of an AND circuit and a NOT circuit. There can be an output in the presence of all of the AND signals provided the NOT signal is *not* present.

13.11   AND Circuits

A diode AND circuit was presented in Chapter 1, Figure 1.11. Other possible arrangments for AND circuits are presented in this section.

The two circuits of Figure 13.12 have two or more transistors in parallel. (These could be vacuum triodes as well.) The first circuit has direct-coupled input circuits. The second circuit has RC-coupled input circuits. For either circuit, the transistors are biased to a normally *on* state and are in a saturation state. (This is a significant fact regarding AND circuits in which the electronic switching devices are connected in parallel). A negative pulse at

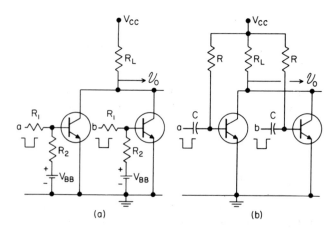

Fig. 13.12. Two or more transistors in parallel to form AND circuit.

the input of any one transistor, for either
circuit, can force that transistor to the *off*
state. The output voltage will remain near
zero, however, as long as any one of the
parallel transistors remains in saturation.
There is an output voltage only if all transistors are *off*. Consequently, all input signals (negative pulses for the represented
circuit) must be present to obtain an
output voltage.

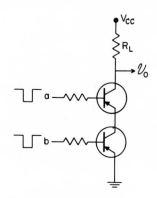

Fig. 13.13. AND circuit with two
transistors in series.

The circuit of Figure 13.13 has two
transistors in series. Both negative input
signals must be present to produce a change
at the output.

Rather than having several transistors
in parallel, or in series, it is possible to form an AND circuit with a single
transistor. Two circuit versions are shown in Figure 13.14. The first circuit
contains diodes while the second circuit does not. In either circuit, the transistor is saturated in the absence of any one negative signal with the *n-p-n*
transistor. The input circuits are designed to make this true. For the
diode circuit, Figure 13.14a, the off-biasing voltage V_1 is effective only if
all diodes are nonconducting. This can happen only if all negative input
signals are simultaneously present. For the proper operation of circuit (b),
the input circuit is carefully designed to cause the transistor to be in
saturation when all but one of the input signals are present, but to cause
the transistor to be *off* if all input signals are present. This requires a careful
selection of magnitudes for R_1, R_2, V_{BB} and the input signals.

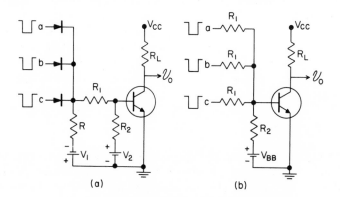

Fig. 13.14. Two AND circuits with one transistor.

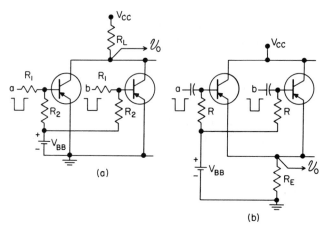

Fig. 13.15. Two or more transistors in parallel to form OR circuit. (a) Direct coupling. (b) RC coupling.

13.12 OR Circuits

One OR circuit, with diodes, was presented in Figure 1.9. Additional OR circuits are presented in this section.

The two circuits of Figure 13.15 have two or more transistors in parallel. The first circuit has direct-coupled input circuits and the second circuit has RC input circuits. For either circuit, the transistors are biased to a normal-ly *off* state. (This is a significant fact regarding OR circuits in which the electronic switching devices are connected in parallel.) The presence of any one of the input signals, in either circuit, will activate the circuit.

There could be some question as to whether circuit (a), a common-emitter configuration, is correctly identified as an OR circuit. In some applications, it may be desirable to identify it as a NOR circuit, since the output *voltage* is at a zero level when the circuit is activated by any one of the input signals. The area of application and the particular way in which the circuit is used will dictate the correct identifying name. The one important common characteristic of the circuit, OR or NOR, is that any one of the input signals will activate the circuit.

13.13 NOR Circuits

The transistor of Figure 13.16 is resistance coupled to two or more input signals. Three inputs are shown. The transistor is biased *off* in the ab-sence of all input signals. The direct-coupling network can be designed to cause the transistor to saturate in the presence of any one of the input signals. If the resulting zero level of output *voltage*, or the inverter action

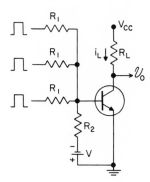
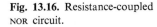
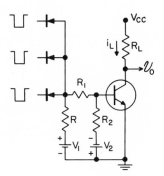

Fig. 13.16. Resistance-coupled NOR circuit.

Fig. 13.17. Diode OR input circuit.

of the circuit, is regarded as no output, then the circuit might be identified as a NOR circuit. If the current i_L is of primary interest, the circuit might be more properly identified as an OR circuit.

The inverse conditions, with regards to an output that could be a voltage or a current, is shown in Figure 13.17. The input circuit is a diode OR circuit. The diodes are normally nonconducting and the transistor is normally in saturation. The network that includes the three resistors and the two biasing voltages is selected to make these conditions true. The transistor is driven *off* in the presence of any one or more of the negative input signals. With i_L as the significant output quantity, the circuit is properly identified as a NOR circuit. With the voltage as the significant output quantity, disregarding the inverter action, the circuit could be properly identified as an OR circuit.

13.14 NOT **Circuits**

The possible NOT circuits with transistors are illustrated in Figure 13.18. Such circuits should not be definitely identified as NOT circuits unless the nature of the output, as required by a particular logic circuitry system, is defined. In other words, what *is* considered as an output and what *is not* regarded as an output? Is the output a voltage, primarily, or is the output a current? If a positive voltage pulse *is* an output, is a negative voltage pulse *not* an output? Is a positive (or negative) d-c voltage an output and a zero d-c voltage not an output? Or is it the steps that are generated in switching from one d-c level to another, that are of special interest as the outputs? Only the logic system as used in a particular area of application can provide the answers to these questions.

In circuit (a) of Figure 13.18, the circuit can be a NOT unit if V_{cc} *is* the

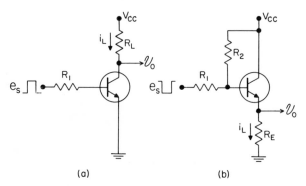

(a)   (b)

Fig. 13.18. Two possible NOT circuits.

output and zero voltage *is not* an output. Thus, there is an output in the absence of the input signal and there is not an output when the positive signal is present. The transistor is assumed to be *off* or in saturation as the two possible states. This circuit is also an inverter, and it is possible that the circuit may be identified as a NOT unit because of the inverter action.

Circuit (b) of Figure 13.18 is an emitter follower configuration. As such, it is not an inverter. Yet, the circuit could be a NOT circuit if V_{cc} and zero are the *yes* and *no* outputs, respectively. The transistor is normally biased to saturation. Thus, in the absence of a negative input signal the output is present. A negative signal can turn the transistor off and the output *is not* present, since the output is now zero (the defined *no* output).

The circuit of Figure 13.19 is another possibility for a NOT unit. It employs a saturable two-winding reactor with square-loop core material. For the represented voltage waveforms, the output voltage, or current, is either a positive pulse or nothing. In the absence of the positive input pulses for e_s, the e_1 pulses (assumed repetitively present) will eventually cause the core to be saturated, after which the output pulses are present and coincident with the pulses at e_1. Now, if the positive pulses at e_s are present and are not coincident with the positive pulses at e_1, then the output pulses will not be present. This happens because of the desaturating effects of the positive

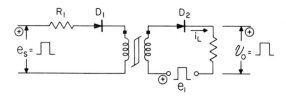

Fig. 13.19. A magnetic-coupled NOT circuit.

pulses at e_s. Notice the polarity marks on the windings and the orientation of the diodes. A detailed discussion of saturable reactors is presented in Chapter 15.

13.15 Volt Ampere Characteristic and D-C Load Lines for Unijunction Transistor

The properties of a unijunction transistor were described in Section 7.15 of Chapter 7. It is now appropriate to consider some of the uses of this device as an electronic switch. However, a study of the volt ampere characteristics is a prerequisite.

Figure 13.20 shows a basic circuit for a unijunction transistor. The circuit is drawn in a manner to emphasize diode properties and to identify v_E and i_E, the emitter voltage and current respectively. The emitter is returned to a d-c supply voltage V_a, through R_L. The base B_2 is returned to a d-c supply voltage through a resistance identified as R_1. This is an external R_1. It must not be confused with the internal resistance that was identified as R_1 in Figure 7.17b.

The emitter current vs emitter voltage characteristic is represented in Figure 13.21. Frequently, this characteristic is represented with the voltage as the dependent variable. It is shown, here, with the current as the dependent variable in order to demonstrate a more clear comparison with the corresponding characteristic for a tunnel diode (see Figure 7.6), and with the corresponding characteristic for a silicon controlled rectifier (see Figure 7.7.).

From the origin to point 3, on the unijunction characteristic, the emitter junction is reverse-biased. Beyond point 3, also identified as V_p, the transistor first exhibits the characteristic of a negative resistance, over the region of negative slopes.

Four d-c load lines are shown on the graph of Figure 13.21. The slope of

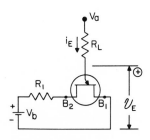

Fig. 13.20. Basic circuit for a unijunction transistor.

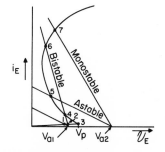

Fig. 13.21. Volt-ampere characteristic and d-c load lines for unijunction transistor.

these load lines is the negative inverse of R_L. Two of these load lines are for a selected value of V_a, identified as V_{a1}, that is less than V_p. One of these two load lines intersects the volt-ampere graph at only one point, point 1. The second line intersects the graph at three points, points 2, 4, and 6. Notice that point 4 is in the negative resistance region.

The second pair of load lines are for a selected value of V_a, identified as V_{a2}, that is greater than V_p. Both of these load lines intersect the graph at only one point. One of these load lines intersects in the negative resistance region, point 5. The other intersects in a positive resistance region, point 7.

The voltage V_p is a function of the V_b/R_1 ratio. Increasing this ratio will increase V_p, assuming this increase is within the rated values for the unijunction transistor. The increase of this current simply increases the reverse bias on the emitter junction.

Capacitive loading of the basic unijunction transistor circuit is of special interest. The possible conditions of operation are considered in the next section.

13.16   Capacitive Loading of Unijunction Transistor Circuit

The unijunction transistor circuit of Figure 13.22 has a capacitor connected from the emitter to the base B_1. Otherwise, the circuit is comparable to that of Figure 13.20 where V_b is equal to V_a.

The capacitive loaded circuit can be astable, monostable, or bistable depending on the position of the d-c load line on the transistor characteristic. Refer again to the load lines of Figure 13.21. The circuit is monostable if the load line corresponds to the one that intersects at point 7. The circuit is astable if the load line corresponds to the one that intersects at point 5, in the negative resistance region. The circuit is bistable if the load line corresponds to the one that intersects at points 2, 4, and 6.

Consider the operating loop for the monostable mode of operation. Assume the capacitor voltage is initially near zero. The capacitor voltage, which is also the emitter voltage, rises along the reverse-emitter-voltage region with a time constant of $R_L C$. At V_p the transistor becomes unstable (enters the negative resistance region) but the capacitor voltage cannot change instantly. The next operating point on the graph is immediately in the positive resistance region, beyond point 7 and at a point where the emitter voltage is identical

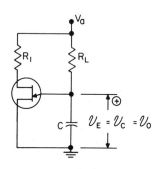

Fig. 13.22. Capacitive loading of unijunction transistor.

to V_p. The quiescent and stable operating point is at point 7. The circuit must be triggered to repeat this cycle. A negative trigger pulse at the emitter will accomplish the trigger action. This forces the transistor out of the positive resistance region by way of point 6. The operating point drops immediately to the reverse-emitter-voltage region when the circuit becomes unstable, and the operating loop is complete.

The operating loop is very similar for the astable mode of operation. Since a quiescent stable point does not exist, however, the circuit is self-triggering and free-running. The output voltage is a sawtooth waveform.

The bistable mode of operation has two stable states. Consequently, the circuit must be triggered in both directions. The external capacitance is not required for bistable operation. The transition time is faster without it.

13.17 Monostable, Astable, and Bistable Modes of Operation for a Tunnel Diode Circuit

The properties of a tunnel diode were described in Chapter 7. Recall the volt-ampere characteristic of Figure 7.6. The characteristics of a tunnel diode has a threshold of current I_p, rather than a threshold of voltage as in the unijunction transistor. Consequently, it is necessary to have an inductance in series with the diode rather than a capacitor in parallel, if the circuit is to exhibit a monostable, astable, or a bistable mode of operation. A series resistance is also required to help establish the position of a d-c load line on the volt-ampere graph. The conditions that must be satisfied are similar to those described for unijunction transistors in the preceding section.

The inductive circuit is monostable if the d-c load line intersects the graph at only one point and in a positive resistance region, preferably in the region of low diode voltage. The circuit is astable if the d-c load line intersects the graph at only one point and in the negative resistance region.

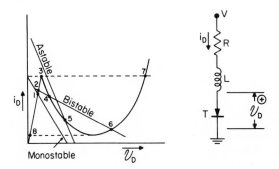

Fig. 13.23. Volt-ampere characteristic and d-c load lines for tunnel diode circuit.

The circuit is bistable if the d-c load line intersects the graph at three points, two of which are in the two positive resistance regions. The other point of intersection is in the negative resistance region. The three representative load lines are shown in Figure 13.23.

The operating paths are current controlled for the tunnel diode circuit. The unijunction transistor required voltage control. Refer to Figure 13.23 and let us examine the operating path that could exist for the monostable mode of operation. Any attempt, by triggering, to force the current beyond the threshold value will make the circuit unstable. The operating point then moves from point 3 to point 7. The current decays to the valley point where the circuit is again unstable and the operating point changes to point 8. The current then increases to the stable point, point 1.

PROBLEMS

13.1 Describe the triggering behavior for the bistable circuit of Figure 13.1 when trigger pulses are applied at point A, and when R_E and R_3 are reduced to zero.

13.2 Describe the triggering behavior for the bistable circuit of Figure 13.1 when trigger pulses are applied at
   (a) Point D with R_E and R_4 reduced to zero.
   (b) Point E with R_4, R_3 and V_{BB} equal to zero.

13.3 For the triggering circuits of Figure 13.3, what are the advantages and disadvantages of a large value for R_5? What are the advantages and disadvantages of making R_5 small?

13.4 Four bistable circuits are available. It is desired to connect these bistable circuits in such a way that an output negative pulse is initiated, repeatedly, on a specified number of trigger input pulses. It may be necessary to use some feedback resets. Assuming it is not always necessary to use all four bistable circuits, design a plan of connections for a required count of
   (a) 8
   (b) 16
   (c) 15
   (d) 10.

13.5 Refer to the resistance coupled AND circuit of Figure 13.12a. The bias voltage $V_{BB} = 6$ volts and the input signals are -10-volt pulses (from zero). In the absence of a signal, a base current of 200 μa is desired. In the presence of a signal, a base voltage of -2 volts is required. Determine the values of R_1 and R_2 that will satisfy these conditions. Assume the transistor input resistance is comparatively low when the transistor is on, and that the reverse input resistance is large.

13.6 Repeat Problem 13.5 if a reverse bias voltage of -4 volts is required in the presence of a signal.

13.7 For the AND circuit of Figure 13.14a, $V_1 = 12$ volts (polarity as shown) and $V_2 = 12$ volts (polarity as shown). The minimum forward current for each of the three diodes must be 100 μa. When the transistor is on, its base current is 200 μa. Its base voltage, when off, must be -1 volt.

(a) Determine the values of R, R_1 and R_2.

(b) What minimum magnitude of negative input pulses is required to open all diodes?

13.8 Refer to the resistance coupled AND circuit of Figure 13.14b. The bias voltage $V_{BB} = 6$ volts, and the input signals are negative ten-volt pulses. The conditions that must be satisfied for the transistor are the same as in Problem 13.5. Determine R_1 and R_2 for

(a) A two-input AND circuit.

(b) A three-input AND circuit.

13.9 State the advantages and disadvantages when comparing the two circuits of Figure 13.4.

14

Other Solid State Circuitry And Techniques For Electronic Switching And Pulse Shaping

14.1 General Discussion

The circuits and problems of this chapter, as in Chapters 12 and 13, are not necessarily new circuits and problems that would require an entirely new method of analysis. The early sections of the chapter, for example, are primarily concerned with the techniques of counting to any desired number with bistable transistorized circuits. The counting techniques represent new material but the bistable circuits, along with possible methods of triggering, have been presented earlier.

Later sections of the chapter present circuit configurations, in which *n-p-n* and *p-n-p* transistors are used in the same circuit. Circuits with complementary transistors can perform some of the same circuit functions that have been presented earlier. Since *n-p-n* and *p-n-p* transistor circuits are frequently used in practical systems, it is important to become familiar with these circuits. Circuits are chosen for reasons of economics, circuit simplicity,

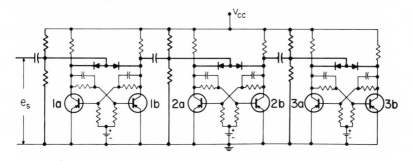

Fig. 14.1. A chain of three bistable circuits arranged for positive triggering with *p-n-p* transistors.

and for the improved characteristics of one type over the other for particular applications.

Other sections of the chapter present additional techniques for using certain solid state devices other than transistors.

14.2   Chain of Bistable Circuits (for frequency division or counting)

Frequency division and especially electronic counting are essential in many automatic control and measurement systems, digital computers included. This and the next few sections are devoted to some of the circuitry techniques and problems of electronic counting using bistable circuits.

A chain of three bistable circuits is represented by Figure 14.1. Here, the output voltage will have a frequency that is one-eighth of the signal

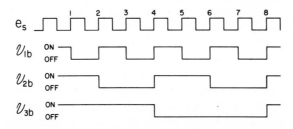

Fig. 14.2. Voltage waveform for the circuit in Figure 14.1.

frequency. Voltage waveforms for the signal and the output of *each* stage are shown in Figure 14.2. Notice that any one of the bistable circuits changes its state whenever a positive voltage step is applied to that particular bistable circuit. Positive steps are normally used for triggering with *p-n-p* transistors.

The diodes, in the circuit of Figure 14.1, are oriented to permit triggering with positive pulses only. With *n-p-n* transistors and with vacuum tubes, the triggering is commonly done with negative pulses. The possible methods of triggering were discussed in Chapters 12 and 13.

Although the waveforms of Figure 14.2 are self explanatory, it is important to appreciate the following:

(a) The three bistable circuits are in the same state just preceding the count of one.

(b) At the count of eight, all three bistable circuits are returned to their initial states.

(c) The third and last bistable circuit is returned to its initial state for the first time at the count of eight.

14.3 Counting to Any Number with Bistable Circuits

Electronic counting is really a method for measuring time intervals. The chain of three bistable circuits, as in Figure 14.1, could be identified as a count-of-eight counter. For example, a count-of-eight represents 800 μs for a signal frequency of 10,000 c/s. The unit of measure is the period of the signal and is 100 μs in this case. The unit of measure (the period) and the time interval to complete a count are significant in practical applications that require bistable circuits for time measurements or for time control. Each application dictates its own specific requirements.

Of course, bistable circuits can give normal counts of 2, 4, 8, 16, . . . , 2^n, depending on the number of bistable circuits that are in the chain. These counts are not always convenient. There are applications in which other counts *must* be used. A count to any number equal to or greater than two can be accomplished by resetting one or more of the bistable circuits during the count. The remainder of this section is devoted to a general procedure for establishing a count to any number.

A symbolic chart for the count-of-eight circuit of Figure 14.1 is shown in Table 14.1. The symbols "0" and "1" represent *on* and *off* states respectively. The first bistable circuit changes state on every count, or for each cycle of the signal. The second bistable circuit changes its state whenever the "b" transistor of the first circuit returns to "0" or the *on* state. The second stage influences the third stage in the same way. This chart is a representation of the waveforms of Figure 14.2. (The chart also gives the binary systems of counting. For example, the count of three is 011 in the binary system. Additional stages are needed to reveal the binary count beyond 7.)

The technique of causing a chain of bistable circuits to count to any number is presented in Table 14.2. Counts of three through 16 are included

TABLE 14.1 THE SYMBOLIC CHART FOR THE COUNT-OF-EIGHT
CIRCUIT OF FIGURE 14.1.

The count:		1	2	3	4	5	6	7	8
State of 1b:	0	1	0	1	0	1	0	1	0
State of 2b:	0	0	1	1	0	0	1	1	0
State of 3b:	0	0	0	0	1	1	1	1	0

KEY: 1b, 2b and 3b are identified in Figure 14.1.
      0—The "b" transistor is *on*.
      1—The "b" transistor is *off*.

here. This table should be examined rather carefully before reading further. Notice that a definite pattern exists.

Now, the conditions of operation are

(a) The count is completed when the last and output stage *returns* to the "0" state for the first time, and the other stages are also at the "0" state that existed initially.

(b) Each reset of the first stage will shift the count by one digit.

(c) Each reset of the second stage will shift the count by two digits.

(d) Each reset of the third stage will shift the count by four digits.

(e) The counts, without resets, are 2, 4, 8, and 16, with one stage, two stages, three stages, and four stages respectively.

(f) To determine the stage, or stages, that need resetting for a given count, merely subtract the required count from the next highest count that would exist without resets. For example, nine is seven less than 16. The count must be shifted from 16 to nine by resets that will shift the count by seven digits. Resetting the first three stages once each will give a count of nine.

(g) Theoretically, the reset of a stage can be done at any time including or preceding the final count. A stage could even be *preset* in advance of the count and have an initial state of "1" rather than "0".

The practical problems associated with resetting depend on the method chosen, or required by a particular application, to accomplish the resets. In general, there are two methods.

(a) The reset of a stage can be done internally by feedback from a stage further along in the chain. This feedback signal must come from a stage that would normally change states on the count at which the reset is to be made.

(b) The reset of a stage can be done externally from outside signals that are properly timed with the input signal to be counted.

There are numerous circuitry techniques for accomplishing the necessary resets. The circuitry is largely dictated by the requirements of each particular application.

TABLE 14.2 Charts that Illustrate the Technioue of Counting
to any Number with a Chain of Bistable Circuits.

(a) Count of three (Reset first stage).

The count:		1	2	3
State of 1b:	0	1	0(1)	0
State of 2b:	0		1	0

(b) Count of four (no resets).

(c) Count of five (Reset first and second stages).

The count:		1	2	3	4	5
State of 1b:	0	1	0(1)	0	1	0
State of 2b:	0		1	0(1)		0
State of 3b:	0			1		0

(d) Count of six (Reset second stage).

The count:		1	2	3	4	5	6
State of 1b:	0	1	0	1	0	1	0
State of 2b:	0		1		0(1)		0
State of 3b:	0				1		0

(e) Count of seven (Reset first stage).

The count:		1	2	3	4	5	6	7
State of 1b:	0	1	0	1	0(1)	0	1	0
State of 2b:	0		1		0	1		0
State of 3b:	0				1			0

(f) Count of eight (no resets).

(g) Count of nine (Reset first, second,and third stages).

The count:		1	2	3	4	5	6	7	8	9
State of 1b:	0	1	0(1)	0	1	0	1	0	1	0
State of 2b:	0		1	0(1)		0		1		0
State of 3b:	0			1		0(1)				0
State of 4b:	0					1				0

(h) Count of ten (Reset second and third stages).

The count:		1	2	3	4	5	6	7	8	9	10
State of 1b:	0	1	0	1	0	1	0	1	0	1	0
State of 2b:	0		1		0(1)		0		1		0
State of 3b:	0				1		0(1)				0
State of 4b:	0						1				0

(i) Count of 11 (Reset 1st and 3rd stages).

(j) Count of 12 (Reset 3rd stage).

(k) Count of 13 (Reset 1st and 2nd stages).

(l) Count of 14 (Reset 2nd stage).

(m) Count of 15 (Reset 1st stage).

(n) Count of 16 (No resets).

14.4 Symbolic Representations of Bistable Circuit Operations

The block diagram of Figure 14.3 is a convenient and simplified representation of a bistable counting circuit. It is arranged to illustrate a chain of bistable circuits that are connected and triggered as in the circuit of Figure 14.1. Refer to this circuit and observe that the output is taken from the "b" side of each bistable circuit. In addition, each bistable circuit is triggered with a single common input such as to always cause a change of state regardless of the state of a bistable circuit before the trigger. The diagram in Figure 14.3 represents these output and triggering arrangements.

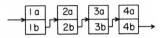

Fig. 14.3. Symbolic representation for a bistable counting circuit.

However, a group of bistable circuits is not always used for counting purposes. There are control and measurement systems that require a *storage* of information that must be collected only on demand from a special signal applied to the bistable circuit that is holding the information. In addition, a group of bistable circuits may be required to serve as a *sequencing* switch where outputs are taken from each bistable circuit in a time ordered sequence. Then, there are *shift registers* in which information that is stored in one set of bistable circuits must be shifted to another set on demand from special signals.

The techniques of counting were explained in some detail in the preceding section. However, the detailed circuitry for storage of information, for sequencing and for shift registers are too dependent on particular applications to present here. Each application has its own unique requirements and demands. For this reason, this discussion is restricted to symbolic representations.

In any case, the bistable circuits are interconnected, triggered, reset if necessary, preset if required, and cleared in accordance with the requirements of proper operation for each particular application. This means that it may be necessary to have several trigger inputs to each bistable circuit. In addition it may be required to take the outputs from the "a" side or the "b" side, or from both sides of a bistable circuit. Figure 14.4 is a symbolic representation of such multiple inputs and outputs.

Symbolic diagrams may be helpful in understanding or designing a particular system. Consider the representation of Figure 14.5. Here the bistable circuits are interconnected such that the "b" output of each stage is the "b" input of the next stage. The "a" sides are triggered from a common input. Individual outputs are shown from the "b" side of each stage. A condition is shown whereby only the first stage has been preset by some method. Assuming the trigger inputs will cause a change of state only if the "a" side is at "0" (consistent with the notations of the preceding section), then the first trigger input will cause the first stage to change its state. The second stage will also change state since "1b" went from "1" to "0" and "2b" was initially at "0". Thus, there is an output from the first stage and the second stage is preset for the next trigger input. The second trigger input pulse gives an output from

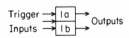

Fig. 14.4. Multiple trigger inputs and outputs of a bistable circuit.

Trigger Input

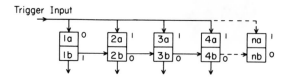

Fig. 14.5. A symbolic diagram to illustrate the principles of sequencing.

"2b" and the third stage is preset, and so on. Figure 14.5 is a simplified representation of sequencing or of a shift register.

An excellent treatment related to the general problem of using computer techniques in automatic control and measurement systems is presented in an article* that is referenced at the bottom of this page.

14.5 A Diode in Collector Circuit Permits Fast Rise Time with Capacitive Loading

The transistor circuit of Figure 14.6 has a diode D_1 in series with R_L of the collector circuit. Capacitive loading is represented by the C_2 branch. The presence of D_1 in this circuit is of special interest. It is used to permit a step voltage to exist at the collector when the transistor is switched off.

Capacitive loaded circuits have been presented in earlier chapters. Recall, in particular, the sweep circuit in Figure 8.21 and the astable circuit in Figure 11.1. In either of these circuits, the collector voltage is an exponential voltage with a time constant of $R_L C$ when the transistor is switched off.

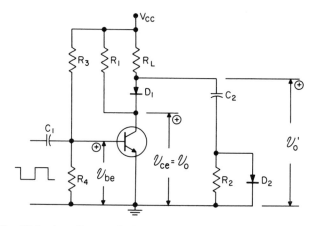

Fig. 14.6. A collector diode permits squaring of collector voltage waveform.

*Michael H. Nothman, "Digital Methods in Measurement and Control," *Electro-Technol* (New York) (September 1959) 125–144.

This exponential function is desired for the sweep circuit, but it is objectionable for the astable circuit, or similar circuits, where a square pulse is required.

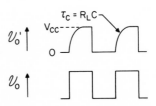

The collector voltage, $V_{ce} = v_o$, for the circuit of Figure 14.6 *is* square pulses when the transistor has an input circuit and a driving voltage that will switch the transistor *on* and *off*. The voltages v_o^1 (identified on the circuit diagram) and v_o could be as represented by the waveforms of Figure 14.7 when the circuit is properly driven to

Fig. 14.7. Voltage waveforms that represent the purpose of Diode D_1 in the circuit of Figure 14.3.

produce these waveforms. Notice that v_o^1 has an exponential identified by $\tau_c = R_L C$. The voltage v_o, however, has steps on both the leading and the trailing edges. This happens because v_o^1 and v_o are isolated by the diode D_1 when the transistor is switched to the *off* state; that is, the diode is subjected to a reverse voltage during the time required for the capacitor C_2 voltage to recover to V_{cc}. The collector voltage rises directly to V_{cc} in the presence of R_1.

The values for R_1 and the parallel combination of R_1 and R_L have special significance. When the transistor is turned *off* there is a time interval during which R_L is isolated from the collector. After recovery for C_2 is completed, R_L and R_1 are in parallel since the diode is no longer reverse-biased. This means that the d-c load line on the volt-ampere characteristics of the transistor is two-valued. The manner in which an equivalent R_L influences the operation of a transistor was explained in Chapter 7.

In review, and with attention to the circuit under discussion, if R_1 is too large, then the collector voltage may be somewhat less than V_{cc} at the

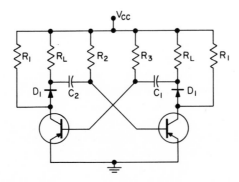

Fig. 14.8. Collector diodes in an astable circuit to permit square pulses at the collector.

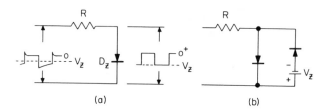

Fig. 14.9. (a) Illustrates the use of a Zener diode. (b) Equivalent circuit.

instant that the transistor is triggered *off*. Now, when diode D_1 becomes conducting (transistor still off) the equivalent load resistance is decreased and v_{ce} will be more nearly equal to V_{CC}. The resulting two possible values for v_{ce} must be nearly equal and near V_{CC} if v_o is to have a flat top for the *off* time of the transistor. In addition, the parallel combination of R_1 and R_L influences the operating values of collector current and voltage when the transistor is *on*. The equivalent resistance must not be too small here. Again, recall the discussion of Chapter 7 concerning this problem.

The astable circuit of Figure 14.8 shows the use of collector diodes, with *p-n-p* transistors, for the purpose of obtaining square pulses at the collectors. Understand, however, that the use of these diodes does not decrease the recovery time nor permit a higher frequency of operation for the circuit. The difficulties related to the values of R_1 and R_L, as explained in the preceding paragraph, prohibit this.

14.6 Zener Diodes for Wave Shaping

The properties of a Zener diode were described in Chapter 7. The use of a Zener diode is especially advantageous wherever two-level limiting is required; this is illustrated by the simple circuits of Figure 14.9. The (a) circuit resembles a single unidirectional diode clipping circuit. The Zener diode, however, has the equivalence of two diodes and a bias voltage as shown in the (b) circuit, where V_Z represents the Zener breakdown voltage. Thus, one Zener diode can replace two diodes and the circuitry necessary to establish a d-c bias voltage.

As another example, the astable circuit of Figure 14.8 could employ Zener diodes in parallel with the transistors of that circuit. The two diodes (both identified as D_1) and the two resistors, identified as R_1, could then be removed from the circuit. The Zener diodes would be oriented toward common ground and V_{CC} should be somewhat greater in magnitude than V_Z in order to have a better square pulse at the collectors.

14.7 Schmitt Trigger Circuit with *npn-pnp* Transistors

Occasionally it is desirable to use a combination of *p-n-p* and *n-p-n* transistiors in switching and pulse-forming circuits. The circuit representation

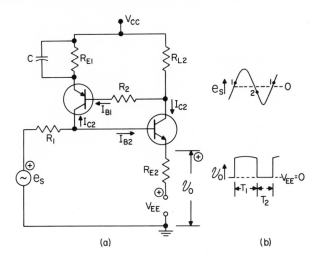

Fig. 14.10. Schmitt trigger circuit with *pnp-npn* transistors.

in Figure 14.10 is one example. This series type circuit can have the properties of a Schmitt trigger circuit. (The parallel type transistor circuit was previously described in Chapter 11. The counterpart with tubes was described in Chapter 10.)

The *npn-pnp* circuit of Figure 14.10 has significant behavior in that both transistors are normally *off* for a zero signal. The power drain on the power supplies is then negligible. This is not true for the parallel type circuits where *one* of the transistors, or tubes, is normally *on*. Let us itemize the sequence of operation for the series Schmitt trigger circuit (assume V_{EE} is zero unless specified otherwise)

(a) When the *n-p-n* transistor is *off* ($I_{c2} = 0$, assuming negligible leakage current), the *p-n-p* transistor is also *off*, or nearly so, since I_{b1} will be near zero. This base current is near zero because the base and the emitter of the *p-n-p* are both returned to the same voltage, V_{cc}.

(b) Now, when e_s goes slightly positive, I_{B2} becomes positive and the *n-p-n* transistor enters its active region of operation. The circuit becomes regenerative with a drop in the *n-p-n* collector voltage, making I_{B1} negative and causing the *p-n-p* transistor to enter the active region. The resulting collector current, $-I_{c2}$, increases I_{B2} and causes the *n-p-n* to conduct more heavily. This regenerative action continues until either or both transistors enters the saturation region. The transition to *on* for both transistors is indicated as Point 1 on the waveforms of Figure 14.10b.

(c) The reverse transition from *on* to *off* requires that the saturated transistor or transistors shall be driven out of saturation in such a way that both transistors are again in their active regions of operation to permit the required regenerative, self-triggering action. The driving voltage must reduce to a value identified as Point 2 on Figure 14.10b to cause the reverse

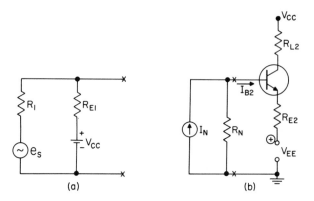

Fig. 14.11. Approximate equivalent input circuits for the *n-p-n* transistor when the *p-n-p* transistor is *on*.

$$I_N = \frac{e_s}{R_1} + \frac{V_{CC}}{R_{E1}}, \quad \text{and} \quad R_N = \frac{R_1 R_{E1}}{R_1 + R_{E1}}.$$

transition. Notice that Point 2 is shown as a considerably lower voltage than Point 1 on the source voltage.

Approximate equivalent input circuits for the *n-p-n* transistor, when both transistors are *on*, will reveal the problems associated with the transition from *on* to *off*. These input circuits are shown in Figure 14.11. They disregard I_{B1} and assume zero collector-to-emitter voltage for the *on p-n-p* transistor. With these assumptions, the input circuit is as shown in circuit (a) of Figure 14.11. The Norton's equivalent circuit is shown in circuit (b). Notice that the current source is the sum of two currents, namely e_s/R_1 and V_{cc}/R_{E1}. The second of these two current terms is significant for the reverse transition. True, this current term provided the necessary contribution to I_{B2} to establish the *off*-to-*on* transition, but it is a handicap for the reverse transition where I_{B2} must be *decreased* into the active region before any reverse transition can take place. The controllable e_s/R_1 current source must work in opposition to V_{cc}/R_{E1}. This condition does not exist for the forward transition when both transistors are *off*. The driving current source is then e_s/R_1 only, with R_1 as the shunting resistor.

The output pulse width, T_1 of Figure 14.10b, is easily controlled with the emitter d-c biasing voltage V_{EE}. Make V_{EE} positive and Points 1 and 2 on e_s will be at higher levels. When Point 1 is at e_s (max.), V_{EE} equals e_s (max.). The triggering action is lost for any larger values of V_{EE}. Make V_{EE} negative and the two trigger points on e_s are at lower levels.

Changes in V_{EE} will also change the magnitude of the output pulse when v_o is the emitter voltage as represented in Figure 14.10. The output voltage can also be taken at the collector of the *n-p-n* transistor. The choice depends on the pulse polarity desired, magnitude of the pulse required, and required limitations on distortion of the pulse when the transistors are *on*. The capacitor C, shown on the circuit diagram, is for commutating purposes to decrease transition times.

14.8   Direct Coupled Circuits with *npn-pnp* Transistors

One method of interconnecting *n-p-n* and *p-n-p* transistors is shown in Figure 14.12. Other circuits will be discussed and illustrated later in this section. For now, let us concentrate on the circuit of Figure 14.12.

Assuming the *p-n-p* transistor is either entirely *on* or *off*, then the output voltage v_o is two-valued and is equal to V_{EE2} or V_{CC2} respectively. These two values are selected in accordance with the requirements of the system in which this circuit may be used. The *p-n-p* transistor requires, of course, that V_{CC2} shall be algebraically less than V_{EE2}. Correspondingly for the *n-p-n* transistor, V_{CC1} must be greater (algebraically) than V_{EE1}. The *n-p-n* emitter voltage has either of these two limiting values.

A further demand on the relative magnitudes of the supply voltages is that V_{CC1} shall be equal to or preferably greater than V_{EE2} to insure that the *p-n-p* transistor is *off* when the *n-p-n* transistor is *on*. For the reverse states, I_{B2} must be sufficiently negative to drive the *p-n-p* transistor fully *on*. This means that V_{EE1} must be sufficiently less than V_{EE2}, for a given R_{E1}, to establish the required negative magnitude for the *p-n-p* base current.

The four separate d-c supply voltages are not always necessary for the circuit of Figure 14.12. The circuit could operate reasonably well with only one source of d-c voltage, as illustrated by circuits that are discussed later in this section. It is only important to realize that the practical system, in which the circuit is used, will dictate the voltage requirements in addition to certain inequalities of these voltages to insure stable operation in the *on* and *off* states.

Another *npn-pnp* direct-coupled circuit is shown in Figure 14.13 with

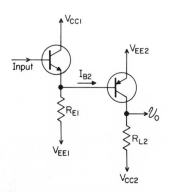

Fig. 14.12. Direct-coupled *npn-pnp* circuit.

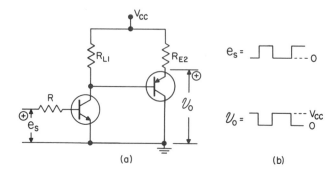

Fig. 14.13. (a) Another direct coupled *npn-pnp* circuit. (b) Waveforms to show inversion.

accompanying waveforms to illustrate phase relations. This circuit is somewhat similar to the preceding circuit of Figure 14.12. The circuit has only two (not four) possible voltage limits, namely zero and V_{CC}. This and the preceding circuit both have one emitter follower. There is one significant difference in the two circuits. Both transistors in the circuit of Figure 14.13 can be *off*, or *on*, at the same time. This is not true for the preceding circuit.

Other *npn-pnp* direct-coupled circuits are illustrated in Figure 14.14. Circuit (a) is a series type circuit where both transistors can be *on*, or *off*, at the same time, assuming that the circuit is used as an electronic switch or for squaring a waveform. There are two conflicting demands on the magnitude for R_{E1}. When both transistors are *on*, R_{E1} should be small enough to give a required value of base current for the *n-p-n* transistor. However, R_{E1} should not be small if overloading of the source is to be avoided. Otherwise, there is not much need for the *p-n-p* emitter follower.

The circuit of Figure 14.14b is a good squaring circuit, as illustrated by the waveforms on the figure. Observe that the first stage is an emitter follower.

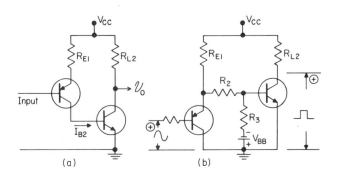

Fig. 14.14. (a) A series *pnp-npn* circuit. (b) Two-stage direct coupled circuit.

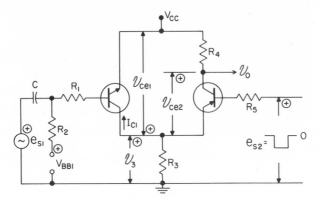

Fig. 14.15. A gating circuit.

14.9 A Gating *npn-pnp* Circuit

The circuit of Figure 14.15 can serve as a gating circuit as illustrated by the oscillograms of Figures 14.16 and 14.17. The circuit has a sinusoidal driving voltage on the *n-p-n* transistor and gating pulses on the *p-n-p* transistor.

For the oscillogram in Figure 14.16, the upper trace is the gating pulses and the lower trace is the output voltage, v_o. For the results shown here, the circuit quantities are adjusted for linear operation of the *n-p-n* transistor when the *p-n-p* is driven *on* and into saturation by the negative-going, gating pulse. (A more detailed explanation of the circuit will follow in later paragraphs of this section).

The squared gated pulses at the output, lower trace of Figure 14.17, are the result of overdriving the *n-p-n* transistor with the sinusoidal input voltage.

A general analysis of the circuit will reveal the manner in which the circuit quantities must be adjusted to obtain desired results. First of all, observe that v_3, for the indicated reference polarity, is always a negative voltage. Any magnitude increase of v_3 will require an increase in magnitude of col-

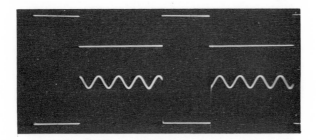

Fig. 14.16. Gating sine waves with the circuit in Figure 14.15.

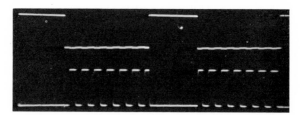

Fig. 14.17. Squaring and gating with the circuit in Figure 14.15.

lector current from either or both transistors. Recall, however, that the collector current is positive for the *n-p-n* transistor and negative for the *p-n-p* transistor.

Observe, for the circuit configuration, that the *p-n-p* transistor will be *off*, or nearly *off*, unless e_{s2} is negative. Any collector current from the *n-p-n* transistor will cause the *p-n-p* transistor to be more *off* because of the voltage established across R_3 by I_{c1}. If the *p-n-p* transistor should be operating in

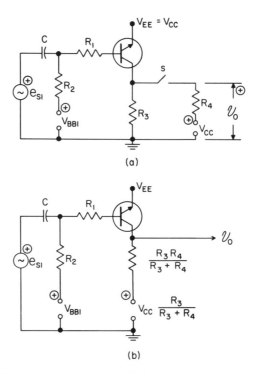

Fig. 14.18. Equivalent circuits for the gating circuit of Figure 14.15. (a) The switch represents the *p-n-p* transistor. (b) The *n-p-n* equivalent circuit when the *p-n-p* is in saturation.

the active region, then the collector current from the *n-p-n* will influence the operation of the *p-n-p* for two reasons: (a) any increase of v_3 magnitude produced by I_{C_1} will of itself cause less conduction in the *p-n-p*; (b) any increase of v_3 magnitude produced by I_{C_1} will aslo cause the base current of the *p-n-p* to decrease in magnitude which will also decrease conduction in the *p-n-p* transistor. This double action does not exist on the *n-p-n* transistor when the *p-n-p* is made to change in conduction—the base current of the *n-p-n* will not change because of any change of collector current in the *p-n-p* transistor.

The circuit of Figure 14.15 functions very well as a gating circuit by operating the *p-n-p* as a switch rather than as an amplifier. In other words, the *p-n-p* transistor is driven *to saturation* by the negative-going, gating pulse to open the gate. The equivalent circuits of Figure 14.18 represent this method of operation where the switch in the (a) circuit approximates the *p-n-p* transistor as an ideal switch. Circuit (b) is the simplified equivalent circuit when the switch is closed, or when the *p-n-p* transistor is in saturation. The indicated d-c supply voltages, V_{EE} and V_{CC}, are equal negative voltages. Observe, from Figure 14.18b, that the *n-p-n* transistor operates under reduced values of load resistance and *d*-c supply voltage when the *p-n-p* transistor is in saturation.

14.10   A Two-Stage RC-Coupled Circuit Using Complementary Transistors.

A two-stage, RC-coupled circuit using *npn-pnp* transistors is shown in Figure 14.19. Two oscillograms for this circuit are shown in Figure 14.20. In oscillogram (a), the driving voltage (not shown) is a rectangular waveform. The top trace is the collector voltage of the *p-n-p* transistor and the lower trace is the collector voltage of the *n-p-n* transistor. In oscillogram (b), the driving voltage (top trace) is sinusoidal; the remaining two traces are the two collector voltages as in (a). For these two illustrations, the circuit is designed to give output pulses of controllable time duration.

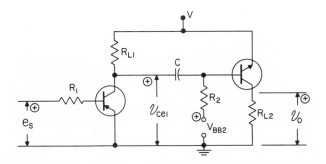

Fig. 14.19. One example of RC coupling with complementary transistors.

An examination of the circuit in relationship to the generated waveforms will reveal the following information:

(a) Since each transistor is either *on* or *off*, the upper limit and the lower limit of the two collector voltages are zero and the negative supply voltage, respectively.

(b) When the *p-n-p* transistor is switched off, the *n-p-n* transistor is also switched *off* and the output pulse, of controllable time duration, is initiated.

(c) The time duration of the output pulse is evaluated from the exponential voltage that exists at the base of the *n-p-n*. Evaluation of such exponentials has been done many times in the circuits of preceding chapters. The *n-p-n* transistor returns to the *on* state when the exponential relaxes back to V, which is a negative voltage to which the emitter is connected. The significant quantities of the base-voltage exponential, while the *n-p-n* is *off*, are $E_{as} = V_{BB2}$, $\tau_c = C(R_{L1} + R_2)$, and $E_o = (2V - V_{BB2})R_2/(R_{L1} + R_2)$. If V_{BB2} is zero and R_2 is much greater than R_{L1}, then $E_o = 2V$ and the time duration of the output pulse is approximately equal to $\tau_c \ln 2$.

(d) In the presence of R_{L1}, the collector voltage of the first stage does not go immediately to V (a negative quantity) when this *p-n-p* transistor is switched *off*.

(e) Comparing this circuit that uses complementary transistors with a

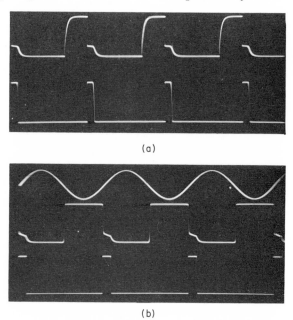

(a)

(b)

Fig. 14.20. Oscillograms for the circuit in Figure 14.19. (a) For a rectangular driving voltage (not shown), the top trace is the collector voltage of the first stage and the bottom trace is the collector voltage of the second stage. (b) Same as (a) for sinusoidal driving voltage.

similar circuit that uses like transistors, it is found that R_{L1} influences the response of the two circuits differently. In this circuit, R_{L1} is significant during the entire time of the output pulse, since the *p-n-p* transistor is *off*. With like transistors, the controllable output pulse is generated after the transistor in the first stage is switched *on*, so R_{L1} is essentially shorted out by this *on* transistor.

14.11 A Second RC-Coupled Circuit Using Complementary Transistors.

The RC-coupled circuit of Figure 14.21a is very similar to the circuit discussed in the preceding section. The first stage has an *n-p-n* transistor rather than a *p-n-p* transistor. The two transistors, still of the common emitter configuration as before, are oriented in such a way that the supply voltage must be a negative voltage, as in Figure 14.19.

An oscillogram for this circuit is shown in Figure 14.21b. The driving voltage is sinusoidal. The middle trace on the oscillogram is the collector voltage of the first stage and the bottom trace is the collector voltage of the second stage. Except for inverted waveforms, the same observations can be made for this circuit as for the preceding circuit. The upper and lower limits

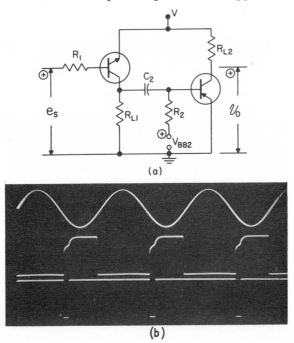

(a)

(b)

Fig. 14.21. (a) RC coupled circuit using *npn-pnp* transistors in the reverse order of Figure 14.19. (b) Oscillogram, showing the source voltage and the collector voltages of the first and second stages, respectively.

of the two collector voltages are respectively zero and V (a negative voltage), the same as in the preceding circuit.

14.12 A Third RC-Coupled Circuit Using Complementary Transistors

In the circuit of Figure 14.22a, the first stage has a p-n-p emitter follower and the second stage has a common-emitter n-p-n transistor. The voltage, V, is a negative supply voltage.

An oscillogram for this circuit is shown in Figure 14.22b. The driving voltage (not shown) is sinusoidal. The top trace is the emitter voltage of the first stage and the remaining two traces represent the collector voltage of the second stage for two conditions of operation. For the middle trace, the n-p-n transistor is *off* during the time of the positive-going pulse. For the bottom trace, the n-p-n transistor is *on* during the time of the negative-going pulse. This second condition of operation is also possible in the preceding two circuits although it was not shown. Notice, for the bottom trace, that the recovery time on the trailing edge is not so good. The two conditions of operation are made possible by adjusting the quiescent base current (V_{BB2}/R_2) of the n-p-n transistor to hold this transistor normally *on*, or normally *off*, under quiescent conditions.

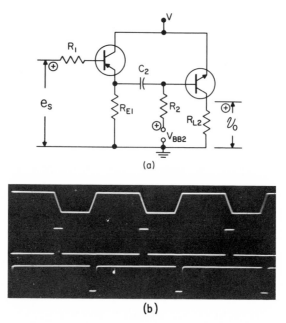

(a)

(b)

Fig. 14.22. (a) A third RC-coupled circuit with npn-pnp transistors. (b) Top trace is collector voltage of p-n-p (e_s is sinusoidal). The middle and bottom traces are the collector voltage of the n-p-n for two values of V_{BB2}.

Although the emitter voltage of the first stage is shown on the oscillogram as a trapezoidal waveform, this emitter voltage would be a good rectangular wave if the p-n-p transistor is driven a little harder. The trapezoidal voltage was used to illustrate the reasonably good results that are possible for the positive-going pulses at the output.

Again, all three waveforms in the oscillogram have upper limits and lower limits of zero and V (a negative voltage).

14.13   Inverted-Transistor Circuits

This section is presented primarily for the purpose of defining the "inverted-transistor" and to call attention to the significance of its use in a circuit.

Each circuit of Figure 14.23 is a common-emitter circuit with the output voltage taken at the collector. Circuit (a) shows the conventional common-emitter configuration while circuit (b) shows the transistor inverted. To distinguish the two circuits, it is convenient to identify the second circuit as an inverted-transistor circuit. The only difference in the configuration of the two circuits, of course, is that circuit (b) has the emitter connected directly to the supply voltage (negative for *n-p-n*) rather than to ground while R_L is returned to ground rather than to the supply voltage (positive for *n-p-n*).

On comparing the response of the two circuits, the collector voltage of circuit (b) cannot be positive, while in circuit (a), the collector voltage cannot be negative. Electrically, either common-emitter circuit is an inverter. The two circuits have the same kind of response except for the d-c voltage levels as illustrated by the pulses shown on the diagrams in Figure 14.23.

By referring to the *npn-pnp* circuits of the preceding sections, it may be observed that the use of complementary transistors requires that there must

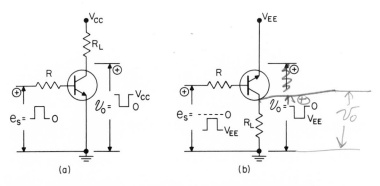

Fig. 14.23. (a) Conventional common-emitter circuit. (b) Common-emitter circuit with inverted transistor.

be only one inverted-transistor when a single common supply voltage is used. If it is desired to avoid using inverted-transistors in such circuits, then a single common supply voltage cannot be used.

14.14 Thirty-Two Possible Combinations with Complementary Transistors

Three RC-coupled circuits using complementary transistors were presented in earlier sections. There are thirty-two possible combinations. This is not to imply that all of these are practical. The thirty-two possibilities are the result of assuming the first stage could be either an *n-p-n* or a *p-n-p* and that either stage could be any one of four configurations. The four configurations are: common emitter, "inverted" common emitter, common collector, or "inverted" common collector. The total possible combinations add to thirty-two.

Restrict the use of the emitter follower to just one of the stages and the possible combinations reduce to twenty-four. Further restrict the circuit to the use of only one d-c power supply and the possible combinations reduce to twelve.

14.15 The Unijunction Transistor Circuit as a Pulse Source

The physical and electrical properties of the unijunction transistor were presented in Chapter 7. The behavior of a unijunction transistor circuit as a monostable, bistable, or astable circuit was described in Chapter 13. See Figures 13.20, 13.21, and 13.23 in particular.

The unijunction transistor, with its negative resistance characteristic and the three possible modes of operation, is one device that finds frequent

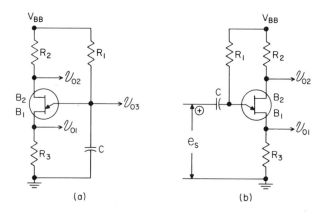

Fig. 14.24. Two unijunction transistor circuits to illustrate its use as a pulse source.

use in automatic control and measurement systems because of circuit simplicity. Conventional transistor circuitry, to perform the same functions, would be much more involved.

Two circuits, each with a unijunction transistor, are shown in Figure 14.24. Circuit (a) resembles the circuit in Figure 13.22, where the principles of operation were described. It is redrawn here, with R_3 added, to illustrate the three likely points in the circuit from which output voltages are available. As a relaxation oscillator (astable operation), a negative-going voltage pulse is available at B_2 and a positive pulse is available at B_1 each time the unijunction transistor is made to conduct as the capacitor voltage increases to the threshold voltage. The capacitor voltage, v_{o3}, is a sawtooth waveform .The positive pulses, or the negative pulses (whichever is needed), can be used to trigger other circuits that require triggering or synchronization. These other circuits could be bistable circuits, monostable circuits, astable circuits, or blocking oscillators. The circuit of Figure 14.24a, then, can perform a number of circuit functions. In addition to the fact that this simple circuit is a waveform *generator*, it can provide a sawtooth voltage, it can provide positive pulses of short time duration, or it can provide negative-going pulses of short time duration (the positive and negative pulses are generated during the discharge time for the capacitor).

Circuit (b) of Figure 14.24 is shown to illustrate a condition where the unijunction transistor circuit would probably be designed for bistable operation.The circuit must be driven, in this case, by an external signal. The input circuit is shown as capacitance coupled to the source. Other types of input circuits, as required, could be used. A bistable circuit could be either *on* or *off*, and must be triggered by e_s if it is to change its state. If the unitransistor should be *off*, then a positive pulse is required at the source to turn it *on*. See Figure 13.21 and observe the load line conditions for bistable operation.

14.16   Circuits with Silicon Controlled Rectifiers

A few circuits to suggest possible uses for a silicon-controlled rectifier (SCR) are presented in this section. The physical and electrical properties for this device were presented in Chapter 7.

Before presenting any circuits, attention should be called to the fact that technical literature does not always refer to this device with the same identifying name or symbol. In the true sense, the device is a four-layer solid-state diode and is frequently referred to as a *p-n-p-n transistor* or simply as a *four-layer-diode*. The device is also

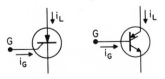

Fig. 14.25. Two symbols to represent the four-layer diode.

identified as a *trinister-controlled-rectifier* (TCR) and as *thyrister*. Recall that the device has three junctions and has electrical characteristics that are similar to the thyratron.

Two symbols for representing this solid-state controlled rectifier are in common usage. They are shown in (a) and (b) of Figure 14.25.

The solid-state controlled rectifier, having electrical characteristics that are very similar to the grid-controlled gas tube (thyratron), is made to conduct or not to conduct with very much the same techniques that are applicable to the thyratron. With regard to the circuitry techniques for the control of these two devices, there is one important difference to keep in mind. The thyratron is a *voltage* controlled device while the solid-state controlled rectifier is a *current* controlled device. This means that the solid-state device may seriously load and distort a control source and will, therefore, place certain limitations on the kinds of control circuits that may be used. The solid-state controlled rectifier has definite advantages, however, over the thyratron. Its recovery time from *on* to *off* is much faster. Its anode voltage, when conducting, and power losses are much less. It is much more compact. It is not subject to mechanical damage and has a long electrical life.

In general, the solid-state controlled rectifier is made to conduct by either of two methods. Conduction (anode current exists) is initiated when the anode source voltage is more positive than the forward breakdown voltage. The forward breakdown voltage is decreased considerably in the presence of a positive gate current. Once conduction starts, however, the gate current loses control. To stop conduction, the anode current must be reduced to a low value (usually done by causing the anode voltage to be small or negative).

Two simplified circuits are shown in Figure 14.26. These two circuits are chosen to illustrate the possibility of having an anode source voltage that is (a) time-varying, or (b) constant. Let us consider these two circuits

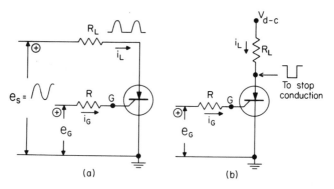

Fig. 14.26. Two ways to use a four-layer diode. (a) The diode source voltage is time-varying; (b) The diode source voltage is a d-c voltage.

(other circuits are presented later) in order to describe the behavior and possible methods for control of solid-state controlled rectifiers.

Circuit (a) of Figure 14.26 shows a sinusoidal applied voltage. The circuit could be identified as a single-phase half-wave rectifier circuit. A d-c voltage for e_G, to establish small positive values of gate current, will insure that the diode starts to conduct when e_s is only a few volts positive. When conducting, the diode voltage is in the order of about one volt. Diode conduction will stop when the source voltage returns to this low voltage. Disregarding this low voltage, the source voltage is applied directly to the load resistance during the positive half-cycle and directly to the diode ($i_L = 0$) during the negative half-cycle. The diode must have a voltage rating to withstand the peak inverse voltage (P.I.V.) that is applied while the diode is nonconducting.

The average current for the half-wave rectifier circuit can be controlled if the control voltage is a time-varying voltage that lags e_s by some angle less than 180°. (Phase-shifting circuits are presented in the next chapter). The problem is to postpone positive gate current to a desired instant of time in each positive half-cycle of the source voltage. For full control the forward breakdown voltage of the controlled rectifier (for zero gate current) must be greater than the peak value of the applied voltage. The gate control voltage e_G could be sinusoidal, but short positive pulses, accurately timed and phased, are often used. Pulse control is suggested by the circuit represented in Figure 14.27. In this circuit, e_G must come from a phase-shifting circuit in order to control the average load current. The coupling transformer could be a peaking transformer (presented in the next chapter) or a pulse transformer. If it is a pulse transformer, then the pulses must exist at e_G also.

Now, let us turn to circuit (b) of Figure 14.26. Here, the anode source voltage is a d-c voltage. For this representation, we are thinking of the controlled rectifier as a switch and the possibility of using the circuit as a memory, storage of information, or (with some changes or additions) as a logic element. The anode supply voltage must be less than the forward breakdown voltage for zero gate current. If the gate voltage is a positive d-c voltage then the diode will conduct at all times except during a time interval when the anode voltage is pulsed to a zero or negative voltage. If the control voltage consists of positive pulses then the diode conduction is initiated by the positive gate pulses provided the stop pulses are not simultaneously present.

A few additional circuits with solid-state controlled rectifiers are now presented. Two circuits are shown in Figure 14.28 to illustrate two techniques for *turn-off* of the

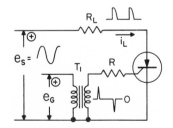

Fig. 14.27. Control of average current with *pulses*, phased back from the source voltage.

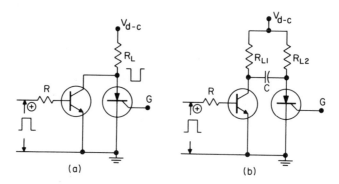

Fig. 14.28. Transistor coupling for *turn-off* of four-layer diodes.

controlled rectifier with transistor coupled circuits. In circuit (a), the *n-p-n* transistor is directly connected in parallel with the diode. Pulsing the transistor *on* for a few microseconds will leave the diode, or controlled rectifier, nonconducting provided the gate current is then zero. With capacitive coupling, as in circuit (b), the anode voltage of the controlled rectifier will go instantly to $-V_{d-c}$ when the transistor is pulsed *on*. Nonconduction is more certain for this circuit and the capacative coupling forces a more rapid recovery of the controlled rectifier.

The circuit of Figure 14.29 illustrates the use of a controlled rectifier in an AND memory circuit. (The resistance coupled input circuit for AND operation with transistors was presented in the preceding chapter.) The operation is identical for this circuit except for the fact that the controlled rectifier remains conducting after the AND operation takes place. The controlled rectifier must be switched *off*.

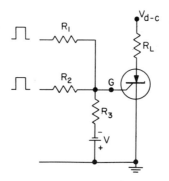

Fig. 14.29. AND memory circuit with controlled rectifier.

PROBLEMS

14.1 The waveforms of Figure 14.2 are for a chain of bistable circuits for positive triggering with p-n-p transistors. Show corresponding waveforms for negative triggering using n-p-n transistors.

14.2 Design a decade counter using a chain of bistable circuits, employing feedback to perform the necessary resets. Illustrate with symbolic block diagrams.

14.3 A counting circuit, using bistable circuits, is required to give a count of eight *followed* by a count of seven. In other words, the circuit counts to eight and 15. Illustrate, with symbolic block diagrams, the procedure for accomplishing this result. Use no more than four bistable circuits.

14.4 Sketch a circuit diagram, using three stages of bistable circuits with p-n-p transistors, that will count to six.

14.5 Refer to the symbolic block diagram in Figure 14.5. Sketch a complete circuit diagram, using p-n-p transistors, that will perform the indicated operation.

14.6 Repeat Problem 14.5 using n-p-n transistors in the circuit.

14.7 For the circuit of Figure 14.6, $V_{CC} = 15$ volts, $R_L = 5$ K, $R_1 = 20$ K, $R_2 = 60$ K, $C_2 = 0.005$ μfd., diodes D_1 and D_2 each have a forward resistance of 100 ohms, the transistor (for a selected n-p-n) is held alternately *on* and *off* for intervals of 1000 μs. Plot a steady state cycle for the two indicated output voltages, showing all significant quantities for these waveforms.

14.8 For the circuit of Figure 14.8, $V_{CC} = -24$ volts, $R_L = 5$ K, $R_1 = 15$ K, $R_2 = R_3 = 100$ K, $C_1 = C_2 = 0.005$ μfd., and assume the diodes and transistors are ideal.
(a) What is the frequency of operation for the astable circuit?
(b) Plot the collector and base voltages for one of the transistors.

14.9 For the circuit of Figure 14.19, $V = -15$ volts, $R_{L1} = R_{L2} = 3$ K, $R_2 = 50$ K, $C = 0.003$ μfd., $V_{BB2} = 0$, the first stage is driven with a square wave having a period of 500 μs and of sufficient magnitude for a given R_1 to cause the p-n-p transistor to be either *off* or in saturation.
Plot a steady state cycle for the output voltage and for the base voltage of the n-p-n transistor. Indicate all significant quantities for these waveforms. Assume ideal transistors.

14.10 Repeat Problem 14.9 if $V_{BB2} = -10$ volts.

14.11 Repeat Problem 14.9 if $V_{BB2} = +10$ volts.

15

Rectification And
Magnetic Amplifiers

15.1 General Discussion

The contents of this chapter are carefully selected and restricted to give the kind of assistance that is considered most valuable to a further study of rectifier circuits and magnetic amplifiers. A thorough treatment of either of these two general topics would require a complete volume.

Circuitry techniques are of less concern in this chapter than in the other chapters. The material on rectification, for example, is primarily concerned with the current and voltage waveforms from which significant quantities, pertinent to rectifier circuits, are calculated. Complete circuits are not always shown. Sufficient information is given, however, to permit a determination of the waveforms. Concentration on the waveforms permits a condensed discussion and a more thorough understanding of the techniques for making calculations of the significant quantities.

Some of the calculation techniques for rectifier circuits are also applicable to a study of saturable reactors and magnetic amplifiers. Again, only the basic types of magnetic amplifiers (there are three basic types) and their principles of operation are included. These principles of operation are not simple and cannot be presented briefly. It is considered sufficient, therefore, to include in this chapter a discussion of only the *basic* magnetic amplifiers.

Further study of magnetic amplifiers and related problems will be considerably enhanced if the principles of operation are clearly understood.

The principles of magnetic amplifiers are also closely related to the problems of magnetic storage, to static control devices, and to logic circuitry using magnetic devices.

15.2 Single-Phase Rectifier Circuits

The circuit diagrams of Figure 15.1 show three single-phase rectifier circuits. Circuit (a) is a half-wave rectifier circuit, circuit (b) is a full-wave rectifier circuit that requires a center tap on the transformer secondary, and circuit (c) is a full-wave rectifier circuit that does not have a secondary center tap and therefore, requires a bridge circuit for the diodes and the load.

The voltage and current waveforms of Figure 15.2 are for a single-phase half-wave rectifier circuit with a resistive load and (a) a gas diode, which has a constant voltage drop E_{bo} when conducting, or (b) a diode that has an

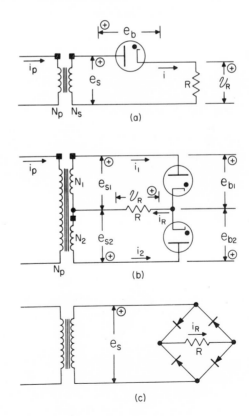

Fig. 15.1 Single phase rectifier circuits, (a) half-wave, (b) full-wave, and (c) bridge circuit.

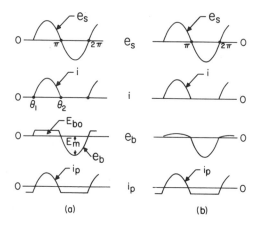

Fig. 15.2 Waveforms for single-phase half-wave rectifier circuit: (a) with gas diode and (b) with solid state diode.

assumed constant value of forward resistance r_b. Given that $e_s = E_m \sin \omega t$, then for a gas diode the load current is

$$i = \frac{E_m \sin \omega t - E_{bo}}{R} \qquad \theta_1 < \omega t < \theta_2 \qquad (15.1)$$

where

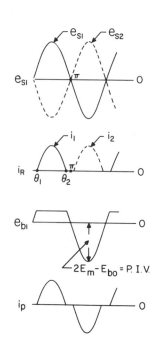

$$\theta_1 = \pi - \theta_2 = \sin^{-1} \frac{E_{bo}}{E_m}$$

This current minus its average value is the component of the secondary current that is transformed into the primary winding.

For a diode having an assumed constant forward resistance, the load current is

$$i = \frac{E_m \sin \omega t}{r_b + R} \qquad 0 < \omega t < \pi$$

$$(15.2)$$

from which we can observe that r_b, along with its probable nonlinearity, becomes less important as R is made large in comparison to r_b.

A comparison of the two groups of rectifiers (E_{bo} and r_b groups) is important. In the one case the tube voltage E_{bo} becomes insignificant if $E_{bo} \ll E_m$, while in the other case r_b becomes insignificant if $r_b \ll R$. The demands of a particular rectifier circuit application (efficiency, initial cost, current and voltage requirements, space limitations, reliability) dictate the choice of available rectifiers.

Fig. 15.3 Waveforms for single-phase full-wave rectifier circuit, as in Figure 15.1b.

The voltage and current waveforms of Figure 15.3 are for the single-phase full-wave rectifier circuit of Figure 15.1b.

Given $e_{s1} = -e_{s2} = E_m \sin \omega t$, observe that

$$P.\,I.\,V. = 2E_M - E_{bo} \tag{15.3}$$

is the peak inverse voltage to which each tube is subjected. Neglecting exciting current, the primary current approaches a sinusoidal function. This is true since

$$(i_1 - I_1 \text{ ave}) - (i_2 - I_2 \text{ ave}) = i_1 - i_2 \tag{15.4}$$

is the component of secondary currents transformed into the primary.

Additional calculations for single-phase rectifier circuits will follow a study of voltage and current waveforms for multiphase rectifier circuits.

15.3 Multiphase Rectifier Circuits

Three multiphase rectifier circuits, including transformer windings, are shown in Figure 15.4; they are (a) a three-phase, one-way rectifier circuit, (b) a three-phase, two-way rectifier circuit, and (c) a six-phase, one-way rec-

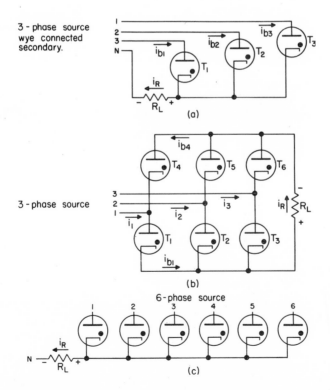

Fig. 15.4 Multiphase rectifier circuits: (a) three-phase one-way, (b) three phase two-way, and (c) six-phase one-way.

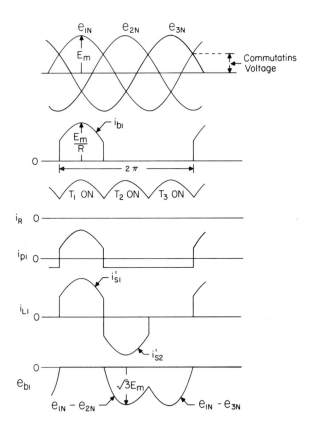

Fig. 15.5 Waveforms for the circuit in Figure 15.4a.

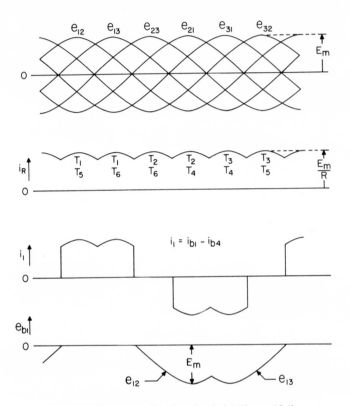

Fig. 15.6 Waveforms for the circuit in Figure 15.4b.

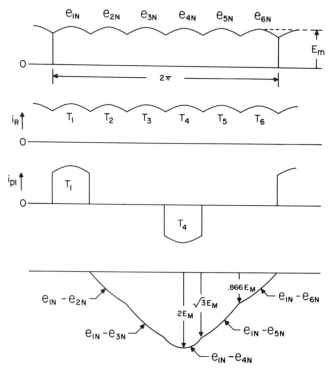

Fig. 15.7 Waveforms for the circuit in Figure 15.4c.

tifier circuit. Voltage and current waveforms for these three rectifier circuits are shown, respectively, in Figures 15.5, 15.6, and 15.7 for resistive loads and assuming ideal diodes and transformers.

Three single-phase transformers connected delta-star are assumed in the first circuit. The same transformer connections apply for the three-phase, two-way rectifier circuit in Figure 15.4b, except that it is a three-wire system. The six-phase source for the third circuit requires a center tap on the secondary of each transformer to convert a three-phase source to a six-phase source. The neutral N is then obtained from the common center-tap connections, and the secondaries, so connected, provide a balanced six-phase source when the delta primary is energized from a balanced three-phase source.

Zero time reference is purposely omitted in the figures for the voltage and the current waveforms. The significant points in time are the points of intersection on the graphs of appropriate source voltages. These commutating times are determined from the phase voltages for the two circuits that use the neutral return. In the three-phase, two-way rectifier circuit, however, the commutating instants of time are determined from the *line-to-line* voltages.

Various calculations for rectifier circuits are given in the next few sections. The voltage and current waveforms are a valuable aid in making the calculations. No two rectifier circuits behave in exactly the same manner. Any attempt to group all rectifier circuits into one general type of problem, or formulation, could lead to false conclusions. We can, however, take advantage of the symmetry that exists since each rectifier circuit has an integral number of symmetrical positive current pulses in the load.

15.4 Current Calculations

A single current pulse for any of the given rectifier circuits with E_{bo} type rectifiers can be expressed as

$$i/\text{pulse} = \frac{E_m \sin \omega t - E_{bo}}{R} \qquad \theta_1 < \omega t < \theta_2 \qquad (15.5)$$

provided θ_1 is defined as the initiating angle for the pulse and θ_2 is defined as the terminating angle for the current pulse. For the single-phase rectifier circuits, these angles are determined from the definition of θ_1, which follows Equation (15.1). The relationship of $\theta_1 = \pi - \theta_2$ is also true for the multiphase rectifier circuits of Section 15.3. In these circuits, however, the time duration of a current pulse is not influenced by E_{bo} provided the commutating voltage (see Figure 15.5) is greater than the voltage drop across the conducting diode or diodes. The three-phase, two-way rectifier circuit, for example, always has two diodes conducting in series. In the three-phase, one-way rectifier circuit of Figure 15.4a, θ_1 has a value of $\pi/6$. For the remaining two circuits of Figure 15.4, θ_1 has a value of $\pi/3$.

The average value of a single current pulse for any of the given rectifier circuits is expressed in general form as

$$I_{\text{ave}}/\text{pulse} = \frac{1}{2\pi} \int_{\theta_1}^{\theta_2} \frac{E_m \sin \omega t - E_{bo}}{R} \, d(\omega t) \qquad (15.6)$$

The particular rectifier circuit determines the limits of integration. The average value of current in the resistive load is

$$I_{\text{d-c}} \text{ (load)} = I_{\text{ave}}/\text{pulse} \times \text{(No. of current pulses in load)} \qquad (15.7)$$

The rms value of a single current pulse for any of the given rectifier circuits is expressed in general form as

$$I_{\text{rms}}/\text{pulse} = \left[\frac{1}{2\pi} \int_{\theta_1}^{\theta_2} \left(\frac{E_m \sin \omega t - E_{bo}}{R} \right)^2 d(\omega t) \right]^{\frac{1}{2}} \qquad (15.8)$$

The particular limits of integration are the same as for Equation (15.6). The rms value of load current is

$$I_{\text{rms}} \text{ (load)} = I_{\text{rms}}/\text{pulse} \times \sqrt{(\text{No. of current pulses in load})} \qquad (15.9)$$

Now, for any periodic waveform

$$I_{\text{rms}}^2 = I_{\text{d-c}}^2 + I_{\text{a-c}}^2 \qquad (15.10)$$

where $I_{\text{a-c}}$ is the effective (rms) value of all the sinusoidal components combined. This gives a convenient relation for calculating the effective value of sinusoidal components in rectifier circuits. For example, in the single-phase, half-wave rectifier circuit, assuming an ideal diode,

$$I_{\text{d-c}} \text{ (load)} = \frac{E_m}{\pi R} \qquad (15.11)$$

$$I_{\text{rms}} \text{ (load)} = \frac{E_m}{2R} \qquad (15.12)$$

Then

$$I_{\text{a-c}} \text{ (load)} = \sqrt{\left(\frac{E_m}{2R}\right)^2 - \left(\frac{E_m}{\pi R}\right)^2}$$
$$= \frac{E_m}{\pi R}\sqrt{\frac{\pi^2}{4} - 1} \qquad (15.13)$$

Assuming an ideal transformer, Equation (15.13) also gives the true rms value of primary current for an equivalent 1 : 1 turns ratio. This is true since the d-c component of current in the secondary cannot be transformed into the primary.

In the single-phase, full-wave rectifier circuit of Figure 15.1b, again assuming ideal diodes,

$$I_{\text{d-c}} \text{ (load)} = \frac{2E_m}{\pi R} \qquad (15.14)$$

$$I_{\text{rms}} \text{ (load)} = \frac{\sqrt{2}E_m}{2R} = \frac{E_m}{\sqrt{2R}} \qquad (15.15)$$

Then

$$I_{\text{a-c}} \text{ (load)} = \sqrt{\frac{Em^2}{2R^2} - \left(\frac{2E_m}{\pi R}\right)^2}$$
$$= \frac{2E_m}{\pi R}\sqrt{\frac{\pi^2}{8} - 1} \qquad (15.16)$$

The rms value of primary current, for an equivalent 1 : 1 turns ratio, is given by Equation (15.15) for this circuit (see Figure 15.3).

Notice that Equations (15.13) and (15.16) are written in such a way that the radical term gives the ratio of $I_{\text{a-c}}$ to $I_{\text{d-c}}$ in the load. This ratio is the ripple factor.

By applying Equations (15.6) through (15.10), with proper limits of integration, the three load currents ($I_{\text{d-c}}$, I_{rms} and $I_{\text{a-c}}$) can be determined for the multiphase rectifier circuits. A determination of general expressions for these currents is not recommended in a study of these rectifier circuits. Immediate insertion of known quantities is much easier and is recommended for each particular problem.

EXAMPLE

Given: A six-phase, one-way rectifier circuit

$$E_m = 200 \text{ volts}$$
$$E_{bo} = 20 \text{ volts}$$
$$R = 10 \text{ ohms}$$

Determine:
(a) $I_{\text{d-c}}$ (load)
(b) I_{rms} (load)

Solution:

(a)
$$I_{\text{d-c}} \text{ (load)} = \frac{6}{2\pi} \int_{\pi/3}^{2\pi/3} \frac{E_m \sin \omega t - E_{bo}}{R} \, d(\omega t)$$

$$= \frac{3}{10\pi} [-200 \cos \omega t - 20 \omega t]_{\pi/3}^{2\pi/3}$$

$$= (60/\pi) - 2 = 17.1 \text{ amp}$$

(b) I_{rms} (load) $= \left[\dfrac{6}{2\pi} \displaystyle\int_{\pi/3}^{2\pi/3} \dfrac{E_m^2 \sin^2 \omega t - 2 E_{bo} E_m \sin \omega t + E_{bo}^2}{R^2} \, d(\omega t) \right]^{\frac{1}{2}}$

$$= \left\{ \frac{3}{100\pi} \left[(200)^2 \left(\frac{\omega t}{2} - \frac{\sin 2 \, \omega t}{4} \right) \right. \right.$$
$$\left. \left. + \, 2(20)(200) \cos \omega t + (20)^2 \, \omega t \right]_{\pi/3}^{2\pi/3} \right\}^{\frac{1}{2}}$$

$$= 17.2 \text{ amp}$$

Since the rms value is only slightly greater than the d-c value, this indicates a rather low a-c value. The ripple factor is also small.

Because of the symmetry of current pulses, the rms and d-c values of current at various locations in a circuit are simply expressed in terms of load current. For example, the rms value of line current (i_1, i_2, i_3) in the three-phase, two-way rectifier circuit is

$$I_{\text{rms}} \text{ (line)} = I_{\text{rms}} \text{ (load)} \times \sqrt{\frac{4}{6}}$$

since there are four current pulses in the line compared to six pulses per cycle in the load. The d-c line current, however, is zero. (See Figure 15.6.) In this same circuit,

$$I_{\text{d-c}} \text{ (tube)} = \frac{1}{3} I_{\text{d-c}} \text{ (load)}$$

and

$$I_{\text{rms}} \text{ (tube)} = \frac{1}{\sqrt{3}} I_{\text{rms}} \text{ (load)}$$

15.5 Power and Efficiency

Multiplying both members of Equation (15.10) by the load resistance R, gives

$$I_{\text{rms}}^2 R = I_{\text{d-c}}^2 R + I_{\text{a-c}}^2 R \tag{15.17}$$

or

$$P_{\text{(rms)}} = P_{\text{(d-c)}} + P_{\text{(a-c)}} \tag{15.18}$$

A little care is needed in an interpretation of the three power terms of Equation (15.18). Each term of the equation is an *average* power, but is not average in the usual sense. For example, $P_{\text{(rms)}}$ is the *total* actual average power in the load. The power $P_{\text{(d-c)}}$ is the average power in the load due to the *average current* or *voltage* in the load and is the desired usable portion of the total power. The power $P_{\text{(a-c)}}$ is that portion of the total power due to the undesirable sinusoidal components of current or voltage and should be considered, therefore, as a power loss.

$$\text{The rectification efficiency} = \frac{P_{\text{d-c}} \text{ (load)}}{P_{\text{rms}} \text{ (load)}} \times 100 \tag{15.19}$$

The maximum rectification efficiency for a single-phase rectifier circuit with a resistive load, for example, is $\frac{4}{\pi^2} \times 100$, or 40.6%.

The rectifier circuit efficiency, as distinguished from rectification efficiency, is

Rect. Ckt. Eff.

$$= \frac{P_{\text{d-c}} \text{ (load)}}{P_{\text{d-c}} \text{ (load)} + P_{\text{a-c}} \text{ (load)} + \text{diode losses} + \text{transformer losses}} \times 100 \tag{15.20}$$

The power loss in a diode of a rectifier circuit is expressed by

$$\text{diode loss} = \frac{1}{T} \int_0^T i_b e_b \, dt \tag{15.21}$$

For an E_{bo} type of diode this loss becomes

$$\text{diode loss} = (I_{\text{d-c}} \text{ in diode}) E_{bo} \tag{15.22}$$

However, a diode having a constant forward resistance r_b has a loss of

$$\text{diode loss} = (I_{\text{rms}}^2 \text{ in diode}) r_b \tag{15.23}$$

15.6 Transformer Volt-Ampere Ratings

One of the identifying characteristics of a distribution transformer is its volt-ampere rating, which is actually the volt-amperes available at the output terminals of the transformer. It is not necessarily a direct indication of the volt-ampere rating of the various windings in the transformer. The volt-ampere rating of the several windings should be referred to as the *parts* rating. The volt-amperes available at the output terminals of an autotransformer, for example, could be identical to that available from an isolating transformer, but the *parts* rating of the two transformers would not be equal. The *parts* rating is lower for the autotransformer.

In rectifier circuits, the transformer *parts* rating is influenced by the circuit arrangement external to the transformer as well as by the transformer connections. It becomes essential to identify the volt-amperes of the secondary windings and the volt-amperes of the primary windings for each type of rectifier circuit. The single-phase, full-wave rectifier circuit of Figure 15.1b, as one example, has a total volt-amperes in the two halves of the secondary that is larger than the volt-amperes in the primary by the $\sqrt{2}$, assuming an ideal transformer. This ratio is determined by expressing the total volt-amperes of the secondary as the sum of the volt-amperes (rms current multiplied by rms voltage) of the two secondary windings and dividing this sum by the volt-amperes of the primary. The six-phase, one-way rectifier circuit also has a secondary to primary volt-ampere ratio of the $\sqrt{2}$.

However, the single-phase, full-wave rectifier circuit of Figure 15.1c and the three-phase, two-way rectifier circuit of Figure 15.4b have a volt-ampere ratio of unity. This is true since the d-c current is zero in each secondary winding of these circuits.

15.7   Controlled Rectification

The discussion of this section is an introduction to the topics of several sections to follow in this chapter.

The general problem of controlled rectification is illustrated by an instantaneous plot of load current i_L in Figure 15.8. A single-phase, full-wave rectifier circuit is implied here. The point of interest, however, is the variable value of θ_1.

Referring to Figure 15.8, the average load current I_{d-c} is a function of I_m and θ_1. With i_L a portion of a sinusoidal function,

$$I_{d-c} = \frac{1}{\pi} \int_{\theta_1}^{\pi} I_m \sin \omega t \, d(\omega t)$$

$$= \frac{2 I_m}{\pi} \left(\frac{1 + \cos \theta_1}{2} \right) \tag{15.24}$$

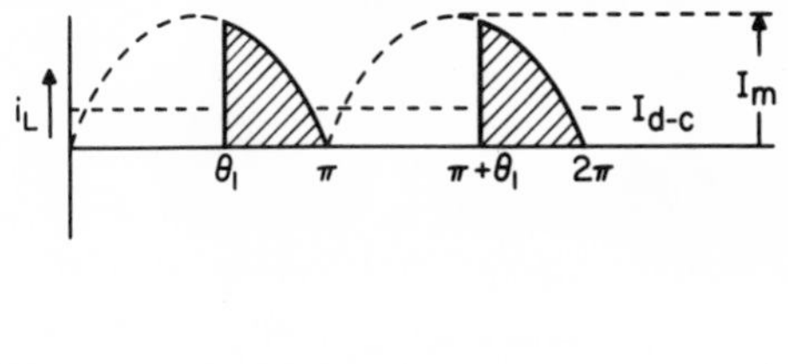

Fig. 15.8 Average current is a function of the firing angle θ_1.

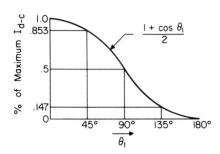

Fig. 15.9 A graph of $(1 + \cos \theta_1)/2$.

where $2I_m/\pi$ is the maximum value of *average* load current occurring for $\theta_1 = 0$. In a single-phase, half-wave rectifier circuit this coefficient is I_m/π.

The parenthetical factor of $(1 + \cos \theta_1)/2$ is a significant variable indicating the influence of θ_1 on the average load current. It is plotted in Figure 15.9 which clearly shows that θ_1 has the greatest effect when varied about 90°. The graph also emphasizes the insignificance of varying θ_1 near zero or near 180°.

The objective of controlled rectification is to control the time intervals of current pulses in a load, with a selected type of rectifier circuit arrangement; in other words, the circuitry is not to be changed. This implies the need of a voltage or current signal of some sort that will serve to influence the instant when the controllable device of a rectifier circuit is changed from a nonconducting to a conducting state.

There is more than one type of device that has the required characteristics to permit control between nonconducting and conducting states. There are rectifiers that inherently have the characteristics to permit direct control, as illustrated by the block diagram of Figure 15.10a. A grid-controlled gas tube, or thyratron, and silicon-controlled rectifiers are such devices.

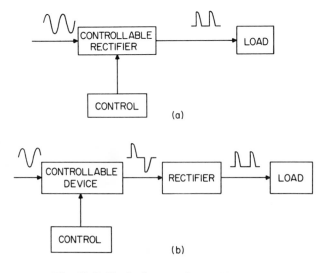

Fig. 15.10 Block diagrams for rectifier circuits.

Other devices have the desired controllable characteristics but are not rectifiers; for example, the magnetic amplifier is such a device. The block diagram of Figure 15.10b is representative of these devices.

15.8 Delayed Firing

The waveforms of Figure 15.8 illustrated that the average value of load current can be changed by controlling the firing angle θ_1. The available techniques for controlling the firing angle depend on the type of controllable rectifying device that is used. One method that is applicable to any of the devices is a control of the phase-angle for the control voltage or the control current. Phase-shifting circuits, required for this purpose, are discussed in the next section.

15.9 Phase-Shifting Circuits

Two phase-shifting circuits are shown in Figure 15.11. The phaser locus diagrams illustrate the behavior of these circuits. Notice that the magnitude of E_s, for the RC circuit or the RL circuit, is a constant independent of R and C, or of R and L. The phase angle of E_s, with respect to the transformer secondary voltage V_{ab}, is adjusted or varied by an adjustment or variation of one of the circuit parameters in either circuit. The voltage references on the circuit diagrams, and the phasor notations on the locus diagrams, are selected in order to have E_s *lag* the voltage V_{ab} by some angle ϕ.

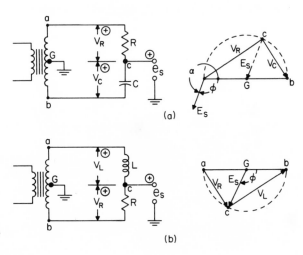

Fig. 15.11 RC and RL phase shifting circuits.

The significant voltage relationships in the two circuits, as represented by the locus diagrams, are verified by writing appropriate voltage equations. For the RC phase-shifting circuit,

$$E_s = V_c - \tfrac{1}{2} V_{ab} \qquad (15.25)$$

and for the RL phase-shifting circuit,

$$E_s = V_R - \tfrac{1}{2} V_{ab} \qquad (15.26)$$

The phase relationship of E_s with reference to V_{ab} is determined by expressing V_C (RC circuit) and V_R (RL circuit), of the last two equations, in terms of V_{ab}. Thus, in the RC circuit,

$$V_c = V_{ab} \frac{-jX_c}{R - jX_c} \qquad (15.27)$$

Then, Equation (15.25) simplifies to

$$E_s = \frac{V_{ab}}{2} \left(-e^{2j\tan^{-1}(X_c/R)} \right)$$

$$= \frac{V_{ab}}{2} \left(e^{\pm j\pi} e^{2j\tan^{-1}(X_c/R)} \right) \qquad (15.28)$$

With $+j\pi$, or $-j\pi$, Equation (15.28) gives the angle by which E_s respectively leads or lags V_{ab}. These angles are designated as α and ϕ in Figure 15.11a. Since the angle of lag is of primary interest, the following equation is set up:

$$\phi_{RC} = -180° + 2 \tan^{-1} \frac{X_c}{R} \qquad (15.29)$$

for the RC phase-shifting circuit.

In the RL phase-shifting circuit,

$$V_R = V_{ab} \frac{R}{R + jX_L} \qquad (15.30)$$

which, by substitution in Equation (15.26), gives

$$E_s = \frac{V_{ab}}{2} e^{-2j\tan^{-1}(X_L/R)} \qquad (15.31)$$

where the angle of lag is

$$\phi_{RL} = -2 \tan^{-1} \frac{X_L}{R} \qquad (15.32)$$

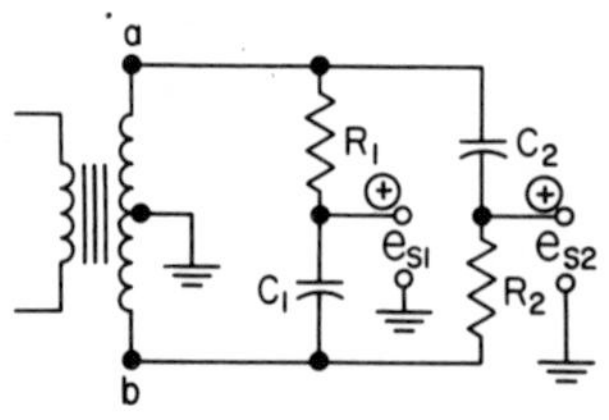

Fig. 15.12 Double RC phase shifting circuit.

Now, a single-phase full-wave rectifier circuit requires two signal voltages that are in series but 180° out of phase. One circuit arrangement that will satisfy this requirement is illustrated with Figure 15.12. An analysis of the phaser relationship of E_{s2} reveals that

$$E_{s2} = \frac{V_{ab}}{2} e^{2j\tan^{-1}(X_{c2}/R_L)} \qquad (15.33)$$

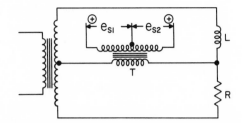

Fig. 15.13 Phase shifting circuit with center tapped transformer - coupled output.

Since E_{s1} of Figure 15.12 is identical to E_s of Equation (15.28), it is observed that

$$E_{s2} = -E_{s1} \quad \text{if} \quad \frac{X_{c2}}{R_2} = \frac{X_{c1}}{R_1} \quad \text{or if} \quad R_2 C_2 = R_1 C_1 \qquad (15.34)$$

Another method of satisfying the requirements for the two signal voltages is to use transformer coupling from the output of either phase-shifting circuit of Figure 15.11, as illustrated by transformer T of Figure 15.13. A center tap is required on the secondary of this transformer. The coupling transformer can be one that is designed to approximate a linear response, or it can be designed to operate as a nonlinear device so that the output voltage waveform is a series of peaks, rather than a sinusoidal waveform. The transformer is then identified as a peaking transformer.

15.10 Peaking Transformers

A peaking transformer is designed to yield pulses of voltage at the terminals of one winding when a sinusoidal voltage is applied to the other winding of a two-winding transformer. This is accomplished by using an unsymmetrical magnetic circuit as illustrated by Figure 15.14. The core within the coil N_2 has a much smaller area and has higher permeance than the remainder of the magnetic circuit. Consequently, this part of the core saturates at a lower flux level than other parts of the magnetic circuit.

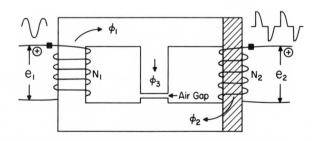

Fig. 15.14 Peaking transformer.

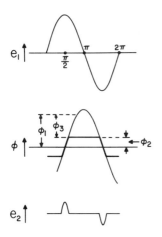

Fig. 15.15 Voltage and flux waveforms for the circuit in Figure 15.14.

The voltage and magnetic flux waveforms for the peaking transformer are shown in Figure 15.15. When a sinusoidal voltage is applied to the terminals of N_1, the resulting magnetic flux in each leg of the core is as indicated. The magnetic flux ϕ is represented as a sinusoid, which it must be if the resistance of N_1 is small. Since the core within N_2 saturates at a low level, it is then possible to obtain a trapezoidal waveform for ϕ_2. The voltage induced in the coil N_2 is proportional to the rate of change of ϕ_2, or

$$e_2 = N_2 \frac{d\phi_2}{dt} \qquad (15.35)$$

The magnitude of the resulting short time-duration pulses of e_2 is dependent on the steepness of the leading and trailing edges of ϕ_2 which, in turn, is dependent on the maximum value of ϕ_1.

The center leg of the magnetic circuit provides a low reluctance magnetic circuit for the *leakage* flux during the intervals when ϕ_2 is at saturation. This keeps the magnetizing ampere turns low for N_1. Consequently, the input impedance remains high to avoid excessive loading of the source, which provides the input voltage e_1. However, the reluctance of the center leg must be high compared to the reluctance of the unsaturated ϕ_2 path. This is the reason for the short air gap. The two conflicting requirements of the center leg account for the fact that the leading and trailing edges (with rounded corners) are less steep than ϕ_1, over the corresponding time intervals, as illustrated in Figure 15.15.

15.11   The Saturable Reactor as a Variable Inductor

The possible requirement of an *automatic* phase-shifting circuit creates the need for an inductor, capacitor, or resistor that can be caused to vary on demand in accordance with error signals of a particular control system. A saturable reactor, represented by Figure 15.16, can be caused to represent a wide range of inductance values merely by changing the d-c control current I_c.

Referring to Figure 15.16, the windings N_1 and N_2 have the same number of turns and are connected series-aiding when considered as a two-winding transformer. For linear operation, this arrangement will not cause a voltage to be induced in the control winding N_C when an a-c voltage, e, is applied.

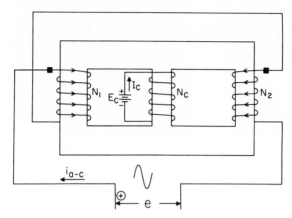

Fig. 15.16 Common core saturable reactor.

The control-ampere turns establishes a bias *mmf* in each outer leg of the magnetic circuit, thereby influencing the magnitude of inductance exhibited by coils N_1 and N_2. This effect is explained with the aid of Figures 15.17 and 15.18.

The sense of the windings and the current references on the two-core saturable reactor of Figure 15.17 are in agreement with that shown in Figure 15.16. Notice that the d-c ampere-turns and the a-c ampere-turns are additive for core 2 but subtractive for core 1, with the winding and current

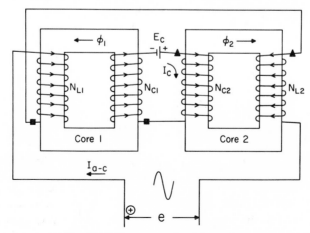

Fig. 15.17 Two-core saturable reactor.

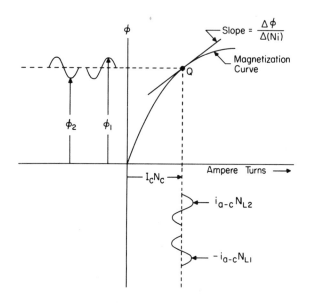

Fig. 15.18 Magnetization curve illustrating inductance and phase relationships for Figure 15.17.

references as shown on the diagram. Thus, when an a-c voltage, e, is applied, the resultant ampere-turns in each core are:

$$\text{Resultant } Ni \text{ of core } 1 = I_C N_{C1} - i_{a\text{-}c} N_{L1} \qquad (15.36)$$

$$\text{Resultant } Ni \text{ of core } 2 = I_C N_{C2} + i_{a\text{-}c} N_{L2} \qquad (15.37)$$

These ampere-turn relationships are illustrated in Figure 15.18. The magnetization curve of this figure is idealized to the extent that hysteresis effects are neglected. The diagram clearly illustrates significant characteristics of a two-core saturable reactor when it is used as a variable inductor. The significant characteristics, the most important of which is the variable inductance, are now stated in the itemized paragraphs that follow.

(a) The a-c ampere-turns in the two cores are in *time-phase opposition* when the d-c ampere-turns in the two cores represent the common reference. The inverse, with a different choice of references, is to have the a-c ampere-turns *in time-phase*.

(b) The resultant magnetic flux ϕ_1 in core 1 and the resultant magnetic flux ϕ_2 in core 2 have components that are in *phase opposition* when the positive references are as indicated in Figure 15.17. This choice of references merely permits a study centered at a single quiescent point Q on a common magnetization curve (see Figure 15.18) for the two cores. Any other set of positive references for magnetic flux could require a second Q point, symmetrically located on the negative portion of the magnetization curve.

(c) With only the one Q point established, the a-c ampere-turns have the effect of driving the two cores in opposite directions. More significantly, when the a-c ampere-turns drive one core closer to saturation the other core is driven further away from saturation. This is a physical fact regardless of the choice of positive references for magnetic flux. The one exception is for zero d-c ampere-turns, in which case the cores are equidistant from either level of saturation.

(d) An approximate linear relationship exists between the changing components of magnetic flux and ampere-turns, provided only a small swing about the Q point is permitted.

(e) The slope of the saturation curve at any Q point is an indication of the inductance exhibited by the winding N_{L1}, or N_{L2}, since inductance can be defined as

$$L = N \frac{d\phi}{di} \tag{15.38}$$

For the coordinates indicated in Figure 15.18, however, the slope of the saturation curve is $\Delta\phi/\Delta \, (Ni)$. Thus

$$\text{Slope (Figure 15.18)} = \frac{\Delta\phi}{N \Delta i_{\text{a-c}}} = \frac{L_1}{N_{L1}^2} = \frac{L_2}{N_{L2}^2} \tag{15.39}$$

where $N_{L1} = N_{L2}$, and $N_{C1} = N_{C2}$, and the saturation curve for the two cores are identical as assumed in all of the preceding itemized paragraphs.

15.12 Controlled Rectification With a Two-Core Saturable Reactor (Magnetic Amplifiers)

Except for the addition of a series load resistance R, the circuit diagram of Figure 15.19a is a schematic representation for the two-core saturable reactor of Figure 15.17. This circuit can yield alternately positive and negative pulses of load current as represented in Figure 15.20a. The angle θ_1, or $\pi + \theta_1$, at which these current pulses are initiated, is controlled by the average value of control current I_c. Thus, by including a rectifier circuit, Figure 15.19b, the two-core saturable reactor provides a unique and reliable method of controlled rectification.

The behavior of the circuit cannot be explained briefly. There are too many interdependent quantities that influence the angle θ_1 at which the current pulses are initiated. True, for a given circuit (number of turns, core material and dimensions, load resistance, and applied voltage), the angle θ_1 is controlled by adjusting the control-circuit current I_C. A calculation of θ_1 includes all of the circuitry components, as well as the applied voltage, as dependent quantities. One equation involving θ_1 is easily recognized from Figure 15.20 (also, see Figure 15.9) as

$$I_R = \frac{2E_m}{\pi R} \frac{(1 + \cos \theta_1)}{2} \tag{15.40}$$

where I_R is the rectified average value of load current and E_m is the maximum

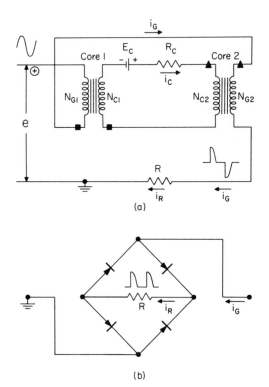

Fig. 15.19 Simplified schematic diagram for a magnetic amplifier.

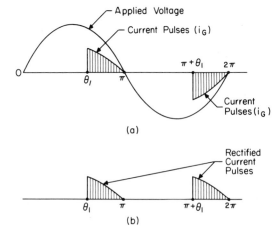

Fig. 15.20 Applied voltage and possible current pulses for magnetic amplifier circuit in Figure 15.19

value of a sinusoidal applied voltage. The equation is true provided the two reactors have two states, one state of full conduction during the intervals of current pulses and a second state of no conduction (at least low conduction) during the intervals between current pulses. Further study, provided later in this section, is required to determine how the two reactors can exhibit either of the two states of full conduction or no conduction.

In a magnetic amplifier circuit, the rectified average value of load current can also be calculated from an equation that does not include θ_1. This equation involves an equality of ampere-turns within certain limits of operation. For the circuit of Figure 15.19 the ampere-turns relationship is

$$N_G I_G = N_C I_C \tag{15.41}$$

where N_G is the number of turns on the *gate* windings N_{G1} or N_{G2}, N_C is the number of turns on the *control* windings N_{C1} or N_{C2}, I_G is the *rectified* average value of gate current, and I_C is the average value of control current. The term "*gate*" is descriptive of the *on-off* characteristics required for the two reactors.

The two significant Equations (15.40) and (15.41) are presented early in this discussion to direct attention to their importance, before continuing with a more detailed study of the magnetic amplifier circuit of Figure 15.19. Let us now direct our attention to this circuit.

If either of the two reactors are to exhibit *on* and *off* characteristics, the B-H curves of the magnetic core should be rectangular with low hysteresis. A typical B-H curve for square-loop core material is shown in Figure 15.21. With this type of core material, windings will exhibit either a very low inductance when the core is in saturation, or a very high inductance when the core is not in saturation. The resulting *on-off* characteristic of a *single* reactor must now be distinguished from the *on-off* characteristic of the *two* reactors, when connected in series as shown in Figure 15.19. The two reactors can exhibit the state of high conduction even though only one of the cores is in saturation. This is true because the unsaturated reactor is coupled to an impedance load of R_C only. If R_C is small, the unsaturated core acts like a current transformer and therefore has an *on* state when the other reactor is *on* because of satura-

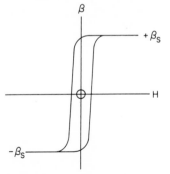

Fig. 15.21 Hysteresis loop for square-loop core material.

tion. Actually, the firing angle θ_1 is controllable provided the two cores are not simultaneously in saturation. This gating of current pulses is explained in the next section.

15.13 Gating of Current Pulses in Magnetic Amplifiers

The diagrams of Figures 15.22, 15.23, and 15.24 show instantaneous time functions of applied voltage, magnetic flux and ampere-turns for three different values of control ampere-turns. In Figure 15.22, the control ampere

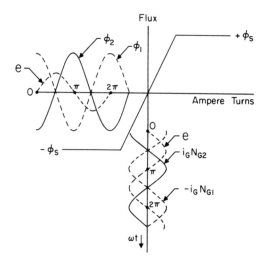

Fig. 15.22 Zero control ampere-turns and idealized saturation curve.

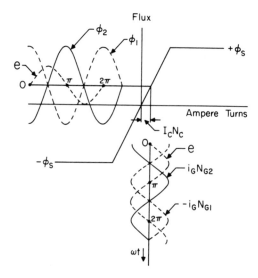

Fig. 15.23 Control ampere-turns adjusted to permit cores to just reach saturation.

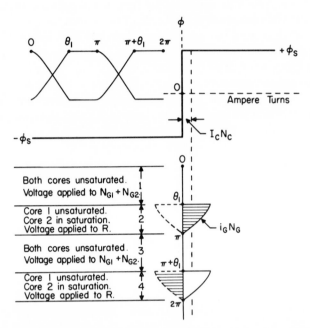

Fig. 15.24 A study of relationships in the two cores of a magnetic amplifier.

turns are zero. In Figure 15.23, the control ampere-turns are adjusted in such a way that the magnetic flux and the net ampere-turns of either core and reactor just reach saturation at one instant of time each cycle. In Figure 15.24 the control ampere-turns are increased considerably, thereby causing the two cores alternately to enter saturation at θ_1 and $\pi + \theta_1$. Comparing these three diagrams, the first two have an expanded ampere-turn scale to illustrate the excitation ampere-turns as a function of time. The diagram of Figure 15.24 has a more normal ampere-turn scale that emphasizes the *gated* ampere-turns. The excitation ampere-turns are neglected in this third diagram. (These three diagrams will be studied in more detail in the following paragraphs.)

The phase relationships for e, ϕ_1, ϕ_2, $-i_G N_{G1}$, $i_G N_{G2}$, $i_C N_{C1}$ and $i_C N_{C2}$ are in agreement with the selected positive references of the two-core saturable reactor, Figure 15.19. *It is very important to have an exact understanding of these phase relationships and their relation to the actual physical conditions in the circuit.* To aid in this problem of analysis, the magnetic polarity marks on the schematic diagram of Figure 15.19 (or Figure 15.17) have an additional significance beyond that which is conventionally associated with magnetic polarity marks. Except for the winding N_{G1}, observe that the *reference* current (i_C or i_G) enters the marked end of the coil. This means that $i_C N_{C1}$, $i_C N_{C2}$ and $i_G N_{G2}$ shall be written and preceded by a positive (+) sign while the ampere-turns in N_{G1} shall be written always as $-i_G N_{G1}$, when expressing the algebraic sum of ampere-turns. Now, observe the positive reference that was selected for the flux in the two cores and note that (+) ampere-turns agree with (+) flux for *either* core. What we wish to do here, is to avoid the necessity of always referring to a schematic diagram that shows the direction of wrapping each coil on the cores. Conventionally, for example, the two magnetic polarity marks on the windings of core 1 could have been placed at the opposite ends of the windings. If this were done, however, then it would be necessary to state that (−) ampere-turns agree with (+) flux for core 1, and we do not have the same defining notations for the two cores.

A study of the diagrams of Figures 15.22 through 15.25 leads to an understanding of the gating action of the magnetic amplifier represented by the circuit diagram of Figure 15.19. Significant relationships are now discussed in outline form.

(A) When both reactors are operating entirely within the steep linear portion of the saturation curve, Figure 15.22 and Figure 15.23, then

(1) The net ampere-turns and the resultant magnetic flux variations are continuous sinusoidal functions. Observe that the two cores are driven in opposite directions from saturation; that is, when one core is headed toward saturation the other is headed away from saturation.

(2) As illustrated in Figure 15.23, ϕ_2 or $i_G N_{G2}$ just reaches the saturation level at π, and ϕ_1 or $-i_G N_{G1}$ just reaches the saturation level one-half cycle later at 2π.

(3) The control ampere-turns are simply $I_C N_{C1}$ and $I_C N_{C2}$, since the net induced voltage in the control circuit is zero. There is an induced voltage in N_{C1} and also in N_{C2}, but these two voltages are in *phase opposition*.

(B) The diagram of Figure 15.24 illustrates a condition in which $I_C N_C$ has sufficient magnitude to cause the two cores to enter saturation on alternate half-cycles. This generates the desired and controllable current pulses in the load. Before considering these current pulses in detail (paragraph C), it is well to examine the four significant time intervals indicated in Figure 15.24.

(1) In the interval from $0°$ to θ_1, both cores are unsaturated. Neglecting the exciting current, the source voltage is applied entirely to $N_{G1} + N_{G2}$. The magnetic flux of core 1 is headed away from saturation while the magnetic flux of core 2 is headed toward saturation, reaching saturation at θ_1. Also, neglecting the exciting current, all

ampere turns must be zero for both reactors since both cores are out of saturation during this interval.

(2) In the interval from θ_1 to π, core 2 is in saturation but core 1 is well out of saturation. The two reactors now have a condition of full conduction since core 2 is in saturation and reactor 1 is acting like an ideal current transformer, provided R_C is small. The source voltage is now applied entirely to the load R for this interval.

During this same interval, the ampere-turns in each of the four windings require special attention since pulses of current also exist in the control circuit because of the current-transformer action of reactor 1. Now, since core 1 is not in saturation the net ampere-turns of reactor 1 must instantaneously add to zero during this second time interval. Similarily, since core 2 *is* in saturation then the ampere turns of reactor 2 must not add to zero at any instant during this interval. (The exciting current is still being neglected, of course.) See Figure 15.25 and paragraph (C) of this outlined discussion.

(3) In the interval from π to $\pi + \theta_1$, both cores are again unsaturated where the magnetic flux of core 2 is headed away from saturation and the magnetic flux of core 1 is headed toward saturation, reaching it at $\pi + \theta_1$. Again, the net ampere-turns of both cores must be zero for this interval.

(4) In the interval from $\pi + \theta_1$ to 2π, core 1 is in saturation and core 2 is out of saturation. The two reactors again have a condition of full conduction, but this time it is due to the saturation in core 1 and the current-transformer action of reactor 2. Consequently, the net ampere-turns of reactor 2 must instantaneously add to zero but

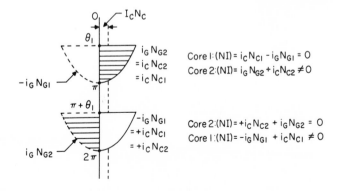

Core 1:(NI)= $i_C N_{C1} - i_G N_{G1} = 0$
Core 2:(NI)= $i_G N_{G2} + i_C N_{C2} \neq 0$

Core 2:(NI)= $+i_C N_{C2} + i_G N_{G2} = 0$
Core 1:(NI)= $-i_G N_{G1} + i_C N_{C1} \neq 0$

Fig. 15.25 Ampere-turn relationships.

must not add to zero at any instant for reactor 1 over this fourth time interval.

(C) The current and ampere-turn relations are now summarized for the four significant time intervals. (See Figure 15.25.) Exciting currents are neglected.

(1) From $0°$ to θ_1, the current is instantaneously zero in each of the four windings.

(2) From θ_1 to π,

$$i_C N_{C1} - i_G N_{G1} = 0 \qquad (15.42)$$

$$i_C N_{C2} + i_G N_{G2} \neq 0 \qquad (15.43)$$

$$|i_C N_{c1}| = |i_G N_{G1}| = |i_C N_{C2}| = |i_G N_{G2}| \qquad (15.44)$$

(3) From π to $\pi + \theta_1$, the current is instantaneously zero in each of the four windings.

(4) From $\pi + \theta_1$ to 2π,

$$i_C N_{C2} + i_G N_{G2} = 0 \qquad (15.45)$$

$$i_C N_{G1} - i_G N_{G1} \neq 0 \qquad (15.46)$$

and Equation (15.44) is also true for this interval; that is, the *magnitudes* of the four ampere-turns are equal.

(5) For each half-cycle of the supply voltage, the four existing ampere-turns ($i_C N_{C1}$, $i_C N_{C2}$, $-i_G N_{G1}$, and $i_G N_{G2}$) have the same magnitude of *average* ampere-turns. Observe the symmetry in Figure 15.25. This average value is $I_C N_C$. Thus

$$I_C N_C = I_G N_G$$

as previously represented by Equation (15.41).

15.14   Load Current Calculations

From Equation (15.41), the rectified average value of gate current I_G is

$$I_G = I_C \frac{N_c}{N_G} \qquad (15.47)$$

provided the equality of control circuit ampere-turns and gate circuit ampere-turns is applicable. Neglecting exciting current, this equality is true if the firing angle θ_1 is within the limits of $0°$ and π. Expressed as a function of θ_1, the rectified average value of gate current [see Equation (15.40)] is

$$I_G = \frac{2E_m}{\pi R} \left(\frac{1 + \cos \theta_1}{2} \right) \qquad (15.48)$$

where E_m is the peak value of the sinusoidal source voltage. This equation indicates that the supply voltage, the load resistance, and the firing angle θ_1 are the three possible variables influencing the magnitude of the gate current and therefore the load current. In view of these three variables, the equation is easily misinterpreted if considered only as a mathematical expression. Actually, the firing angle θ_1 is inherently determined by the magnetic amplifier. Only the supply voltage and the load resistance are adjustable quantities external to the magnetic amplifier. It is important to remember that I_G is fixed in magnitude by the equality of the gate circuit ampere-turns to the control circuit ampere-turns. Thus, with I_G *fixed*, any change of supply voltage or load resistance will cause the firing angle θ_1 to automatically change such that Equation (15.48) gives this constant value for I_G. This means that I_G *is independent of the supply voltage and the load resistance*, provided θ_1 is within the limits of $0°$ and π.

The supply voltage and the load resistance primarily determine the *maximum* rectified *average* value of gate current that is possible when θ_1 is zero. Thus

$$I_G \text{ (max)} = \frac{2E_m}{\pi R} \qquad (15.49)$$

Although the maximum value of I_G is directly proportional to the ratio of the supply voltage to the load resistance, this does not mean that the ratio can be increased without limit. Normally the supply voltage is adjusted to cause a magnetic flux swing that is within the saturation levels of the cores when the control current is zero, as illustrated in Figure 15.22. If the supply voltage is excessive, both cores are driven to saturation, one at $+\phi_s$ and the other at $-\phi_s$. This makes it impossible to reduce the gate current to the excitation level and still have control of the firing angle.

For the series connected reactors (Figure 15.19), the flux swing is determined from Faraday's law expressed in integral form

$$\phi = \frac{1}{N_G} \int \frac{E_m}{2} \sin \omega t \, dt \qquad (15.50)$$

$$= -\frac{E_m}{2\omega N_G} \cos \omega t \qquad (15.51)$$

where $E_m \sin \omega t$ is the supply voltage, one half of which is applied to each

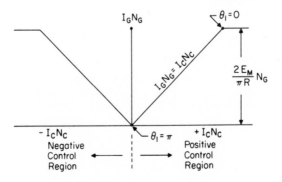

Fig. 15.26 Rectified-average $I_G N_G$ as a function of $I_C N_C$.

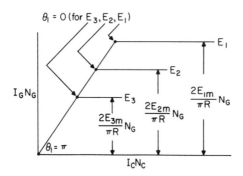

Fig. 15.27 Magnitude of source voltage influences range of control.

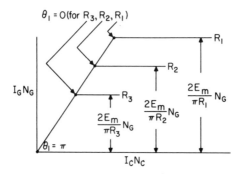

Fig. 15.28 Magnitude of load resistance influences range of control.

gate winding when I_c is zero, assuming the load resistance is much less than the reactance of the gate windings. For the condition that neither core ever enters saturation, the peak-to-peak flux swing from Equation (15.51) is

$$\phi_{p-p} = \frac{E_m}{\omega N_G} = \frac{E_m}{2\pi f N_G} = \frac{E_{\text{ave}}}{4 f N_G} \qquad (15.52)$$

which is applicable to the conditions shown in Figure 15.23 where I_c is not zero, as well as to the conditions shown in Figure 15.22 where I_c is zero.

The characteristics of the magnetic amplifier discussed in this and pre-ceding sections are represented graphically by the diagrams of Figures 15.26, 15.27, and 15.28. The graphs are ideal, assuming ideal core materials and neglecting exciting current.

15.15   Other Magnetic Amplifier Circuits

The series-connected type of magnetic amplifier circuit, as discussed in the preceding three sections, is only one of many magnetic amplifier circuits. Also, the applications of magnetic amplifiers are not restricted to controlled rectification problems.

A complete and detailed study of magnetic amplifiers should include the **effects of the exciting current, the true nonlinear characteristics of the**

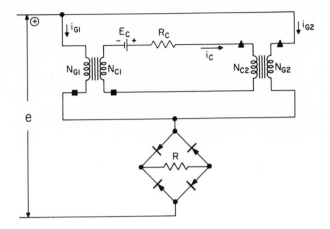

Fig. 15.29 Parallel connected saturable reactors.

saturation curve, the characteristics of any diodes included in the circuit, and the practical circuitry arrangements including feedback. It is not the purpose of this text to include an extended treatment of magnetic amplifiers.

The magnetic amplifier circuit with series-connected saturable reactors is, however, a basic type. Two other circuits are shown in Figure 15.29 and Figure 15.30. Respectively, these two circuits are the ordinary parallel-connected saturable reactors and the self-saturating parallel-connected reactors. Observe that the only difference in the circuitry is the addition of diodes D_1 and D_2 in series with the gate windings of the latter circuit.

Characteristics of the parallel-connected circuit of Figure 15.29 is very similar to the series-connected circuit. When either core is in saturation,

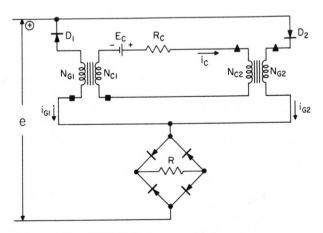

Fig. 15.30 Diodes in gate circuits.

the other reactor becomes a current transformer if the control-circuit resistance is small. Thus, the ampere-turn relationships as represented in the preceding sections for the series-connected circuit also apply to the ordinary parallel-connected circuit. In other words, the two gate currents i_{G1} and i_{G2} are equal in the parallel circuit when R_C is small. In the series circuit, i_{G1} must equal i_{G2} since they are one and the same current. The supply voltage for the parallel circuit is, of course, one half that required for the series circuit with identical reactors.

The addition of diodes in series with the gate windings, as indicated in Figure 15.30, has the effect of blocking the current-transformer action of either reactor when the core of the other reactor is saturated. Still, the circuit can have controllable pulses of current in the load that are similar to the ordinary series or parallel circuits. The study of a single-reactor circuit with diodes, as presented in the next section, will reveal more clearly the behavior of the two-reactor circuit with diodes.

There are a few significant facts that can be observed by reference to Figure 15.30 before studying a single-reactor circuit. Assuming, for the present, that the firing angles θ_1 and $\pi + \theta_1$ can exist as before, then when either core enters saturation, a pulse of current is initiated and exists in the gate winding of the reactor that is saturated. This load component of current is not caused to exist in any of the remaining three windings, since the unsaturated reactor cannot act like a current transformer in the presence of its diode, during the current pulse interval. For example, referring to Figure 15.30, a positive pulse of i_{G2} only can exist during the positive half-cycle of the supply voltage, and a negative pulse of i_{G1} only can exist during the negative half-cycle of the supply voltage.

Now, when either reactor comes out of saturation at π or 2π the unsaturated reactor is driven toward saturation. During this same interval, the reactor which came out of saturation is driven away from saturation by the *voltage-transformer action* of the other reactor. Referring to Figure 15.30, when reactor 2 comes out of saturation at π the negative half-cycle of the supply voltage is applied to N_{G1}, neglecting the voltage across any other part of this gate circuit that is present because of exciting current. By voltage transformer action, the voltage induced in N_{C1} is applied to N_{C2}, assuming that R_C is small. This voltage applied to N_{C2} has the proper polarity to reset the flux level of core 2 away from saturation. The excursion from saturation is dependent on the time interval required for reactor 1 to reach saturation.

15.16   The Single-Core Reactor

The self-saturating magnetic amplifier of Figure 15.30 has two reactors with the two gate windings, and their respective diodes, connected in parallel.

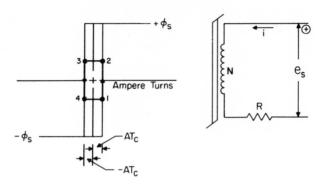

Fig. 15.31 A study with a single winding on square-loop core material.

The behavior of the self-saturating magnetic amplifier becomes more easily understood after a study of a single-core saturable reactor. Actually, the single-core reactor has a number of unique applications of its own, especially when the core is of square-loop material. It may have a single winding or a number of windings. The presence of diodes in the circuitry has an important influence on the characteristics of a single-core saturable reactor. It is the presence of these diodes, or a unidirectional current in the absence of diodes, that can give the reactor a self-saturating or storage property. As an energy storage device, it can be triggered *on* and *off*. Consequently it can be used in applications that require such characteristics of an electrical device. Systems employing circuit logic, as in digital computers and in the automatic control of certain manufacturing processes, are significant general applications.

A one-winding saturable reactor having an assumed square-loop magnetization curve is shown in Figure 15.31. The magnetization curve is represented with flux as a function of ampere-turns. The magnitude of AT_c, as defined on the diagram, is commonly identified as the coercive ampere-turns. Regardless of whether the core has one winding or more than one winding, the reactor can be in any one of three possible states. Two of these states are illustrated by the time diagrams of Figure 15.32. Here, a condition is represented in which the source voltage is less than that required to cause the flux to reach the saturation level. Consequently the ampere-turns of the single-winding reactor cannot be greater than $+AT_c$ nor less than $-AT_c$. The significant points (1-2-3-4) on the Ni time diagram correspond to the positions (1-2-3-4) on the magnitization curve. From Point 1 to Point 2, $Ni = AT_c$ and the flux is increasing toward $+\phi_s$ during this interval. From Point 2 to Point 3 the one-winding circuit with a series R is resistance limiting. From Point 3 to Point 4, $Ni = -AT_c$ and the flux is forced away from

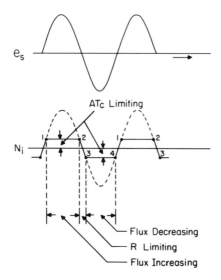

Fig. 15.32 Waveforms corresponding to the conditions shown in Fig. 15.31.

$+\phi_s$ during this interval. From Point 4 to Point 1 the circuit again becomes resistance limiting and the cycle is completed. Of course, with a larger voltage the reactor could be forced into saturation at $+\phi_s$ during an interval of the positive half-cycle of the source voltage, but also into $-\phi_s$ during an interval of the negative half-cycle of the source voltage. Normally, it is desired to have the reactor saturate at only one of the two saturation levels, either $+\phi_s$ or $-\phi_s$. In any case, the three possible states of a single-core reactor are

(a) The net instantaneous ampere-turns, assuming the possibility of more than one winding, are *within* the limits of $+AT_c$ and $-AT_c$.

(b) The net instantaneous ampere-turns are exactly $+AT_c$ or $-AT_c$. The flux can be caused to increase or decrease, respectively, only if this condition exists.

(c) The net instantaneous ampere-turns are greater than AT_c. For this state, the reactor is in saturation.

The diagrams of Figure 15.33 illustrate the behavior of a single-winding saturable reactor having a series diode and a series load resistance, when the source voltage is sinusoidal. The significant points (1 through 9) on the Ni time diagram and the corresponding positions (1 through 9) on the square-loop magnetization curve are of particular interest. For the results, as shown, it is assumed that the circuit is initially energized at $\omega t = 0$. From Point 0 to Point 1 the circuit is resistance limiting. After Point 1, the ampere-turns are limited to $+AT_c$ since the reactor cannot be driven instantly to saturation. From Point 1 to Point 2 the flux is increasing toward saturation. The change in flux from 1 to 2 is

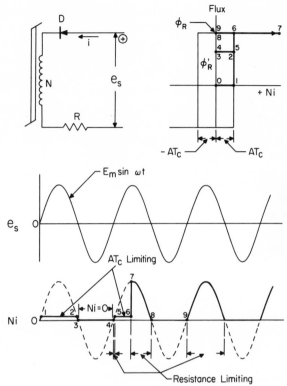

Fig. 15.33 A study of a single winding saturable reactor when a series diode is used.

$$\phi_2 - \phi_1 = \phi_2 = \frac{1}{N} \int_{t_1}^{t_2 = (T/2) - t_1} E_m \sin \omega t \, dt \qquad (15.53)$$

where the subscripts have reference to the significant points on the diagrams of Figure 15.33.

Knowing that $Ni_1 = Ni_2 = AT_c$, the time t_1 can be calculated. The current at Point 1 is

$$i_1 = \frac{E_m \sin \omega t_1}{R + r_d} \qquad (15.54)$$

where r_d is the forward resistance of the diode. The value of R should include the resistance of the winding. Now, since

$$Ni_1 = AT_c \qquad (15.55)$$

then

$$N\left(\frac{E_m \sin \omega t_1}{R + r_d}\right) = AT_c \qquad (15.56)$$

and solving for t_1 gives

$$t_1 = \frac{1}{\omega} \sin^{-1}\left(AT_c \frac{R + r_d}{NE_m}\right) \qquad (15.57)$$

In many instances, t_1 is much less than half the period $T/2$, and the limits of integration in Equation (15.53) are then approximated by zero and $T/2$.

Continuing with the sequence of significant points (Figure 15.33) the circuit again becomes resistance limiting from Point 2 to Point 3. It is assumed that the saturation level is not reached during the first positive half-cycle of the source voltage. If the diode can block negative currents, the flux will not decrease. Hence, the residual flux ϕ_R at Point 3 remains constant until the succeeding positive half-cycle of the supply voltage drives the reactor still closer to saturation, starting at Point 5. The diagrams indicate the reactor entering full saturation on the second half-cycle of the source voltage. With the reactor firmly clamped in saturation, the circuit is entirely resistance limiting $(R + r_d)$ for each succeeding positive half-cycle. The circuit is diode-blocked on the negative half-cycles of the source voltage. To keep the reactor clamped to saturation, the diode must have a sufficiently high back resistance such that the negative ampere turns remain less than the magnitude of $-AT_c$. Thus, the development of saturable reactors, having a lower coercive ampere-turns than previous reactors, requires the use of diodes that have a higher back resistance.

To reset a self-saturating reactor requires the presence of at least one additional winding on the core. There are a number of circuitry arrangements, as dictated by the particular applications, for accomplishing the reset. Whatever the circuitry for the second winding might be, for the additional winding or windings, the three possible states of *net* ampere-turns must be considered. The circuitry of the additional windings must permit the reactor to recycle through these three states.

Let us consider a second winding added to the self-saturating reactor, as illustrated in Figure 15.34, where the circuitry of the second winding N_C is specified as a general network only. In this case, the winding and diode of the main, or gating circuit is identified as N_G and D_G respecitvely. Normally the desired operation is to have the reactor driven to saturation by the N_G circuit and to have the reactor reset, or driven away from saturation by the N_C circuit.

Let us examine the possible behavior of a two-winding, self-saturating reactor by referring to significant points in a cycle of operation. Let the first significant point be that in which i_C is zero (Figure 15.34) and $N_G i_G$ is just

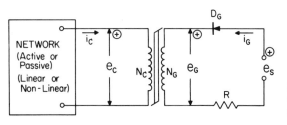

Fig. 15.34 Two windings on a core of square-loop material.

equal to $+AT_c$, as it is at Point 1 or Point 5, Figure 15.33. The source voltage e_s can now drive the reactor toward saturation by action on the N_G winding only, provided i_c remains instantaneously at zero or nearly zero. Since a changing flux will cause an induced voltage in the N_C winding, either of two conditions must exist in the N_C circuit in order to keep i_c at zero (or nearly so) *during the time interval when the reactor is being driven toward saturation*.

One condition is that the N_C winding shall be connected to a high impedance passive network. A low impedance load on N_C will permit the reactor to act like a current transformer, in which case the input impedance to N_G is low compared to the load resistance R. The voltage applied to N_G is therefore low and the flux change toward saturation is small.

The second condition is that the N_C winding shall be connected to an active network with an output voltage that is equal, or nearly equal, and in *phase opposition* to the induced voltage in N_C. In addition, a blocking diode is required in the N_C circuit to prevent the network output voltage from acting on the N_C winding and helping the N_G circuit to drive the reactor to saturation. Remember that the two possible conditions, as specified in this paragraph and the preceding paragraph, apply specifically to the time interval when the reactor is being driven *toward* saturation.

At the instant the reactor enters saturation, the N_G circuit is resistance limiting. The current pulse is initiated and continues until the source voltage returns to zero, at which time the reactor is self-saturated at a residual flux of ϕ_R. Since the diode D_G blocks negative values of i_G, the reactor can be reset by action on the N_C winding only. For the next half-cycle of the source voltage, the N_C network must definitely be an active network to overcome the $-AT_c$ coercive force and to reset the reactor. While the reactor is being reset, a voltage is induced in the N_G winding that is in phase opposition to the source voltage e_s. This induced voltage should not be greater than e_s because the induced voltage would unblock diode D_G and, consequently, partially block the reset by permitting positive values of i_G to exist during the reset interval. In any case, however, the net ampere-turns must remain at $-AT_c$ during the reset time. In other words, if i_G does exist then i_C must increase negatively, causing a larger voltage across the output resistance of the N_C network with a resulting decrease of voltage on the N_C winding.

PROBLEMS

15.1 For the single-phase, full-wave rectifier circuit of Figure 15.1b, the primary turns $= N_1 = N_2$, the applied voltage is 230 volts (rms), $R = 20$ ohms, and the diode voltages (when conducting) are assumed to be negligible. Determine the average value and the rms value for the load current.

15.2 For the circuit and given conditions in Problem 15.1, calculate all significant quantities for the circuit: the d-c power in the load, the total true power in the load, the rectification efficiency, ripple factor, peak inverse voltage on the diodes, volt-amperes of the transformer primary, volt-amperes of the secondary windings, utilization factor for the transformer and the rms value of the current in each of the transformer windings.

15.3 The peak value of load current in a three-phase, one-way rectifier circuit is 50 amperes, assuming a balanced three-phase sinusoidal source voltage and assuming ideal diodes and transformers. Determine the average value and the rms value of current in (a) the load and in (b) each phase.

15.4 Repeat Problem 15.3 if the circuit is a six-phase, one-way rectifier circuit and the peak load current is 50 amperes.

15.5 Repeat Problem 15.3 if the circuit is a three-phase, two-way rectifier circuit and the peak load current is 50 amperes.

15.6 Determine the three significant powers (d-c, a-c and rms) for each of the three preceding problems, if the load resistance is five ohms.

15.7 Determine the d-c component of current for the waveforms of Figure 15.8, if $I_m = 24$ amperes and $\theta_1 = 30°$. Also for $\theta_1 = 60°$, $90°$, and $120°$.

15.8 For the phase-shifting circuit of Figure 15.11a, $R = 1000$ ohms and the frequency of the sinusoidal applied voltage is 60 c/s. Determine the value of C that will cause e_s to lag the applied voltage by
   (a) 20°
   (b) 45°
   (c) 90°
   (d) 110°
   (e) 150°.

15.9 Repeat Problem 15.8 for a frequency of 400 c/s.

15.10 For the phase shifting circuit of Figure 15.11b, $R = 10,000$ ohms, and the frequency of the applied voltage is 60 c/s. Determine the value of inductance to produce a phase lag of
   (a) 60°
   (b) 120°.

15.11 Repeat Problem 15.10 if the frequency is 400 c/s.

15.12 Draw the complete phasor diagram for the double RC phase-shifting circuit in Figure 15.12, for the condition $e_{s1} = -e_{s2} = 45°$ lag with V_{ab} as reference. What are the values of C_1 and C_2 if $R_1 = R_2 = 5000$ ohms for a frequency of 60 c/s?

15.13 The series-connected magnetic amplifier of Figure 15.19 is a schematic diagram having magnetic markings that are in agreement with the winding diagram of Figure 15.17. Why are the two markings on the windings of core 1, for example, positioned at the bottom rather than at the top of the diagram?

15.14 Assume that someone had the task of writing a voltage equation for the a-c loop in Figure 15.19. Discuss the problem of doing this, keeping in mind the different modes of operation that are possible for the circuit. Either core, both cores, or neither core may be in saturation. The windings may have finite values of inductance. It might be desirable to assume that the inductance is either infinite or zero. Also, there are core losses that may or may not be negligible. The actual problem is, what voltage equations could one write for the circuit and under what conditions of operation is each equation applicable?

15.15 The graph of Figure 15.27 could be described as a plot of $I_G N_G$ vs $I_C N_C$, for a *family* of applied voltages, E, and for constant gate-circuit resistance R. Sketch the graph for each of the following conditions and identify significant quantities for each.

(a) $N_G I_G$ vs $N_C I_C$, R family, E constant.

(b) $N_G I_G$ vs E, $N_C I_C$ family, R constant.

(c) $N_G I_G$ vs R, E family, $N_C I_C$ constant.

15.16 For an ideal current transformer, the primary current is a half-wave rectified current; that is,
$$i_p = 20 \sin \omega t \quad (0 < \omega t < \pi)$$
$$\text{and } i_p = 0 \qquad (\pi < \omega t < 2\pi)$$
Write the expressions for the secondary current for the two corresponding half-periods, for a secondary-to-primary turns ratio of 5. Are the net ampere-turns equal to zero?

15.17 Is the solution of Problem 15.16 applicable to the current-transformer action of the nonsaturated reactors of the magnetic amplifier? Explain.

15.18 For a series-connected magnetic amplifier, $N_C = N_G$, $I_C = 0.1$ ampere, $R = 400$ ohms (includes resistance of gate windings). What is the minimum value of applied sinusoidal voltage for which $N_C I_C = N_G I_G$ (magnitudes)? *Hint:* What is the value of θ_1 for this condition?

15.19 A single coil of 400 turns is wound on a core that has an ideal rectangular B-H curve. A single triangular pulse of voltage is applied. The voltage pulse is positive only, having a peak value of 40 volts and a time duration of 0.05 seconds. Assuming the flux is initially zero, what is the magnitude of the flux (in webers) at the end of the pulse?

15.20 Repeat Problem 15.19, for a positive rectangular pulse of the same peak value and time duration.

15.21 Repeat Problem 15.19, for *one* half-cycle of a sinusoidal voltage having a peak value of 40 volts and a time duration of 0.05 seconds.

FOR FURTHER STUDY OF MAGNETIC AMPLIFIERS

1. Martin, Thomas L., Jr. *Physical Basis for Electrical Engineering*, Englewood Cliffs, N.J.: Prentice-Hall, Inc., 1957.

2. Dekker, A. J., *Electrical Engineering Materials*, Englewood Cliffs, N.J.: Prentice-Hall, Inc., 1959.

3. Geyger, William A., *Magnetic Amplifier Circuits*, New York: McGraw-Hill Book Company, Inc., 1954.

4. Milnes, A. G., *Transductors and Magnetic Amplifiers*, New York: The Macmillan Company, 1957.

5. Attura, George M., *Magnetic Amplifier Engineering*, New York: McGraw-Hill Book Company, Inc., 1959.

6. LaFuse, David L., *Magnetic Amplifier Analysis*, New York: John Wiley and Sons, Inc., 1962.

7. Lynn, Gordon E., *Self-Saturating Magnetic Amplifiers*, New York: McGraw-Hill Book Company, Inc., 1960.

8. Platt, Sidney, *Magnetic Amplifiers, Theory and Application*, Englewood Cliffs, N.J.: Prentice-Hall, Inc., 1958.

9. Storm, H. F., *Magnetic Amplifiers*, New York: John Wiley & Sons, Inc., 1955.

10. Gerhart W. Heumann, *Magnetic Control of Industrial Motors.* New York John Wiley & Sons, Inc., 1961.

REFERENCES

(Applications of Electronic Control and Measurement Systems)

1. Weeks, R. W., "Rotating Raster Character Recognition Systems," *Communication and Electronics*, AIEE Trans., No. 56 (September 1961), 353.

2. Butterfield, M. H. and J. Dowsing, "Two Ideas for Character Recognition," *Control Engineering*, 9 (August 1962), 113.

3. Doran, G. A. and M. Jobes, "An Automatic Track (Pulse) Following Device," *Nucl. Instr. & Methods*, 13 (1961), 124–126.

4. Rockwood, Curtis C. and Michael G. Strauss, "Three-Parameter Multichannel Recorder—Analyzer System," *Rev. Sci. Instr.*, 32 (December, 1961), 1211–1221.

5. Barnett, Ray H. and Robert M. Maxham, "Infra-red Phosphorescence Detection Using Pulsed Excitation," *Rev. Sci. Instr.*, 32 (June 1961), 740–741.

6. Wheeler, George W., "500–Kw Pulse Modulator for Accelerator Applications," *Rev. Sci. Instr.*, Vol. 32 (November 1961), 1130–1131.

7. Maeder, D., "Photographic Recording Methods in Nuclear Pulse Spectrometry," *Nucl. Instr. & Methods*, 2 (1958), 299–331.

8. Luszczynski, K. and J. G. Powles, "Nuclear Spin Pulse Apparatus," *J. Sci. Instr.*, 36 (February 1959), 57–63.

9. Neilson, G. C., W. K. Dawson, and F. A. Johnson, "Fast Neutron Time-of-Flight Spectrometer," *Rev. Sci. Instr.*, 30 (November 1959), 963–975.

10. MacNichol, E. F., Jr. and Jay A. H. Jacobs, "Electronic Device for Measuring Reciprocal Time Intervals," *Rev. Sci. Instr.*, 26 (December 1955), 1176–1180.

11. Flanagan, James L., "Models for Approximating Basilar Membrane Displacement Part II. Effects of Middle-Ear Transmission and Some Relations Between Subjective and Physiological Behavior," *The Bell System Tech.* (May 1962), 959–1009.

12. Bushor, William E., "Review of World-Wide Progress in Medical Electronics," *Electronics* 34 (August 25, 1961), 41.

13. Rich, Ottis, Jr. and R. V. Hill, "R–F Spot Welder Reattaches Retina of Human Eye," *Electronics* 34 (August 11, 1961), 160.

14. Littauer, R. M. and C. Walcott, "Pulse-Height Analyzer for Neuro-Physiological Applications," *Rev. Sci. Instr.*, 30 (December 1959), 1102–1106.

15. Wyatt, D. G., "A Heart Pulse Amplifier and Ratemeter," *J. Sci. Instr.*, 33 (November 1956), 440–444.

16. Skinner, R. L., D. K. Gehmlich, and F. W. Longson, "Blood Pressure and Heart Rate Regulator," *Electronics* 32 (January 2, 1959), 38–41.

17. Hughes, H. A., "Electronic Instruments in Diagnostic Medicine," *Electronic Engineering* (March 1950), 88.
18. Baxter, I. G., "An Electrical Flowmeter for Recording Blood Flow," *Electronic Engineering* (April 1952), 162.
19. Wood, M. C., "The Amplification and Recording of Foetal Heart Sounds," *Electronic Engineering* (March 1953), 90–93.
20. Gilford, S. R. and H. P. Broida, "Physiological Monitor for Anesthesia," *Electronics* 28 (October 1955), 130.
21. Hilton, Alice M., "Computing Machines in Control Systems," *Electro-Technol* (New York) 66 (December 1960), 94–101.
22. Kirkham, E. E., "Digital Positioning Control," *Electro-Technol* (New York) (March 1957), 118–125.
23. Berry, T. M., "Optical Contour Follower," *G. E. Review* (June 1950), 44.
24. McKelvie, John L., "Principles of Data Processing in Numerical Control of Machine Tools," *Electro-Technol* (New York) 67 (March 1961), 135.
25. Adamson, Colin and Ahmad M. El-Serafi, "Principles of a Simulator for Studying Synchronous Machine Voltage Regulator Problems," *Power Apparatus Systems, AIEE Trans*, No. 53 (April 1961), 36.
26. Thompson, Francis T., "High-Accuracy Digital-Analog Sold-State Speed Controller," *Applications and Industry, AIEE Trans*, No. 59 (March 1962), 23.
27. DiVincengo, A. P. and C. E. Robinson, "Press Control Speeds Auto Body Production," *Electronics*, 26 (December 1953), 154.
28. Phillips, A. H., et al., "Excitation Improvement—Electronic Excitation and Regulation of Generators as Compared to Conventional Methods," *AIEE Trans.* (1950), 338.
29. John, K. W., et al., "Coordinated Electric Drive for Rubber Calendar Train," *AIEE Trans.*, 65 (1946), 128.
30. Allen, L. W., "Thyratron-Controlled Vibration Drive," *Electronics*, 24 (December 1951), 106.
31. Johnson, R. O., "Current Slope Control for Resistance Welding," *Electronics*, 26 (November 1953) 158.
32. Ciancaglini, H. R., "Spot and Seam Welding," *Electronic Applications Bulletin*, 14 (December 1953), 187.
33. Hills, W. B., "Slope Control for Resistance Welding," *Electronics*, 25 (May 1952), 124.
34. Myers, R. G. and D. L. Waidelich, "A System for Gaging Plating Thickness," *Communication and Electronics, AIEE Trans. No.* 39. (November 1958), 770–774.
35. Hanysz, E. A., "Swept Frequency Eddy-Current Device to Measure Overlay Thickness," *Rev. Sci. Instr.*, 29 (May 1958), 411–415.
36. Savage, F. M., "Ultrasonic Method of Gauging," *British IRE* (September 1954), 436.
37. Colten, Robert B., "Noncontacting Gages for Nonferrous Metals," *Electronics*, 29 (March 1956), 171–173.
38. Waidelich, Donald L., "Pulsed Eddy Currents Gage Plating Thickness," *Electronics*, 28 (November 1955), 146–147.

39. Sampson, E. S., "Photoelectric Width Gage for Hot Steel Mills," *Electronics*, **26** (March 1953), 114.

40. Clapp, C. W. and S. Bernstein, "Non-Contacting Thickess Gauge Using Beta Rays," *AIEE Trans.*, **69**, Part I (1950) 488.

41. Landall, W. N., "X-Ray Thickness Gauge for Cole-rolled Strip Steel," *AIEE Trans.*, **67**, Part I (1948), 83.

42. Bell, R. E. and J. A. Ferstle, "Electronic Weighing on the Production Line," *Electronics*, **28** (June 1955), 152–155.

43. Thurston, A. S., "Scale for Weighing Moving Trucks," *Electronics*, **29** (January 1956), 142–143.

44. Pedersen, S. R., "Liquid Weighing Scale Controls Rate of Flow," *Electronics*, **25** (June 1952), 104.

45. Klein, E., "Remote-Control Automatic Weighing," *Electronics*, **25** (July 1952), 98.

46. Riley, Oliver V., "Precision Measurement of Shaft Speeds," *Electronics*, **24** (October 1951), 104.

47. Hellar, M. W., "Precision Speed Measurement of Rotating Equipment," *G. E. Review* (October 1949), 22.

48. Downie, E. G., "Making Short-time Motor-coast Measurements," *G. E. Review* (March 1948), 18.

49. Strassman, A. J., "RPM Indicator Provides Expanded Scale," *Electronics*, **27** (August 1954), 146.

50. Punnell, S. W. and H. G. Jerrard, "A Precision Electronic Tachometer," *Electron. Eng.* (February 1951), 55.

51. Harrington, E. L., "A High Speed Revolution Counter," *Electron. Eng.* (April 1955), 142.

52. Cowie, E. G. and J. H. Gregson, "Variable-Speed Control for Integral H-P Motors," *Electronics*, **28** (April 1955), 162–163.

53. Kubler, E. E., "New Industrial Motor Control Circuits," *Electronics*, **25** (March 1952), 110.

54. Shulman, J. M., "Accurate Tachometry Methods with Electronic Counters," *AIEE Trans.*, Part I (1952), 452.

55. Hesselgrave, D. H. and M. H. Kebby, "The 57A Microwave Path Protective System," *Communications and Electronics, AIEE Trans.*, No. 52 (January 1961), 654.

56. Matthys, R. J., "A Precision Torque Balance for the Measurement of Small Torques," *AIEE Trans.* (September 1955), 485–490.

57. Bousky, Samuel, "Precision Balancing at Mass Production Speed," *Electronics*, **20** (September 1947), 98.

58. Lynch, F. J. and J. B. Baumgardner, "New Fluorescence Photometer," *Rev. Sci. Instr.*, **26** (May 1955), 435–440.

59. Bishop, F. W., "Exposure Timer for the Electron Microscope," *Electronics*, **28** (March 1955), 206.

60. Edgerton, H. E., "Double-Flash Microsecond Silhouette Photography," *Rev. Sci. Instr.* (October 1952), 532.

61. King, R. W., "Image Converter—A High Speed Photographic Device," *IRE Trans.*, (May 1955), 8.

62. Johnson, S. E. J. and P. D. Schnelle, "Precision Reading Refractometer," *Rev. Sci. Instr.* (January 1953), 26–35.
63. Wessel, A. B., "Universal Shutter Tester," *Electronics*, **29** (February 1956), 162.
64. Popkin-Clurman, J. R., "Portable Color-Signal Generator," *Electronics*, **29** (September 1956), 171.
65. Sziklai, G. C., "A Tristimulus Photometer," *J. Opt. Soc. Am.*, **41** (May 1951), 321.
66. Bullock, B. M. and S. Silverman, "A Rapid Scanning Spectrometer," *J. Opt. Soc. Am.*, **40** (September 1950), 608.
67. McDuffie, T. E., "Spectrum Analyzer, for Quartz Crystals," *Electronics*, **28** (October 1955), 160.
68. Lyman, R. C. and C. I. Jones, "Electroluminescent Panels for Automatic Displays, *Electronics*, **32** (July 10, 1959), 44.
69. Isaacs, J. P. and G. Grey, "Testing Hardness with Flux Gate Magnetometer," *Electronics*, **29** (April 1956), 142–143.
70. Diamond, W. J., "Hardness Tester Sorts Auto Engine Parts," *Electronics*, **27** (December 1954), 160.
71. Sanford, A. C., "Precise Parts Sorting on Production Lines," *Electronics*, **26** (July 1953), 142.
72. Smith, T. J. and R. A. Huggins, "Tomato Classification by Spectrophotometry," *Electronics*, **25** (January 1952), 92.
73. MacMartin, M. P., "Sensitive Flow Detector Solves Noise Problems," *Electronics*, **33** (April 15, 1960), 64–66.
74. Vossberg, C. A., "Photoelectric Gage Sorts Pencil Crayons," *Electronics*, **27** (July 1954), 150.
75. Lepri, F. and R. Sanna, "Ceramic Tile Sorter," *Electronics*, **26** (October 1953), 180.
76. Gumpertz, D. G., "Magnetic Sorting of Unlabeled Food Cans," *Electronics*, **25** (September 1952), 100.
77. Strother, F. P., "Industrial Yarn Classifier," *Electronics*, **25** (July 1952), 110.
78. Shepard, D. A. and C. C. Heasly, Jr., "Photoelectric Reader Feeds Business Machines," *Electronics*, **28** (May 1955), 135.
79. Johnson, J. A. and E. M. Stacey, "Application of Electronic Motor Drives to Printing Presses," *AIEE Trans.* **69** (1950), 216.
80. Chalfin, Norman L., "Phonetic Printer of Spoken Words-Speech Typewriter," *Electronics*, **28** (April 1955), 228.
81. Cory, S. I., "A New Portable Telegraph Transmission Measuring Set," *AIEE Trans.*, **73**, Pt. I (March 1954), 59.
82. Gedaminski, B. F. and W. G. Griffin, Jr., "Transmitting Facsimile Messages Over Meteor-Burst Paths," *Electronics*, **34** (May 10, 1961), 85.
83. Fahnestock, James D., "High Speed Printer for Weapons Testing," *Electronics*, **29** (September 1956), 168.
84. Widman, L. C., "Detecting Transmission Errors in Phase-Shift-Keying Systems," *Electronics*, **34** (September 8, 1961), 76.
85. Deubel, J. A., "Flame Detectors for Domestic Fuel Burner Safety Devices," *AIEE Trans.*, **69** (1950), 220.

86. Bradley, Robert W., "Tack Detector for Shoe Production," *Electronics*, **29** (February 1956), 144–146.

87. McLucas, J. L. and R. D. Laughlin, "Moving Target Detector," *Electronics*, **27** (August 1954), 169.

88. Grobtuch, M. and D. J. Williams, "Pulp-log Metal Detector," *Electronics*, **25** (July 1952), 124.

89. Blasberg, E., "An Iron Detector for Protecting Machines," *Electronics Application Bulletin* (October 1953), 152.

90. Jackson, C. E., "Intrusion Alarm," *Radiotronics* (March 1951), 65.

91. Koletsky, Harold, "Temperature Indicator for Aircraft Engines," *Electronics*, **28** (November 1955), 129–131.

92. Adams, J. A., "Miss Distance Indicator Scores Missile Accuracy," *Electronics*, **32** (April 17, 1959), 42.

93. Glaser, P. F. and E. R. Spangler, "Payload Design for a Lunar Satellite," *Electronics*, **33** (October 8, 1960), 63.

94. Lepri, F., L. Meyyetti and G. Stoppini, "New Circuit for the Measurement of Very Short Delays," *Rev. Sci. Instr.* (October 1955), 936–941.

95. Fowler, Fred E., "Accurate Time for Scientific Measurements," *Electronics*, **25** (January 1952), 98.

96. Sandlin, B. J. and J. C. Thompson, "Precision Thermometer System for the Liquid Helium Region," *Rev. Sci. Instr.*, **30** (August 1959), 659–661.

97. Browning, Glenn H., "Balanced-Capacitance Fence Alarm System," *Electronics*, **29** (April 1956), 150–152.

98. Lehman, G. L. and C. A. Meuliau, "Temperature Regulator Used in Producing Germanium Crystals," *Elec. Commun.* (March 1954), 19–26.

99. Siau, J. H., "Crucible Heat Control," *Electronics*, **27** (February 1954), 149.

100. Dauphinee, T. M. and S. B. Woods, "Low-Level Thermocouple Amplifier and a Temperature Regulation System," *Rev. Sci. Instr.* (July 1955), 693–695.

101. Slater, F. E., "Furnace-Atmosphere Control by Dew Point Control," *Instruments and Automation* (October 1955), 1720–1724.

102. Williams, A. J., Jr., "Electronic Recorder with Range and Precision Adequate for the Platinum Resistance Thermometer," *AIEE Trans.*, **71**, Part I (September 1952), 289.

103. Hartley, M. S., "Ultrasonic Machining of Brittle Materials," *Electronics*, **29** (January 1956), 132–135.

104. Chute, G. M., "Remote Control of Positioning Motors," *Electronics*, **24** (July 1951), 92.

105. Harrison, E., Jr., "Beta Gage Controls Cigarette Machine," *Electronics*, **29** (November 1956), 147.

106. Pattison, J. R., "An Apparatus for the Accurate Measurement of Internal Friction," *Rev. Sci. Instr.* (May 1954), 490–496.

107. Pesanto, M., "A New Instrument for Measuring Surface Roughness," *Microtechnic*, **9** (1955), 27.

108. Pochapsky, T. E., "Determination of Heat Capacity by Pulse Heating," *Rev. Sci. Instr.*, **25** (March 1954), 238–242.

109. Parkinson, R. W., "Instrumentation for the Continuous Measurement of Certain Ionospheric Echo Characteristics," *Rev. Sci. Instr.*, **26** (April 1955), 319–323.

110. Carrol, J. M., "Electronic Equipment in Railroading," *Electronics*, **26** (August 1953), 130.

111. Lefevre, H. W. and J. T. Russell, "Vernier Chronotron," *Rev. Sci. Instr.*, **30** (March 1959), 159–166.

112. Washburn, R. P. and E. B. Stavely, "Tape Recorder Cycles Truck Axle Tester," *Electronics*, **27** (July 1954), 130.

113. Smith, L. G., "An Electronic Field Meter with Extended Frequency Range," *Rev. Sci. Instr.*, **25** (May 1954), 510–513.

114. Reich, H. J. and R. L. Unguary, "A Direct-Reading Frequency Meter for the Audio and Supersonic Ranges," *Rev. Sci. Instr.*, **19** (January 1948), 43–46.

115. Ortel, William C. G., "A Multichannel Pulse-Height and Delay Time Recorder," *Rev. Sci. Instr.*, **25** (February 1954), 164–169.

116. Thomas, D. E. and J. M. Klein, "Automatic Transistor Alpha Measuring Set," *Rev. Sci. Instr.*, **30** (June 1959), 458–462.

117. Pine, C. C., "Recorder Amplifier for Flight Testing," *Electronics*, **29** (August 1956), 158.

118. Lippman, S. A., "Tire Tread Noise Analyzer," *Electronics*, **23** (November 1950), 84.

119. Rao, P. V., "Phase Shifter Circuits Test Power Meters," *Electronics*, **29** (January 1956), 156–157.

120. Glass, F. M., "Elastic Constant—Internal Friction Spectrometer," *Rev. Sci. Instr.*, **29** (November 1958), 1034–1040.

121. Lehman, Gerard, "Rotary Amplifiers in Servomechanisms," *Elec. Commun.* (March 1953), 12.

122. Gates, J. L., "Electronic Controllers," *Instruments and Automation* (August 1955), 1338–1341.

123. Young, N. H., "Automatic Control System with Provision for Scanning and Memory," *Elec. Commun.* (December 1953), 279.

124. Yu, Y. P., "Coincident Slicer Measures Phase Directly," *Electronics*, **31** (September 12, 1958), 99–101.

125. Bigelow, S. and J. Wuorinen, Jr., "Extended Angular Range Direct Reading Phase Meter," *Rev. Sci. Instr.*, **28** (September 12, 1957), 713–717.

126. Linlor, W. L., Q. A. Kerns, and J. W. Mark, "Bubble Chamber Pressure Gauge," *Rev. Sci. Instr.*, **28** (July 1957), 535–541.

127. Blakeslee, J. H., "Strobe Techniques Analyze Complex Mechanical Motion," *Electronics*, **32** (June 5, 1959), 62–64.

128. Thompson, F. T., "Sync Generator for Dot-Interlace TV," *Electronics*, **30** (August 1, 1957), 170–173.

129. Staff Report, "Preferred Circuits-I," *Electro-Technol.* (New York) (February 1957), 101–109.

130. Jamnik, D., "Energy Control of 31 MeV Betatron," *Nucl. Instr. & Methods*, **1** (1957), 324–328.

131. Reaves, J. H., "Fast Logical Binary Adding Network," *Nulc. Instr. & Methods*, **2** (1958), 139–145.

132. Woestemeyer, F. B., "Marker Pulse Shows Shaft Position," *Electronics*, **27** (May 1954), 146.

133. Sulyer, P. G., "Temperature Controller Controls Within 0.001°C," *Instruments and Automation* (October 1955), 1726–1727.

134. Vantine, Harry, Jr. and E. C. Johnson, "Modified Transceivers Compute Distance," *Electronics*, **31** (September 12, 1958), 94–98.

135. Soffel, R. O. and E. G. Spack, "SAGE Data Terminals," *Communication and Electronics, AIEE Trans.* (January 1959), 872–879.

136. Watts, B. N., "An Infra-Red Radiation Pyrometer," *J. Sci. Instr.* (May 1955), 167–170.

137. Tait, R. D. and F. C. Chalkin, "A Direct-Reading Microdensitometer," *J. Sci. Instr.* (August 1953), 268–270.

138. Wilkie, M. J., "A Recording Water Velocity Meter," *J. Sci. Instr.* (August 1953), 350–353.

139. Kniayuk and Prediger, "Ultrasonic Gas Analyzer," *Instruments and Automation*, **28** (November 1955), 1619–1627.

140. Brownlee, T., "Advances in Techniques of Lightning Measurements," *AIEE Trans.* (1949), 515.

141. Walsh, C., "Spark Plug Tester," *Electronics*, **22** (June 1949), 104.

142. Snyder, Howard W., "Velocity Meter Has Direct Readout," *Electronics*, **29** (October 1956), 248.

143. Cole, George H., "Transistorized Indicator Measures Jet Exhaust," *Electronics*, **29** (December 1956), 145.

144. Dalziel, R., "Visual Impedance Matching Equipment (80–25 mcs)," *Wireless Engr.*, **32** (April 1955), 103–104.

145. Nelson, V. R., "Gated Amplifier Wave Analyzer," *Electronics*, **25** (August 1952), 136.

146. Sokal, N. O. and Ira L. Resnick, "Staircase Generator Counts Pulses," *Electronics*, **27** (March 1954), 187.

147. Williamson, C. N., "Direct Reading Pulse Counter," *Electronics*, **29** (December 1956), 195.

148. Nakamura, Michiyuki, "Millimicrosecond Pulse Generator Capable of 10 Million Pulses Per Second," *Rev. Sci. Instr.*, **30** (September 1959), 778–782.

149. Gambrill, R. D., "Controlling Extrusion of Foam Plastic on Wire," *Electronics*, **28** (April 1955), 144–145.

150. Dado, F., V. Proscia, and M. Raphael, "Punch Card Reader for the Blind," *Electronics*, **29** (November 1956), 148.

151. Strasser, R. M., "Gas Diode Electronic Organ," *Electronics*, **24** (January 1951), 70.

152. Halstead, W. K. and L. D. Jaffe, "Quench Controller for Steel," *Electronics*, **23** (November 1950), 109.

153. Alcan, R. L., "Thyratron Control of Air Pistons," *Electro-Technol.* (New York) (January 1954), 82.

154 Blumenthal, I. S. and A. R. Eckels, "A High Speed Direct Writing Oscillograph," *AIEE Trans.*, **71**, Part I (January 1952), 50.

155. Yates, C. G., "Free Wheeling Thyratrons Cut Autopilot Weight," *Electronics*, **26** (March 1953), 103.

156. Jaeschke, R. L., "Thyratron Braking for Oil Drilling Rigs," *Electronics*, **21** (April 1948), 92.

157. Carrol, J. M., "Electronics in the Oil Industry," *Electronics*, **27** (September 1954), 120.

158. Hornfeck, A. J., "Computing Circuits and Devices for Industrial Process Functions," *AIEE Trans.*, **71** Part I (July 1952), 183.

159. Coles, R. V., "Automatic Control of Moisture," *Electronics*, **22** (November 1949), 82.

160. Kimmel, R. T., "Electronic Controls-Machine Tool Applications," *Tool Engineer* (May 1952), 69–76.

161. Leaver, E. W. and G. R. Mounce, "Recorder Controlled Automatic Machine Tools," *Electronics*, **27** (November 1954), 124.

162. Galbrath, Hugh J., "Portable Navigator for Ground Personnel," *Electonics*, **35** (January 26, 1962), 48.

163. Harkins, Dwight, "F–M Multiplexing for Studio-Transmitter Links," *Electronics*, **32** (May 22, 1959), 44.

164. Fujimura, Yasushi and Nobuo Mii, "Automatic Frequency Control With Reactance Transistors," *Electronics*, **33** (September 30, 1960), 97.

165. Mann, H., H. M. Straube, and C. P. Villars, "A Companded Coder for an Experimental PCM Terminal," *The Bell System Tech. J.* (January 1962), 173–226.

166. Sullivan, R. J., I. Eastman, and I. C. Chanock, "Using Digital Techniques in Time Encoders," *Electronics*, **32** (November 13, 1959), 80.

167. Goodwin, John K., "Digital Tachometer Aids in Turbine Design," *Electronics*, **32** (April 10, 1959), 58.

168. Bell, Gordon M., "Static Magnetic Frequency Multipliers," *Electro-Technol.* (New York) (November 1960), 94–102.

169. Mittman, Benjamin and Richard B. Wise, "The Digital Computer as a Tool for Design Engineers," *Electro-Technol.* (New York) (August 1960), 116–123.

170. Brubaker, T. A. and G. A. Korn, "Accurate Amplitude Distribution Analyzer Combining Analog and Digital Logic," *Rev. Sci. Instr.*, **32** (March 1961), 317–322.

171. Arunasalam, V. and John D. Trimmer, "Pulse Conduction in Decaying Plasma," *Rev. Sci. Instr.*, **32** (March 1961), 282–285.

172. Court, F. C., "'Logand' A Binary-Coded Data Transmission System for Telecontrol Purposes," *Brit. Commun. & Electron.*, **9** (June 1962), 428–431.

173. Lindahl, J. H. and W. M. McGuire, "Adaptive Control Flies the X-15," *Control Engineering*, **9** (October 1962), 93.

174. Vaeth, James E., "Vapor Jet Control of Space Vehicles," *IRE Trans. Auto. Control*, **AC-7** (October 1962), 67.

175. Wayson, Alan R., "Guided-String Cutter for Single, Metal Crystals," *Rev. Sci. Instr.*, **32** (August 1961), 967–971.

176. Kaplan, D. E., M. E. Browne, and J. A. Cowen, "Pulsed X-Band EPR Spectrometer," *Rev. Sci. Instr.*, **32** (December 1961), 1182–1186.

177. Fujii, Tadakuni, "Electron Beam Analyzer Using a Piezoelectric Scanner," *Rev. Sci. Instr.*, **32** (April 1961), 434–444.

178. Dahnhe, Jack W., "Computer-Directed Checkout for NASA's Biggest Booster," *Control Engineering*, **9** (August 1962), 85.

appendix A

Characteristic Curves
for Tubes*

*Courtesy of Receiving Tube Department, General Electric Company.

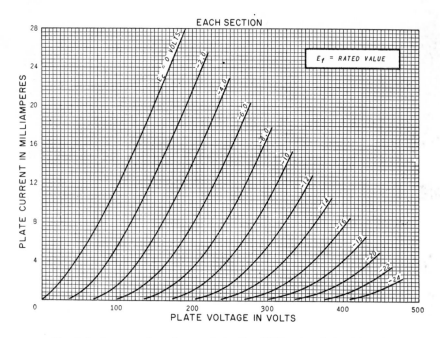

Fig. A.1. Average plate characteristics for 6SN7 twin triode. (Negative grid-voltage region only.)

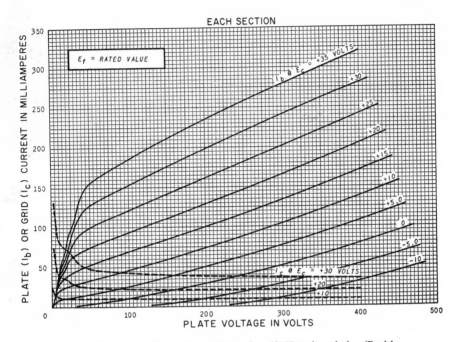

Fig. A.2. Average plate characteristics for 6SN7 twin triode. (Positive grid-voltage region.)

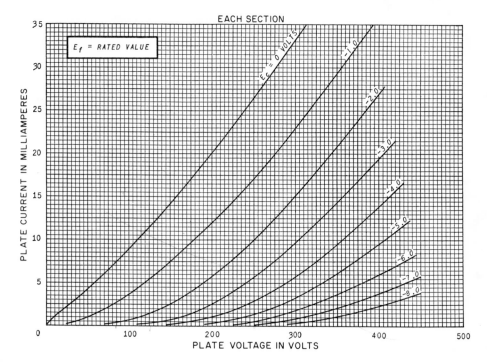

Fig. A.3. Average plate characteristics for 12AT7 twin triode. (Negative grid-voltage region only.)

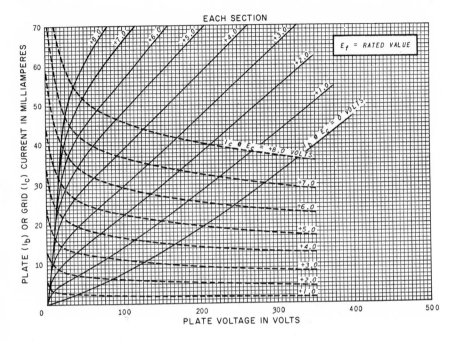

Fig. A.4. Average plate characteristics for 12AT7 twin triode. (Positive grid-voltage region only.)

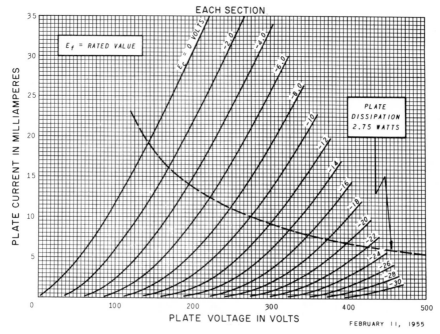

Fig. A.5. Average plate characteristics for 12AU7 twin triode. (Negative grid-voltage region only.)

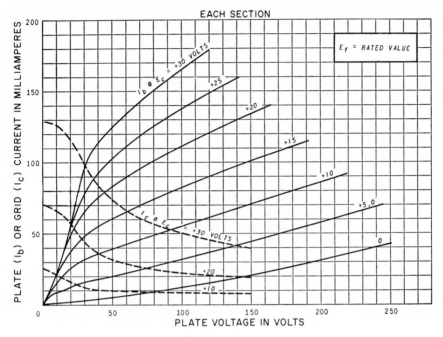

Fig. A.6. Average plate characteristics for 12AU7 twin triode. (Positive grid-voltage region only.)

Characteristic Curves
for Transistors

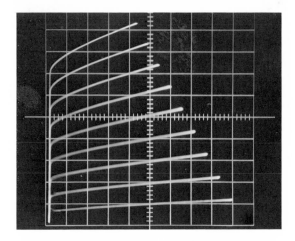

Fig. B.1. The transistor: 2N190 (*p-n-p*)
            Collector-emitter voltage: 2 V (per horizontal
                                         division)
            Collector current: 0.5 ma (per vertical
                                         division)
            Base current: 10 μa (per step)

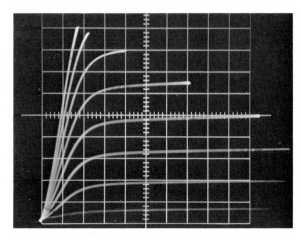

Fig. B.2. The transistor: 2N190 (*p-n-p*)
            Collector-emitter voltage: 0.05 V (per horizontal
                                         division)
            Collector current: 0.1 ma (per vertical
                                         division)
            Base current: 5 μa (per step)

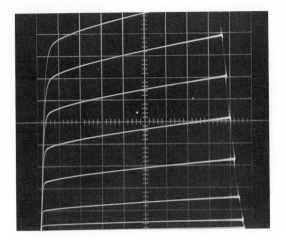

Fig. B.3. The transistor: 2N118 (*n-p-n*)

Collector-emitter voltage: 2 V (per horizontal division)

Collector current: 0.5 ma (per vertical division)

Base current: 20 μa (per step)

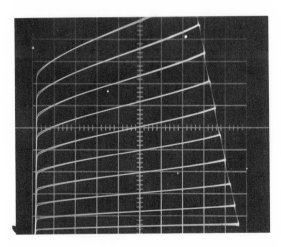

Fig. B.4. The transistor: 2N320 (*p-n-p*)

Collector-emitter voltage: 2 V (per horizontal division)

Collector current: 0.5 ma (per vertical division)

Base current: 10 μa (per step)

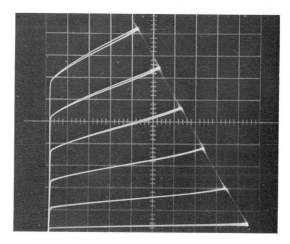

Fig. B.5. The transistor: 2N440 (*n-p-n*)
Collector-emitter voltage: 2 V (per horizontal division)
Collector current: 0.5 ma (per vertical division)
Base current: 10 μa (per step)

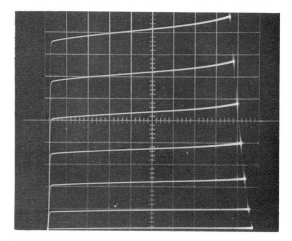

Fig. B.6. The transistor: 2N702 (*n-p-n*)
Collector-emitter voltage: 2 V (per horizontal division)
Collector current: 0.5 ma (per vertical division)
Base current: 50 μa (per step)

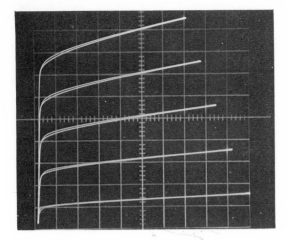

Fig. B.7. The transistor: 2N1038 (*p-n-p*)
        Collector-emitter voltage: 1V (per horizontal division)
        Collector current: 2 ma (per vertical division)
        Base current: 50 μa (per step)

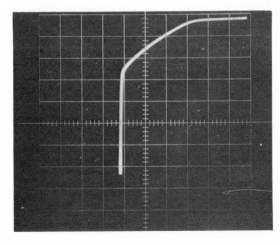

Fig. B.8. Illustrates reverse voltage breakdown of a collector-base junction.

The transistor:	2N190 (*p-n-p*)
Collector-base voltage:	20 V (per horizontal division)
Collector-base current:	100 μa (per vertical division)
Initial breakdown:	55 volts
Limiting reverse voltage:	120 volts

Index

PRAISE FOR
BLINDED BY THE LIGHT

"Timely and significant.
Brancato's latest is also a strong,
well-crafted novel on a vital subject . . .
absorbing the author's message could
save young people, *and* their families,
a lot of heartbreak."
                                        —*Publishers Weekly*

"The plot has the magnetism
of suspense and the issue confronted
is a refreshing change from
beleaguered old stand-bys."
                                        —*School Library Journal*

THE NEW NOVEL
ABOUT THE CULT PHENOMENON
BY THE AUTHOR OF *WINNING*
ROBIN F. BRANCATO

BLINDED BY THE LIGHT

BY ROBIN F. BRANCATO

BLINDED BY THE LIGHT

*A Bantam Book / published by arrangement with
Alfred A. Knopf, Inc.*

PRINTING HISTORY

*Alfred A. Knopf edition published September 1978
Excerpt appeared in Scholastic Magazine February 1979
Bantam edition / May 1979*

2nd printing

For Rick and Jan
and for John

I

1

Gail, propping up a book, stared over the top of it at the L.O.W.s. It was them all right. Lots of other university organizations handed out flyers, but not like this—two people working together, a girl and a boy, buttonholing students so they couldn't escape. Not that they looked any special way—no purple robes, no tambourines. Both of them conservatively dressed. Their style was to blend in with everybody else at Munro on this first afternoon of warm weather, the first day since last fall nice enough for sitting in the outdoor café.

She was surprised at how calm she felt—almost as if she were just another curious observer. Now, for instance, they were stopping a guy who was walking along by himself. They'd probably made their first contact with Jim right here. Jim had always been too polite to kooks on the street. She had a tendency that way herself.

"You're going to have to promise to be more careful than you've ever been in your life," her father had said during the summer. "Otherwise we can't let you go back for your sophomore year." This scene was exactly what he'd been worried about. Amazing that she hadn't run into them until now. She ought to leave, really, except that if she got up, they'd be sure to notice her.

Gail sat on the edge of the seat. Back in September she'd have run off in a panic at the sight of them. Last month, even, she'd probably have hurried to the dorm and thrown herself face down on her bed, and if Marilyn wasn't in the room she'd have lain there in the dark, her stomach knotted, mulling it all over again, starting

1

with the last night she'd seen Jim, up through the most
recent letter her parents had gotten from him. And she'd
have asked herself all over again whether there was
anything more a sister could have done. She'd have
pictured her father writing useless letters and her mother, on tranquilizers most of this year, looking spacier
than the L.O.W.s who were on Sansom Walk right
now.

And lying there in the dark in the dorm, Gail's mind
would have drifted back to the repeated scenes in the
living room in Laurel Ridge on those evenings last
summer when she'd gotten home from her day-camp
job. Her father straining forward in the easy chair. Her
mother sitting stiffly on the antique sofa, looking as if
both she and it might crack from brittleness. Gail,
cross-legged on the floor, listening obediently, trying
not to notice the photographs on the mantelpiece of
Jim as a kid.

"They're criminals, Gail," her father would end up
saying, a line of perspiration above his lips. "They've
taken an innocent boy—yes, Jim's a boy, even though
he's twenty-three—and they've hoodwinked him into
thinking he's serving God. But they won't get away
with it. Other parents may give up—I won't."

"They don't show you this sort of thing right away,
you understand," he would say, flashing the little white
button with the green letters L.O.W. "They usually call
themselves by another name at first. They won't admit
they're a religious cult—not until they've got you
hooked. *Then* they'll tell you you're in the Light of the
World Church."

On these evenings her mother would squeeze the arm
of the sofa, lower her head and start to cry—faintly, so
that the sound could barely be heard over the hum of
the air conditioner. And her father would say again,
"Promise us you won't have anything to do with them,
Gail. Let us know right away if they try to make contact. They make a special play for brothers and sisters
of members—we know that for a fact."

"Stay home this year," her mother would beg. "Go
to college near here. It would make me feel so much
safer."

And Gail would consider giving in, until she thought about what it would mean not to see Doug and Marilyn and the other kids, and she'd claim that Munro had the courses she wanted, and she'd promise automatically whatever they asked her to.

I promise I won't hang around if I see them, Gail remembered saying as she watched the bewildered guy responding to the L.O.W.s. They were working on him, flattering him, so that the rapt smile on his face reminded her of Jim's on that night a year ago when he'd come into Pepe's Pizza Parlor looking for her and Doug. Jim had slipped into the booth on her side, she recalled —excited, his mind somewhere else. She had examined him closely, not knowing then that he'd be fixed that way in her memory—eyebrows arched, hair same dark brown as hers, his wavy, hers long and straight. Brown eyes intense.

"I came to say so long," he had told them. "I'm going away for two weeks. Got a project going."

"Great," she had said. "Connected with your thesis?"

"Yeah, but I think it'll work into something bigger."

"A job?" Doug, leaning forward to hear better, had smoothed his new moustache with the tips of his fingers. The beginning of a habit.

"Maybe a job," Jim said.

"What kind?" Gail asked. Jim had looked happy. A little kid onto something.

"It's a chance to help start the ideal school," he'd told them.

"Yeah? Did your adviser set it up?"

"No . . . I just lucked into it."

"Who's behind it?"

"Some beautiful people I just met. The Model Schools Unit."

"Here at Munro?"

"No . . . they've got a base here in Philadelphia, but they've got branches all over."

"How did you find out about them?" Doug had asked.

"From a guy named Charlie Hafer," Jim said. "Know him?"

"No."

"And you're going for two weeks?" Gail asked. "Can you get excused from classes?"

"Excused?" Jim shrugged. "What does it matter? I can't miss this chance. These people are already doing the stuff I'm proposing in my thesis. I want to *do* for a change."

"Won't missing classes mess up your grades?"

"You mean I should give up a great chance because I might get a *C* instead of a *B* in some course in my last semester in college?"

"I guess not," she'd said. "Where is this you're going, anyway?"

"To a farm, sort of. Not far."

"In Pennsylvania?"

"Yeah, north of here. I'm not sure of the exact location myself."

Doug had poured him a beer, she remembered, but Jim had pushed it away.

"Do Mom and Dad know you're going?" Gail had asked.

"Not yet. I'll wait until I get there to call, so I can give them a phone number."

It had sounded perfectly logical that night. Seniors often did special projects. Jim had been into the idea of free schools for months—the latest in a series of his passions that came and went. Even the bit about the new friend, Charlie Hafer—nothing strange about that. Jim was always meeting new people he temporarily got excited about. He wasn't a person who did things moderately, who plodded along with the same two or three best friends, the way she did.

So she hadn't thought a thing about it at the time. Not even that Sunday when her parents had made their weekly call.

"We tried to reach Jim this morning," her mother had said, "but he wasn't in."

"He's fine."

"When did you see him?"

It had taken her a minute to think. "Thursday night. Didn't he call you? He was going to call and give you the number when he got to this place. Didn't he?"

"No—what place?"

"This farm upstate, where he's going for his project."

"Jim went away for the weekend?"

"For two weeks—for his thesis. You'll probably hear from him tonight."

Her mother had suspected right away that something was wrong, but her mother always worried, so Gail hadn't paid much attention. And the next night when her parents had telephoned again to say they still hadn't heard from Jim, she'd only thought it was inconsiderate, not that it was such a big mystery. But by Wednesday when her father had taken off from work to come to Munro, Gail had begun to take it seriously. She and Doug had skipped classes. They had described the scene in Pepe's again and again for her parents, and had gone with them to look for Charlie Hafer and to talk to Jim's professors and the dean of students and finally to the chief of police. One thing that made it tough was that Jim hadn't had a close friend—only acquaintances who didn't know any more than they did. They'd run into dead ends mostly. No Charlie Hafer registered at Munro. No Model Schools Unit in the phone book.

"I'll lay odds it's a front for a cult," the chief of police had said, "in which case there's nothing we can do, since he's over eighteen. First Amendment—freedom of religion."

The next two weeks had been hell, she recalled, glancing angrily at the L.O.W.s across the way. Her parents, after issuing a missing persons report, had gone home. Meanwhile, because it was midterm time, Gail had stayed at school. Not that she'd been able to concentrate.

Had she misunderstood anything Jim had said on that Thursday? Had there been anything different about his behavior that night or in the weeks before? Nothing she could think of. To tell the truth, she hadn't seen him much her whole freshman year at Munro. Not her fault, Doug insisted—it worked two ways. If Jim had wanted to see more of her, he could have made the effort. She had looked forward in high school to going on to "Jim's college," but by the time she'd gotten there, their lives seemed very different. Brothers and sisters grew up and apart, wasn't that the way it was?

Gradually though, and in a natural way, not like this. Not here one day, gone the next. Not with mystery and hurt and confusion that went on long after the night two weeks later when he'd finally called. She'd been there—home in Laurel Ridge for a depressing weekend.

Her mother, picking up the phone, had let out a cry. "I'm so relieved, I'm so relieved!"

"Jim—where are you, Jim?" her father had asked, snatching the receiver. Gail had seen him take off his glasses and pull out the clean white handkerchief he always carried in a suit pocket.

"I don't understand," he'd said. "Yes, well, I've heard of the Light of the World, but aren't they the ones that sell peanuts and candy on the street—the ones that follow what's-his-name?"

A terrible pause, her mother dead still, her father's face screwing up and darkening, Gail's stomach tensing up.

"What about graduating?" Another pause. "Jim, I said *where are you?* Just tell me where you are. We'll come up there right now and talk things over." A pause. "Why not? *I'm* your father!"

After he'd hung up, the three of them had looked at a map, gotten into the car, and driven for several hours over lonely mountainous roads to the spot in Pennsylvania that Jim had described, even though he'd said not to come. Finally, very late at night, when they had arrived outside a town called Mercy, a gas station attendant had explained to them where the place was, and they had proceeded up the long road to the L.O.W. house— a mansion, really—where her father had knocked on the door and heard from the young man who answered that Jim had left in a van two hours earlier with a group who were going on the road for six months.

Dazed, she and her parents had spent the rest of the night in a nearby motel with horrible pink walls. Her father had sat up until four or five practicing arguments, as if Jim were in the next room and might come in any minute.

"We always encouraged you children to make up

your own minds," she remembered him saying. "Too much freedom, I guess. That's the trouble!" Meanwhile her mother had kept on asking, "What's wrong with what we've given you? What's wrong with our church?" On and on until morning, when they'd returned to the L.O.W. road and found the gate locked so that no cars could enter. The Mercy police, a couple of deputized farmers, had offered sympathy but no help.

Just like the rest of the people her parents had consulted in the last year: Mr. Cooper, their minister, who suggested they pray for guidance; the congressman in their district, who wrote her father a really nice thank-you letter for his campaign contribution, with no mention of congressional action against cults; and some psychologist at Munro. Not that they'd told Gail about that one—she'd overheard them talking during the summer. For a while, right after the trip to Mercy, there had been a few weeks in limbo when they'd kept reassuring one another that Jim was no dummy—he'd come back before graduation. Once her father had said without thinking, "I know he's going to wake up and see the light." None of them had laughed.

Gail sat up abruptly. The L.O.W.s were coming closer, away from the congestion on Sansom Walk and into the café area. The boy—blond, curly-haired, baby-faced, wearing slacks and a sport jacket. The girl, large-boned, with long reddish hair, dressed in a skirt and sweater. They were sizing up the situation, scanning the rows of tables as if they were looking for a place to sit. Still closer now, joining a couple of students at a table across the way, starting to talk to them—about how much the world needed love and peace, probably. Was she imagining it, Gail wondered, or was the girl looking at her?

Leave, she told herself. Alone here, she was a sitting duck. Go to the library and come back in time to meet Doug at five-thirty.

"The reason it's so important to be on your guard," her father had warned her, *is that they make a special play for brothers and sisters.*" How come they hadn't gotten to her then in a full year? They probably didn't even know she was Gail Brower, Jim's sister, and if they did, they didn't give a damn. It was possible her parents were exaggerating.

"So that's what you think," her father would say if he saw her now. Shaking his head with disappointment, he would take off his glasses and rub his eyes.

"There's no harm in staying," she would protest. "Maybe I can find out something."

"We know all we need to know about this outfit," he would tell her.

"I'm against them as much as you are, Daddy, but it's hard to prove they do anything illegal."

"Brainwashing's legal? You approve of brainwashing?" His hurt eyes would grow stern.

"No—"

"Gail," he'd say wearily so that she saw he was a whole different person in the last year from the calm giant of her childhood, "think of your mother. Think what it would do to her if anything happened to you."

She'd already thought about it. That's why she'd get up and go now, as soon as she was sure the L.O.W.s weren't paying any attention to her—for her parents' sake. Curiosity killed the cat. She didn't need to know one more thing about these creeps who went around worshipping an ordinary pale-faced little businessman named Father Adam, whose picture was plastered all over the city these days on posters that said COME TO THE LIGHT OF THE WORLD RALLY IN PHILADELPHIA. Divine—that's what his followers said about him—son of God, head of the Light of the World Church.

Forget them. Wipe them out of her mind completely. She would, except that one of them was Jim, who was somewhere on another campus probably, cut off from the family except for the letters without return addresses that came every few months from different faraway places. Letters that said, "Everyone is so loving! I'm so happy pursuing the work of Father!"

Depressing letters. But how could it help matters to sit here watching them operate? Don't mess around. Especially now that her life was just vaguely beginning to get back to the way it had been before Jim went away. Being with Doug—going to crew races, like this weekend, and staying over with him. Fooling around and arguing late into the night with Marilyn and the other kids in the dorm. Taking a couple of decent courses. Trying to get a summer job away from home so she wouldn't have to listen again this year to their sad voices and the hum of the air conditioner.

"I'm Michael."

The nearness of his voice surprised her.

"I'm Michael. I represent STIC—Students and Teachers for Improved Communications." He was introducing himself at the table next to hers. "This is Zora."

They'd be coming her way next—she knew it—a tide creeping from table to table. She could escape now, or she could stay and ask them point-blank, "Do you know Jim Brower? He's one of you. How can I find him?"

Her parents would kill her. She pushed back her chair and picked up her books.

On the other hand, she might find out something.

And if she did?

Go to him.

Sure, just like that.

It would be worth breaking a promise, if she could only talk to him in person.

Decide. They were coming toward her. Zora's red hair swirling around her face, Michael offering a flyer.

Gail, getting up, avoided their eyes. "Excuse me," she said faintly. Her blazer caught on the chair as she turned, and she heard the pocket rip. Clutching her books, she darted between tables toward Sansom Walk. Her torn pocket flapping, she dodged people on both sides of her. She was dying to look back, but she didn't, as if doing it would be bad luck. Instead she kept going, eyes straight ahead, past the entrance to the student union, until a little farther, afraid that she'd heard her name, she stumbled and dropped one of her books. A hand tapped her on the shoulder.

"Gail-babes! Hey, what's the matter?"

Turning around in confusion she saw him—work shirt, unruly light brown hair, moustache. She caught her breath. "Doug—I'm so dumb," she said. "I'm so clumsy."

"I love dumb, clumsy women." Doug picked up her book. "They make me feel superior. What's happening? Did you just get the lead in the remake of *Breathless?*"

"It's"—she glanced over her shoulder—"I don't see them now."

"Who?"

"Some people from the Light of the World."

"Yeah? Coincidence or they knew you?"

"Coincidence."

"Did they give you the pitch?"

"No, I left."

"Good. Let 'em sell stale peanuts to somebody else. We're going to Pepe's for mushrooms and pepperoni."

2

"I don't blame you," Doug said, stretching one arm across the back of the seat. "You did right to take off. Try to forget them now, O.K.?"

"I'll try," Gail said. They faced each other on opposite sides of the booth, the Formica tabletop between them.

"You're looking good, babes, in spite of it all. You washed your hair?"

"Yes, this morning."

"It's got shimmering highlights and luxurious body. I like your body, babes."

She sat back and began to relax.

"So what else did you do, before you ran into them?" Doug stared absentmindedly at the graffiti on the wall. "Wait a minute, before you tell me—get Irene's attention so we can order. She won't look at me. She hates men."

"She hates her *job*," Gail said, glancing around. Customers were lined up now at six o'clock waiting for takeout orders. The fluorescent light flickered over the hand-painted mural of the Bay of Naples. Pepe, behind the cash register, mumbled to himself. The jukebox thumped, and Irene stared at the ceiling waiting for the kids in the next booth to order.

"Yeah, O.K.," Doug said, "I'll try not to take Irene personally. She's probably having a mid-career crisis. Just catch her eye if you can."

Gail nodded. "Why do we come here, anyway?"

"Because it's so honest—so completely unphony." Doug patted the green vinyl seat. "Because the atmos-

11

phere's so openly tacky. And no—no deception with Irene. She hates people. And the pizza's so honestly mediocre. Now, go on, tell me—what did you do today?"

Gail stretched. "I went to psych and comparative lit. I had lunch with Marilyn at the dorm, and we studied geology, sort of. Marilyn kept fooling around, imitating Dr. Furman."

"Furman." Doug shook his head. "No wonder that course is driving you up a wall."

"What do you mean? He's a very gneiss guy! If we're good, he's taking our class to see an outcropping of gneiss next week."

"Terrific. Can I come along?"

"Only if you're deeply into gneiss."

"I am." Doug brushed his moustache with his fingertips. "So, Gail, what about the weekend?"

"You mean the races? Sure, I'm coming."

"Good. If it's nice we'll take a blanket and I'll shoot some film and we'll tap a keg. Afterward"—Doug looked up slowly—"we're invited to Billy's parents' place overnight. They're away."

"I have to write my lit paper. Could we come back Saturday night? Do we have to stay over?"

"Because of your parents' calling, right? Not the lit paper."

She hesitated. "Yes."

Doug's eyes roamed, rested again on her. "Good old Ed and Frances. You don't want to just tell them where they can reach you?"

"No. You know how they feel—"

"You're not the cause of their worries."

"I know. But I don't want to do anything that'll upset them."

Doug raised his eyebrows. "You mean you don't want them to *find out about* anything you do that will upset them."

"I guess so," she said. "What does that make me—a hypocrite?"

He shrugged. "Skip the labels. It makes you a person who wants to be with me, because we care about each other and because we both know there's nothing wrong in it, and at the same time a person who's sensitive to her parents' values and who's loving enough so that she doesn't want to cause them pain."

"That sounds better than hypocrite."

"Look, Gail." He laid his hand on hers. "I don't want to lean too hard on you—I don't—I know we've been over this ground before, but when are you going to explain us to your parents in a way that'll make them appreciate how great we are?"

"They know we go out all the time," Gail said.

"They know it, but they aren't happy about it." Doug hunched in the corner of the booth and stretched out his legs.

The kitchen door swung open. Irene swept by with a steaming pizza.

"Get her attention when she comes back," Doug said. "Promise her anything—a Korvette's charge account—dinner for two at Pepe's. . . ."

Irene doubled back to the kitchen.

"See?" Doug shook his head. "She hates me. Just like your parents."

"They don't hate you," Gail said.

"I know. I'm exaggerating. They're . . . wary."

"They've gotten to be wary of everybody."

Doug nodded. "I'm trying to dig that, I mean, I really am. But man, it ain't easy. I'm a hometown boy, for Pete's sake! I could see it if I were some freak —some thug, or dope fiend, or a religious nut! No offense! Or even some poor anonymous slob who didn't have the supreme good fortune to be born and raised in Laurel Ridge, New Jersey. But here I am, an old friend of the family. Childhood comrade of the departed son—long-time protector of the daughter—"

"At least remember it right," Gail said. "You were the one who used to push me into the pool. Remember?"

"Oh." Doug rubbed his moustache. "Well, that's the highest form of flattery at that age, right—a boy pushing a girl into the pool? And mocking you out when you played baseball with us. *Gail-babes*—that's how the name got started. 'Stick one over the fence, Gail-babes!' " Doug sat up suddenly, rested his arms on the tabletop. "Gail, why don't Ed and Frances appreciate me like the whole rest of the world does? Hmm, why?"

"You want a serious answer?"

"Yeah, I do."

"Their being cool to you doesn't have anything to do with you. You shouldn't take it personally."

"I'm not taking Irene personally, I'm not supposed to take your parents personally . . . who can I take personally?"

"Look," Gail said, "I've said this before. Losing Jim's been an awful shock to them, as bad as if he'd been killed in a war. Worse, because that way he'd be a hero—they'd have *that* as a consolation. This way, it's an embarrassment."

"That's their problem! What does it have to do with you and me?"

"They figure I'm all they have left," Gail said. "I've gotten to be more important to them than I ought to be. They're much more uptight about what happens to me than they would be otherwise."

"Brilliant," Doug said. "That might get you accepted as a psych major, but it doesn't do much for my ego. Why should they be uptight about you hooking up with a straight, reasonably presentable, reasonably ambitious, brilliant young architecture student and potentially great filmmaker from their own lilywhite hometown?"

"I think they're afraid of losing me. First, they're afraid we might get married—"

"Let's shake them up!" Doug said, jiggling her hand. "Let's do it, then they won't have to fear it anymore."

Gail smiled. "First, they're afraid we might get married, and second, they're afraid we might not."

Doug nodded. "That about covers the possibilities. You mean they're afraid we might live *in sin*—is that the expression they use?"

"I don't think even *they* say that, but—yeah, that's what they're afraid of." She folded her hands. "Whatever we do, I don't see any way it's going to make my parents happy."

"That's not your job."

"Yes, in a way."

"Another great chasm between us then." Doug leaned back. "Their love would have been perfect, except that she loved mushrooms, and he loved pepperoni; she liked to sit on the edge, and he pushed her in the pool; she believed children should live for their parents, and he believed—"

"I didn't say that."

"O.K., O.K." Doug put his finger to his lips. "To be continued—hold everything."

Irene, scowling, was standing by the booth, her hand on her hip. "Ready to order?"

"Yes, yes," Doug whispered. "One large, half mushroom, half pepperoni. And a pitcher of beer. Thanks." He squeezed Gail's hand as Irene walked away. "Hey, did you notice?"

"What?"

"Did you notice her expression—the serenity, the sense of dedication, the inner illumination?"

"What . . . ?"

"She's one of *them*, Gail. Irene—Light of the World, definitely. Doesn't she look beatified?"

Gail laughed so that she started to cough. "Come on, don't mock me."

"I'm not." Doug said. "I'm mocking the goddamn *situation*. I want to help you with this thing, Gail. It's still haunting you, isn't it? These characters you saw today—they're bugging you now, right? I said you should forget them, but you can't. You can't make up to your parents for Jim. And you can't let an incident like this . . ."

". . . go by without doing something," she said quickly.

"Doing what?"

"I could've talked to them today. Somebody must have heard of Jim. He left from here."

"That doesn't mean anything. They keep shifting people around. The ones you saw probably just arrived from the West Coast. Look." Doug drew a circle with his finger on the back of her hand. "Your father's already done all he could."

Gail paused. "I know, but *I* haven't."

He looked up. "What do you want to do?"

"Find them again. Ask them about him."

Doug let out a deep breath. "You mean, go up to one of them on the street, 'Hey, man, what'd you do with Jim Bower? Like that?"

"I'm serious," Gail said. "I'd be cool."

"Gail." Doug sat back. "If your father's right, then it's a messy business. I mean, these L.O.W.s might've had their eye on you—on us—all along. Like right now"—he leaned over and whispered—"Irene planted over there, reporting our activities—can't you see snaggle-toothed Irene as an angel in the Light of the World Church?"

"You don't think I'm serious."

"I'm afraid you are, babes. That's why I'm going on like this—I'm trying to distract you. What do you want to get mixed up with these bozos for?"

"I don't want to."

"Then don't."

"I won't get mixed up."

"That's probably what Jim said on his way to Mercy. What's the logic, Gail? What do you expect them to tell you?"

"Where he is."

"And then?"

"I could go there."

"Ed and Frances'll really dig that."

"They don't have to know."

"You're supposed to be working on being straighter with them, remember?"

Gail shifted impatiently. "I know, but—afterward. It's worth a try. Let me try."

"*Let you?*" Doug blinked. "Since when do I not let you? Ed and Frances are the ones who don't let you do things." He glanced toward the kitchen. "Irene's still out there meditating." Then he turned back to Gail. "So what would you do?"

She sat stiffly. "I don't know. Try to find this Michael and Zora."

"They aren't students, are they?"

"I doubt it."

"Where would you look?"

"In the café again—along the Walk."

"What would you say?"

"I'd say I'm interested in the movement."

Doug folded his arms. "How far are you willing to play that role?"

"Just long enough to ask who gets sent where, whether there's a list of members—"

"Beer," Irene said, suddenly, sliding the pitcher and mugs across the Formica. "Pie in a minute."

Irene went away, and Doug poured the beer.

"Nancy Drew takes on the Light of the World Church, huh?" he asked.

"No, not really," Gail said, staring at the foamy head.

Doug lifted his mug and drank. "You don't think there's any risk?"

"Of what?"

He hunched. "Of making your parents upset—of getting in trouble—getting emotionally involved—"

"Attracted to it?"

"Yeah."

Gail looked at him over the rim of the thick glass. "You're kidding, aren't you?"

"Yeah, I guess so."

"Watch out!" Irene lowered the aluminum tray onto the table. "Hot!"

The aroma of oregano surrounded them. The mozzarella glistened with oil. Gail picked up a slice in one hand and a napkin in the other. Spicy tomato scalded her lips. She held the pizza away from her and watched the steam rise.

"You don't think I should look for them, do you?" she asked.

"I'm for doing what feels right," he said.

"It didn't feel right this afternoon. Now I'm looking at it differently. Doug"—she tasted the sauce again cautiously—"if we find him, what do you think he'll be like?"

"I don't know." Doug chewed slowly. "Stubborn, I guess—full of plans and energy—fun to talk to until he goes on about the some thing too long—"

"The same, in other words."

"Yeah."

Gail smiled.

Doug filled her mug from the pitcher. "You remember a lot of good stuff from when the two of you were kids, don't you?"

She nodded.

"That's cool. Not everybody has that." He held his beer in both hands. "Go on, then, if you've got a hunch. Look for what's-their-faces tomorrow. I'll come with you." He paused, glancing idly at graffiti on the wall. "What about Saturday night, Gail? What do you say? I have to tell Billy."

"The only thing is—"

He sat up suddenly. "Gail, look . . . incredible." He pointed to where the plaster crumbled around worn names and phone numbers.

She gazed at the graffiti on the peeling wall.

Carol and Andy   Power to
                             the third
    Tom loves Georgette   world!

        Free haircut? Call 458-8754
          (Get one or give one?)
                Either!

Godfather sez
    eat PEPE's PIZZA

"Which?" she asked.

"Here. The one in pencil. I don't believe it."

She followed his finger.

    Come see the Light. Ask for Charlie Hafer
                458-2403

Gail laid down her slice of pizza. "Charlie Hafer," she said. "It's a joke. You wrote it—right?"

"Gail, for God's sake, even *I* wouldn't pull that."

"How come we never saw it before?"

"It must be recent. It's gotta be the same Charlie— Jim's Charlie."

She stared at the number.

Doug, finishing his beer, set down the mug. "Here's your chance, then, if you want it."

"You mean, call?"

"Yeah. Ask if we can see him." He cleared his throat. "Want me to?"

"No," she said.

"Why not?"

"I'll do it."

Doug wiped his moustache with a napkin. "You're sure?"

"Yes."

"You have change for the phone?"

"Yes."

"What'll you say?"

"I'll say I want to see the Light as soon as possible."

He looked at her intently. "I'm coming with you, wherever it is."

"Good."

"You're sure about this now?"

Getting up shakily, she nodded. "Yeah. I think it feels right."

"Across the street," Doug said. "Is that it? Hell, it's practically right on campus, Gail. Which number again?"

"Thirty-nine eighty." Gail lowered her head as a gust of wind blew at them from between two buildings. Doug led her past a dry-cleaning establishment toward the front steps of the house.

"It was definitely Charlie on the phone?" he asked.

"He said so."

"What else? Tell me again."

"I said, 'I want to see the Light. I'm interested in your group.' He asked where I got the telephone number. I told him. He asked my name. I said Gail."

"No last name."

"No."

"Did he ask if you were with anybody?"

"No."

"And he said there was a lecture going on?"

"Yes."

"What do you think we're getting into?"

"I don't know." Gail stopped at the bottom of the steps. Four brownstones in a row, all the same. Four stories high. Faded number 3980 on the transom above the entrance.

Doug put his arm around her. "Ever notice this building before?"

She shook her head.

Doug put his arm around her. "What would you do if we walk in and he's here?" He pushed a strand of her hair gently behind her ear.

"Who?" .

"Jim."

Gail turned toward him. "His last letter came from Kalamazoo."

"This is a big school, babes. Fourteen thousand students. A guy could go and come back and even his own sister wouldn't have to know it."

Gail was silent. Her eyes blurred as she looked from one lighted window to another. "If I saw him, I'd laugh, I guess—or cry—don't know which. Come on, let's get it over with," she said.

Doug held her hand as they walked up the steps. Groping for the knob, she opened the outside door and they entered the foyer.

"What number?"

"He said ring 3A." Gail searched the list of apartment numbers.

"Does it say Hafer?" Doug asked.

"No, just 3A. Here."

"Gail," Doug said, "is there anything you and I should discuss?"

"Like what?"

"Like—I don't know."

She paused. "If they're all strangers and they ask, I'm not Gail Brower. I'm Gail—Gail something else."

He shrugged. "You really want to make it complicated."

Gail pushed the button. They heard the sound of a buzzer. Doug opened the inside door, and Gail, her hand on the railing, went first up the two narrow flights of stairway carpeted with a worn, fake-oriental runner. Their own long, thin shadows fell in front of them on the landing. They walked slowly without looking back.

When they reached the third floor, the two of them stood, breathing heavily, facing the door marked 3A. They looked at each other. Gail hesitated, rang the bell.

Silence. A faint creaking of floorboards. The door opened. "Gail? Hi, there. I'm Charlie Hafer." A heavy-set young man offered his hand.

Gail, awkwardly returning the pressure, stared at the bland face, the rimless glasses, and the blond hair cut

amateurishly, as if he'd called the haircutting number
on the wall in Pepes. So this was Charlie. She'd pictured somebody more sinister. Odd. He was wearing a
double-knit suit but no shoes.

"You brought a friend," Charlie said heartily, ex-
tending his hand to Doug.

Doug shook it. "Good to see you, man."

"Come in." Charlie rubbed his palms together.
"Here, give me your coats—and your boots. We like to
keep the floors clean around this place."

Exchanging another quick look, Gail and Doug followed him into a long hallway, where they saw a row
of footwear lined up against the wall. Doug pulled off
his boots and handed them to Charlie.

"Here, let me help, Gail," Charlie said, supporting
her as she slipped out of hers. He set them in the row
with the others. "Gee, good to see you," he said, his
hands on his hips. "You're both students at Munro?
Senior?"

"I'm a sophomore," Gail said. "This is Doug. He's a
senior."

Charlie, nodding briefly at Doug, studied her face.
"Have we met, you and I?"

"I—I don't think so." Her mouth felt dry.

"Well then, a special welcome to newcomers! We're
having the best time here tonight. Really, I'm glad you
could come." He laid a hand on the arm of each of
them. "So you saw my invitation in Pepes—a little
Light creeps into the most unexpected places, doesn't
it? You've visited our group before?"

"No," Gail said, surprised at the evenness of her
voice. "I've heard about the Light. I've wanted to
come." She glanced around the center hall. Floor bare,
except for the rows of shoes. Slightly dirty cream-col-
ored walls bare, too. High ceilings. Nobody else in
sight. Quiet, except for someone talking in the distance.

"Doug, you're looking for the Light, too?" Charlie
asked.

"Could be." Doug cleared his throat.

"I'm dying to talk to you two," Charlie said. "Listen,
we're just finishing up a little lecture down the hall. Too

bad you missed the beginning. I'd like you to catch the end though. Dr. Ram's speaking to us. Have you ever heard of Dr. Ram?"

"No," Gail said.

"Well, then, you've got a treat in store. He's a professor of theology, a brilliant man. You'll love him. Come on." Charlie, motioning, led them past several unoccupied rooms.

Gail's pulse pounded. At the end of the hall Charlie stopped. A door stood open. She peered in.

"See those empty seats in the back row?" Charlie whispered.

The room was small and sparsely furnished, she saw. Dr. Ram, a slender little man in well-tailored clothes and stockinged feet, stood in front of the group, drawing on a chalkboard. A half-dozen people sat on folding chairs, their backs to Gail. Four women, two men.

"Go ahead," Charlie urged. "Go in and make yourselves at home. I'll see you as soon as it's over."

Gail stood still in the threshold, waiting until the one young, dark-haired man turned his face. Then she let out her breath, surprised at the depth of her relief. No Jim.

Doug nudged her, and the two of them, tiptoeing to the back row, sat down. The dark-haired man and one of the women turned around as they came in. Dr. Ram, chalk in his hand, smiled at them.

"We are all tempted sometimes, aren't we, to hold back our love?" he was saying in a high-pitched voice with an accent she couldn't place. "It's human nature! Just as it's human for ourselves." He drew a circle on the chalkboard and divided it into unequal parts.

"You see?" he said, looking directly at Gail. "Oh, yes, we give ourselves all sorts of good reasons for this selfishness. We say, 'Only *this* much to my parents—they're already old! They have modest needs—they don't have long to live! And only *this* small piece to my friend. He's richer than I am to begin with. And *this* tiny sliver to my brother. He really ought to learn to manage for himself! I don't want to encourage him to be dependent on me.' "

Gail, lowering her eyes, sneaked a look at Doug. Why was Ram singling her out?

"Have you ever offered a delicious morsel to someone," Dr. Ram asked, "and been *so glad* when he said, 'No, thank you'?"

Someone in the audience chuckled.

"Ah, yes," he said with a laugh like a snort, "isn't that how it is? We hold back when, in fact, we ought to *share* our bounty, whether it be spiritual love or material possessions." He looked from one of them to the other, smiling broadly so that he revealed a gold tooth. "Some of you may be sitting here thinking to yourselves, 'Dr. Ram doesn't know what he is talking about! I have offered my love to my parents, my friend, my brother and my sister, and it was *rejected*.' You know what I say to that?" he asked Gail.

She blinked.

"I say," he went on, drawing another pie, "I say, make the slice more generous and offer it again! Make it so generous that the receiver is *overwhelmed. Offer the whole thing.* Offer your whole self to your friend, to your brother!" He laughed aloud. "I am speaking of spiritual love, of course," he said, his face suddenly clouding. "Physical love is *not* like a pastry." He turned and drew a narrow rectangle on the board. "Physical love is a stick of dynamite."

Gail felt Doug poking her with his elbow.

"Let us ask for help," Dr. Ram continued, "in handling this explosive. And at the same time, let us try to give of our spiritual selves unstintingly, for the larger the gift of ourselves, the larger-hearted is the giver." He bobbed his head up and down. "I am pleased to be seeing some of you for the first time tonight. I hope to see much more of you. Amen, in the name of Father."

Gail joined halfheartedly in the staggered, hollow clapping. That was it? That was the brilliant Dr. Ram? Everybody stirred. Doug got up.

"Man, watch the dy-na-mite," he whispered. "Babes, you sure we dropped in on the right bunch?"

She nodded.

Doug cast his eyes upward. "Heavy!"

Dr. Ram was circulating now, shaking hands with everybody.

"Gail, I've got to go out in the hall," Doug said in a low voice. "If I stay, I'll laugh."

As Doug walked away, Gail saw Dr. Ram coming toward her.

Same height as she was, she noticed. Their eyes met. He was looking at her strangely.

"I know you," he said, grinning slyly.

"I—I don't think so." She felt very warm suddenly.

"Oh, yes! Your name is—"

"Gail," she said, wishing she'd waited.

"Gail, yes! Gail, I *know* you."

"How?" she asked weakly.

Dr. Ram smiled. "How, from past lives perhaps? I noticed you immediately when you came into this room. You and your boy friend?" He laughed. "I have something to say to you. . . ." He paused, taking her hand.

"What?" Her hands were sweating. Could he tell?

"Follow the Light," he said, squeezing her fingers. "If you do, you will find what you're looking for." He turned and moved on.

Gail stared after him. He knew her. Did he mean it literally? If he knew her, then he knew Jim. She made a move to go after him, but his back was turned as he spoke to the young dark-haired man.

"Isn't he amazing?"

Gail wheeled around. Charlie Hafer's hands were resting on the back of her chair.

"Dr. Ram's remarkable, isn't he?" Charlie said. "He's got this charisma. You should have heard his lecture from the beginning. It *builds*. See how everybody just naturally gravitates to him?"

"Yes," Gail said feebly.

"He's going to be one of the speakers at the rally. Do you know about the rally?"

"Yes," she said. "I saw the posters."

"It's going to be great. Thousands of supporters from around the world. . . ." He clapped his hands together. "Hey, how about some refreshments, Gail? Your friend

Doug's having himself a good time. Come on, you come with me."

Turning around, she saw that Doug was trapped in a corner with two women. Maybe she ought to rescue him and get out of here right now. This whole thing was stupid.

"What are you waiting for, Gail?" Charlie asked jovially. "Come have some of the best cookies this side of the Mississippi River!"

No thanks, she was about to say, but before she could catch Doug's eye, Charlie had his hand on her back and was steering her through the hall into the next room where a plastic punch bowl and paper plates were set on a table.

"Here, Gail, sit down and relax," Charlie said. "Isn't it great to have a little privacy? How about some punch?"

"O.K." Sitting uneasily on the edge of a convertible couch, she examined the tackily furnished room, the framed poster of a bridge in the sunset, with the caption *Like a bridge over troubled waters, I will lay me down.* "Is this your apartment?" she asked.

"Ours," Charlie said, handing her a cup. "It belongs to the Light of the World. Isn't it homey?" The springs of the couch creaked as he sat down beside her.

She sipped the punch, a watery, orange-colored drink. Did Ram really know who she was, she wondered. And what about Charlie? *Have we met?* he'd asked her. *Where's Jim?* she felt like shouting at him out of the blue.

Charlie leaned back against the wall. "Do you live in the dorms?"

"Yes."

"Where are you from originally?"

"New York City," she heard herself saying. She hated to lie, could never remember later what she'd said.

"The Big Apple! Fabulous!"

"Yes," she said. What a bore. She was going to have to put up with small talk if she wanted to find out anything. Others were coming into the room now, helping themselves to refreshments and moving out into the hall again, where someone was playing a guitar.

"This is nice, isn't it?" Charlie said, smiling so that his big teeth were prominent.

"Yes," she said stiffly.

"You know," he said, "when I saw you at the door a little while ago, you know what I thought?"

Gail glanced up quickly.

"I thought—there's a person who *loves people.*"

She nodded. That's the kind of line Jim might have fallen for.

"I bet you're taking . . . let me guess. I bet you're studying to be . . . a nurse?" He watched her reaction. "A . . . schoolteacher?"

"No," she said. "I want to major in psychology."

"Good! See, I was close, wasn't I? I knew you were interested in people."

She thought for a second. No Charlie Hafer registered at Munro last spring. "What're you majoring in?"

"Business."

"Oh?" She raised her eyebrows. Last spring there hadn't been a Charlie Hafer registered. "Oh, are you a senior?"

"Almost."

"Almost?"

"I'm a part-time student. I took off most of last year to work for the church, so I have some credits to make up."

"What work did you do?"

"I traveled. Spent some time in a beautiful place."

"Where?" Gail coughed.

"North of here, about two hours. In a place called Mercy. Then I was on the road for a while.

She felt herself perspiring. "Did you go with a group?"

"With a bunch of the most beautiful people in the world."

"From Munro?"

"Yes."

"Where are they now?"

"All over. Most of them are heading back this way

for the rally. A lot of them'll be stopping in Mercy on their way to Philadelphia. I'm heading up to Mercy myself this weekend." He rested his hands on his knees. "Say," he said brightly. "I just got a terrific idea."

"What?"

"You could use a break from your routine, right?"

She looked at him.

"We have room for one more person up at Mercy. How would you like to come with us this weekend—be our guest?"

Gail stared straight ahead.

"Oh, I know what you're thinking," Charlie said. "You're thinking, 'I don't even know this Charlie Hafer! I just met him, and he wants me to go away for the weekend!' Listen, Gail—I don't know about you, but I feel as if we're old friends. Do you ever feel close to people you've just met?"

Gail nodded hesitantly.

"Good! You'll love the group. Girls stay together, boys stay together—that's the kind of bunch we are." He raised his cup as if offering a toast. "Come up to Mercy for the weekend with us, will you? There're so many great individuals I'd like you to meet up there." He sighed. "It's so beautiful. I tell you, sometimes when I get a load of that fresh air, I don't want to come back to the city at all. How about it? There's a whole gang going from Munro. We have a van. No expense!"

"For how long?"

"We're leaving tomorrow after classes."

"When will you be back?"

"Sunday night."

"I've got schoolwork," she said.

"Bring it along! We'll help you. What've you got?"

"A 'lit' paper. A geology midterm on Monday."

"Geology—I took geology! Where are you, at the Paleozoic?"

"Further. Up to the Devonian."

"Bring your books! Come, Gail—O.K.? We're leaving from here tomorrow at six. From the apartment. Just bring your books and a change of clothes. You'll love the people."

"A lot of kids from Munro?" she asked, setting her cup on the table.

"Yes, the greatest people you'll ever meet." Charlie jumped up. "A little more punch, Gail? Let me get it for you."

"No, thanks." She glanced toward the hall, where the singing was louder now. More people must have come in. Where was Doug? What should she do?

"Hey, let's join the party then," Charlie said, taking her hand. "Gail," he whispered, light glinting off his glasses, "come with us, please. Whatever you're looking for, we can help you find it. We can help you turn your life around." He looked into her eyes. "Will you?"

"Yes," she said numbly. "Yes, I'll come."

"Fabulous!"

"But I've got to go now," she said, pulling away from him.

"Go? You're kidding. The party's just starting."

"I have to." She breathed quickly. "I'll come to Mercy. I will." Avoiding his eyes, she brushed past him into the hall.

"Gail, wait!" he called.

But she didn't. There were people all over the place now, singing and clapping in time to the music. She stopped short. On one side of the guitar player was blond, baby-faced Michael. On the other side, Zora.

"Gail!"

She jumped.

Doug took her by the hand. "I can't take any more —let's split. I'll get the coats. Get your boots on."

Charlie would follow, she knew, as she pushed her way to the end of the hall. Doug came up behind her with the coats, and the two of them sat on the floor to put on their boots. "The L.O.W.s from this afternoon," she said in a low voice, "they're here."

Doug looked over his shoulder. "Which?"

"Girl with the red hair. The blond boy with curly hair. Here comes Charlie," she whispered. "I agreed to something. You're going to flip."

"What?"

"I'll tell you when we're out of here."

"Gail? Doug? You've really got to go?" Charlie, blinking behind his glasses, was clutching two fresh cups of punch.

"Sorry, man," Doug said, one hand on the doorknob, "got some studying to do. You know how it is. Thanks a lot for everything."

"Gee, that's too bad." Charlie stood by the door. "Gail—see you tomorrow?"

Nodding, she followed Doug.

"Thanks for coming!" Charlie called.

Doug, grabbing her arm, hurried her down the stairs. "What's happening?" he asked as soon as they were out of Charlie's sight.

"I told him I'd go to Mercy for the weekend."

He stopped abruptly on the landing. "How come?"

She looked up at him. "Jim might be there."

Doug snapped his eyes closed for a second. "Was his name mentioned?"

"No."

"Then it's a shot in the dark. It could be a big nothing."

She nodded.

"Do they know who you are?"

"I don't know. Ram said, 'I know you.' "

"He's a jerk. He was talking like that to everybody," Doug said, leading her slowly down the next flight. "Now let me get this straight. If they don't know who you are, the advantage is they won't think you're up to anything. You'd catch Jim off guard."

"Yeah. I'd see things the way they really are."

"This weekend, huh?" Doug looked at her. "What about the crew races—Billy's—?"

"Would you come too?"

Doug sighed. "I don't think I could take them. This, tonight, wasn't anything, but a whole weekend—I'd laugh in their faces, or I'd start mouthing off." He took her hands in his. "Look, I'm not all for your doing this, but if it's going to make you feel better, I'm behind you."

"Then come."

He shook his head. "If I thought there was any danger involved, that'd be another story. They're idiots but they aren't going to hurt you, and I'm sure you're not going to let them mess with your mind."

She looked at him steadily. "Come."

"No."

"Then—tell me not to."

"Nope." He smiled gently. "You know what? I think you'll be annoyed at your self if you don't go. I think you should."

4

Gail, bored out of her mind, swayed from side to side along with everyone else in time to the song.

> *"Country road, country road,*
> *Take me back, where I belong . . ."*

Last night she had jumped whenever somebody came up behind her to pull her into the circle. Once she'd almost said Jim's name out loud. By now, though, halfway through Saturday morning, she knew by sight everybody at the "workshop," as they were calling it. About twenty-five people in all, most in their midtwenties, some from the city, who'd come up with her in the van, and some who were passing through on their way to Philadelphia. So far, no sign of Jim.

> *"West Virginia, mountain momma,*
> *Take me home, country road."*

They were widening the circle now as they sang, pushing back against the walls of the huge room, carpeted but unfurnished, that once must have been the main parlor. And they were starting to clap along with the guitar and tap their feet, though the sound was only a muted *thump, thump* because the shoes, as usual, were piled at the door. An old oriental custom, she'd been told this time.

Gail mouthed the words and glanced from one L.O.W. to the other: Charlie Hafer, smirking at her; blond, baby-faced Michael, leader of the workshop, in the center of the circle; Zora, singing her heart out;

Dan Wong, the clean-cut Chinese guy who was next to Scott; Scott Halloran, the guitar player with straight blond hair, delicate features, and thick glasses. Who else? Kurt, a high school dropout with an arrow tattooed on his arm. Claudia, a black woman with a beautiful singing voice, who had come to the church looking for her daughter. The daughter had left, but Claudia had stayed. A couple of foreign students. Everybody pretty ordinary, except for their high tolerance for listening to dumb, repetitive lectures and singing the same folksongs over and over. Some of these people must know Jim, she thought, but nobody had mentioned him. So—a false lead. Just as well, maybe. She could get out of here early now, and get back to school. Catch Doug, maybe, and go down to the river with him. Study a little for the midterm. Be in her room tomorrow morning when her parents called, instead of relying on Marilyn to give them a story.

And if she was going to leave, she could quit this ridiculous business of pretending to be interested in everything. She stopped singing. Anybody watching? Michael, in the middle, was gazing at her soulfully. And on her right, Zora was looking hurt.

"Next verse, sisters!" Michael called.

Gail moved her lips. *Sisters.* The last thing she felt like was a sister. Wasn't it hard enough working things out with one set of parents, one brother? What made them crave this oversize family? Eight at a table for a supper of chili and Kool-Aid. Ten women stretched out last night on the floor of a bedroom. Twelve in a van riding up here. Two dozen doing early-morning calisthenics. No privacy. Zora always there beside her, chattering, even in the bathroom.

"That was so beautiful," Michael said at the end of the verse. "Really beautiful, sisters. Now, brothers, the last chorus!" He winked at Gail.

Was he flirting with her? she wondered as she swayed next to Zora. Charlie, too, was always taking her hand, putting his arm around her waist. Touch, touch. Not sexily, though. A replacement, sort of. Members could not marry, Zora had told her. They had to devote them-

selves totally to Father. *Father.* So far the lectures had
been mostly about love, peace, serving mankind. Hardly
a mention of Father.

> *"West Virginia, mountain momma,*
> *Take me home, country road."*

"Repeat the chorus!" Michael shouted, and the sound
of Scott's guitar swelled.

Not again, Gail sighed. Fifth time for this one. She'd
leave at the end of it. They'd try to convince her to stay
until tomorrow night, but she'd refuse. She'd tell them
the closest thing to the truth—she hadn't studied
enough geology, had to go back early. How to get out
of here, though? Hell of a long walk to the bus stop in
Mercy. Unless she could call Doug and ask him to pick
her up somewhere. If there was a telephone, that is.

Where's a phone? she was about to ask Zora as the
song ended, but Michael came from the center of the
cirlce and took her hand.

"Guess what, Gail?" he whispered. "I asked for you
in my discussion group. We're calling ourselves The
Happiest Family."

Gail cleared her throat. "I have a family," she said,
feeling her palm grow moist as it touched his.

Michael smiled. "So now you're blessed with two!
Hey, brothers and sisters," he said, "what do you think
of this weekend so far?"

"Great!" Twenty-some people pounded their feet on
the floor.

"Are we glad we're together?"

"Yes!"

In unison, as if they were cheering on a high school
football team. Gail, backing away, felt Zora's arm en-
circle her waist.

"And what do we think of our guests?" Michael
asked, holding Gail's hand up in the air. "What do we
think of Bob and Marc and Gail?"

"Terrific!"

"Do we love them?"

"Yes!"

"Then let's show them *how much,*" he said. "Let's

overwhelm them with our love. Let's separate and join your family leaders, brothers and sisters. This is a time for really getting to know each other." He took Gail by the hand.

O.K., so she'd hang in for a few more minutes and slip out when she wouldn't attract so much attention.

"Welcome home," Michael said to them as they sat in a circle on the floor. "Zora—Dan—Charlie—Scott—Gail. Some of us have been brothers and sisters for a long time; others we hardly know at all. This is the time in our workshop when we tell who we are and how we came here. I'll begin, O.K.?"

Gail fixed her eyes on the space between his front teeth. He looked like a little kid. A lot of them did. As a group they were plain-looking, sickeningly cheerful, slightly grubby from living like kids at summer camp.

"I'm Michael Royerson," he said. "I come from Indiana. I started out studying accounting because that's what my dad wanted me to do. But my heart wasn't in it. Something was missing. I was empty. I was just going through the motions of practicing my parents' religion—they're Protestant. I was going along with their values without thinking.

"Anyway, I left college after two years and headed for California. Thought I'd like to try living in a commune. I did for a while, but things were terrible. Everybody argued—over money, over sharing the work, over women. I was more lost than ever—really turned off to people. So I left. I was just wandering aimlessly, at my wit's end. . . ."

Zora's eyes were large as she listened. Dan studied his hands. Scott sprawled out on the carpet.

Michael looked up. "Then, one day in Berkeley, by accident, I met up with a girl who told me about a wonderful group of people who wanted to make the world a peaceful place. I told her, 'Yeah, I've heard that before!' I was skeptical—but I was curious. So I went to a meeting and then to a weekend like this. And I met some beautiful people. And that's how I first found the Light of the World, four years ago. Since then I've been all over the country."

"Were your parents behind you?" Dan asked.

"Well," Michael said, his cheeks glowing, "to tell you the truth—"

Scott smiled ironically. "They sent the Snuffer after you, didn't they?"

"They tried," Michael said. "That was one of his early attempts. He failed."

Snuffer? Gail looked from face to face.

"What did he do to you?" Scott asked.

"Kidnapped me as I was waiting for a bus to return from my grandmother's funeral. Wasn't that about as low as he could get? He got me all right. Tied me to a bed for about eight hours, tried to argue me out of my beliefs, but he couldn't keep me. When he let me go to the bathroom, I bolted out the window, borrowed a bicycle, and rode thirty miles back to the church."

"Michael!" Zora covered her mouth with her hands. "That's so amazing! You must have felt so betrayed by your parents, so alone."

"Yes, alone, until I got back here—to safety."

"I felt alone until I got here, too," she said, her voice subdued, "and do you know why that was so strange?"

"Why?"

Zora tilted her face. "Because I grew up in a family of fourteen."

"Fourteen? Really?"

"Yes, two parents and eleven brothers and sisters, and I still felt alone—can you believe that?"

Michael nodded. "Sometimes one family isn't enough, no matter how big it is. Tell us how you came, Zora."

"I'm from Ohio," she said. "From a little stick of a town. As far back as I can remember I wanted to get out of there. I often thought of running away, but I was scared to because I had no money. I couldn't afford college, so right after high school, last June, I went to Cleveland and got a job in an office, but the work was boring and I didn't know anybody.

"Then one night in summer, after I'd been in Cleveland a month, the Light of the World Sunbeam Chorale came to town. They sang for free in the park. I had always wanted to be a singer. I hung around afterward and tried out for the chorale. Well, I made it. I gave up my job and came here with the chorale. I've been a member of the Light of the World ever since."

"You're a different person now, aren't you, Zora?" Michael asked.

"Yes," she said. "I used to be so shy. Now I'm confident. I travel. I get to stay in beautiful places like this."

Gail watched her smoothing her skirt over her knees. "Do you miss your brothers and sisters at home?" Gail asked her.

"Sometimes," Zora said. "But I have my brothers and sisters here. And my Father is everywhere."

"That's right, Zora," Michael said. "You're very lucky. We all are. Dan, will you tell us about your life now?"

Dan, in a neat white sport shirt, fingered the dark rims of his glasses.

Gail, leaning back against the wall, listened to the overlapping voices as people around the room told their stories. Jim must have sat here once telling his. What had he said? "I'm from suburban New Jersey. I had what most guys want—nice house, decent parents, a sister who looked up to me—but that wasn't enough. . . ."

"My name is Daniel Wong," Dan said, his speech precise, clipped. "I was born on the mainland of China. My family fled from the Communists. We came to California. We were very poor at first and were discriminated against. I went to school on the West Coast and studied political science in college. When I graduated I looked for a job for a full year. Nothing was open. I was prepared to devote myself completely to my work, but there was no work.

"Then one evening at a lecture, I met Mr. Brock, our East Coast director, who was then in California. I was impressed with his leadership. He introduced me to others, and I began to see a future for myself in the family of Father Adam. Since I became a member I've met a lot of important people and I've gained a lot of valuable experience."

"Wonderful, Dan," Michael said. He put his hand on Charlie's shoulder. "It's your turn, Charlie."

"I come from near Washington, D.C.," Charlie began, biting his lower lip. "I had an unhappy childhood. I was overweight and had almost no close friends in school. My older brother was an athlete and very popular, and I figured I couldn't ever match him so I might as well give up. I hated him then. Since I've found the Light of the World I don't hate anymore. Luckily I was good at science. I did pretty well in that, so I got accepted at Munro."

"Did things go better for you then?" Zora asked sympathetically.

"Not at first," Charlie said, "but at the end of my freshman year, I found this wonderful group where everybody was welcome—Protestant, Catholic, Jew; black, white, brown, and yellow; old and young; male and female. It was a group called STIC—Students and Teachers for Improved Communications. And through it I came to the Light of the World."

Michael smiled. "Charlie's had a few interesting experiences since then, haven't you, Charlie?"

"Yes," he said ruefully. "My brother decides every once in a while I ought to be rescued."

Scott sat up. "Pity the poor Snuffer if he ever lays hands on Charles!"

"You know it!" Charlie said. "So far a Snuffer or two has trailed me, but I've never been captured. I have new courage since I found the Light."

"Oh, Charlie," Zora cried.

"He's an inspiration to all of us," Michael said. "How about it, Scott? How did you come to the church?"

"A hopeless wreck," Scott said, stretching languidly.

Gail watched him. Very expressive face. A talented musician. Generally sharp. Tense, though. Fingernails stubby from being bitten.

"I'm Scott Halloran. I'm originally from North Carolina, but I've been everywhere, including hell. I was the only child in a Catholic family. That's unique right there, isn't it? My father was a career officer in the U.S. Army and my mother played bridge a lot. They seldom remembered they had me, but I didn't care, because all

I was interested in was music. I wanted to be a star!" he said in a tone of self-mockery.

"Well, I left home six years ago when I was seventeen, and I worked in New Orleans in a piano bar, where I got a taste of bourbon. I played guitar and dropped acid for a while in the Village in New York. Then I snorted coke in Paris, where I went to study and wound up being kept by an older woman. I wrote poetry and played music, but what I was producing got worse and worse, because I debauched myself by night and slept by day. You can't imagine how badly I wanted to get out of that scene, but I just couldn't do it by myself. Well, brothers and sisters," he said, pushing his hair off his forehead, "after six month of that—I could go into much more sordid details, but I'll spare you—I woke up one morning in Paris—didn't know who I was or where I was—and decided . . . enough. *Enough.* I'll kill myself."

He paused. "Now here you see the Father's wondrous ways. On the way to the Seine—I figured in Paris, if I was going to do myself in, it had to be the Seine—I happened to run into a beautiful brother singing like crazy right on the street. I ran up to him, blissed out at the thought that somebody could be that happy. He took me to a café and spoke to me about my music and my poetry, and he told me about a family that was so high on love they didn't need anything artificial, not even cigarettes. And he brought me back to America. And"—he bowed slightly—"that's the story of a lost soul who went off to drown in darkness and found instead the Light of the World!"

"Scott!" Zora sobbed.

Gail joined the others as they clapped.

"In spite of your expressions of appreciation," he said with a twisted smile, "I remain most humble and self-effacing. I live to serve others."

Gail watched him. Was the story for real? There was something studied about it—rehearsed, almost. Still, he was interesting. Did he know Jim? she wondered.

"Scott," Michael said, "you've been through a lot—more than the rest of us put together, maybe. In this world of evil and temptation, what do you fear the most?"

Scott, looking at his hands, thought for a minute. "Myself," he said.

Michael nodded knowingly. "Gail." His voice was gentle. "It's your turn. Will you tell us who you are?"

She coughed, uncertain what he meant. Make up a last name. Not that they seemed to care what her name was. I'm—Gail—Gail Brown," she began, suddenly overpowered by an unpleasant odor. Feet, she realized, glancing around. Stockinged feet.

"Yes, Gail, go on," Michael said. "Tell us your story."

Brown—dumb choice of name. They were all looking at her. "I—I grew up in New York," she said. "I've lived there all my life. I came to Munro last year. There's nothing terrible in my life, really—"

"Everybody's got some problems, Gail," Zora said. "You can tell us."

"Do you have any brothers or sisters?" Michael asked.

His blue eyes were looking right through her. She blinked. "No—no, I'm an only child."

"Don't feel alone," Zora said. "We're your brothers and sisters now."

Michael was still watching her closely. "You live with your parents?"

"Yes."

"Where did you go to high school?"

"I—I went to a small private school. You probably never heard of it." She was glad suddenly that Doug wasn't here. She could never lie like this if he were.

"Are you happy, Gail?" Michael asked. "Do you get along with your parents?"

"Yes . . ."

"All the time?"

She shrugged. "Well, that's impossible—"

"So you disagree with them sometimes," Dan said.

"Yes—"

"About what?" Michael asked.

"Oh, they don't like me to do certain things."

"I know what you mean," Dan said. "They don't

think you're old enough to make up your own mind, and you find that insulting."

"Yeah, that's it."

"And they probably don't always approve of your friends," Dan went on.

"That's true, they don't," she said. *Why don't Ed and Frances appreciate me?* Doug had asked her the other night at Pepe's, and she'd avoided the truth. Because they like people who're just like they are, she should've said. You're too different. You like art and films and talking about serious stuff, and you're sarcastic and frank and too liberal for them. And they don't like your moustache.

"It's tough when your parents try to alienate you from your friends," Michael said. "By the way, what do you think of all the different kinds of people here this weekend?" He waved his hand.

"Great," Gail said.

"Is that why you came to us, Gail?" Dan asked. "To expand your friendships?"

"Sort of," she said. Why were they giving her the third degree?

"I think you're looking for a place to let out your feelings, Gail," Zora beamed. "Here you can let everything out—you really can."

"I think I know why Gail's here," Michael said.

She met his eyes. Could it be that he'd known all along and was trying to torment her?

"She's looking for a person—to believe in. Is that it, Gail?"

"I don't know," she said impatiently.

"We can help you find whatever you're looking for," Zora said, hugging her. "Let us!"

"She's right, Gail," Michael said. "Stay with us and you'll find what you're looking for. We have a seven-day workshop starting Sunday night when this one ends. How about staying?"

"I can't!" she said sharply. "I have to go to classes."

They were quiet suddenly, surprised, she saw—and hurt by the tone of her voice.

"O.K.," Michael said agreeably. "We understand. If you change your mind, let us know. Brothers and sisters, let's end the meeting of The Happiest Family by saying a short prayer for Gail."

The six of them bowed their heads. "Dear Father," Michael prayed, "thank you for bringing our sister Gail to us . . ."

"Father!" Zora repeated.

"Help our sister see that although her life may seem full now, it can only be at its fullest when it includes thee, Father."

"Father!" Charlie and Dan cried in unison.

Gail, opening her eyes, watched them quiver.

"Lead the rest of us on the right path, Father, away from the temptations of drugs and alcohol and the terrible lusts of the flesh that some of us have known, and away from sinners—some of them our blood relatives, who want us to leave our work and sink with them into the pit . . ."

"Father!" Zora moaned.

"We ask, finally, that our sister Gail come to love us as we already love her, and that she come to see the Light," Michael said. "Amen."

"*Amen!*"

"Let's gather all the families together now," Michael announced. "Put your shoes on. It's time to go outside for Spirit-World Hide-and-Seek!"

Gail stood up shakily. Zora was hugging her again, and Scott was kissing her hand in an exaggerated way. How was she going to get out of here?

"You know, Gail," Charlie said as they hovered over her, "I keep thinking we've met before."

He'd said that at his apartment, too. She forced a smile.

"You mean she reminds *you* of somebody too?" Michael asked. "You know who she reminds me of a little?" he said, his blue eyes flashing. "Jim Brower."

"Yes!" Zora said.

"Hey!" Charlie laughed.

"What a wild coincidence, Gail," Michael said. "But you said you're an only child, right?"

Gail, biting the insides of her cheeks, nodded.

"Jim Brower's a really beautiful person. If you come

to the Philadelphia rally with us, I'll introduce you to him. It's amazing—this guy could be your brother!"

Zora took her arm again and led her toward the door, where everyone scrambled for shoes. Gail, pulling her boots on, felt weak and sick. They knew who she was. Why were they pretending to believe her lies? Devious creeps. What did they stand to gain by it?

"You," she imagined her father saying, *"You. They've gotten you all the way to Mercy, haven't they? Now they're trying to get you one step farther. And all the time they're getting you to think that it's your own idea."*

"Let's be straight with each other!" she felt like yelling out.

"They like deception better," a voice in her head told her. "Deception leaves you confused. All the easier to trap you, then, my dear!"

"Hurry, Gail!" Michael was calling. "Come with me. Time for Spirit-World Hide-and-Seek!"

5

"You'll like our game, Gail. It'll make you feel free and innocent, like a child again."

"In the L.O.W. you can feel free and innocent all the time, Gail."

"Stay, Gail. Stay for the seven-day workshop."

"And come to the rally with us. Dr. Ram will be there. And Mr. Brock. And Father Adam. We're going Monday, some of us, to set up for the weekend. We're staying at Father's home in Philadelphia—the New World Hotel. Won't you come with us?"

They were flocking around her now on the lawn outside the big house—not only Michael's group but others, too—treating her like a bride, welcoming her as if she'd already admitted she was Jim's sister and had agreed to become a member. Could Jim himself know about this?

She'd find out—that and a lot of other things. She'd go to Philadelphia somehow. Not with these jerks though. With her parents, maybe. Or Doug, if she could convince him. Meanwhile, the sooner she got out of here, the sooner she'd be with Doug. The minute the game was over—that's when she'd tell them she was leaving, Gail decided as they competed playfully to hold her hands. Tell them she wasn't feeling well. That way maybe they'd offer her a ride to the bus stop.

"Spirit-World Hide-and-Seek!" Michael called. "Ward, you'll be captain of your family and Bob's family. We'll call you team Father's Seekers. Scot'll be captain of the other two families. You'll be Adam's Angels, Scott. O.K., Father's Seekers, you'll hide, and

Adam's Angels, you'll look for them. I'm the timekeeper. Play hard, everybody, and remember—nobody loses —we all win with Father!"

"Follow me, Adam's Angels," Scott shouted, twirling a soccer ball in his hand.

Gail felt herself being pulled across the lawn between Zora and Charlie in a human chain that wound around Scott.

"OK., brothers and sisters," Scott said, drawing them into a huddle. "You know the rules: We close our eyes and count to one hundred. While we're counting, they go off and hide. When I say, 'One hundred,' we start looking until Michael calls time. Ready?"

"*Yes!*"

"And what do we do when we see one of 'em?"

"Heave the ball!"

"Bombard them with our love!"

"Send them to the World of the Spirits!"

Scott nodded. "Remember, they'll resist us," he said in a low voice. "They'll try to escape us and join Satan, but we won't let them. We'll search until we find them all, and we'll overwhelm them, down to the last wayward soul. Another thing, brothers and sisters, let's show our spirit with a cheer."

"Beautiful!" Charlie said.

Scott crouched down. "Listen now, this is it:

> *"Adam's Angels, from above,*
> *Crush opponents with their love!*
> *Win for Fa-ther A-dam!*

Everybody join in!"

Gail pulled back from the huddle.

"Come on, Gail."

She mouthed the words as they cheered again.

> *"Adam's Angels, from above,*
> *Crush opponents with their love!*
> *Win for Fa-ther A-dam!"*

Now the other team had linked hands and were swinging their arms high in the air as they danced in a circle:

"We don't know the word DEFEAT . . .
Father's Seekers can't be beat!
Hoo-rah for the Father!"

They were kidding, weren't they? Gail thought.
They'd quit this nonsense, admit they'd been joking
and go back in for another lecture. Lectures were bad
enough, but *this* . . .

"O.K., everybody, ready?" Scott asked.

They weren't kidding.

"Shut your eyes, Adam's Angels! Fathers Seekers—
go hide! One, two, three, four . . ."

Gail stared at the sight of the others running in all
directions while her teammates stood in a circle and
covered their eyes with their hands.

"Hide your eyes, Gail," Michael called.

She snapped them shut angrily.

". . . eight, nine, ten . . ." Scott counted.

Gail shifted from one foot to the other. This was
ridiculous—insane. Having to play, having to close
her eyes. What were grown people doing, anyway, on
a beautiful Saturday morning, hiding and chasing each
other across a lawn? Damn, she could be back at Munro now, down at the races with Doug, watching—watching what? She thought suddenly. Watching grown people chase each other down a river in sculls. There was
a difference, wasn't there, or was the whole world just
one big lunatic asylum divided into different wards?

". . . thirty, thirty-one, thirty-two . . ."

The idea flickered in her mind: their life wasn't any
crazier than hers. She followed routines, too, at Munro
—went to lectures that were often boring, did things
because she was told to do them, knocked herself out
working for grades, wasted a lot of time on nonsense. . . .

"Don't be absurd!" she could hear her father's voice
contradicting. "There's no comparison. Father Adam's
a charlatan who's turning innocent kids like your brother into liars and cheats who'll do anything to further
this international movement."

"Anything?"

"Yes, *anything*," he'd said. "I believe that, Gail."

". . . forty-nine, fifty . . ."

If her father meant violence, he had to be wrong, she thought. There was no way she could picture baby-faced Michael and flabby Charlie hurting anybody physically. Killing them with boredom, maybe. Her teammates were counting in unison now, louder and louder: ". . . *fifty-nine, sixty* . . ." Gail tried to shut out the counting, but the sound swelled.

". . . *sixty-seven, sixty-eight* . . ."

"Gail!"

She opened her eyes and saw Zora squinting at her.

"What's the matter, Gail?" Zora asked.

"Nothing."

"Why aren't you counting? Aren't you having fun?"

"Sure." She moved her lips. What *was* wrong with her that she felt she had to keep faking? *Nothing.* Just easier to play along until she left. "Seventy-nine, eighty . . ." She sneaked a look around the circle at the earnest faces.

How could she manage to take off without attracting a lot of attention? When the game was over, she'd pretend—wait a minute, why pretend anything? At the end of the game she'd go to the bathroom. Quickly, so Zora couldn't come with her. Then she'd pick up her bag from the girls' dormitory and sneak downstairs. If they didn't notice her, she'd leave without saying good-bye. If they saw her, she'd ask for a ride. With or without a ride, she'd be out of here in an hour.

". . . *ninety-eight, ninety-nine, one hundred!*"

"Coming, ready or not," Scott shouted. For a minute they all stood still, listening. Then the circle of Adam's Angels broke up and spread out. "Call when you see somebody! Call for this," Scott said, holding the ball aloft. "Call for the word of Father."

"Gail, let's follow Scott," Zora said, linking arms. "It's more fun to stay together."

Scott led them across the grass and under the portico to the rear of the house. An enormous, sturdily built place, Gail noticed, seeing it now for the first time in daylight. Huge unkempt gardens, a garage with six or eight cars and vans in it, more lawn behind that.

Scott stopped short. The rest of them waited and

listened to a rustle in the bushes by the garages. "I spy a Seeker," Scott whispered. "Surround him!"

Zora, Gail, and the others fanned out.

"Trapped!" Scott raised the ball over his head.

The Seeker dashed out of the bushes, but the ball zinged toward him and hit his ankle.

"A very palpable hit!" Scott said, retrieving the ball. "Go to the Spirit World, Marc! You're too beautiful for this one. Onward, Adam's Angels."

"Look over there." Zora pointed. In the garden Charlie was signaling. The group of them tiptoed in his direction. As they drew closer they saw a dilapidated arbor shaking. A head stuck out of the shrubbery underneath.

"Heave!" Charlie called.

Scott let go of the ball. It bounced off a branch and came back to him.

"Heave again!"

The Seeker squirmed as the flying ball hit him between the shoulder blades. One of his teammates darted out of the same clump of shrubs, and Charlie, picking up the ball, hit him on the seat of the pants.

"The Word strikes again!" Scott said.

Scrambling for the ball, he handed it to Gail. "I'm entrusting you with the Word of Father," he said solemnly. "Are you worthy of it?"

Gail stood, dazed, with the ball in her outstretched hands.

"Time's almost up!" Michael's voice rang out.

"Follow me, Gail." Scott, motioning to her to come along with the ball, led her in and out among the bushes. "Wait," he said, suddenly, his eyes narrow. "I sense a direct confrontation with Satan, and you are to be the instrument of Good. There," he whispered, "behind that tree. Satan is lurking in the form of Ward Garner, captain of Father's Seekers."

Gail looked at the shadow slanting away from the thick trunk. She inched closer. Scott and Zora backed her up.

"This is a test of true mettle, Gail," Scott said. "Don't let us down."

The shadow swayed, a figure moved. Gail, running toward it, aimed the ball and fired.

Ward leaped and landed on the ground, with the ball at his feet.

"Satan is conquered!"

"Win for Fa-ther A-dam!"

"Gail, we love you!"

"Time's up!" Michael called.

Arms were flung around her as both teams returned to the side lawn.

"Will you come with us to Philadelphia, Gail?"

"You must've played this before—you're so good."

"Be my partner, Gail."

"Let's hear it for Gail," Charlie shouted.

"Rah, rah, rah!"

"You sure have made a lot of friends," Michael said, grinning. "Let's switch now, everybody. Father's Seekers count to one hundred, Adam's Angels hide."

"Ready?" Ward asked as everyone gathered around him. "Close your eyes, Father's Seekers. One, two, three . . ."

For a second Gail watched the others on her team starting in different directions. Charlie was heading toward the garage. Scott, after a few steps, caught onto a branch as if he intended to climb the tree. Then, shaking herself out of her fog, she ran too, past the portico to the front of the house.

"Gail, let's hide together!"

Zora's high-pitched voice spurred her to move faster, filled her with the urge to get out of its range. Even as she half turned and beckoned to Zora to follow her, Gail knew she would never let her catch up. And she knew even at that moment what she was about to do. With long, loping strides—easily, at first, as if she were winning a race in a dream—she broke into a run around the forsythia bushes in front of the house and on down the long blacktop driveway that led to the gate. After that would be the road, and the highway and the town of Mercy. At the edge of town was a gas station, she remembered. She would go there and call Doug collect.

Ahead of her on the deserted driveway lay acres of trees on one side and a pond on the other. L.O.W. property, paid for by the sweat of Jim's brow, as her father would say. Breathing spasmodically, she looked back. Even though Zora didn't seem to be following, Gail veered off the blacktop and ran parallel to it, behind a row of evergreens. Her hair blew in her face. Her jacket flapped open. Tiny nuggets of dirt leaped into her shoes.

She'd regret this, probably. She gulped in air—crazy, leaving without her bag. They'd be angry . . . Michael and Charlie and the rest . . . they'd look her up at school . . . make her life miserable. . . .

Pressure in her chest now. Lungs straining like cheap balloons overinflated. Sharp stitch in her side. Slowing to a walk, she stepped over fallen branches and piles of leaves back onto the blacktop surface. Up ahead— the gate. It was open.

Gail! No, she was imagining it. Glancing nervously behind her, she saw only the driveway, the pond, and the evergreens. They'd have missed her by now, for sure. She laughed at the thought of them running around like maniacs, looking behind bushes and up trees, thinking that any second they'd find her and bombard her with the ball, when instead she'd be exiting through the gate. She walked faster.

Until she saw it, that is—the car. A small, gray foreign job, parked outside the fence—and a man getting into it fast, slamming the door, idling the motor, waiting.

Hesitating for only a second, she held up her head and went through the gate. It could be anybody, this driver who was watching unseen from the car. All sorts of people came here and gaped—parents, reporters. Her stomach churned though, as the car pulled up alongside her. It could be a gatekeeper. Somebody assigned to handle departures like hers.

They wouldn't dare try to keep her by force, would they? She glanced quickly at the car, which was inching along next to her. Another one of their teases maybe— to follow her until she couldn't stand it anymore and got in of her own free will. She wouldn't. *She wouldn't.*

She moved over farther onto the shoulder. The car kept even with her. The gas station was far off. The bus stop even farther. Still, the only thing to do was to make a break for it, away from the road, down into the ditch and into the woods. Unburdened, she jumped down easily, but climbing up the other side, she tripped on a tuft of long grass and lay, panting, in the dirt. You'll never get me, she felt like calling out as she got up on her hands and knees. Until she looked over toward the road again and saw that there wasn't any reason to be dramatic. The gray car, well beyond her already, was speeding along on the way to Mercy.

6

Safe. She threw her arms around Doug and buried her face in his sweater. He reached over to close the door on her side of the car. Then he turned off the ignition and pulled her toward him.

"Hey, it's O.K.," he said. "Jesus, you're cold. Here, take my sweater." Struggling behind the wheel, he took it off and put it around her shoulders.

Gail pressed her head against his chest and laughed softly. "Before I was so hot, now I'm cold."

"What'd they give you, laughing gas?"

She shook her head. "No, I don't know what's wrong with me. I can't stop." But as she said it, she did. Sitting up, she looked at Doug, at his green eyes, wispy brown newly washed hair, slightly reddish moustache. *What are you doing here?* she had the urge to ask, as if she hadn't called him two hours before with the dime borrowed from the gas-station attendant. Here he was now, in his friend Billy's beat-up Chevy, kissing her like the hero in a Western. Twenty-four hours—that's all it had been.

"Don't go away anymore," Doug said, relaxing his hold on her.

She glanced up at him. "He's going to be in Philadelphia next weekend for the rally."

"I'll come with you."

"You changed your mind. How come?"

He tied the arms of the sweater in a loose knot at her neck. "I don't sleep right when you're off with those creeps."

A car pulled up at the pump a few yards away from

them. "Let's go, Doug," she said. "Please let's get out of here."

"It was grim, huh?" He started the motor, looked over his shoulder and pulled out onto the highway. "O.K. Tell all. What did they do to you?"

"They lied."

"About what?"

"They pretended I was a complete stranger."

"You told them—what name?"

"I told them Gail Brown."

"And they didn't believe you? How do you know?"

"They kept saying things that showed they didn't. 'Do you have any brothers?' 'You *remind* me of somebody —oh, yes—Jim Brower! He could be your brother.' "

Doug took his eyes off the road for a second. "They said that?"

She nodded.

"So you think they knew all the time—even at Charlie's apartment the other night?"

"Probably. Your father says they make a play for siblings."

"I know."

"So what the hell are they up to, Gail?" Doug shifted behind the wheel. "There's no way you'd . . ."

"I'd *get hooked?*" she said ironically.

Doug kept his eyes on the road. "Yeah," he said.

"Are you kidding?" she said. "They disgust me."

"That's what I thought," Doug said. "Good. So, what else?"

Gail stared idly at a Howard Johnson's on the right, a bowling alley, a skating rink. "At first I thought I was being followed."

"By who?"

"A car was waiting at the gate. Somebody was watching me."

"Who?"

She shrugged. "A man."

"Did you get a look at him?"

"No. He drove up beside me—pretty close—and then he took off."

"He didn't speak to you?"

"No."

"What kind of car?"

"Gray. A foreign car." She paused. "Probably it was a coincidence."

"Just a plain, ordinary strangler-rapist, you mean, who follows girls on deserted roads."

"Yeah." She curled up in the seat. "I'm a wreck," she said. "It was awful."

"Sorry you went?"

She hesitated. "No."

Doug glanced at her as he slowed down. "Maybe it'll all seem funny someday when you look back on it." He stopped at the intersection. "So, Jim's in Philadelphia."

Gail glanced at the sign: WELCOME TO MERCY. "He will be next weekend," she said.

Doug put his foot on the accelerator. "We're going to go there and see him, you and I."

"What about my parents?"

"Oh, yeah!" Doug said. "They called you this morning. I spoke to Marilyn."

"My parents called this morning—Saturday?"

"Yeah. They broke tradition. Marilyn did what you said—she told them you went to somebody's house to study for the geology midterm."

"Did they believe her?"

"Why wouldn't they? You've got an honest reputation, babes. When you tell people lies, they're likely to believe you. But why don't you make your life simpler and tell the truth?"

"Some people don't want to hear it. My parents, for instance, a lot of the time."

"I say you don't give them enough credit. Try them. Come on, Gail, call them up. Say, 'Look, Ma, you may not like this, but I went off with the L.O.W.s this weekend, and it was worth it because I found out where Jim is, and Doug and I thought we'd go to see him. And by the way, Ma, Doug and I are more than good friends. You may not like that, either, but that's the way it is. And if you can't reach me at the dorm on Sunday mornings when you call, try Doug's number or Billy's parents' house.' "

"Easy for you to say." Gail turned to look out the window. "After what they've been through, they just want to feel I'm a nice, innocent kid who does what they want."

"They've got to get used to you growing up, Gail. And you do, too."

They were silent as they drove along Main Street with its old-fashioned white frame storefronts. Larson's Soda Shoppe, Dingman's Furniture, the Mercy Pharmacy.

"See that?" Doug asked.

She nodded. Grinning at them from a poster was Father Adam.

Light of the World
Philadelphia Rally
Saturday, April 22

Come out of darkness into the Light

"We'll be there, man," Doug said with a mock salute as they passed. "What'd you find out, Gail? What's the guy's racket?"

"They say he's all-loving and he's everywhere—"

Doug passed the car ahead of them. "You mean omnipresent? In this car right now, watching over us?"

"Yeah."

Doug shook his head. "Gail, do they *believe* it? I mean, it's a racket, isn't it, that a few naive good guys like Jim have been sucked into? A money-making proposition. Or a cover for a political organization."

"He believes he's the son of God," Gail said. "So do they. They'll do anything he says."

Doug stepped on the accelerator as they came to open highway at the end of town. "What else do they believe?"

"That the world's full of evil."

"So what else is new?"

"They want to wipe out Satan and unite all countries in peace," she said. "They think they can be as pure as children again, with Adam as their perfect father. They want to model themselves after him."

"After that sawed-off shyster?"

"He's got personal magnetism, Michael says, and an inspirational quality, and—"

"Money," Doug said. "Fifty million bucks a year just from sending your brother and his buddies out on the streets to sell candy and peanuts. How do they rationalize that?"

"They say they have to sell stuff to get the money to further their goals and spread the word."

"And to buy more tax-exempt real estate for that playboy to loll around in," Doug said. Shifting gears, he took a steep incline. "So what were they like—full of crap like Ram?"

"Yes, they keep saying everything's 'so beautiful' and 'real spiritual.' They weren't stupid—not at all. A couple of them seemed very bright. Scott—a guy named Scott. Strange, though."

"College kids?"

"All ages," Gail said. "Mostly in college or college dropouts. All different backgrounds."

"What the hell attracts them?" Doug asked as they sped down the hill and braked for shopping-center traffic.

Gail watched the cars jockeying in and out. "I don't know—most of them seem like they'd have a rough time out in the world. They want things to be perfect —by magic. They love *everybody* but no one special person. Maybe they're afraid of sex."

"They really practice what they preach—no sex?"

"They seem to."

"Oh, yeah, sex is dy-na-mite! Ram says. I go along with that," he said.

Gail sat up. "I guess they think eliminating sex makes their lives easier—"

"Easy—*easy*, babes? Who wants *easy?*"

"Me sometimes," she said quietly. "When I'm lazy."

"We're going to have to deal with that." Doug smiled. "I don't tolerate lazy women." Glancing into the rear-view mirror, he pulled out to pass. At the sound of a horn he swerved back. "Yeah, man, yeah, I see you!" He fixed his eyes straight ahead. "Jim never found a steady woman. Think that's what's at the bottom of it?"

"Maybe."

"Well, one thing that fits—he always had big impractical ideas. Remember the tree house? I guess you weren't old enough to be involved in that. We built it in the neighborhood. It looked terrific, but it collapsed before our backs were turned."

"I remember," she said. Suddenly she ached to see Jim.

"I'm proud of you for making this trek, babes. I am." Doug said after a minute. "It took guts. Look, I got a plan of action." He steered with one hand and put his other arm around her. "Let's look for a place to have lunch—are you hungry?"

"I guess so. What time is it?"

"Going on two."

What would they be doing back there now? she couldn't help wondering. Whispering about her. Going through her bag, maybe.

"Look for a place," Doug said. "Over lunch we'll figure it out, about next weekend—how we're going to handle it. Then we'll call your parents—"

"They called me this morning? That's odd."

"Yeah. Then I'll take you back to the dorm, and you'll shower and pick up some stuff, and we'll go to Billy's. Hey, are you listening?"

"Yes." Gail was looking into the side mirror now.

"What're you staring at?"

"Go a little faster," she answered. "I want to see something."

"I'm trying. He's tailgating."

"Doug, what kind of car—?"

"A Volvo."

Gail swiveled around in her seat. "That's the car," she said.

"The car? The gray—the *gray* car?"

"Yes."

"How do you know it's the same?"

"It is."

"You're sure you're not just spooked over this?"

"*It's the same car.* Pull over and see what happens."

"There's gotta be at least nine thousand gray Volvos in Pennsylvania."

"Pull over," she insisted.

"Here's a McDonald's. Should I?"

"Yes."

At the sign he veered suddenly into the lot without giving a signal. They skidded on gravel and stopped abruptly.

The gray car sped on. For a minute the two of them sat in silence staring at the steady flow of traffic.

"Well, whoever he was," Doug said, "he gave up his chance for a Big Mac."

She nodded.

"Look," he said, opening the car door, "it's a big nothing. Another strangler-rapist off into oblivion. Be happy!"

She got out of the car.

Doug came around to her side. "Come on, babes, let's have lunch." He put his arm around her. "You know," he said as they walked across the lot, "this heavy thought just hit me. I mean, here we are, analyzing Jim, and chasing around like Charlie Chan, and plotting like madmen. And yet, what if Jim's right and we're the jerks? Wouldn't that be the divine screw? What if Father Adam really *is* God, then where are we?"

7

Church bells. Sunday morning. Gail rolled over, saw
bands of light streaming through the blinds of her room
in the dorm. Doug hadn't wanted to bring her back here
from Billy's at two in the morning. She was glad now
that she'd insisted. A couple of hours alone to think
things out—that's what she needed. Where was Marilyn? She raised her head and watched the gentle rise
and fall of the sheet on the other bed.

Her limbs felt heavy. Too much beer last night maybe. Not enough sleep. Too many dreams. The one, for
instance, where she and Jim were kids again, hiding in
the attic at Laurel Ridge, and she was looking for him.
And the other dream: she was in Doug's apartment—
lying on his bed—and Scott Halloran from the L.O.W.
had appeared all of a sudden in a kind of angel costume. "The worst sin is carnal knowledge!" Scott had
whispered. "Worse than murder!" She had felt terrible
and had tried to sneak out of Doug's room without being seen. Stupid as the dream was, she realized as she
looked around the room, it had left her with an eerie
feeling of being watched.

Maybe she'd feel better if she got out of bed. She
should study for the geology midterm, start the paper
on *Antigone*. . . . How could she concentrate, though,
with so many other things buzzing in her head? The
idea of going to see Jim, for instance. And what to tell
her parents . . .

Let this be the day of beginning on a new footing with
them, she thought. Call them—now, early, before they

59

went to church. Tell them right away that she'd been to
the workshop. Ask their advice about going to Philadelphia with Doug on Friday.

She tried to imagine their reaction. Anger? Maybe
not. "It's too dangerous," her father would say. "Let's
keep this in the family, Gail," she could hear her mother
adding. "It's nice of Doug to volunteer, but it's not
necessary." What would her parents suggest instead?
The three of them going after him again—arriving like
tourists at the hotel, being spotted a mile away as a
family that was there to make trouble. Jim being fore-
warned so that he wouldn't even agree to see them.
No, she couldn't let them talk her into anything like
that.

Sitting up, she threw off her blanket and put her feet
on the floor. The truth was she didn't want to go to the
rally at all. Not with Doug or her parents or anybody.
No matter what the arrangements were, it would be
awful facing Charlie and Michael and Zora again. If she
called her parents and poured out everything, they'd
stop her from going. That's what she really wanted,
wasn't it?

She stood up tentatively, swaying a little. "Country
road, country road, take me back where I belong." That
fool song was still haunting her. So was everything else
about the L.O.W. after only one day. Here she was,
obsessed by it after being there only twenty-four hours.
What about Jim though? she thought as she reached for
her jeans. Soon he'd have been there too long to remember anything else. Like it or not, she had to go to
Philadelphia and give it a try.

O.K., she'd go. Gail pulled her sweater over her head.
Wait a second. When her parents called, what should
she say? Play it safe. Not a word about Jim. Give them
the usual small talk—the crew races, studying for the
geology exam. She splashed some water in her face and
brushed her teeth. The exam—damn. She could flunk
that course if she wasn't careful—if she messed up the
test and missed the field trip on Friday. Gail patted her
face dry with a towel and sat down at her desk. Time
to get down to business. Her eyes roamed over the backs
of her books. Where the hell were they—*Principles of*

Physical Geology, Rivers and Geologic Formations of
. . . Oh, God! She closed her eyes. Stupid! *Stupid!*
They were with the rest of her stuff in the girls' room
at Mercy. How could she have been so dumb?

"Hey—" Gail looked up. Marilyn's blond curly hair,
flat from sleeping, appeared from under the sheet. "I
thought you were staying over with Doug," she said, her
voice hoarse.

"I came back."

Marilyn raised her head groggily. "Something
wrong?"

"I left my books up in Mercy."

Marilyn, gathering the sheet around her, sat up.
"Yeah?" She paused. "Don't worry. You can use mine."

"Now, maybe, but not for the rest of the course. I
even left my notebook."

"Can't you go and ask them for your stuff?"

"I don't ever want to see them again," Gail said.

"They're that bad?" Marilyn propped herself up on
her pillow. "I'll go ask them for your books, if you
want me to." She stifled a yawn. "Tell me where this
Charlie character lives. I'll get your stuff."

"No, don't. Forget it."

She smiled. "You're not afraid of them, are you?"

"No. No!"

"Gail, you are! That's bizarre!"

"I know it is. I—I'm not."

"Then . . ." Marilyn looked at her intently. "Is anything else wrong? With you and Doug?"

"No, I just asked him to bring me home, is all."

"You had a fight."

"No, I just wanted to be here this morning. I'm glad I
am."

Marilyn reached for a cigarette on her bedside table.
"Your parents called again last night after you went
out," she said.

"What did you tell them?"

"That you were with Doug."

"What'd they say?"

"You should call them as soon as you got up."

Gail coughed. "It's going to be awkward talking to
them."

"You're sure . . ." Marilyn lit the cigarette and inhaled slowly. "You're sure you're going after him?"

"Yes."

"Why?" She blew out a thin line of smoke.

Gail looked at her. "Because now I know where he is and I see what they're like."

"You saw what they were like and you walked out on them."

"Yes."

"Jim could've walked out, too, couldn't he?" Marilyn tapped an ash into the seashell ashtray on her table.

"Maybe he tried to," Gail said. "Maybe they came after him in a gray car."

"Maybe." Marilyn looked at her steadily. "Gail, I've been thinking a lot about this. What if he really wants to stay in the Light of the World because he believes in it? What about his freedom to choose his own religion?"

"Jim's not free."

"Nobody's completely free," Marilyn said testily. "I said *free to choose.* Listen, would you try to stop him if he wanted to be a priest in a regular church?"

Gail hesitated. "Probably not."

"That goes to show, you're against this just because it's different."

"No, not just different—rigid."

"Doesn't a person have the right to choose *not to be free?"* Marilyn flicked another ash.

"This isn't philosophy class!" Gail said. "This is my brother's life I'm talking about!"

Marilyn rocked forward on the bed. "I know. I know! That's why I'm asking you if you're sure. It's *his* life."

"That's *living,* what he's doing?"

"Can one person judge what's good for another?"

"Yes, sometimes, if the other person is temporarily out of it, and you care about them."

Marilyn, stubbing out her cigarette, rose up. "Do you think you should impose your values on other people?"

"He's not *other people.* He's my brother!"

"Don't you want him to do what makes him happy?"

"I can't believe he's happy!" Gail said, putting her head down on the desk.

"Gail . . ." Marilyn, still wrapped in the sheet, slid out of bed and came toward her. "Hey," she said, standing behind her, "I didn't mean to get you upset. I didn't mean you should forget about Jim. Gail? I think it'd be great if you went and visited him. I just—"

Gail lifted her head slowly. "You just wouldn't try to change his mind." Her voice was flat.

"I think . . ." Marilyn ran her hand through her hair. "I think I'd respect him for choosing such a hard life."

Gail shook her head. "You don't know how you'd feel. You don't know what they're like. *You don't have a brother!*"

"You're right," Marilyn said, resting her hand on the back of Gail's chair. "But if I did, I'd want to care about him as much as you do. That's cool."

Gail looked up. "Thanks."

"Why don't you call your parents?" Marilyn said quickly. "I told them you would."

"Yeah. All right."

"Are you O.K.?"

"Yeah." She got up.

"Want me to come with you to the phone?"

"No."

"Go ahead," Marilyn said. "Call."

"O.K."

"Come on back then and we'll talk rocks."

Gail, nodding, went into the corridor.

"Gail?"

She heard Marilyn call, but she didn't go back. She was going to Philadelphia—no amount of heavy philosophizing was going to change that around. Everything quiet as she walked past closed door. *Do Not Disturb* signs dangling from a couple of knobs. At the end of the hall, she lifted the receiver, gave the operator the number.

"Reverse the charges, please."

Phone ringing. Twice. Three times. Good, maybe they'd already left for church.

"Hello?"

"Collect call from Gail. Will you accept—?"

"Yes—why, *yes!* Wait, Gail, I want to call Dad. Ed! It's Gail! . . . He's upstairs. How's everything, dear?"

"Fine," Gail said. Her mother sounded cheerful. Or was it giddy?

"We called yesterday."

"I know. I was out. How come you called Saturday?"

"Oh, Dad has something special he wants to talk to you about. He'll come to the phone in a minute, Gail. How are you, dear?"

"Fine. What is it? What's new?"

"Dad'll tell you. Your test's this week—the one you're worried about?"

"Geology, yes—tomorrow."

"Did you study?"

"Some. I have more to do."

"Good. It makes us feel good, you know, that you're working so hard. Dad says stick to it. You can't expect to like everything you take. A lot of time something'll seem useless and years from now it'll pay off."

"I know."

"Where were you yesterday, Gail? With Doug?"

"Yes."

"Did you have a good time?"

"Yeah. We went to—this friend's house."

"Somebody I know?"

"No, I don't think so. What've you been doing?"

"Oh . . ." Her mother's voice trailed off.

Was she still taking those pills that made her foggy, or did she always talk that way now?

"Grandma was with us for a few days. Did you remember she was coming?"

"Yes, how is she?"

"Oh, fine. Physically she's strong as a horse. Uncle Jim brought her down. It's still so hard when she's here. She keeps asking questions. She says if it's an organization like the Peace Corp, why doesn't Jim get a leave like they do. You know how strongly she feels about her church. I don't know what it would do to her if she really understood—" She paused. "Uncle Jim says hello."

"How is he? Did Aunt Lil come down too?"

"No. No. Lil avoided coming, I think."

"What do you mean?" Gail asked.

"She thinks it's our own fault, the way we brought Jim up. She as much as said that at Christmas. She's a very judgmental person, Lil. I don't care to see her. I hope she stays away."

"Well, that's stupid, if she said it was your fault. You brought me up the same way as Jim."

"Gail, people can be very cruel. It's taken me a lot of years to see that. I used to think the best of people. If you ask me, Aunt Lil ought to be the last person to pass judgment on how to raise children."

"You mean because of Doris?"

"Well, yes."

"Is she getting the divorce?"

"I didn't ask. Grandma says she thinks so. Here's Dad, Gail. I'll come on afterward."

"Hi, Gail."

"Hi, Daddy."

"Good to hear you. How's everything?"

"O.K."

"Just O.K.? Listen, we called ahead of schedule because we want you to keep Tuesday evening free for us. Mother told you we're coming over?"

"No, what's—?"

"Well, we've got something to talk over with you. I don't like to be mysterious, but I don't want to discuss this over the phone. You'll understand when we see each other what I mean."

"It's about Jim?"

"Yes."

"What?"

"I'm serious, honey, when I say I can't talk on the phone. Trust me, O.K.? It's nothing bad. Something good very possibly. How's everything with you?"

"Fine. Can't you just tell me—did you hear from him?"

"I'll give you the full story Tuesday, Gail. Don't worry! Listen, we'll be over early in the day for an appointment. Then we'll meet you at seven at the Steak Pub for dinner. Is that all right with you?"

"Yes."

"It won't interfere with studying for your exam, will it?"

"No, I have that tomorrow."

"Good. I'd like to see you do real well in that one. I know you can."

"Yeah."

"So we'll see you at the Steak Pub at seven on Tuesday night. I think I'm going to have a lot to fill you in on."

"Daddy . . . ? About Jim . . ." *He's in Philadelphia,* she felt like saying. *Is that what you have to tell me?*

"Wait, honey, please. I've been advised on this by somebody I trust. All right?"

"Oh."

"All right? Mother wants to get back on the phone, but I'm going to convince her to wait until Tuesday. You'll have time for a good long talk then."

Gail could hear him whispering to her mother.

"Listen, Mother says study hard, and write Grandma if you get a chance, and lots of love, O.K.?" He paused. "Everything's fine down there?"

"Yes."

"How's the young fellow with the moustache—behaving himself?"

"Yeah."

"O.K., then, get back to that geology. See you Tuesday."

"Yes."

" 'Bye!"

" 'Bye." Click. Dial tone. She stood with the receiver pressed to her ear. What was it all about? Awful, to keep her dangling. She had wanted to tell them everything—would have—if they hadn't held out on her.

She hung up the receiver. They knew where he was, too, probably. Maybe she'd be saved from going to Philadelphia.

Good. Let them be the ones to take action, she thought as she walked back through the corridor. Let her get back to her own normal routine. A stereo blared now. Doors were opening. She'd borrow Marilyn's books, start right in. . . . Gail hurried along to her room. There in the doorway stood Marilyn, shaking her head, shrugging. "What's happening?" Gail asked.

"I see what you mean," Marilyn said.

"About what?"

"Them."

"Who?"

"Her, anyway, the girl with the red hair."

"Where?"

"Look." Marilyn pointed to Gail's desk.

"My books," she said, coming closer. They were lying on her desk next to the canvas bag she had left in Mercy. "She brought them? She was here?"

Marilyn nodded. "Two minutes ago—long red hair —freckles—"

"What'd she say? They weren't even supposed to be back until tonight."

"She asked for you. I said you were out. I pretended I didn't know where."

"Then what?"

Marilyn backed up and sank down on Gail's bed. "First she smiled at me like an idiot. Then she handed over your books. 'Please give these to Gail Brower,' she said. 'Tell her we're counting on her to come to the rally with us.'" Marilyn glanced up mockingly. "'Tell her we think it's going to be the most beautiful experience of her life.'"

8

"Here, give me your coat," Doug said, taking it from her.

"Are Billy and Gene in?" she asked.

"No, they went to class for a change. Just you and me, babes. Come over here and take it easy until you have to go to the exam, O.K.? When did you finally get to bed last night?"

"Two."

Hanging her coat over the back of a chair, he smoothed the bedspread and motioned for her to lie down. "You studied all that time?"

"Till midnight," she said, sitting on the edge of his bed. "After that, I don't know—my mind went haywire."

Doug sat beside her and played with a strand of her hair. "What time did you get up?"

"Seven thirty. I made my eight o'clock class."

"Did you eat anything?"

"No."

"Gail, when are you going to observe the basic principles of nutrition? You're looking peaked—isn't that a wild word—*peaked?*"

"Yeah. I look it?"

"You do, I swear. Want something to eat?"

"No, thanks."

"How about two over easy with bacon and a toasted English on the side?"

"No, really, I'm not hungry."

"Then rest." He pushed her gently by the shoulders

until her head lay on the bolster pillow. "Come on, stretch out—relax. Take off your shoes. That's it." Dropping his boots on the floor, he lay down beside her. "Want a blanket?"

"No," Gail said. She reached for his hand. "I can't stay long, Doug. I've got to meet Marilyn before the exam." Through half-closed eyes she examined the design tacked to Doug's drawing board and watched the particles of dust that floated by the apartment window where the sun poured in. "This is nice," she said.

"Nice enough to move in permanently?"

"Don't I wish."

"It could be arranged. Who knows what the future has in store."

She breathed deeply. "I'm just trying to get through today."

"What time's the midterm?" he asked.

"Noon."

"Good. No rush. Will you pass?"

"I think so. I knew it backward and forward last night. *'A typical trilobite has a segmented body roughly resembling a wood louse. . . .'* "

"Let's see, backward . . . Louse wood a resembling—

"Idiot!" She turned her face toward his on the pillow.

"Peaked, huh? So that's how I look."

"Peaked but beautiful." Supporting himself on one elbow, he leaned over and kissed her.

"It's true, isn't it?" she said, their foreheads touching, "I'm not looking good."

"Good enough for me, Gail," Doug said softly. "But looking good or bad isn't the point. You're so damned tense. I can feel it. Look at that." He pried open her clenched fist. "Come on, go limp! Here, roll over and let me rub your back."

She turned onto her side. "I've felt so strange lately," she said. "At night I think and think, and then I finally fall asleep, like last night, and then I wake up suddenly and start shaking so hard I can't stop. This morning I was sure I was going to jump out of my skin. Do you ever feel like that?"

"No. Sounds like a woman's thing. Hormones or something. Describe it."

"I can't sit still or lie still when it hits me. My legs start twitching. My eyes won't focus."

He locked his arms around her waist. "She didn't come back, did she—Zora?"

"No."

"Zora. Man, what a name. Zora, Queen of the Amazons . . . Zora the Girl Wonder. She sure returned your books quick enough."

"I know. She must've come back early just for that. She didn't say a word about me running away."

"Maybe she ran away, too."

"No, never. They've got her for life." Gail stretched. "They want me to come with them to the rally."

"Over my dead body," Doug said, hugging her closer. "You're expecting one of them to pop up every time you turn around, aren't you?"

She nodded.

"Have you ever heard of them picking somebody up off the street—I mean, carrying them off bodily?"

"My father says they do that to get back a member who tries to leave."

"Listen," Doug said, "how about staying here at the apartment, at least till tomorrow night when you see your parents?"

"Here?" She half turned. "What about Gene and Billy?"

"Hell, they'll move over, that's all."

"What about my parents?"

"What about them?"

"If they're trying to reach me . . ."

Doug smoothed her hair with the back of his hand. "Leave my number. Come on, Gail, for your own safety. For your own peace of mind. There's plenty of room here. I'll feel a hell of a lot better if you stay. *You'll* feel better, won't you, with Gene, Billy, and me between you and Zora the Jungle Girl? Not to mention Smilin' Charlie and Michael the Choirboy?"

"I guess so." She hesitated. "O.K. I'll stay here. I'll tell Marilyn at the exam. I'll have to go back to my room and get some stuff though."

"That's all right." Doug rolled onto his back. "Tell me again, now, about this call from your parents. They couldn't tell you what was up?"

"No, and it's so unlike my father. Usually he can't stop talking when there's something going on with Jim. He was advised—that's what he said—he was advised not to discuss it over the phone."

"Advised by who?"

"I don't know."

"Not to discuss what? Do you think they know where Jim is, too?"

"It's possible."

"Yeah, well, you don't have to have inside dope to guess where most L.O.W.s are going to be this weekend. It's in all the papers that they intend to pack the Civic Center. That's it, Gail!" Doug said. "Zora and Charlie are after your body to fill a seat at the Center."

"Don't laugh. It's probably true."

"But they're not going to get it," Doug whispered, sliding his arm around her. "I won't let them."

Gail lay very still, her eyes closed. The jumpiness had gone away now. She felt Doug's thigh pressing against hers.

"Let's say your parents know he's in Philadelphia at this New World Hotel," Doug went on. "Do you think they're planning to go over there?"

"Maybe."

"And they want you in on it, whatever it is?"

"My father said he wanted to talk to me. That's all I know."

"Alone?"

Gail looked at him. "What do you mean?"

"He—he didn't say, 'Bring a friend—bring a starving undergraduate to dinner'? Nothing like that?"

"No, no, if the whole thing hadn't been so strange, I would've asked if you could come."

Doug stretched and took a deep breath. "This kind of puts our plans on the shelf, doesn't it—you and me going to look for Jim on Friday?"

"Until we hear what my parents say, at least."

"You didn't say anything to Ed and Frances about your trip to Mercy?"

"No. I wanted to. He cut me short."

"Excuses, excuses," Doug said. "Too bad Ed doesn't see me as part of the family. I think I could be very effective talking to Jim."

"I think so, too."

"I can't believe the bum is so spaced out that he wouldn't respond to an old buddy—you know, in-jokes, wry anecdotes of our boyhood." He turned to her. "Do they laugh in the L.O.W.?"

Gail thought for a second. "Yeah, they do. In fact you *have* to smile. That takes the fun out of it. Who wants to smile when you *have* to?"

"Man, I'd never make it. I need a little mild depression every now and then."

Gail laughed. "Yeah, me too. You feel so good when it lifts."

Doug, taking her hand suddenly, touched her fingertips to his lips. "Speaking of feeling good," he said, "what would you say to his novel idea? We could try to wipe out this whole past weekend— the L.O.W.s and coming back in the middle of the night from Billy's. We could get comfortable—right now."

"Doug." She shook her head. "We can't."

"Not true," he said. "We've proven again and again that we can. And I, for one, hope we always will."

She smiled. "I mean, we can't *now.*"

"Why not?"

She looked up at him. "Because I—I couldn't. I've got too much on my mind."

"What—Zora, Queen of the Zombies? Gray Volvos? Trilobites segmented like wood lice?" Leaning close, he brushed her lips lightly with his moustache. "Come on, babes," he said, his eyes meeting hers, "they're *nothing* They don't exist. Not for *us.*"

"There isn't enough time," she said quietly. "I've got to meet Marilyn before the exam."

Doug sat up and looked at his watch. "There is. Enough for us and Marilyn and the trilobites too." He took off his watch and laid it on the table by the bed. "We'll keep an eye on it, O.K.?"

"O.K." She turned toward him.

Eyes closed, she slowly entered a world large and small enough for two, where faces and memories and thoughts of everyone and everything else had the courtesy not to intrude, because *this was private*. And, to make up for the loss of faces and memories, in the private darkness there were gently lapping sounds, and the same faint aroma as the sweater, and lights of various shades of violet, and finally, whorls of gold, shining concentric circles, to signal the triumphant end of the world.

"Where are you?" Doug asked reaching out.

"Back in reality," she said. The other people's faces that had been so polite before were parading in front of her now—Scott Halloran's, so white; Michael's, rosy-cheeked; Marilyn, trying to tell her something that she couldn't understand. Then darkness again, of another sort, this time, bringing loss of consciousness. Until . . .

Bell ringing. Church bell? No, Monday, this was. Gail twitched. Doug rolled over and stumbled to the telephone by the door. *Don't tell anyone I'm here,* she thought of saying. She opened her eyes.

Doug was back by the bed now, standing over her, his hair tousled, his hands on his bare hips. "We goofed."

"What?" She sat up. "Who was it?"

"Marilyn."

"What did she want?"

"She says how come you didn't show up for the midterm?"

"Didn't show up? What time is it?"

Doug held his watch in the palm of his hand. "Ten after one."

"Ten after one?" Gail stared at the flecks of dust suspended in the sunlight.

"Yeah," Doug said, sitting down on the bed beside her. "Very dumb, Marilyn says. Furman's a gneiss guy, she says, but not *that* gneiss."

9

The doors opened and Gail got off the bus. Waiting on the corner for the light to change, she glanced at the clock outside the Steak Pub—7:05. Perfect. They'd be here already, her father drinking Scotch as he did every evening now before dinner. Her mother would be waiting anxiously, probably sipping some concoction served in a scooped-out coconut or a tall glass with a cherry in it. The light turned green, and Gail headed for the canopied entrance.

She hadn't felt much like leaving Doug's apartment, especially not after running around like a maniac all afternoon trying to find Dr. Furman, begging him to let her take a makeup exam. Thursday at four. One more thing to worry about. Now that she was down here though, she was glad to be seeing her parents. Her father, even after all this trouble—still solid, dependable, *there*. And her mother reliable too, in her own way. In a mood like this Gail could even picture them somehow accepting ideas like her trip to the workshop, staying at Doug's, missing the exam, taking the Pill.

She walked up the steps and through the heavy outer door, handed over her coat at the checkroom, and looked into the main dining room. Nearly empty. Where were they? She had a fleeting fantasy of finding them and blurting out: "I know where Jim is!" And then the rest of it: "I'm scared. Take care of me like you used to!" Instead she stood behind a potted palm on the thick red rug, looking at the red flocked wallpaper and ornate chandeliers.

"Excuse me, are you Miss Brower?"

"Yes," she said to the maitre d' behind her.

"Your parents are waiting for you in the California Room. I'll show you to their table."

"Thank you." She followed him through a passageway hung with framed reproductions of historical documents.

"Here, Miss Brower."

"Gail!"

There they were at a table in the corner, the two of them and a stranger—a man. Had they told her they were bringing somebody?

"Gail." Her father stood up. "Good, you're right on time. How's everything?"

"Fine," she said.

He was wearing the tie she'd given him for his last birthday, and he was bending down now to give her one of his pecks on the cheek. Her mother leaned over to kiss her, too—her lipstick a little too bright. The man was getting up, offering her his hand as her father introduced them.

"Gail, I'd like you to meet Mr. Mat Ferrar."

"Hello," she said. A business friend? He didn't look like it in a sport shirt and checked jacket.

"Hello there, Gail. Call me Mat."

Mat? *I have an appointment.* That's all her father had said on the phone. Somebody connected with Jim— it had to be. Middle-aged guy with black hair graying at the temples, well built, one eyebrow across both eyes. Like a bear, sort of. Not mean, though. The maitre d' was pulling out her chair now. Her father seated her mother and then himself. The guy—Mat—settled back, watching her.

"Did you have any trouble getting down here, Gail?" her mother asked.

"No, it was easy."

"You look a little tired," she said. "Did you study late?"

"Not so late."

"How was your exam?"

"Not too bad." Great start. An outright lie.

"Was it as hard as you expected?"

"The test?" Gail asked distractedly. Her father and

Mat Ferrar were listening, sitting there with their hands folded. "Marilyn thought it was hard."

"Oh, how's Marilyn?"

"Fine," Gail said.

Her mother was fluffing up her hair with her finger-tips, looking around nervously. Her father took off his glasses and rubbed his eyes. Mat sipped water. There was an awkward silence.

"Gail," her father said, "I'm not going to beat around the bush. How are you, O.K.?"

"Yes."

"Good. I'm sure you're curious about why we're here and why we've invited Mr. Ferrar—Mat. So I'll get right down to what's on my mind. We'll catch up on your news later. Gail," he said. "We've asked Mat to come here because he's very experienced in dealing with situations like Jim's."

Gail nodded.

"He's the one who advised us not to discuss this with you on the phone for a couple of reasons. One, it's easy to misunderstand somebody over the phone, and two, he knows of cases where phone calls—weren't private."

Gail glanced at Mat, who was sitting with his arm stretched casually across the back of the chair. Who was he, a cop?

Mat smiled. "I was just showing a little consideration for you when I suggested meeting for dinner, Gail. I figured you could use a good meal after that dormitory cooking. Was I right?"

"I guess so." Friendly type.

"Really nice to meet you," he said. "I've heard a lot about you, Gail, from your parents. They're pretty proud—I can see why."

What had her parents said?

Her father hesitated. "If you're wondering why we'd talk to a stranger about you—well, the thing is, we only met Mat in person today, but we've heard so much about him lately that we don't think of him as a stranger. I was put in touch with Mat through some-body I met this week, Gail—a man named Nelson Hafer. Do you remember that name?"

"Charlie's brother," she said. She felt her face growing warm.

"That's right." Her father sipped his drink. "A year ago, you recall, we tried to track down Charlie or a member of his family and we couldn't. Now here this week, Hafer contacts me. Somebody passed my name along to him. He's active in an organization called Save Children in Cults. I tell you, Gail, if I'd found SCC a year ago, I think our troubles would've been over before they started. Hafer's had a tough time with his brother in the L.O.W.—almost got him out a couple of times. Now, while he's waiting to make a next move, he's working for the SCC, advising other relatives of cult members. So when he spoke so highly of Mat here, I had to find out for myself if it was all true. Your mother and I came down this afternoon to his office—he's got one here and one in Philadelphia—and, well, after a couple of hours with him, we've got a new lease on life."

Gail looked from one of them to the other.

"After that buildup you must be wondering who I am, Gail. Am I right?" Mat asked.

"Yes."

He took a sip from his glass and leaned forward. "I'm in a line of work that's a little hard to explain to your average person," he said. "My guess is you've heard about what I do, but just in case you have any misunderstanding of it, I'd like to clear it up. I'm a deprogrammer, Gail. Do you know what that is?"

Deprogrammer. The Snuffer. The bad guy of Michael's and Charlie's stories—somebody who snatched kids in cults and tied them to beds. Is that what her parents were planning for Jim? They were watching her, waiting for her to say something. "Yes," she said, "I've heard of it. I—I read an article—"

"So have I," her father said. "Several. Mostly pretty unfair accounts, I think, now that I've talked to Mat." He turned at the sound of the waiter's footsteps.

"Would you like to order dinner now, sir?"

"We'll let you know when we're ready. Something to drink, Gail? Mat?"

"No—no, thank you, nothing," Gail said.

"Give me another club soda, please." Mat watched the waiter go away. "What've you read about deprogrammers, Gail?"

"That they're hired by parents to—kidnap kids—"

"Wait a minute," Mat said patiently. "Sounds like you read an article in the *National Enquirer*. Your dad's right, the media don't usually love us guys. I guess it helps them sell papers if they show us as hired strong-arm men, using methods that make us look as bad or worse than the cult, but that just doesn't hold up. Not in ninety-nine percent of the cases, at least. There're four or five of us around the country now who do this work, but the L.O.W. lumps us all together with the nickname 'Snuffer.' They say we're trying to snuff out the Light, even though most of us have rescued kids from all different cults. They may joke about us, but they sure spend enough time instructing their people how to give us the slip. *They* call what we do 'kidnapping,' by the way. *We* call it 'rescuing.' "

Gail lowered her eyes.

"I see by your expression you're not sure what to think of all this," Mat said. "I don't blame you. Your parents were leery at first, too. Sounds pretty crazy, I admit—especially before you hear the whole story. Mind if I give you a little rundown on myself, Gail?" he asked.

Mat rested his forearms on the table. "I've held a lot of jobs in my life. You name it—professional ballplayer, salesman, swimming instructor for many years with the Red Cross—working with young people mostly, and then two years ago I got a call from my sister. My nephew—her son—got caught up in a cult out on the West Coast, she told me. She was beside herself. Well, I was between jobs, so I went out there to see what it was all about, and what I found was a good-hearted, intelligent kid turned into a windup doll. I liked this kid. I like *all* kids, and I tell you, this made me sick."

Gail looked at her mother. There were tears in her mother's eyes.

"So I decided to see what I could do about it," Mat went on. "First I looked up a well-known deprogrammer out there, but he had more cases than he could handle. Another fellow was available, but I thought he was asking too much money. Not that a kid isn't worth all you've got, but well—I believe the best deprogrammer is one who's in it mostly for other reasons. So I said to myself, 'Look, you've got as good a chance with Bobby as anybody else.' I read everything I could get my hands on about the L.O.W., and I spoke to a fellow who'd recently come out on his own, and he agreed to help me. We picked up Bobby one day as he was leaving the house where they all stayed. We took him to a motel and talked to him on and off for six days—tried to put a little independent thinking back in his head.

"Well, at first he ignored us—threatened to run away, back to the cult. But came a certain point and he started to doubt one thing, then another, and after six days he came back of his own free will to his mother. Don't misunderstand me," Mat said. "This didn't come easy. After that he needed special rehabilitation for a couple of months. There are halfway places that handle that. But the happy ending is, he's back in college today and doing fine."

The waiter set down Mat's club soda. "Nothing for you, miss?"

"No, thank you," she said, her voice faint.

"So after that," Mat said, sipping, "my sister sent somebody else to me. I said, 'No, I've got to go home to my own family,' but when I came back East, I got requests here, and I didn't want to let these people down. I wasn't looking to get into this. It was fate, I tell myself. It started with a personal crisis and now I'm helping others in their crises."

"How do you get them?" Gail asked with an edge to her voice.

"It varies with the situation," Mat said, scratching his eyebrow. "First I get a rundown from the family and I check out the locations where the youngster might be . . ."

They knew where Jim was then. They must.

". . . and on the basis of the details I decide how to get him—or her—I've rescued plenty of girls."

"But they don't want to come, do they? You have to use force," Gail said. She saw her mother's lips quivering.

"Depends on what you mean by the term." Mat folded his arms across his chest. "I don't like rough stuff, but—let's face it—I can't work on a kid, can't deprogram him, until I've got him off by himself. So if he puts up resistance, doesn't want to get into the car or tries to push me out of his way in the motel—I've got to keep him." Mat shifted in his seat. "I've got an assistant, a nice young fellow name of Lee Grady who was in the L.O.W. for three years. His parents asked me to get him out. That's one case where I didn't succeed right away. I got him on the third try. He's been out now over a year. I'd like you to meet him, Gail. Your parents talked to him this afternoon."

"He's helped Mat in over twenty rescues," her father said.

Her mother nodded. "A very nice boy."

"At any rate," Mat went on, "Lee and I have had to contain certain kids—yes . . . for their own good. But I can honestly say that in my lifetime I've never intentionally hurt another human being, and I've helped a lot of them—at least that's what they tell me afterward."

Gail looked from one of them to the other. *Get to the point,* she felt like saying. Were they asking if she approved of kidnapping Jim? It was crazy. She tried to picture it: Mat grabbing him on a Philadelphia street —like a mugger. "Can't you get into trouble doing this?" she asked.

Mat nodded. "You can bet your bottom dollar I wouldn't suggest this to relatives if there was any alternative. 'Do it legally if you can,' I always say. In some states you can get legal custody of a kid over eighteen in a situation like this, but not here in the East. Here the cops generally look the other way, but you never know. I've been arrested twice—spent the night in jail once—so I'm very careful. Some deprogrammers take the risk on account of the money in it. Believe me, there's got to be an easier way to make a buck. Only reason I'm willing to stick my neck out is because I

like to see families together, and I like to see young
fellows and girls thinking for themselves."

"Even if you get him," she stammered, "you don't
know whether you're going to be able to change his
mind, do you?"

"That's what my reputation stands on," Mat said.
"I'm batting about eight hundred. Takes somewhere between three and eight days, usually."

"What do you do?"

Mat rested his arms on the table. "Use facts, logic.
I've got notebooks full of clippings, for instance, criti-
cizing Father Adam. Written evidence that the man's a
fraud. Copies of financial records that prove he's ripping
off the government and his own followers. Allegations
about his personal life that would make your hair stand
on end."

Her father nodded. "Mat's got quite a collection."

"You just show them clippings?" Gail asked.

"I cite them the facts over and over. I play tapes
made by kids who've already been deprogrammed. Lee
tells them his story. I fire questions at the cult member
—find a chink in the foundation of his beliefs and work
from there. It's a matter of finding the right psycholog-
ical approach for each individual kid."

"You've made up your mind then," she said, surprised by the loudness of her own voice. "You're going
to kidnap Jim."

Her father fingered his necktie. "Rescue," he said
softly. "Yes, we're considering it."

Her mother looked as if she'd just swallowed something sour.

"If you want your brother back, Gail," Mat said, "I
recommend it."

There was a minute's silence. What would Marilyn
say? Gail thought. *It's his life.* What would Doug think?
This would kill their plan of going together to see Jim.
They were watching her again, her mother biting her
lower lip, her father immobile as a rock. "I can't believe
it'll work," Gail said in confusion.

"The chances are good," Mat said.

"It's worth it," her father said, rubbing his eyelids.
"We've tried everything sensible. This is all that's left."

His eyes were puffy, Gail noticed. His cheeks sagged. Looking like a rock was a coverup. "Do you know where he is?" she asked.

Her mother brightened. "Yes, Gail. Yes, we do."

"He's in Philadelphia," her father said quickly, "at a place called the New World Hotel—owned by Father Adam. Hundreds of cult members are going to be at that rally Saturday—you've seen the publicity?"

Her hands were sweating now.

"He went to Philadelphia a few days ahead of time to help set up for the rally." Her father reached into the inside pocket of his suit jacket. "We know, because he sent us this letter from there—and because Mat saw him on the street there yesterday. He recognized him from a photograph."

Gail breathed quickly. "How did he look?"

"In good shape, as far as I could see," Mat said.

"The same as the picture?"

"His hair's short."

Her father cleared his throat. "Like a prisoner's."

Gail watched her mother flinch.

"That's the least of it, Mrs. Brower," Mat said. "Hair grows back, doesn't it, Gail?"

Why was he playing up to her? Why did they need her blessing? Hell, let them do this crazy thing if they wanted to, if they weren't worried about Jim's getting hurt or the thing misfiring and making him even more loyal to the cult—like Michael and Charlie. But don't drag *her* into it.

Her father took the letter out of the envelope. "This is what makes us think the time is right. He wrote to ask us for seven thousand dollars."

Gail stared.

"Typical request," Mat said. "They're all pressured into doing that."

"Maybe we *should*—" her mother began.

"No." Her father shook his head. "We're not giving a dime to the cult. This letter's the best thing that could have happened though. It tells us where he is and it gives us a means of getting him out." He turned to Gail. "Mat's working on a plan that sounds good to me.

I'm to send Jim a telegram saying I'll bring him the money."

"But you're not——" Gail said.

"No, I'm not. The offer of money is the means of luring Jim out."

"Then you're lying to him."

Her father rubbed his eyes again. "Nobody knows better than I do that a thing like this takes a lot of getting used to. We could talk about it more now, Gail, but I think it's better if we take one step at a time. The only thing I'd like you to agree to tonight is to see Mat tomorrow at his office and let him explain his plan in detail. Then if you come to see it the way we do, Mat has an idea about how you can help us." He looked up quickly. "Will you go down to Mat's office tomorrow?"

"I—what time?"

"Afternoon," Mat said.

Gail stared straight ahead. "Why tomorrow?"

"If we go on with this," Mat said, "it'll be set for Saturday—the day of the rally. We'll send him the telegram Friday night. I like to interview family members separately before we make a definite agreement, Gail. How about it—tomorrow afternoon?"

"I guess so." She looked from her mother to her father. "What makes you think I can help?"

Her father and Mat exchanged a glance.

"Show her the letter, Ed," Mat said.

Her father, laying it on the table, pointed to the postscript.

Gail examined Jim's round, oversize handwriting.

Waiting for a reply, I send you the brightest and best blessings of Father,

Love to all humanity,
Jim

P.S. How's Gail? Tell her I'd like to see her.

So Jim hadn't forgotten her.

"That's the first time he's shown a personal interest," her father said in a low voice. "That's why Mat thinks you can help."

"But . . ." The waiter was coming toward them now.

"Gail." Her father, ignoring the waiter, reached over and laid his hand on hers. "We're at the end of our rope, you know that. And we trust Mat. What he suggests I'm willing to go along with." He looked at her mother. "Your mother and I just want to tell you that we'd never intentionally do anything to hurt you. We'd never force you into anything." He patted her hand. "So, after you talk to Mat tomorrow, if your heart says, 'Yes, this sounds right,' then come along with us on this. But if, after you talk to Mat, your heart says, 'No, I can't do this in good conscience,' then we'll accept that." He closed his eyes. "Call us up as soon as you've spoken to him, and tell us how you feel. We've always trusted you to decide things for yourself, Gail, haven't we, Mother?"

"Yes." Her mother was trembling.

"If I decided I couldn't help," Gail asked, "would you go on with the rescue anyway?"

Her father nodded. "Yes," he said, looking at her steadily, "we believe it's the only thing left to do. We won't give up on a child of ours. We'd feel the same about you, if it were you in there. Give Mat and Lee a fair hearing tomorrow, will you, Gail?" He squeezed her hand. "Waiter," he called suddenly, "I think we're ready to order now, please."

10

Doug looked at the directory in the lobby. "His office must be down here at the end of the hall, Gail. First floor. *Matthew M. Ferrar.* How do you suppose the guy advertises? 'Custom-designs in kidnapping'? How much does he charge, anyway? Did he say?"

"Expenses plus so much per day," Gail said. "My father thinks it's fair. Come on."

"Think he'll be annoyed I came"

Gail shrugged. "They told me last night, 'We've always trusted Gail to decide things for herself.' I decided you should come."

Doug, shaking his head, put his arm around her as they walked down the hall. "I can't believe this. Did you tell Marilyn where we were going?"

"No."

"She thinks your whole family's gone off their rocker, doesn't she?"

"Yeah. I couldn't even talk to her about this."

"You think Mat's basically all right though?"

"Yeah, basically—sort of a nice old football coach type."

"I never knew any coaches like that," Doug said. "Nice ones, I mean. He's old, you say?"

"Middle-aged."

Doug stopped. "This is it. *Matthew M. Ferrar, Consultant.* Man, *consultant.* . . . Want me to wait out here, till you see what—?"

"No, come in with me." She knocked and turned the knob at the same time. The door opened.

"Gail?" Mat's voice came from a room beyond the foyer.

"Yes." *What was she doing here?* She could've refused to come. "It's me. I brought a friend."

"Come on in."

She and Doug stood in the doorway and looked into the office. Simple, impersonal, makeshift almost, Gail noticed. Fluorescent lights, plain white walls. Nothing on them but a calendar. Two desks—a kid sitting on the edge of one of them—file cabinets, a couple of straight-backed chairs.

"Like you to meet Lee, Gail," Mat said, getting up. "Lee Grady, Gail Brower and —"

"Doug Howard," she said. "I hope you don't mind. He's my boy friend."

"Sure, O.K.," Mat said, shaking hands with Doug. "Sit down, the both of you." He pulled up two chairs close to the desks. "Go ahead, take a seat. How're you?"

"Fine," Gail said.

"Got back all right last night?"

"Yes."

"You slept on the idea, I hope."

"I tried to," Gail said. "I didn't sleep much."

Mat smiled. "Cup of coffee, anybody?"

"No, thanks," Gail said.

Mat looked from her to Doug. "What I'd like to do is go through a few of the preliminaries, and then I'm going to send Lee and your friend here out for a beer, Gail, and you and I'll have a private talk. That all right with you?"

"Yes."

Mat sat down and propped one foot on an open desk drawer. Lee leaned against his desk. "You both go to Munro?" he asked.

"Yes," Gail said, looking at him with curiosity. Not what she'd expected. Slight build. Reminded her of a small animal. A chipmunk? "Are you in school?" she asked.

"I'm going back next semester," he said. "Munro's accepted me as a transfer. Right now I'm working pretty much full-time."

Mat looked at Doug. "How much does your friend here know about the line of work we're in?" he asked Gail.

"About as much as I do," she said. "I told him everything you told me last night."

"He's a friend of the family?"

"Yes," Gail said.

Mat studied him. "Doug, do you know Jim?"

"Yes. I'm from Laurel Ridge. I've known Jim just about all my life."

"And Gail's parents?"

"I know them, too."

"I don't mean to give you the third degree—I'm just interested, you understand. What do you think of the Light of the World Church, Doug?" Mat asked, folding his arms. "Have you had any experience with them?"

Doug opened his mouth, hesitated. "Not really."

"What's your attitude toward them? Think they're dangerous?"

"Yeah," Doug said. "They bore people to death."

Mat, unsmiling, nodded. "Tell me, if you had a kid in there, would you try to rescue him?"

Doug took a deep breath. "Yeah, I'd try. I'd try *myself*, I think, before I'd get a—professional."

"Yes, well, a lot of relatives think they can handle it. Usually they blow it. What about you, Gail, if you were in your parents' position—if *you* were a parent with a kid in the L.O.W., would you attempt a rescue?"

Gail looked down at her hands. "I've been thinking about it. . . .I'm not sure."

"What makes you balk?"

She fidgeted. "Wondering if it was my right. Wondering if my child—or my brother—should be allowed to decide what he wants even if it's not what I want."

"You think Jim *decided*, then, to join the L.O.W.?"

"Sure, I guess so."

"You know he thought he was joining a Model Schools group, don't you?"

"Yes." She cleared her throat. "But at some point they must have told him they were connected with the L.O.W."

"Do you think at that point he was free to *decide?*"

"I don't know. I think he could have left if he wanted to."

"What do you think, Lee?" Mat asked. "You're the one who's been there—long enough to know."

Mat was looking at her fixedly, Gail noticed. So was Lee.

"I never met your brother, Gail," Lee said. "But if his situation was anything like mine, then from the minute he went off with them, he was a victim of mind control."

"Brainwashing?" Doug asked.

"Mat and I use the term 'mind control,'" Lee said. "'Brainwashing' sounds so outrageous people don't take you seriously if you accuse the L.O.☐. of it."

"Did they control your mind?" Gail asked.

"Oh, sure," Lee said. "First of all, I was lied to all along. In the beginning they told me the group was a student organization. I had no idea there was a connection with Father Adam—I'd heard of him and I thought he was a buffoon." Lee hitched himself up onto the desk top. "The first stage was pretty subtle," Lee went on. "Everybody flattered me, surrounded me every minute, told me what I wanted to hear, kept me going until I was bleary-eyed. Then they laid their principles on me—their beliefs. And every time I asked a question, they'd say, 'You'll understand that in time—if you have enough faith.' I figured if I had so many questions I must be weak in the faith department, and that made me feel guilty. That's just what they wanted. They count on getting you to feel so guilty you'll do anything to atone."

"You knew you were lied to all along and you never argued?" Gail asked.

"Right," Lee said. "Because the means justified the end. For instance, they said, 'Tell people on the street we're collecting money for an orphanage.' I knew it wasn't true, but it didn't matter. All that mattered was that we got as much money as possible to continue Father's work. 'A fib for Father,' we used to call it."

"Didn't it disgust you?" Doug asked.

Lee leaned back on his hands. "No, not at all. Not then. It didn't bother me because I thought I was right. And all my friends were involved in it, too. Including the girl I thought I was going to marry. I figured, if they're here, it must be all right. *I* must be the booby who's got problems."

"Where are they now?" Gail asked. "Your friends?"

Lee was quiet for a second. "Still in."

"Do you miss them?"

"Yes."

Doug crossed one leg over the other. "Your parents had you kidnapped?"

"Rescued—yes."

"How?"

"Well, I used to canvass for money in a certain area of Chicago. My parents hired Mat. He found out my schedule by watching me leave and come back, but just by coincidence twice when he tried to get me I wasn't where I was supposed to be. On the third try, though, he managed it."

"Did you know right away what was happening to you?" Gail asked Lee.

"Yeah, I'd seen a picture of the bum," Lee said, glancing at Mat. "I recognized him."

"What'd you do when you saw him coming?" Doug asked.

"I tried to punch my way out. You can see what luck I had with that."

"How'd you do it?" Doug asked Mat. "I mean, put a bag over his head or what? Crazy!"

"I just came up from behind and hugged him, right, Lee?"

"Yeah." Lee laughed. "This guy hugs you and you know it."

"If you'd of only gone limp," Mat said, "I'd of just carried you into that van like a baby. But you—you had to try to prove something!"

"Yeah, well," Lee said, "if you escape, you know, and get back to the cult, you're a hero. I dreamed of that my first twenty-four hours in—captivity." He looked up. "But then Mat started with the rack and the thumb-screws and lighting the kindling under my feet—"

Doug smiled. "Where was this, in a motel?"

"Yeah."

"Did he have to get rough with you at all while you were there?"

"No, I decided to give him a break. I mostly read my Bible and ignored him and his assistant for two days."

"You slept and ate?"

"Oh, sure. This softie even let me make a phone call."

"What happened after two days?" Gail asked.

"Nothing physical, that's for sure," Lee said. "No, the thing that threw me was—would you believe—he showed me a certain verse in the Bible. Mat showed me how Father Adam had quoted it wrong in his book *Meditations on the Blessed Light*, gave it a completely opposite meaning."

"That made your whole faith fall apart?" Doug asked.

"Not all at once, but I looked at that verse in the Bible, and I couldn't believe it. It was the basis of a very important principle in the L.O.W. I said, 'Bring me another Bible—this one's a phony!' So Mat sent out for two different editions. The verse was the same in all three and exactly the opposite of the way Father Adam quotes it. That put the first crack in the structure," Lee said. "After that, point by point, I came to see how I'd been had, how I'd been used. I'd given up everything—my bank account, my sex life, my health for a while there—and mostly—my *self*. I had no self in the L.O.W."

"But you got it back," Doug said.

"Hell, yes, I sure hope so," Lee said. "It started coming back during the deprogramming. That's what a deprogramming's all about—not to talk you into or out of specific things, but to get you to start exercising the old questioning powers again."

The room was silent.

"How did you feel toward your parents that night when they had you rescued?" Gail asked him.

"I cursed them, naturally."

"And now?"

"I thank them every day. Well, I don't see them every day, but I would if I did."

"Have you ever regretted being out?" Gail asked.

"No." Lee clapped his hands together. "Now I'm free to make *my own* stupid decisions—instead of Father Adam's."

"What's the plan?" Gail asked Mat suddenly.

Mat sat up. "You want to hear—?"

"Yes."

"Let's find an excuse to send these two out—what do you say? The next round's got to be between you and me, Gail. Lee, go buy this young fellow a beer. Size him up while you're at it. See if his intentions are honorable."

Gail watched as Doug got up.

"O.K. with you?" Doug asked her.

"Yes."

"Don't be long," Mat said. "Two beers is all Lee can handle, anyway. He still sees the devil coming at him on the third one."

Lee laughed. "Takes a while to wipe out those heavy influences." Putting on his jacket, he held the door open for Doug. "See you, Gail."

" 'Bye," Doug said, with a backward glance.

Mat waited until the door had closed. "So," he said, resting the palms of his hand on his desk, "anything you'd like to say to me, Gail, before I lay my cards on the table?"

"No, I don't think so."

Mat paused. "You *do* want your brother out of the Light of the World—is that right?"

She glanced up at him. "Naturally."

"That's what I figured. Do you see any other way besides a rescue?"

"I—I guess not."

"Oh." Mat looked at her intently. "I thought maybe you had some idea of going there and trying to talk him out of it."

Her face felt warm.

"Look, Gail," he said, "I think it'll be easier on both of us if I tell you right now that I know you went to Mercy last weekend. I also know you called yourself Gail Brown, and you left in a hurry."

She sat very still, but the walls seemed to be waving anyway. The fluorescent lights were suddenly too bright. "How——?" She thought for a second. "That was you in the gray Volvo," she said with annoyance. "I thought it was *them*."

"I know you did," Mat said. "Now wait a minute, though, before you start thinking your parents hired me to spy on you. Are you listening, Gail?"

"Yes."

"I wasn't up there looking for you, or for Jim either. I went to Mercy to check out——another possible assignment."

"Charlie," she said.

"Yes, Charlie."

"Did you tell my parents you saw me there?"

"No. That's the kind of thing I figured you and I ought to discuss first."

"I was afraid to tell them. I thought they'd be mad."

Mat rubbed his chin. "Maybe——maybe. Not necessarily——if they understood your reason."

"How did you know it was me?" she asked. "You didn't know anything about me then, did you?"

"I spoke to your father on the phone the day before, but I didn't know you——no." Mat tilted his chair back. "I get information, Gail. From inside the cult."

"Somebody informs? Somebody told you I was there?"

"That's it."

"Who? Who was it? Zora?"

"It doesn't matter who it was," Mat said firmly. "It's a source that's generally reliable. I protect my sources."

"Was it Michael?"

"I'd terminate business with your parents before I'd break a confidence, Gail. It's someone who helps me in exchange for another kind of help. Don't try to find out."

Gail's eyes wandered around the room. "What did the person say? Did the L.O.W.s know me before I came to Mercy?"

Mat nodded.

"This person told you that?"

"Yes."

"How did they know?"

"They keep lists of relatives—names, ages, locations. I know that to be true."

"How come they didn't notice me till now?"

Mat shrugged. "Chance, maybe. They wait, sometimes, until a relative shows interest—to play down the reputation they've gotten for pouncing on people. This is what I need to know, Gail. Look at me. Tell me why you went there!"

"To look for him."

"With what idea in mind?"

"To talk to him. To see for myself if there was any hope of convincing him to come out."

"Somebody told you he was there—at Mercy?"

"Charlie said he might be."

"Where'd you meet Charlie? How long have you known him?"

"Only since Thursday. I called a number on the wall of the pizzeria."

"Why did you call?"

"It was the first chance I saw to try to contact Jim."

Mat paused. "Why'd you leave Mercy so suddenly?"

"Because I'd found out what I came for—where Jim was."

"You had to leave like that? Run down the road?"

"They made me sick."

Mat looked at her. "How about *scared?* Scared that you might be vulnerable, like Jim?"

"No!"

"You're certain?"

"Yes, the only thing that scared me was the gray car—*you.*"

Mat smiled faintly.

"Wait," Gail said, her stomach beginning to churn. "If you weren't spying on me, why did you follow us as far as McDonald's?"

"McDonald's? Where? Who's 'us'?"

"Doug and I."

"Saturday Doug was up there with you?"

"I called him and he came for me."

"Yeah?" Mat said. "I missed that. Last I saw of you was when you ran down off the road. I went on into Mercy and came back Saturday afternoon around two. You saw a car like mine?"

"There was a gray Volvo right behind us just before the bridge."

"That's something," Mat said. "And you thought they were on your trail, huh? That's the only thing that scared you? You're sure?"

"Yes."

He closed his eyes for a second. "Good. That's what I figured. That's what I hoped. You see why I'm badgering you like this, don't you? I can't ask what I'm about to ask you, if there's even a shadow of a doubt about where you stand with the L.O.W. If you think you could be attracted in the slightest degree, or if you're scared of them after your experience last weekend, then I'd never ask for your help with this."

"Help with what?"

"Wait a minute. One more thing. You wanted to go and reason with Jim, right?"

"Yes."

"What do you think now? Do you still think that's realistic?"

She examined her hands. "I don't know. You said last night you thought you had as good a chance with your nephew as anybody. That's the way I feel about talking to Jim."

"I'm a pretty big fellow, Gail," Mat said. "Not that size is so important. But I had help, and I'd read up on deprogramming. I was psychologically prepared for it. And I had the time. Are you prepared to get Jim alone someplace and keep him there for a week or more?"

"I guess not."

"Then the rescue's the best way, isn't it?"

"How are you thinking of doing it?" she asked after a few seconds.

Mat, closing his eyes briefly, leaned forward. "Your father sends the telegram late Friday. We don't want to give Jim too much time to set up protection. The telegram says that your father'll deliver a check in person—into Jim's hands—in the hotel lobby on Saturday at eleven. Your father says it can't be later because he's leaving town on a business trip.

"O.K., then," Mat went on, "Lee and I are in Philadelphia early Saturday morning. We're stationed at a parking lot in the same block as the New World Hotel. Your father drives over in his two-door car— very important, the two doors—and he double-parks by the lot. Now." Mat sat back. "Here's the thing, Gail. This is where we could use your help."

She fixed her gaze on Mat's one eyebrow.

"We've got to get Jim out of that lobby and onto the street," he said, "so that Lee and I can maneuver him into your dad's car. Now if your father goes into the hotel and asks Jim to come out, Jim'll be suspicious. Plus, your dad's driving—he's got to be able to make a quick getaway. But if *you* go into the hotel and greet Jim warmly and say, 'Dad can't find a parking space—he wants you to come out to get the check'—we think there's a better chance. He's more likely to trust you."

"I hate lying," Gail said.

"Then help us," Mat said impatiently. "Jim's life in there is one big lie."

Swaying in her chair, she tried to concentrate, but her head grew fuzzier the more she thought. Saying yes to Mat meant forgetting the trip to Philadelphia with Doug, lying to Jim. Saying no to Mat meant disappointing her parents and letting Jim go—forever, maybe. "If I don't help," she asked, "how will you do it?"

"Your father, Lee, and I will wait until he leaves for the rally. That's one place we're sure he'll be going."

"And if I help and you get him, then what?"

"Lee and I'll keep him in the back seat between us. Your father'll drive over the Ben Franklin Bridge to the motel in Jersey. After you see us leave you'll take a bus home to Laurel Ridge, and by the time you get there we'll have gotten word to your mother on how it's going. What do you think?"

She looked at the floor. "I'm not sure."

"Your boy friend can come in with you Saturday morning if he wants to," Mat said. "He can wait for you at the terminal and keep you company going back on the bus."

"Let's call my parents," she said suddenly. She sat very still.

"To say what?"

"To tell them yes, I'll do it."

11

Gail, waking up with a start, stared in confusion out the window at the lineup of chimneys and gas tanks on the horizon. What was she doing, rumbling along with exhaust fumes in her nostrils and too much heat coming up from the floor? Where . . . ? She glanced over at the seat beside her and suddenly remembered everything—shelving Mat's plan that had called for Doug and her to go home to Laurel Ridge Friday night. Substituting the new arrangement—this arrangement—so that she must be somewhere on the turnpike right now, close to Philadelphia. She looked over at her companion again. They'd both slept most of the trip, after those first few minutes of talk about Jim. Now she alone was awake—coming to, slowly.

Country road, country road, take me back where I belong. . . . No, not that song again. Why couldn't it come true, though? Back where she belonged—in Furman's room, taking the geology makeup—rather than here in this Greyhound bus on Thursday, doing this wild thing because of the letter that had come directly from Jim, delivered by hand to the dorm, and announced by a phone call to her room that had brought her downstairs only two hours ago. Gail laid her head back against the seat.

If she hadn't gone back to the dorm—if she'd stayed on at Doug's the way he'd wanted her to—then none of this would have happened. Ironic. She'd returned to the dorm to spare her parents' feelings and now look how it had turned out. What had possessed her?

The acrid smell of smoke from chemical factories seeped through the closed windows and made her nauseous. Behind her a newspaper rustled. Beside her all was quiet. Changing plans had seemed so right two hours ago as she'd stood by the mailboxes reading Jim's letter. First she'd been shocked, of course, by the whole idea that they were well organized enough to get a message through like this. She'd had to excuse herself, sit down while she absorbed it. But the idea of acting on Jim's request—that had seemed perfectly natural. So that after only a minute's hesitation she had taken the elevator upstairs and purposely avoiding Marilyn, had thrown a couple of things into her canvas bag. It had seemed logical to leave without signing out or writing anyone a note. She'd call them when she got to Philadelphia to explain what had happened.

Now, though, rolling along the turnpike in semi-darkness, the logic of it seemed fuzzier. Mat and her parents wouldn't see it the way she had. They'd think she was wasting her time, taking risks, sabotaging their plan. They'd be mad at her for making a decision without telling them. But she would tell them. She'd call as soon as they got to the bus terminal, before going to the New World Hotel. She'd call everybody involved—Furman, even. She'd call Dr. Furman and tell him she was sorry about the makeup exam and the field trip tomorrow. *Pressing family problem,* she'd say.

Looking out again, she saw her own dim, wavy reflection now as darkness made a mirror of the window. Scary half-face gazing back at her. Maybe she was cracking up. It was possible. Happened all the time to people under stress. Like her. People forced to make awful decisions on the spur of the moment.

Wait a minute. She turned away from the reflection and closed her eyes. There was nothing wrong with what she was doing. Showing concern for Jim, that was all. Taking a chance on something that might make the rescue unnecessary, might eliminate the need for shoving Jim in a car, confining him in a motel. They'd end up thanking her, all of them, if she pulled this off. And if she didn't? Nothing lost on her part—

except a passing grade in geology maybe. Was that so much to risk for a brother? On their part—nothing lost either. If this didn't work, they could still try the rescue Saturday.

The letter, though, made her hope for better than that. Where was the letter? Had she dreamed it, like the other wild things that had gone on in her head since they'd gotten on this bus? Thrusting her hand into her bag, she felt the envelope, knew it was real, pulled it out and unfolded the paper. She switched on the light above her and made sure the little eyeball was directed to her side. Lines jumping. Light blinking off for a second. Eyes fogged up.

> Dear Gail,
> Even though I haven't seen you for a long time, little sister, thoughts of you have been in my heart, and I have heard things about you. This weekend is the World Rally for Father. Soon after the rally I expect to be sent on a new mission—maybe out of the country. I would like to see the family before I go. If you could come to see me Thursday, the day you get this note, we could talk a little. I know that is a lot to ask of you—but I hope you will find a way. In the last year I have learned the true value of brothers and sisters, and there are certain things I would like to say to you privately. I am at the New World Hotel. Just ask for me at the desk. Everybody knows me here!
>
> > Blessed in the love of Father,
> > Jim
>
> P.S. I beg you not to share this note with anyone. Let us trust each other.

Folding the letter, she put it away. What did trust mean to him now? she wondered. The only way to find out was to go there—today—even if it meant upsetting other people's plans. Go, not with impossible hopes—Mat was right about that. She wasn't prepared to deprogram him. All she could aim for was to get him to come home for a visit, now that he'd admitted he wanted to see the family.

Remembering phrases from the letter, she pressed the button on the arm of her seat and tilted back. "Little sister." He'd never called her that. "I beg you," "Blessed in the love of Father"—that phony talk. He was a different person, she thought suddenly with horror. They'd have nothing to say to each other. She might not even recognize him.

Wait a minute—she was losing the whole point. "Let us trust each other." That's the phrase that had brought her on this spur-of-the-moment trip. Outside, a string of lights glittered in the distance. They were almost there. She'd better get her head clear fast. He had written finally, *that* was the point—he had written asking her to be straight with him. It was worth a try, even with so many unknowns.

She felt a stirring in the seat beside her and she sat up abruptly. In just a minute now they would be picking up where they'd left off in the conversation about Jim and the Light of the World. And she'd be getting more and more nervous about arriving, actually seeing Jim face to face. Suppose Jim was happy— suppose he was happy without a doubt? Should she warn him about the rescue?

Bus making rude noises as it slowed for the toll booth, honking as the driver jockeyed for a place, trailing the sluggish bus ahead of it.

"Hey, did I sleep the whole way?"

"Almost," she said.

"You won't want to travel with me again, I'll bet!"

"That's O.K. I was thinking." She glanced over at the sport jacket lying across his knees and up at his face, at the space between his teeth and the rosy cheeks and the curly blond hair.

"Isn't it beautiful the way this is all working out?" Michael asked. "Perfect timing. One minute I'm asking for you in the dorm, and then I'm handing you the letter, and the next thing, here we are in Philadelphia! I'm sure glad I was scheduled to come over today."

She nodded, still shy, still unused to the idea of his sitting in the place where Doug should have been. That was the worst part of this—leaving without seeing Doug, without explaining. She'd call him first. If anybody could undersand this, he would.

Michael pulled out a pocket comb and ran it through his hair. "Jim's down at the Civic Center, Gail, but he's going to get back as fast as he can. I spoke to him this morning, you know. He can't wait to see you."

"I—I can't wait either."

"Everybody's going to be so thrilled. Zora's there, and Charlie, and Scott. You'll meet Mr. Brock. This is going to be the best night of your life."

She cleared her throat as the bus stopped for a light. "I have to make a call when we get to the bus station."

"Ward'll be waiting for us in the van," Michael said. "We don't want to hold up traffic. You can call from the hotel."

"I should do it right away."

"What's more important than a reunion with your brother?" Michael smiled. "Just think, if you hadn't wasted time playing 'Guess who I am?' I could've brought you to him sooner!"

12

"Hey, we're home," Michael said as he helped Gail out of the van. "So long, Ward. Thanks for the lift. You're going down to the Civic Center. Tell Jim Brower to hurry back!"

Gail, standing under the dilapidated marquee, looked up. A band of white neon lights marked the entrance. In the glow of the street lamp she counted the eight stories of the building. Higher, on the windowless brick wall, she saw letters in peeling paint— *Metropolitan Arms*. At ground level was a stretch of plate glass painted blue and another entrance—to the storefront chapel. Next to that, an alley.

"This is it." Michael stopped at the bottom of the steps. "It used to be one of Philadelphia's best-known hotels."

Not now, Gail thought. No name outside, no advertising, no posters. A half block west, people swarmed in front of movie houses and restaurants, horns honked, a fire siren wailed. Here, though, off Market Street, it was deserted and quiet, except for the soft sound of wind that blew particles of soot in her face.

Michael set down his overnight bag. "Hey, before we go in—again, I'm sorry I slept the whole way on the bus."

"That's O.K., really," she said.

Michael put his hand on her arm. "You *are* glad you came, aren't you?"

"Oh, sure."

"Good," Michael said. "Some people thought you left Mercy on Saturday because you didn't like us."

"Oh."

"You don't have to tell *me*," he said. "*I* know you do! Wait'll you see the welcome you're going to get in this place. Your brother is *so loved,* Gail. I'm dying to see the two of you together." Michael smiled at her. "This is a special thing for me, you know. Charlie recognized you before I did. He'd seen a picture of you that Jim carries in his wallet. But I was the one who told Jim first about your interest in us. So I feel as if I've had a small part in reuniting two wonderful human beings. This is such a great time to be coming to the Light of the World, Gail," he said, glancing up at the marquee. "You couldn't have hit it better. We're expecting thousands of people in the Civic Center the day after tomorrow. Do you know what that means to us, when nobody even heard of us until three years ago? After being misunderstood and mocked and hassled all this time? The media are going to *have* to take us seriously. And you're going to be in on all of it, Gail. You can say you were there when the Light of the World really got off the ground."

"Yes," she said quietly. No matter how this turned out, she'd be gone by the rally. Had they missed her at Munro yet? she wondered.

"Wait'll you see the spirit around here," Michael said. "And the enthusiasm of your brother! He's such a beautiful person, Gail."

He picked up his bag and led her up the steps. She felt his hand pressing against the small of her back, urging her into the compartment of the revolving door. The door spun, and she walked into the lobby of the New World Hotel.

Michael was behind her. "So quiet!" he said. "Saturday you won't recognize this as the same place."

Gail looked around. More like the lobby of an office building than a hotel. Enormous, empty, cold. Scuffed tan marbelized floor, thick columns overlaid with mirror, an occasional vinyl-covered chair. A few people talking, over by a bank of elevators with heavy bronze doors.

Michael motioned her toward the reception desk.

"Welcome, brother." A young Oriental in a dark suit and narrow black tie reached across the desk and shook hands with Michael. "Welcome, sister."

Gail nodded.

"Gail, this is Brother Sam Li. Sister's name is Gail Brower, sister of Jim Brower. We can find her a place in the women's dorm, can't we?" Michael looked at his watch. "I'm supposed to be in a meeting with Mr. Brock."

"The meeting started," Sam said. "Want me to find sister a place so you can go on up?"

"No, that's all right. I'm just going to get her a cup of tea. Then I'll be heading up to the meeting. Listen, call me immediately when Jim comes in, O.K.?"

"Sure, brother."

"Follow me, Gail," Michael said. "Isn't this place impressive?"

Her heels clacked on the hard floor. "It's big." She looked up at the scaffolding and the ornate molding—half discolored, half freshly painted over in high-gloss white.

"It'll be magnificent when we finish," Michael said. "We're doing the work ourselves, of course. All the brothers and sisters pitch in, in the evenings. There's so much important work to do, it's hard to find time to sleep."

"Except on buses," she said.

"You won't let me forget that, will you?" Laughing, he ushered her into a small unoccupied room off the lobby with a hand-lettered sign on the door: *Coffee Shop.*

"I don't know why we call it that," Michael said. "Most of us drink tea. I'm going to make you the best cup you ever had. It's terrific for calming you down, relaxing you."

"Good." Gail looked around the room at the mustard-colored walls, the half-dozen small tables with chairs, the kettle on the hotplate.

"Put your bag down, Gail," Michael said, measuring tea. "Help yourself to the newspapers and magazines over there while you're waiting." He poured boiling water into a cup. "Very relaxing, this stuff. Wish I had time for some." He looked up quickly. "Sorry to leave you by yourself, but everybody's pushing like mad here—planning, rehearsing. You'll be all right till I bring Jim?"

"Sure. I'll be fine."

He set the tea in front of her. "Here, sip slowly and drink all of it. I'll be back soon." He touched her hand. "This is going to be a night to remember."

She nodded. A night to remember. Sounded like a film title. Clark Gable? Doug would know. Where would he be now? She'd call as soon as Michael left her alone.

"O.K., then," Michael said, "help yourself to those papers." He backed away from her. "I'll be quick."

Gail watched him go. She'd wait until he was out of sight. Then she'd look for a telephone. Lifting the cup to her lips, she felt steam rise up her nostrils, make her eyes tear. She swallowed. Powerful stuff, superhot, slightly bitter. She took another mouthful and felt a sharp contraction in her stomach. From the bitterness, probably. Or panic, at the idea of seeing Jim. Or hunger, she thought, her stomach rumbling. She hadn't eaten since breakfast.

In the distance a siren moaned. The room, though, was scarily quiet. Hard to believe she was here, so close. She sipped more tea and felt a slow unknotting inside her. She glanced nervously toward the door. If she went to a phone now, she might not be here when Jim came. What would he look like? she wondered again. That picture on the mantel at home, where his hair was short? Or like the high school graduation picture, pale and serious—one of three kids who'd refused to wear a cap and gown?

The sound of a scraping chair caught her by surprise. Gail sat up. She looked at the patterned sweater, the hair falling in his eyes, the guitar case.

Scott Halloran was sitting down across the table from her. "You're back," he said matter-of-factly. "You bolted at Mercy, but you came back. We met last weekend, remember? You're Jim Brower's sister, they tell me."

She nodded. *They,* she thought. The same they, probably, who told things to Mat Ferrar.

"You jumped when I came in," Scott said.

"You surprised me."

"I came in on little cat feet," he whispered. "That's my style. You must be waiting for your brother."

"Yes."

"Michael brought you here, didn't he?"

"Yes." Was there anything they didn't know about her?

"Ah, so," Scott said, sliding his guitar case under the chair. "Welcome, welcome to the sister of Jim Brower—rising star."

"I don't know what you mean."

"Only that Jim is a man with a future. Rising star in the universe of Mr. Brock, East Coast director. He's much loved, your brother. Have you seen him yet?"

"No, he's supposed to be here any minute."

"Back from his work—yes. From his vital work at the Center. How long has it been since you've seen him?" Scott asked.

"A year."

"As long as that. You must have a lot to say to each other."

"Yes," she said awkwardly, watching him. His eyes were red rimmed; his fingernails, drumming the edge of the table, were bitten short.

"You're staring at me," he said. "Go ahead, say it. There's something different about me."

She paused. "You're—you're not wearing your glasses."

"Right."

"How come?"

He pushed the blond hair off his forehead. "They broke this afternoon."

"How?"

"While I was working the street. Witnessing for new recruits—without any luck, of course. Somebody bumped me, and my glasses broke on the sidewalk." He smiled grimly. "An occupational hazard."

His eyes were glittery, she noticed now. Was he high? Impossible. They didn't believe in drugs—not even cigarettes. "Can your glasses be fixed?" she asked.

"No. They'll have to be replaced."

"How are you managing? Can you see?"

"Barely. You *are* Gail, aren't you?"

"Yes," she said. "It must be awful not to see."

"Yes, insufferable. But I deserve it."

"Are you serious?"

"Quite," he said. "I deserve to be punished. I'm weak. I'm imperfect."

Gail shrugged. "Yes, well—nobody's perfect."

"That's just an excuse," Scott said hostilely. "We should try to be perfect—like Father."

He *was* different, she thought. And it was more than the glasses. "Do you really think it's possible to be perfect?" she asked.

"With Father as an example, yes." His mouth twisted. "Unfortunately, though, I'm often tempted to follow another example—Satan's."

"What does Satan tempt you to do?" She strained not to smile.

"He tempts me to be lazy," Scott said in a monotone. "He tempts me to write heresies, and to be jealous of my brothers, and to talk too much, like I'm doing with you right now."

"Oh, come on," she said lightly, "don't you think you're being too hard on yourself?"

He shook his head. "No, too easy."

He was serious. "I remember at Mercy your telling about your past life," Gail said. "So, O.K., you hit a low back then, in Paris, but here—*now*—what do you do that's so bad?"

"I haven't turned in enough money. I have no one to write to for money."

"What else?"

"I've given up on bringing in my quota."

"What quota?" she asked.

"Of recruits. I haven't witnessed enough recruits. I haven't brought in three new members yet this year."

Gail slowly rotated her teacup. "Everybody has to do that?"

Scott looked at her coldly. "It's not a matter of *having* to. Everyone who loves Father *wants* to do those things."

"But if you try and don't succeed—"

"Trying isn't enough, Father says in his book, *Meditations on the Blessed Light.* You must succeed or be excluded from the Spirit World."

Gail stared at him. He was crazy. Is this the way they got after they were in awhile? "Did you say everybody has to bring in three members per year?" she asked again.

"Yes, but that's not my worst failing." He lowered his eyes. "Satan tempts me sometimes to—"

She watched with curiosity as his face flushed. "To what?"

He leaned toward her as if he were about to whisper and then drew back.

Sex, she thought. Something about sex.

"He's tempting me right now," Scott said hoarsely.

Right now? She felt like smiling, but he looked so miserable.

"He's tempting me," Scott repeated, "but I won't give in! I'll do whatever I have to, to fight it. I'll confess publicly tomorrow night."

"Publicly? Why tomorrow night?"

"The pre-rally celebration for Father Adam here in the auditorium. He's addressing those of us who worked here this week. We're putting on skits for him, and anyone who wants to confess is invited to." Scott looked up. "You'll be coming, won't you?"

"I don't know. When does it start?"

"About eight. Your brother's one of the people in charge of it." Scott's face was suddenly animated.

She turned. Michael was coming through the door. She shivered and felt herself tense up. Behind him was Jim, smiling at her. Not so changed, not on the surface, anyway. He was wearing dark pants and a white shirt and gray V-neck sweater. Slightly thinner, hair cropped short, cut unevenly. Same crinkles around the eyes, though. She rose out of her chair awkwardly, but the awkwardness disappeared as he came toward her without embarrassment and hugged her hard. As the tears rolled down her cheeks, she buried her face in his sweater.

"Welcome home, Gail," he said.

13

Home, home free! she remembered calling out as a kid. Waving her arms, so happy to have come in safe for their side—hers and Jim's. Happy to be playing with the big kids. What made her think of that now, riding up in a creaky old elevator with him? He'd called this place *home*—maybe that was it. The two of them alone, finally, after all the greetings and introductions downstairs. Zora running into the coffee shop, asking her if she'd gotten her books. Charlie shouting, "Gail, am I glad to see *you!*" Scott picking up his guitar and starting a chorus of "We'll all go out to meet her when she comes." Everybody hugging her, even people she'd never met before. Better that than asking embarrassing questions about why she'd left Mercy. Jim had smiled proudly through it all, as if she'd scored a point for their team.

"Rehearsal for tomorrow night—upstairs ᵢ twenty minutes, everybody!" Michael had called out then, and Jim had said, "Hey, Gail, quick. You've got to see my room."

Here he was now, pushing the button so the elevator stopped at the second floor. The doors opened and Gail stepped out.

"This way." He led her down the deserted hallway.

Hey, it's good to see you! she wanted to say, but she was shy. Not that he wasn't trying hard to make her feel welcome. Something was missing though, she thought as they walked in silence. He hadn't asked anything yet about her or the rest of the family. Maybe he was waiting until they were alone.

112

"Isn't this place great?" he asked her.

Same old tone of voice she remembered—enthusiastic about things most people would knock. In this case, the hotel with its faintly sweet mothball odor, faded wallpaper, and worn grayish green carpet. Depressing to her, but he obviously loved it.

"Are these bedrooms?" she asked as they passed a row of doors.

"Meeting rooms mostly. We have two huge dormitories—one for women on the fourth floor and one for men on the sixth."

"But you sleep on the second?"

"You'll see."

Be on the lookout for a telephone, she reminded herself as they turned the corner. By now Doug would be starting to worry. Maybe if she waited there'd be good news to tell them.

At the end of the hall Jim pushed open a wide door and flipped on a light switch. "This is it," he said. "Come on in."

The door closed behind them. There was a funny smell, musty like a storage room. Gail looked around. "It's an auditorium," she said.

He turned on another bank of lights. "It sure is. How do you like the size of it?"

"Great." It had been elegant once, she saw, like the estate at Mercy. Dark paneled walls and ceiling. At one end, a stage; rows of folding chairs set up haphazardly, scuffed vinyl tile on the floor. "Did you say this was your bedroom?" she asked.

"Temporarily, anyway. There's my bed," he said, pointing to a pile of striped mattresses in one corner. "I moved out of the dorm to make room for visitors this weekend. Don't feel sorry for me—I'll have plenty of company!"

She looked at the lumpy mattresses and at the shelf stuffed with sleeping bags and personal belongings. "Do you like living like this? I mean, sleeping here?"

"Sure," he said, walking over to the pile of mattresses. "It's not like a double bed in Laurel Ridge, but here, try one." He pulled down the top mattress. "Sit. Make yourself at home."

Home. Plunking herself down in the middle of the mattress, she felt it sag under her weight. Jim hoisted himself up on the pile and dangled his legs over the edge.

"Hey, little sister," he said with a grin, "it's good to have you here."

"Thanks." That name again—*little sister.* Silly. His facial expression was familiar, though. One eyebrow raised. "I'm really glad you asked me to come," she said. "I've thought about you so much. We—we all have."

"You didn't worry about me, I hope. I've never been better in my life."

"Well . . ." She stared at a spot on the mattress. "So you're really happy here, with your work—and everything?"

"Oh, sure. It's beautiful, Gail. I'm busy from morning till night."

"Isn't it hard?"

"All important work is hard," he said. "I wouldn't want it to be easy."

"I know." She paused. Awkward. What had he wanted to tell her? Was he waiting for her to begin? "I was so happy to hear from you," she said. "I'm so glad you're thinking of coming home for a visit."

Jim looked at her quizzically. "Oh, you mean— you misunderstood me, Gail. I said I'd like to see the family." He nodded patiently. "I meant *here,* at the hotel, before I leave."

"But . . . Oh."

"When you're as deeply involved in your work as I am," Jim said, smiling, "you can't get away. You understand that, don't you?"

Gail, without answering, traced a line between the buttons on the mattress. "I—I'm not sure. How's— how's your school doing?"

"School?"

"Your model school. That's your work isn't it?"

"Oh, *that,*" Jim said, stretching out languidly. "My work's gotten much more diversified than that."

"You did leave Munro to work in a school, didn't you?"

"Yes."

"So how was it? As good as you thought? Is it still operating?"

"It's still in the planning stages, actually."

She looked up quickly. "You mean, it never got started?"

"Not yet. We're still waiting to get accredited. But—it's really going to be something once it's underway. I'd like you to see it."

That placid smirk on his face—through everything.

"I thought there already was a school," Gail said. "I thought that was the reason you. . . . There're so many things I don't understand, Jim—why you left without letting us know. Why you sent such—*nothing* letters home. Why you didn't write to me until today. . . ."

Jim sat upright. "I did. I *did* write to you. You never got any letters?"

"No. Where did you send them—to Munro?"

"To Laurel Ridge."

"But—they never came. Where did you mail them from?"

"One from Minneapolis, I think. Or Detroit. And another one from—let's see—I don't remember where from."

She rose up on her knees. "I never got a single letter addressed to me—until today."

He looked at her steadily. "Then they must have been intercepted."

"You mean—somebody in the church—?"

"No! I mean on the other end."

"Mom and Dad?" She swayed slightly. "You're not serious, are you? You mean you think they opened letters and read them and never told me?" She thought for a second. "What was in them?"

"I always asked you to come for a visit."

"All year long?"

He nodded.

"But Jim, you know Mom and Dad, they *wouldn't*—"

Jim shrugged. "That's the kind of thing I never believed either, until I saw it happen in other families.

I'm a lot less naive now than I used to be. I've seen things firsthand. Zora—get this—Zora sent presents home for all her brothers and sisters last Christmas—things she took months to make by hand. Her father mailed them all back to her still wrapped. I could tell you stories, Gail, until the sun comes up about relatives doing the cruelest things imaginable—"

"Other people's relatives . . ." She trailed off, thinking of her father, of Mat. "You really wrote to me?" she asked, her voice faint.

"Yes."

"But when you didn't get any letters back, didn't you suspect I hadn't gotten yours?"

"No," he said. "I thought you didn't want to have anything to do with me—and it hurt me—a lot."

He was sitting there swinging his legs like—like she remembered him a long time ago. "I never felt that way," she said. "I thought about you every day. We did so much to try to find you. But—" Weren't they both forgetting an important point? "The way you left! It was as if you didn't give a damn about us. I don't care about myself. I'm thinking of Mom and Dad, Jim. Frankly they haven't been able to handle this very well. And Grandma—they haven't even been able to tell her where you are. Unless you talk to them right away, I'm afraid—" Her throat felt tight. She cleared it. "I mean, I know how important your work is to you, but can't you come home for a short visit?"

"Sure."

She looked up. "When?"

"As soon as my work's completed. As soon as I'm no longer needed here the way I am now."

He was sitting there smugly almost. "But that could be—years, couldn't it?"

"It could be. I'm optimistic though."

"Aren't there other people who could take over for you—for a few days, a week—while you're away?"

"Even if there were," he said, "who would do that person's job? We all contribute here. We all count."

"But just for a couple of days!" she nearly shouted. "Everybody gets time off. Whoever heard of a person not getting any time off?"

He spoke patiently. "Does God take vacations? Does Father Adam? Remember it's their work I'm doing."

She felt heat rising inside her. "What work? What do you do that's so important?"

"I organize things. I travel with the orchestra sometimes. I'm probably going to be sent out of the country, I told you. Mr. Brock's recommending me for lecturer. I've been given a lot of responsibility for the rally. I'm assistant producer of the show for tomorrow night. See that curtain there?"

She looked at a mass of dark velvet lying on the floor of the stage.

"I've got to get that decorated and hung for tomorrow. That's just one thing I've got to do. It's got to be perfect for Father when he comes tomorrow night."

"Father?" she repeated, suddenly confused. "Dad?"

"Father. Father Adam."

She felt the heat creeping up her neck and cheekbones.

"I'm doing so many exciting things, Gail," he said in a rush. "You can't imagine. I could never find work in a job outside the church that would be so varied. I'm always meeting people, always handling special problems. . . ."

"I understand that you feel needed," she said, "but why can't that stuff wait a day or two? Wouldn't you get a kick out of seeing Mom and Dad after all this time—and Grandma and Uncle Jim, and the neighborhood, and friends—Doug? Doug cares about you."

"Sure," Jim said quietly. "I told you I'd like to see Mother and Dad—here." He sat erect. "I wrote to Dad this week, in fact."

Asking for money, she thought. She bit her lip.

"I wrote them," Jim said, "but they didn't answer. They'd like to forget me, I think."

"That's not true! They can't get you off their minds!"

"You've seen them then—recently?" He looked at her suspiciously. "Do they know you're here?"

"No. No, they don't. I came because of your letter."

"Did they know you went to Mercy?"

"No."

"Why did you go there, Gail? Why did you come here?"

"To see you. To talk to you—because I care about you."

"You weren't sent by Mother and Dad?"

"No."

"Or anyone else?"

"No."

Jim sat perfectly still. "Word of honor? Remember when we were kids that's what we always said?"

"Yes."

He kept his eyes on her. "Mom and Dad didn't send you after me—*word of honor?*"

"Word of honor," she repeated softly.

"Good." He sat back. "I'm glad to hear that. I'm glad we trust each other."

"Prove it, Jim," she said, her eyes blurring. "Come home for a weekend."

He looked at her sadly. "That's what you want," he said, shaking his head, "but do you know what I want?"

"What?"

"For you to stay here a few days."

She felt dizzy. What a jerk she'd been to think she had a chance of reasoning with him. "It's impossible," she said.

"Why? Are you going to say you can't miss school? What's a day or two of classes?"

"It's not that—I can't stay."

"You'll thank me later if you do," he whispered.

"No, I won't." *And you won't either,* she felt like saying. Even now Mat and her parents might be guessing where she was, so that he'd be getting visitors sooner than he expected.

"Please stay, Gail. You just got here."

"I can't. Just tonight. Until tomorrow morning." Staying—was that the matter he'd wanted to talk to her about in private?

"Stay for the rally, please! You have to!"

"What do you mean, *have to?*" she asked, getting up. "*Are you short on your quota?*"

Jim sat stiffly. "Who's been talking to you about quotas? That sounds like Scott Halloran."

"Yes, it was."

"We love Scott," Jim said quickly. "He's our brother—but he's not very reliable. He exaggerates. He's had nervous breakdowns."

"Are there quotas?" she asked, her eyes meeting his.

"We—we want as many people as possible to share in the happiness we've found, but—"

"Have you brought in three new members this year?" she asked.

Jim hesitated. "That's beside the point. Scott misled you."

"Why did you invite me here?"

"Because I missed you."

"If that's true, prove it. Come see Mom and Dad, for my sake."

He paused. "How about this?" he said, speaking fast. "I have so much to do—so little time to talk to you. We're rehearsing in a few minutes. Tomorrow I'm in charge of a cleanup project around the Civic Center. Stay here tomorrow—all day. Help me with my work, and I'll give you—and Mother and Dad—a day in return."

She looked at him skeptically. "At home, in Laurel Ridge?"

"Yes."

"Just one day?"

"Yes. A day for a day."

"You'll come—word of honor?"

"Yes."

"What work?" she asked. "What would I have to do?"

"Help Zora sew that curtain," he said, nodding toward the stage. "We have to sew a sun motif onto it."

"Me sew? You know I'm bad at it."

"It won't be hard. A day of yours for a day of mine—that's fair, isn't it?" Jim said, his cheerful tone returning.

"Wait—only until early in the evening," Gail said. "I have to get home before dark. Seven. I'll stay till seven. When will you come to Laurel Ridge? What day? Sunday," she said. "Make it Sunday."

"All right," Jim nodded. "The rally will be over. I'll stay with the family till seven. Is it a deal?"

"Yes," she said hesitantly. Why hesitate—what was one more day of her life? So long as she called home now, told them to hold off. Once he got there, maybe —no, take one step at a time. For now, though, tell them to wait with the rescue.

"Great, little sister," Jim said, bouncing down off the mattresses. "I'm so glad you'll be here tomorrow. We'll have some more good talks. Say, did you have dinner?"

"No."

"Gee, too bad. Let me see if I can find something for you to nibble on. How about . . ." He went over to the shelf behind the mattresses and brought back a tin container. "Look what I've got—remember these? You used to love these when we were kids—malted milk balls." He pried off the lid and offered them to her. "Remember when these were twelve cents a box at the Paramount?"

"Yeah," she said, popping one into her mouth. "We used to have to go out for a drink every ten minutes to wash the chocolate down. Doug would get so annoyed at us. He still does, if anybody disturbs him in a movie."

"Does he?" Jim laughed. "You'll have to fill me in on Doug later. Here, help yourself."

"I guess I am hungry," she said, scooping up a handful. She felt hopeful suddenly. He was coming on Sunday. He'd promised.

Jim glanced toward the door by the stage. "They're starting to come in now, Gail," he said. "Make yourself comfortable. Here, sit down and take the milk balls with you. I've got to get into my costume. You'll love the rehearsal."

Returning to the mattress, she watched them coming through the door loaded with props and costumes. Zora was draping herself in a sheet. Michael was setting up folding chairs. Scott stood in front of a mirror trying on a top hat. Claudia was twining artificial flowers in her hair. Jim was putting on a turban. She'd better go down and call home now. He's coming home Sunday, she'd tell them.

"Hey!" Michael's voice startled her. "Are we ready? Can you all hear me?"

"*Yes!*"

The whole crowd of them were humming now and beginning to link their arms together. Gail edged slowly toward the door.

"O.K., brothers and sisters," Michael's voice rang out, "let's everybody join hands! Are we one big happy family?"

"*Yes!*"

One big happy family, she thought, except for her and the informer, whoever it was. She kept on going, ignoring the stomping of feet and the crescendo of voices around her. Let them do their thing, she thought, until reaching for the doorknob, she felt a hand close over hers. A warm, chubby hand. She turned, and Charlie, grasping her firmly, pulled her into the circle. "I was going downstairs to make a phone call," she said, resisting.

"Now?"

"I want to get a drink," she protested. "My throat's dry from chocolate."

"What's the rush?"

"I've got to call now, *tonight!*"

"Later," Charlie said brightly, clutching her hand. "You can't go anywhere now. We need you!"

14

"We are required to do those tasks we like least, for Father says there is joy in humility, and . . ."

Scott's voice was straining, Gail noticed. No wonder. Long rehearsal last night. Not much sleep for any of them. And now, today, how many hours had he been here on the stage, sitting cross-legged, his back so straight, reading to her and Zora as penance for his sins? Six hours, seven? He'd only left them briefly once or twice in all that time. Outside the sun was going down, but inside the satin sun on the curtain was almost ready to rise. If she sewed a little faster, Jim would be pleased when he came back. "I want it hanging by the time I come," he'd said. "It's got to be perfect for Father."

Sitting on the floor of the stage, on top of the thick velvet curtain, Gail tugged at the slippery needle until it came through the material. Watch it. Stitches getting too big again. If Zora came over to look, she'd make her rip them out like before. Hard enough to do it once, with thumb and two fingers so red and tender. Watch the gold satin, too. Don't let it pucker. Must be perfect, Jim had said. One semicircle of gold on each half of the curtain so that when it was hung they'd form a symmetrical sun in the center.

"The simplest, most menial job done enthusiastically in the name of Father, will bring spiritual blessings beyond reckoning."

Stupid book Scott was reading from, Gail thought—*Meditations on the Blessed Light* by Father Adam. At first the words had gone in one ear and out the other. Still, you had to put your mind on something, sitting here all this time. An idle mind is Satan's garden, the book said. Your life is not your own. The salvation of the whole world depends on you. That's what Jim thought—the whole world depended on him. He was giving up his important work though, for one day, to come home. Sunday. Because of her. It was worth it. She'd stay another day here even, if she had to, to get Jim home. Because when he came, he'd see how bright it was, and comfortable. He'd see the forsythia bushes that would just be opening in the yard, and his room with the plaid wallpaper and the snapshots still pinned up on the bulletin board where their mother had left them. And mostly he'd see Mom and Dad and he'd know that they weren't against him. He'd know that they hadn't kept any letters from her. . . .

Gail pulled the needle roughly. The thread broke. "Damn it!"

Scott paused.

Zora looked up. "Don't curse. I'll thread it for you, Gail."

"No," Gail said. "No, it's all right. I can do it."

"Patience in dealing with the trivial cares of life is a sign of being full of love for Father," Scott recited from memory.

Gail tore off a piece of thread so that it cut her at the joint of her little finger. Painful, like a paper cut. She threaded the needle and smoothed out the material again. Be neat. Doug should see her now. "I hate to sew," she'd always told him. Her mother should see her—her mother, who'd always tried so hard to find something nice to say about the awful home ec projects she'd brought home. "Look, Ma, I'm sewing!" she should tell her when she called. Called—to say what? "I'm safe, Ma! You weren't worried, were you? Just a little hard to get to a phone in this place. No problem, though—Jim's coming home. Isn't that terrific? Make chicken cordon bleu, Mom. That's still his favorite. Not much gourmet stuff around here. By the way, Ma . . . Dad? Did Jim ever send me a letter?"

Forget it. Don't worry about phone calls. Just sew.

Not too bad, sewing, once you got used to it. Clear what you had to do. Goal in sight at the end of the rainbow? No, end of the golden semicircle. Easy, sewing. Not complicated like figuring out rescue plans, and arguments for what you believed in, and ways to get calls through. Plus, how could you concentrate on those things when you were tired from sleeping only four hours on the hard floor in a sleeping bag? When you were weak from eating only milk balls for supper and toast for breakfast—because the eggs looked rubbery and you weren't hungry anyway because you were nervous about what was going to happen? Gail sat up with a jolt. What if they picked up Jim today, while he was down at the Civic Center, before she could tell them to wait?

"Physical hardship, in the long run, strengthens the body," Scott was reading, *"but even more important, physical hardship strengthens character.* Do you believe that, Zora?" he was asking.

"Yes," Zora said, her needle poised in the air. "There for a while when I was working in Cleveland, I was so lazy! Just sitting at my desk all day and then going home and sleeping as much as I wanted—too soft! I was getting spoiled."

Spoiled, Gail thought. Maybe that's what was wrong with her. After the first hour or two she'd almost quit. Her fingers had ached so. Her thumb throbbed. Pain in her back was so bad she couldn't straighten up. If Jim had been there she'd have called off the deal. She had imagined herself at that point running away, like at Mercy—going down in the creaky elevator, calling Mat from the nearest phone booth, begging him to pick Jim up right away outside the Civic Center, where he was collecting trash. Half decided to make a dash for it, she had said to Zora, "I have to go to the bathroom."

"Wait till we get halfway around the sun," Zora had answered.

But by the time they'd gotten there, Gail had been so numb that she'd long since stopped complaining.

At lunchtime Zora had given her an apple and taken her to the bathroom. On the way there they had met

Mr. Brock with his thin lips and pointy nose and built-up shoes, and he had complimented her on her devoted work and good attitude and said that she was worthy of being a sister to Jim and to all of them.

In the bathroom, splashing water on her face, she had suddenly come alive enough to walk out on Zora and head for the telephone in the lobby. The booth had been occupied though, and when she'd seen it was Scott in there, holding the receiver and speaking with great concentration, she'd decided not to wait her turn. Besides, Zora had come looking for her.

What happened after that she didn't remember too clearly. Scott had come back, *"Forgive us, Father,"* he had prayed, *"we who are tempted to serve two masters."* And then, *"Envision yourself giving up your life for Father,"* he had commanded, and she'd gone along with him, picturing herself dead, half dozing, slipping into a state of lifelessness that had seemed alluring, until . . .

"Gail? *Gail!*"

She had sat up abruptly.

"Shake those sleepy spirits off your shoulder!" Zora had said.

But she'd fallen asleep again anyway, and the next thing she knew, Zora was shaking her, and Scott was singing a hymn:

> "When we're weak and battle scarred
> And the way seems grim and hard
> Father Adam sees our plight
> And he guides us with his Light."

Gail hummed to try to keep awake. Odd sensations were coming over her now. Joints loose—head aching—a ringing in her ears. Telephone—pick up the phone, somebody! Had she taken her exam, by the way? No, too late. Too late for the field trip. Too late to do anything—anything but continue around the semicircle of gold.

"Where's your needle, Gail?"

She felt around in the velvet. "I've got it."

"Good. We must rush now. Jim's back. He'll be here in a minute."

Finish. Yes. She stitched quickly. "Ouch!" She looked down at the drop of blood, tiny and red as a ladybug.

"Suffer willingly. The salvation of the whole world rests on your shoulders. . . ."

"We're close, Gail. Keep going. Mr. Brock's sending in help to hang the curtain."

Hurry, she told herself. If she hurried, she'd beat Zora. Satin shimmery. Bright. Hurting her eyes. But beautiful! A few more inches.

"They're coming, Gail."

Scott was standing up now and closing the book as the brothers and sisters came into the auditorium. Gail kept sewing. Two inches—one inch—finished! Ahead of Zora.

"Fantastic! Gorgeous!"

Everybody hugging her now, admiring her sun. Zora rushing to do her last inch. Half a dozen brothers and sisters on each side, then, pulling, straining, lifting. Some on ladders, some bringing down the baton and tying the curtain. Curtain off the floor, hoisted by pulley. Cheers and clapping as folds of dark velvet unfurled and the golden semicircles met.

"Perfect!" Scott called. "Gail, this will be a night to remember."

"Here comes Jim!"

Jim raising his arms in the air like a champion in the ring. Coming over to her, examining the curtain. "Beautiful! It's beautiful, Gail!" Jim reaching down and offering her his hand. Pulling her to her feet. "Are you as happy as I am right now, little sister?"

She looked at him, dazed. "Is it almost seven?"

"Hey, it's later than that," Jim said. "Father's here. He's about to begin his talk. See how time flies when you're involved in your work? It's past eight o'clock!"

15

". . . and most of all for the presence of Father who has put aside his manifold responsibilities to come to us at the New World Hotel this evening . . ."

"Father! Thank you, Father!"

Jim, on the folding chair next to Gail's in the middle of the crowded auditorium, was murmuring along with everybody else as Mr. Brock continued the prayer. Jim's head was bowed, his expression rapt. Incredible how she'd lost track of time, Gail thought. Too late to go home tonight, Jim had told her firmly. Dangerous traveling at this hour. "Stay one more day," he'd begged. "Stay for the rally."

"Not for the rally!" she'd said.

"Why not?"

She pictured going to rally with Jim, walking along and all of a sudden her father and Mat. . . . "I'll stay—till early tomorrow morning," she said quickly. "If you'll stay over Sunday night at Laurel Ridge."

"All right."

"Good." She nodded. She'd get through till morning somehow. It was worth it, to get Jim home for extra time.

"I'm so glad you're going to see Father Adam," he'd said.

"Where is he now?"

"In his suite, preparing himself. He always meditates in private before an appearance."

If I'm staying another night, I've got to call, she was on the verge of saying, but suddenly she knew it was too late for that. Yesterday, if she'd called immediately, there might have been a chance of making them understand. Now, though, to call and say she was staying still longer . . . They'd tell her Jim was stringing her along, she was crazy to trust him.

She couldn't win. If they didn't hear from her, they'd go through with the kidnapping without her. And it would be a bust, so that Jim would be more committed to the L.O.W. than ever. Only thing to do now was to get out of here early tomorrow. Early enough to telephone her father before he left home and plead with him to wait. Ask him to trust her to get Jim home on Sunday. Keep Mat and Lee away, she'd beg her father.

". . . to be at Father's side forever . . ." Brock droned on. Forever. That'd be one solution. Stay. Avoid decisions. No more hassles with parents. Spend her life sewing on curtains and taking a vacation from thinking. From sleeping and eating, though, too. That was the trouble.

"When's dinner?" she had whispered to Jim before the prayer.

"After Father speaks," he'd said.

"Won't that be late?"

"We won't be thinking of our hunger when we have the chance to be with Father. Aren't you anxious to hear him?"

"Yes," she'd said. Jim was getting a kick out of believing she was here because she wanted to be. Humor him. Otherwise he might not keep up his end of the deal.

"Father, we love you, Father!"

She tried it. *"We love you, Father."* Head tilted slightly, intense concentration, urgency in the tone. Silly. But awkward sitting here being the only one silent. Attracting attention. Jim was nudging her now to sing as the chorus marched in and lined up in rows in front of the main door. Mouthing the words, she looked around the auditorium. In front of her were Charlie and Scott. Behind her was the large group of new recruits who'd been brought in this evening, and the white-robed Sunbeam Chorale, including Zora.

Standing alone near the exit at the bottom of the stage steps was Claudia, singing. Claudia. Gail stared. Why hadn't she thought of it before? It made perfect sense. Claudia'd come here looking for her daughter and had stayed to be Mat's informer. So *that's* who it was.

"*Bless those who gave of themselves today in our efforts to make the streets of Philadelphia cleaner,*" Brock prayed up on the stage.

Gail glanced from Claudia to Brock to Jim, whose face was expressive with delight.

"*Father, wonderful, Father!*" The crowd intoned.

"*And bless those whose efforts resulted in a record-breaking collection of funds for Father's work . . .*"

"*Father!*"

"*. . . and those who have completed the work on the exquisite curtain here on this stage. And bless the members of the Sunbeam Chorale, who will sing our praises to Father tonight.*"

"*Father!*"

"*And let us give thanks,*" Mr. Brock went on, "*for the encouraging number of new friends witnessed today, friends who may, before the evening is ended, turn their lives around.*"

Gail looked over her shoulder at them—people of all ages.

"*We thank Father for the opportunities this night offers,*" Mr. Brock continued, "*for the chance to hear, a few minutes from now, the testimony of a beloved brother, and for the rarest of all opportunities—that of receiving the personal blessing of Father.*"

"*Father! Father!*"

Gail looked again at Jim's upturned face. His eyes were shining, his hands clasped in ecstasy. She watched the other faces. Radiant, flushed. Like Jim's. It must be nice to feel so strongly, so certainly, about something.

"*. . . Amen!*" Mr. Brock said. "And now," he went on, "before we receive Father's blessing, we'll hear the testimony of a brother who has asked to make a public confession. He's suffered much and wants our understanding and forgiveness as he clears his conscience. May we be uplifted by his candid words—Scott Halloran."

Brock left the stage, and Scott came from between Charlie and Michael in the first row and faced the audience. The auditorium was silent.

"I come to you most humbly with my testimony," Scott said, his voice just above a whisper.

"Louder!"

"I come—" He faltered. "I'll come closer." He walked down the center aisle and stood, shaking, in the middle of the crowd. "I'm putting myself on as low a level as I can," he stammered, "to humble myself, for I have knowingly committed acts at Satan's command."

"Help him, Father!" someone called.

"Yes, Father, help me," he said, his eyes shut tight. "I want to make a confession." He opened his eyes again. "I've been remiss in the witnessing of new members and in bringing in a money contribution. I've written heretical verses, which were a waste of my time and a mockery of Father's principles. I've been puffed up with pride and have challenged the authority of those above me—and finally, I have undermined the work of the church by opening my mouth when I should have kept it closed."

"Repent!"

"I repent." He blinked. "I want to be punished. Therefore I resolve to see no evil. I voluntarily renounce my sight. I request that the church not go to the expense of replacing the glasses I so carelessly broke yesterday. I also resolve to hear and speak no evil. From now on, I'll only speak when spoken to. And I'll only write to the glory of Father."

"Father!"

"As an expression of my sincerity," he said, his voice hoarse, "I want to destroy the remainder of my heretical writings." He reached into his jacket pocket and pulled out a sheaf of papers. "These are poems I've written—some of them years ago, before I found the Light of the World, and some of them recently. I'm sorry about them. Because I often find myself

tempted to look back at them, I want to divest myself
of them now." He held the papers up over his head.
"Here, destroy them! I never want to see them again!"

He flung them into the air so that they scattered,
some of them fluttering before they landed on the
floor. Gail reached, grabbed, stuffed one in her bag.
Scott, pale and agitated, tore the last one up into
pieces that he dropped at his feet.

"There," he said with a thin smile, "I feel freer
now." He rocked forward, his eyes glassy. "I wish I
had the nerve to make a complete confession," he
said in a whisper. "I hope I can resist Satan, who
beckons me even now. Pray for me," he said, casting
his eyes upward. Then he turned and sat down again
next to Charlie.

Jim took Gail's hand. "Wasn't that courageous?"

Gail, without answering, looked at Mr. Brock, who
had reappeared on the stage.

"The fact of the matter is," Brock said in a sharp
voice, "we're *all* undeserving of Father's love."

The auditorium was dead quiet.

"Oh, I know what some of you are thinking," he
said, rocking on his heels, his hands behind his back.
"You're thinking, 'Mr. Brock's referring to *other*
brothers and sisters, not to *me*. I picked up *my* trash
today. *I* collected *my* funds. *I* sewed *my* curtain. I'm
beyond criticism. I'm *so* noble.' That's what you're
thinking, isn't it?" he asked smirking.

"Well, just let me tell you one thing," he said, his
voice growing angry. "We've *all* let Father down!"

"Father!"

Brock swiveled around and pointed a finger at them,
"Imploring in his name won't atone for it!" he shouted.

Silence. Gail lowered her eyes.

"See? See how deep our guilt runs? It's written on
our faces. I see it! Don't try to hide! Everyone here
knows I'm right," he said, his own face contorted.
"We've let Father down!"

Sweat glistened on Brock's forehead. Veins stood
out. "We've let him down in countless ways. We crave
owning things," he said in a rush, "while Father
renounces all personal possessions. We wish for

physical comfort, while Father leads the simple life. We yearn for rest, while Father works tirelessly for our benefit."

"Forgive us, Father!"

"You think we have the right to forgiveness?" Brock asked incredulously. He thrust his hands behind him again. "Let's be perfectly honest. How many of you in this auditorium put your own needs before Father's at some point today?"

Gail looked up cautiously. Hands were going up, a few at first, then more. Jim bumped her shoulder as he raised his.

Brock shook his head miserably. "Let's be thankful for one thing at least—that Father isn't here in this auditorium yet to witness our disgrace. Do you think Father put himself before *us* today, for even one second?"

"No!" The cry swelled.

Brock nodded. "And yet you sit there, fully aware of his all-encompassing love, and you fail to give him what he so freely gives you," he said contemptuously. "How many of you—let's get to the bottom of this—how many of you slept longer or sat longer at breakfast or lunch than you really needed to?"

Hands went up again. Gail saw Charlie's, Scott's, Claudia's. Claudia's—she was playing the role all the way.

"How many of you coveted something a brother or sister had?" Mr. Brock asked. "Come on—think about it! A piece of food, maybe, or a better mattress, or a special privilege? That's it—let's face the truth!"

More hands were raised—Jim's. How could it be? Gail wondered. Jim was so selfless already. People all around her were shifting in their seats. She heard a loud sob behind her.

"I see some of you find yourselves beyond reproach," Brock said ironically.

He was looking at her now, Gail thought.

"I realize it takes an awfully big person to admit a weakness," he went on, his voice softening, "but Father wants his children to be as big as he is. Do you know how big Father is?" Mr. Brock asked in a hushed voice. He paused. "He's so big, so generous that while we're sitting here smug and comfortable, he's in his suite, alone, interceding for us. He's torturing himself over our weaknesses."

Gail heard another sob, then another.

"Yes," Brock said, brushing his eyes with his sleeve, "it's painful to think about, but he's taking on our sins himself, purging our souls with his tears. You heard me right—I said *tears*. Because Father's in there right now, alone and miserable, and he's *weeping for us*." Brock reached in his pocket. "I'm sorry," he gasped, unfolding a handkerchief. "I'm sorry—I didn't mean to break down like this, but the thought of Father . . ." Shaking his head, he touched the handkerchief to his eyes. "The picture of that lonely, loving figure, suffering for us . . ." Brock's face was wet and twisted in anguish as he let out a loud, shuddering sob.

Gail glanced from him to Jim, whose head was bowed and whose clenched fists showed white at the knuckles. Low moans rose up around her. She put her hand on Jim's arm, felt her own hot tears overflow. A wave of despair washed over the room.

"What can we do?" a voice finally cried.

Mr. Brock, shaking his head, gestured helplessly. "I don't know. How can we make it up to Father for giving *himself?*"

"Give *ourselves!*"

Mr. Brock, his face still streaming with tears, stood immobile. "You mean give everything—our material possessions, our hearts and minds?"

"*Yes!*"

Brock nodded slowly, recovering his voice. "You mean, come forward and sign a pledge to dedicate— or rededicate—our possessions, our love, our lives to Father?"

"*Yes!*"

"You know," Brock said softly, "I think Father would be deeply touched by that. Do you think he would?"

"*Yes!*"

Gail watched as the auditorium began to rock with spontaneous movement. Chairs scraped. One by one people got up. Feet stamped.

"Father! Father!"

"Are we ready, do you think?" Brock shouted exultantly. "Are we ready to step forward, to come up on the stage and pledge ourselves? Are we ready to sign Father's book and receive his personal blessing?"

"Yes!"

Jim pulled her to her feet. Spontaneous humming began now, chords struck on the piano, people pushed into the aisles.

Brock signaled for the curtain to open, and the golden sun drew apart to reveal a figure raised on a platform. A little man in a suit, Gail saw. *Father.* Smaller than she'd expected. Balding, with a fringe of white hair and a pleasant pinkish face—more sympathetic than the posters. As she stared, the humming grew louder and the movement more frenzied.

"Father, Father!" the cry rose.

She stood still, looking from Father's face to the crowd pushing toward the steps of the stage. There was Charlie with Scott behind him. Scott was motioning to her and Jim.

"Come, Gail," Jim said, offering her his hand. "Come with us to receive Father's blessing. You don't have to sign anything."

"Wait." She reached down for her bag and caught the strap of it on a chair in the next row.

"Everyone dedicate yourselves," Brock was shouting, "loyal brothers and sisters and newcomers alike. We're all the beloved children of Father Adam!"

"Gail," Jim called, "are you coming?"

Scott was linking his arm in Jim's, pulling him toward the stage. Trying to follow them, Gail got caught in a crush of bodies. They were up ahead on the steps now, where Jim was waving to her. She closed her eyes and let herself be carried along with the crowd.

Suddenly she felt a hand grip hers, tug it hard.

She resisted involuntarily and then whirled around, dropping her bag and clapping her hand to her mouth.

"Don't talk," Doug warned, in a single motion picking up her bag and yanking her through the empty row in the opposite direction from the way she'd been going. "Put your head down. Move fast," he whispered, as he bucked the pile-up of people and pulled her through the exit at the base of the steps and into the dark hall.

"How—?"

"I said don't talk!" Wrenching her arm, he led her along the corridor, past the elevator to a door marked *Fire Exit.* "Push," he said.

In the stairwell, instead of slowing up, he ran faster, holding her elbow firmly as he led the way down steps where puddles lay on worn treads.

"Not a word!" he warned again, panting as he steered her down the last flight. "Save your breath. This is stage one." He spat out the words. "I came in with the recruits. Your father and Mat are outside, but we won't see them. We've got to bust out of here and keep going. I'll tell you the rest later."

"When did you—?"

"Shut up!"

She followed silently, trying to ignore the stitch in her side. Doug turned at the bottom of the steps and half dragged her through the dark basement, past piles of old furniture and a row of garbage cans, and out a door that opened onto a small courtyard.

"I can't run anymore," she cried as the night air hit her in the face.

"You've got to."

She stumbled along behind him out into the alley, where a car was parked in the shadows.

"Don't stop!" Doug said, gripping her arm tighter.

"Is that—?"

"Yes, keep going!"

And she did, her side throbbing, until they were away from the hotel and on Market Street where noisy traffic and garish neon signs marked the entrance to another world.

16

"There, that one in the corner, in the back, O.K.?" Doug said to the waiter. He pulled out a chair for Gail. "Let me sit here." He took the seat facing the door. "May we have some bread right away, please, and a carafe of wine? Make it rosé. O.K., *now* I'll talk," he said when the waiter had gone. He breathed quickly. "Two things. One, right this minute Mat and your dad may have Jim. Two. I've got to know why you did this. You had a good reason, right? You had to see him alone, was that it? To try to save him from a rescue?"

She nodded.

"You're going to have to make me understand it, Gail. I'm going to try. Anyway, the important thing is we're out. Safe." He covered her hand with his.

Gail looked over her shoulder.

"Don't worry," Doug said. "There's no way anybody could have followed us. What do you think, they're going to lay seige to the Ikon Restaurant?"

"Why did we come here?" she asked him.

"Because you haven't eaten a good meal in awhile, have you? And this is an O.K. place to be until we call your mother. Give ourselves a little over an hour, your father said, till you feel like talking and she's gotten the word on whether they have Jim." Doug looked up. "Here, have some bread."

As the waiter set down the basket, she tore off a piece of bread and crammed it into her mouth. She swallowed. Sounds around her were exaggerated.

Sirens echoed. Here inside, glasses clinked loud as bells. Was there chanting, or was it only strangers whispering at the next table? "Everything's unreal," she said. Her own voice sounded foreign. "How are they getting him?"

"Mat worked it out with his contact," Doug said. "Jim was supposed to be delivered to the same basement exit where we went out."

"Delivered? How did she manage that?"

"*She?* You know who the contact is?"

"Claudia's got to be. I saw her standing by the door."

"Anybody could be by the door. Mat wouldn't say a thing about who it is. Why would somebody fink like that?"

"She went in to get her daughter out. It figures—she's anti-cult, posing as a member. I can't picture it though. How did she do it? How did you get into this?"

"It's a long story. I was in touch with Mat. He brought me to Philadelphia this afternoon," Doug said. "He gave me instructions how to go in with the recruits. Did you see us come in?"

"The group, sure. I'd have died if I saw you—"

"I played it very cool, but I was quaking in my boots. Anyway," he said, his elbows on the table, "I was supposed to wait until the curtains opened and then when the push toward Father started, I was supposed to bring you out and down the fire stairs."

"That kind of detail—she could tell you all that?"

"Listen, they put on the Father Adam Show over and over, babes. A recruit was telling me. He's caught that crying scene of Brock's before. No wonder they know what happens next. Brock goes around the East Coast giving that spiel five, six times a week—that 'I'm-sorry-I-didn't-mean-to-break-down' crap. Hey, what did you think of Father Adam? Didn't he look like the president of the chamber of commerce?"

"He was cute," Gail said, "a cute little grandfather. Go on—then what?"

"O.K., Mat gave me instructions how and when to go in, where the fire stairs were, and all the rest. My pulling you out was a signal to the contact, who was supposed to be watching for us to go. Then she—if it is a she—tells Jim, 'Gail's split! She went this way!' He'd want to stop you no matter what, right? So while we go down the stairs, the contact takes Jim down in the elevator with enough of a time lag to let us get clear."

"And at the exit?" Gail asked.

"Mat and Lee come to the door when they see us leave. Your father's supposed to bring the car as close as possible."

"It sounds like it'd never work. How did Claudia know she could get Jim down there by himself? What if a bunch of them came with him?"

"Mat thought it was the best we could do under the circumstances."

"I guess I'm responsible for the circumstances," Gail said. She ran her finger along the edge of the table cloth. "So—it's all done. One way or the other."

"Yeah. Mat saw us, I'm sure. They know we got out all right."

"But we don't know about them. When can we call?"

Doug looked at his watch. "I'm keeping track. I'll let you know."

Gail, thinking for a second, shook her head. "Claudia's got to be crazy to devote her life to this."

"Yeah," Doug said. "One shot's enough for me." He folded his arms. "What do you think, Gail? Are you glad we did it?"

She nodded slowly. "You did right to come for me."

"And Jim?"

She paused. "And Jim. I hoped for something else. Now—if this worked—I'll be so relieved."

Doug leaned back. "You weren't so hopped up on the idea of the rescue yesterday, were you, when you disappeared from the scene?"

"No. You must have thought I was crazy."

"As a matter of fact, it did seem a wee bit *whimsical*. What the hell were you doing, Gail?"

"Wait a minute—" She reached in her bag. "First of all, it wasn't whimsical. I went yesterday because Michael brought me a letter from Jim. See? Here."

"From Jim?"

She looked at it. "Oh. No! This is one of Scott's poems, one of the papers he threw in the air."

"Some souvenir," Doug said, laying it on the table.

"Here," she said. "Here's Jim's letter." She pulled out the other paper and showed it to Doug.

"Yeah." He read it once and then over again. "Yeah, well—"

"When I saw this, I had to come. I thought he might listen to me," she said. "And he did, sort of. I got him to agree to come home overnight."

"Yeah?"

"This Sunday."

"He would have come?"

"He said so. I practically signed my life away to make sure he'd keep up his end of the bargain. We made a deal that I'd spend two days there and he'd spend two at home. This way, though—Mat's way —it'll be permanent, we hope."

"So that's why you stayed, because of a deal?"

"Yes."

"That's the only reason?"

"What do you mean?"

"They didn't force you? They didn't wear you down?"

She closed her eyes for a second and then opened them again, "It's hard to admit. I think they were beginning to."

Doug watched her. "If I hadn't come tonight—I mean, if I or somebody else hadn't brought you out— do you think you would have gone up on that stage with the rest of them to sign the book and pledge everything to Father?"

"I don't know," she said. "Sitting here with you now, I think *No, I couldn't have*, but I surprised myself a lot while I was there. I was sure I'd get to a phone to call you. I was sure I'd leave by seven tonight. Would that have messed up the rescue?"

"No, Mat knew you were still there. We were as careful as possible, babes."

Gail shook her head. "I really thought they couldn't touch me. I didn't believe it that Jim or Lee *couldn't* leave." She looked up at him. "I believe it now. I think it's possible I might have signed something tonight."

"Do you think everybody's vulnerable?"

She thought for a second. "No. But I think most people are at some point in their lives."

Doug leaned toward her. "So you're glad I came."

She reached for his hand. "I've never been so happy to see anybody in my life. It's all so unbelievable—running down those stairs, through that smelly basement. . . . I have to know about Jim. Can we call now?"

"A little while longer. Let's eat."

The waiter set down glasses and poured wine. "Are you ready to order, sir?"

"Yes," Doug said. He turned to Gail. "You're starving, right? How about it—shish kebob? Moussaka?"

"It doesn't matter. You decide."

Doug looked at her. "Really? O.K., two moussaka."

The waiter went away.

"Better eat before you drink," he said. "Gail, one little question that's troubling me." He closed his eyes for a second. "I gather from the note that Jim wanted you to keep his invitation secret, but why *did* you? Why didn't you tell somebody? I'm not even hurt—much—that you didn't tell me. But, Gail, you put a bunch of people, including yourself, into a very lousy position!"

"I told you I intended to call. I can't believe I didn't. I tried at the bus station, but Michael talked me out of it. At the hotel they made it so hard. I almost managed today, but Scott was on the phone when I got there. When did you realize I'd left school?" she asked.

"Suppertime last night. I came by the dorm. Marilyn was beginning to wonder. She said you'd been called down to the lobby. The girl at the desk said she saw you leave with a blond guy."

"You knew right away who it was?"

"Well, I figured. Gail, you let yourself be seen leaving the dorm in a hurry with a curly-headed blond goon. . . . You'd never make it as Nancy Drew."

"What'd you do?"

"Wasted time at first looking around for the note I was sure you'd left me somewhere—in your mailbox or at my place. Then I called Mat's office, but he wasn't in, or Lee either." Doug sat back. "Then, let's see. . . . I gave you a couple of hours before I called your parents, just in case you'd gone off to explore the Central Pennsylvania gneiss or something. Marilyn agreed I should call your parents. She's another person who's been going nuts over this, by the way."

"So you did finally call my parents?"

"About ten. Their man Mat was on your trail already. You didn't stand a chance of doing anything in secret with that guy on the payroll. By nine o'clock he knew you were at the New World Hotel."

"Nine? I didn't see Claudia until later. She must've seen me though. What did my parents think? What did they say? Were they mad?"

Doug raised his eyebrows. *"Panicked* is the way I'd put it—conservatively. Remember, babes, they didn't have the benefit of discussing this with you, like I did. And Mat—that tight-lipped son-of-a-gun—he didn't tell them about your Mercy expedition. If that guy gave his word to Jack the Ripper, he wouldn't break it to save his mother's life, I swear. So"—Doug sipped his wine—"so *I* told Ed and Frances what you've been up to lately. I told them the truth because I thought it'd be in the best interests of all concerned."

Gail picked up her wine glass. "What did they say?"

"Well, they were grateful for any explanation, even a dumb one. I told them you had a feeling you could get through to Jim and avoid the rescue. I said I was sure you must know what you were doing—that was loyal of me, wasn't it? I said you hadn't told them about Mercy because you didn't want them to worry.

I told them I'd brought you home safely from there—
thought I'd throw that in to help my own cause.
Frankly, I laid it on good, Gail. They were impressed
as hell. I think they're beginning to love me like a
son-in-law. I would've asked for your hand on the spot
except that none of us was really expecting ever to
see your hand again."

"They were still upset."

"A *tiny* bit, thinking you might have been picked
up against your will, or thinking you might have
followed your will and gone off to join the cult. I said
I doubted it. And I volunteered my services. That
put them completely at ease, naturally."

"Come on. How bad was it?"

Doug laid his palms flat on the table. "Gail, they
were frantic. And if you want to know how *I* took it,
I took it lousy! It scared the hell out of me. Don't
ever do anything so asinine again!"

She looked at him, half smiling. "If you were
scared, you hid it—in there, I mean. You were so
earnest, for a change."

"Man, I was destroyed." He leaned closer. "What
was your first thought when you saw it was me?"

"That they'd gotten you, too. That they get everybody, eventually. Doug," she said, "I'll be so happy
if Jim's out."

Doug, nodding, took her hand in both of his. "Hey,
what's he like? I saw him for about half a second.
How is he?"

Gail waited as the dinner appeared in two stainless
servers. Rising steam and the smell of spices made her
eyes tear.

Doug, leaning over, handed her her fork. "Come
on, Gail, eat. Eat and we'll call your mother. You can
imagine what shape she must be in. Your father said
to call when you're a little relaxed. Come on, eat."

Gail, blotting her face with her napkin, tasted
cautiously. The moussaka was burning hot.

"When's the last time you had something?" Doug
asked, watching her.

"An apple at noon. Candy last night."

"Candy? I was reading about that."

"About what?"

"An article about the way the L.O.W. engineers diets. When they want you to feel down, like that session we were in tonight, they don't give you any dinner, so your blood sugar level's low. And when they want you to feel good, they give you sweet stuff, so you're on a sugar high."

"It's possible."

"They calm you down with this special tea, the article said."

"Tea? I had it."

"And some doctor claims a lot of L.O.W.s suffer vitamin A deficiency—rashes, night blindness—where you can't see in bright light."

"Scott," Gail said. "Scott can't see. What did you think of Scott?"

"Sad. Eat something, Gail. It's not as hot now."

She lifted a forkful to her mouth. "Read Scott's poem," she said. "Read it to me."

Doug unfolded the paper and laid it between them so that they both could see it.

Lush Eden was too beautiful for Eve.
Oh, for a day or so it was all right
   to revel in sweetsmelling grass and toss
A curled up leaf into the water, or
Ankles dangling in a stream, to watch
   a timid minnow nose the riverbank,
But time stood still in Eden.

The weather was too good; and if she fished
Undoubtedly the fish were biting. What's
   the sport? Eve cried, and reaching up she plucked
An apple from a flawless branch, and then
A serpent carping in her soul, she took
   a bite out of the apple
To save us from perfection.

Doug pushed the paper toward Gail. "Not bad for heretical verse," he said, "but then, I'm a heretic."

"I like the poem." Gail picked it up and put it back in her bag. "Unfortunately he's back into perfection now."

"What a bore. Is Jim into perfection, too? *How's Jim?*"

Gail stopped eating. "I miss him. I miss the way he was."

Doug poured wine in both their glasses.

"Am I just being dumb?" Gail asked. "What do you think brothers and sisters ought to be to each other—when they're grown up, I mean? Is it stupid of me to think there ought to be something besides the same parents, the same house to go home to for holidays?"

"Shared memories, babes. Shared memories. They count for something."

"Is that all?"

"If there's more, it's a happy accident. Why, what do you think there ought to be?"

"Oh, I don't know. You grow up being on the same side—on teams often, or against other kids or your parents even. I think you ought to keep on being—allies."

"Well, tell that to Jim when he's deprogrammed."

Gail ate in silence for a minute. "Let's call," she said.

Doug checked the time again. "It's a little early. She may have heard, but—"

Gail laid down her fork. "I can't eat any more until we know. She'll be anxious to hear from us, too. Would—would you speak to her? I think it's better if I wait. . . ."

Doug brushed his moustache. "Yeah, well, don't be disappointed if there's no news yet. O.K.?" He pushed his chair back and laid his napkin on the table. "Take it easy, Gail. I'll be quick."

And he was back almost before she knew it, with an expression on his face that she couldn't figure out even when he sat down across from her again and took both her hands in his.

"What did she say?" Gail asked, her ears buzzing.

"Your father answered," Doug said.

"My father?"

"He—he just got home. They're relieved that you're O.K." Doug locked his hands together. "They want us to take a bus home to Laurel Ridge right now. Mat and Lee are there with them." He paused. "Something went wrong, babes. Even they aren't sure what it was." He shook his head. "Gail, they didn't get him."

17

"Come on, Gail, let's go get a bus. Look at it this way—it may not be as final as it sounds. Maybe they have a follow-up plan."

"If they do, it won't work." Gail, standing on the corner outside the restaurant, resisted as Doug motioned for her to cross the street. Neon lights flashed around them. At the sound of a horn, Doug stepped back onto the curb.

"Come on, it's getting late," he said, glancing up at the green light. "The later it gets, the fewer buses run."

She hung back stubbornly, leaning against the side of a deserted newsstand. "I want to do what I said."

"You can't. We're supposed to go right home. Give your parents a break, won't you? You can figure how they feel."

"It won't take long," she insisted.

"Listen," Doug said, "you don't know what the hell happened there tonight. Jim found out maybe. Or the contact got chicken. Or they called the cops—"

"They'll be glad afterward if we do this. This way they'll know."

Doug came toward her. "For God's sake, Gail, get your head on straight. We're lucky we got out of that place *once* tonight. *We split,* remember? They've got to know that by now. What do you want to do—get trapped in there? Arrested? Why are you being so dense?"

"I've got to see him," she said.

"What makes you think you'll be able to? He could be anywhere by now. What're you going to do, bust back into the lecture and say, 'Excuse me, Father Adam, one little thing I have to ask my brother'?"

"If I can't find Jim," she said, "I'll ask somebody else."

"Who? Mr. Brock? Your friend Michael?"

"Claudia."

Doug was silent for a moment. "Gail, she must've blown it. What're you going to say to her?"

Gail stared past Doug at the light changing from green to yellow. "I want to find out if he's O.K., first of all. And I want to find out—if this is it."

"What do you mean?"

"The last time I'll ever see him."

"Gail . . ." He closed his eyes for a second.

"If he's found out about Dad and Mat, he'll never trust anybody in the family again," she said. "And after the rally, if he's being sent out of the country like he said, then—"

Doug put his arm around her. "Look, let's go see what your dad says."

She shook off his arm. "Doug, listen, *we're here,* three blocks from Jim. Chances are *he's there.* We may never be this close again in our lives. Anyway, what's the risk? I mean, really—what's the big risk? If they call the cops, the cops'll be on our side. Cops hate the cult. We might have trouble getting in the auditorium, I agree," she said. "At least I'd know I tried."

Doug moved closer to her again as a gang of kids passed them. "If I say yes, Gail, what do you picture doing exactly?"

"Going in where we came out," she said, "up the fire stairs to the lobby."

"It's idiotic. He won't be there. Or if he is, he won't agree to see us."

"Let's try."

Doug glanced over his shoulder at the bunch of kids lighting up on the corner. "If I say no, if I refuse to go—then what?"

"I'll go myself."

"And what do I tell Ed and Frances? 'Gail loved it so much she decided to go back?' "

"You won't have to tell them anything. I'll be coming right home."

"If you don't get mugged before you take two steps. Where do you think you are—in front of the Hi-Ho Sweet Shop in Laurel Ridge in broad daylight?"

She shrugged. "So come with me. Either way I'm going."

"All right," he said suddenly. Hooking his arm in hers he led her across the intersection. They hurried down the street past a grocery, a laundromat, a neighborhood bar.

"How did my father sound?"

"In control, Gail. Don't worry."

"My mother—this is going to set her back."

"She'll be O.K., your mother. She's still got you to be frantic about."

They walked in silence past a row of X-rated movie houses to the corner, where they turned east.

"It's my fault," Gail said. "If I hadn't fouled things up, he'd be safe now."

"That's not what your parents are thinking, Gail. They're relieved you're out. Let the L.O.W.s take the guilt trip, O.K.? We're doing what we can. Your parents will try again. It took three times to get Lee Grady, right?"

They crossed the street and saw the marquee outlined in white neon. The block was deserted, except for one car in front of the hotel.

"Look," Gail said.

"What?"

They kept walking toward it, their eyes fixed on the bursts of red light that flashed from the patrol car. When they were close enough, they saw the cop by the revolving door.

"Gail, what do you say let's forget it."

She shook her head. "The cops are here because of the rally. They're expecting a lot of people."

"There's *nobody*."

"We're going around the back anyway," she said.

She turned and waited for Doug. They walked silently, side by side, along the painted-over glass window until they came to the alley. The alley was dark. Sticking close to the wall of the hotel, they edged their way to the courtyard, where earlier her father's car had been parked. Now, suddenly, they heard the revving of a motor and the slam of a car door. High beams blinded them for an instant, and before they knew what was happening, a great hulk of a car swung around the corner so close to them that they jumped back involuntarily and flattened themselves against the wall.

Doug pulled her to him.

The taillights winked as the car disappeared toward the avenue.

"Can we please get out of here," Doug whispered angrily, "before they have to send us home in a box?"

Gail stepped weakly away from the wall. "What happened? Where . . . ?"

"Look, if you're going to get creamed, be happy it's by a Mercedes."

"It was?"

"Yeah. *Now* look."

At the end of the wall they could see into the courtyard, where another patrol car light flashed and dark figures paced inside a wooden barricade.

"Tell me you still want to go in this way," Doug said. "The place is crawling with cops."

"O.K., the front." Without hesitating, she started back down the alley.

"I hope you go through this much to come see me when I'm in the booby hatch," he said, a few steps behind her. They were on the sidewalk now, heading toward the marquee. "You know I'm seriously doubting your judgment, don't you?" he said, his voice even.

"Yes," she said without stopping. At the steps she paused. The cop stood at the top with his arms folded. Doug came up even with her. "Can we go in?" she asked the cop in a low voice.

"You belong to this outfit?"

"No. I have to see my brother."

"I don't know, miss," the cop said. "There's an investigation going on."

"Of what?" Doug asked.

"An accident."

"What happened?" Gail felt heat rising inside her.

"An elevator accident."

She stood still.

"Was anyone hurt?" Doug asked.

"I don't have that information," the cop said. "Inspector's here now. Investigation's still going on."

Gail swayed.

Doug took hold of her. "We can go in, can't we?" he asked.

"Go ahead. You might be restricted once you're inside."

They climbed the steps and pushed the revolving door.

Gail, in a daze, pressed her hands against the cool glass. "Jim's hurt," she said numbly as they came out into the lobby.

"We don't know if anybody was hurt! Hey." Doug looked around. "There's nobody here."

The lobby was empty and dim, as if there were a brownout. Far away they heard the echo of a voice.

"Spookville," Doug said, his heels clicking as he walked toward the reception desk. "Nobody home. Crazy—the eve of the big shebang." He motioned to her. "Hey."

By the elevators was another wooden barrier with a sign that read DANGER BY ORDER OF THE POLICE DEPARTMENT.

"Can I help, please?"

Gail jumped. Without a sound, Sam Li, correct in his black suit and narrow tie, appeared behind the desk.

"I'm looking for my brother," she said.

"Ah, yes! Mr. Brock gave you permission to come downstairs?"

Gail hesitated. "Yes."

"And your friend? He has Mr. Brock's permission, too?"

She nodded.

"You want to see your brother," Sam said.

"Yes, please. Where is he?" Her heart pounded in her ears.

"He's still with the investigator. It was a terrible thing."

She cleared her throat. "Where is he?"

"In the coffee shop. They're not allowing anyone in yet. Except Michael. Michael's with him."

"Is Jim all right?"

"Yes, yes, I understand he is. It was a terrible shock."

"Shock—" she repeated mechanically.

"Do you think they'll be long?"

"I can't say."

Gail, swaying again, willed herself to stand perfectly straight. "We'll wait," she said.

18

She watched the police officers leaving, listened to their nasal voices bouncing off the fake marble walls. "We came to see Jim," she said.

Michael spun around. "Gail! Who let you in here? Nobody's supposed to be let through."

"We want to see Jim," Doug repeated.

"Who are *you?*" Michael asked.

"He's with me." Gail looked through the doorway of the coffee shop. She could see Jim, by himself, slumped in a chair, his head down, showing no sign that he knew they were out here in the hall.

"I heard you left," Michael said coldly.

Gail inched forward. "I left, but I came back to see Jim. What happened?"

"You were going for good, weren't you?" he asked. "And because of it a brother's dead."

"A brother's what?" She looked in confusion at Jim again.

"Scott's dead!" Michael said, his face darkening.

"Scott!" Gail dropped her bag to the floor. "In the elevator—"

Doug held on to her. "What happened?" he asked Michael.

"I only know what Jim told me," Michael said. "He says Scott saw Gail leave. Scott was concerned, naturally, about the well-being of a sister, as any of us would be. 'Jim, something's wrong with your sister,' Scott told him. 'Come with me!' And Jim followed him out of the auditorium."

Gail's mouth was dry. She licked her lips. "Scott saw me go? Who else saw me go?"

Michael looked at her quizzically. "No one that I know of. Why?"

"Not Claudia?"

He shook his head. "Claudia was holding the pledge book for Father on stage."

Gail stared. "No, she couldn't have been. . . ." Doug, she saw, was beginning to understand what she had already understood. *"Scott* told my brother I was leaving?"

Michael nodded.

"Scott . . ." Gail felt a hot, awful liquid rising in her throat. With disgust she swallowed.

"He cared about you so desperately," Michael said. "He cared so much that he pulled Jim off the stage while Father was there. He told Jim he knew where you'd gone." Michael's voice quavered. "Did you tell Scott you were leaving?"

"No!"

"That goes to show, then, the depth of his concern," Michael went on. "Jim says Scott led him to the elevator, and pressed the button—"

"What happened?" Doug asked.

Michael looked up desolately. "Jim's not sure. It all happened so fast. Scott was in a hurry, Jim says. The doors opened but the elevator cab wasn't there." Michael leaned back against the door frame. "The open shaft . . . Scott couldn't see," he said.

"Oh my God," Doug said.

Michael nodded. "Jim says there was nothing anyone could have done."

"Why didn't the cab come up?" Doug asked angrily.

"The inspector doesn't know. It was a freak accident." Michael turned to Gail. "He was taking Jim to find you, you know. How does that make you feel? Where were you going?"

Gail leaned dizzily against the wall. "Let me see Jim," she said.

"He doesn't want to see anyone."

"Did Scott die instantly?" Doug asked.

"Almost. He landed on the cab. Hit his head. He was still alive when the ambulance came. Jim saw it all."

Gail edged toward the doorway, but Michael blocked it. "Seeing you will only upset him more," Michael said. "I don't think you even begin to realize what he's been through because of you. He saw Scott fall. He heard his cries in the shaft. He ran to the lobby and got Sam Li to phone an ambulance. Then he got into the shaft on the main floor and squeezed through the trapdoor in the ceiling of the cab. Scott died in Jim's arms."

Gail closed her eyes. "Horrible! If Scott had had his glasses—"

"If you hadn't left!" Michael shouted.

"She had nothing to do with it," Doug said. "Nobody made Scott leave the auditorium. How could he see that Gail was leaving, by the way, if his eyesight was so bad?"

Michael, puzzled, rose up on his toes. "It may be hard for you—whoever you are—to understand this, but there are certain codes of behavior we value in the L.O.W. Maybe where you come from people ignore each other in time of trouble and let each other go without a word, but we're different here. Scott loved Gail. He loved her like a sister and Jim like a brother. He loved them so much he was willing to give his life for them. What do you say to that, Gail?"

She turned to the wall. He had it all wrong. He'd never believe the way it really had been.

"That's the lowest," Doug said. "Making her feel rotten, making it sound like Scott martyred himself. Scott was unstable. I saw it. I was there tonight. So full of self-hate he renounced his sight. Now I see why he hated himself. Forget it, though. Let us see Jim."

Michael, his nostrils flaring, pointed to Doug. "This is Satan talking, Gail," he said, his voice husky. "He may not even know it, but Satan's speaking through him, sowing seeds of doubt and fear. Trying to corrupt you, Gail." He softened his tone. "Gail, I have something to say to you that's very important. Are you listening to me?"

She nodded dully.

"There's only one way you're going to see Jim. Mr. Brock's put me here to protect Jim's privacy and the privacy of the Light of the World. Nobody's going to hear about this incident tonight, not even our own people upstairs. The rally must go on. Father's peace of mind mustn't be disturbed. *No one's* going to talk to Jim except you, Gail, if you're willing to do what I ask you."

"What?" She looked past him into the coffee shop, where Jim still sat in the same position.

"You owe him something for leaving tonight, Gail. You owe Scott something. His death is an enormous loss to us, Gail. There's only one thing I can think of that would begin to atone for it." He paused. "Jim wanted you here more than anything in the world."

Gail looked at him.

"You know what I mean, don't you? Join us, Gail, fill the empty place. We'll help you learn to repent."

"You're a madman," Doug said, stepping toward him.

"Don't listen to Satan, Gail," Michael said, racing along. "Satan appears in the guise of friends and leads us into evil. I'll let you see Jim, Gail, if you promise to stay. Not forever. Just for a few days, until Jim begins to get over this. That would make him so happy." Michael reached for her hand. "Send Satan away. Stay—"

"No!" She drew back.

Michael, still in the doorway, watched her. "You're loved here, Gail. You're wanted."

"You guys are wanted, too," Doug said. "In fifty states by parents like hers. What did the cops talk to Jim about, by the way?"

"A routine investigation," Michael said, his color rising again. "It's none of your business—Satan!"

"I'm speaking strictly for myself, buddy. The cops thought this might be a suicide or foul play, didn't they? After all, how often does a guy fall down an elevator shaft except in a dump like this, where the bucks go to Father? To hell with keeping up the elevators—buy Father another Mercedes, right?"

"I refuse to answer," Michael said in an angry whisper.

He was bracing himself in the doorway, Gail saw. Doug, the veins standing out on his forehead, took a step toward him.

"I'd like you to go," Michael said to Doug. "Gail is staying. She knows where she's well off."

"I know she does," Doug said, resting one hand on the door frame. "That's why she's leaving here with me. But first she wants to speak to her brother, and you're going to let her."

Michael's body grew rigid. "You can try to get by me, but there won't be much point to it. First of all, Jim's not going to talk to you. Second, Sam Li will be here any minute. Sam can bring me all the help necessary to get rid of you."

Doug laughed. "What're you going to do, get physical? That'd make a hell of a story in tomorrow's *Daily News,* the day of the rally. LONE DISSENTER CLOBBERED IN L.O.W. RIOT. Almost as good as LOONY FALLS TO DEATH IN ELEVATOR SHAFT. Picture that on page one, Michael." Doug nudged him with his elbow. "Let us in. We want to see what condition he's in so we can report to his father—and I don't mean Adam."

Michael, standing firm, looked at Gail. "Don't give in to Satan. Muster all the love you've ever felt for your brother. Ask Satan to go. Ask him to go quietly. He doesn't have Jim's interests at heart. Gail, do you love your brother?"

"Yes," she said, picking up her bag from the floor and coming toward him. "That's why I want you to let me see him right now."

"No."

Doug pushed with his shoulder against Michael's chest.

Michael wedged himself in the doorway. "Sam!" he called. "Sam!"

"Forget Sam," Doug said, throwing his weight at Michael, "and don't make me play Jimmy Cagney, man. I'll feel like an idiot. I'm not a violent guy, but if you don't let Gail in there right now, I'm going to make a hole in the wall the shape of an L.O.W."

"Sam!" Michael didn't move.

Doug squeezed Michael's upper arm so that he squirmed. "Move over, buddy. Let her in."

Michael stared contemptuously.

Doug, hooking one foot around Michael's knee, twisted until he tripped him. He held Michael's arm behind his back. "Go ahead, Gail," he said. "Michael thinks it's a good idea if he and I wait in a secluded spot while you go in and have a little talk with Jim."

19

Gail walked slowly toward the table where Jim sat with his head down, his face hidden. His hands, with fingers spread apart, looked pale. His breathing was shallow. The gray sweater he had worn lay in a heap on the floor, and the white cuffs of his shirtsleeves were turned up, damp where brownish stains showed. She looked at him as she would at a stranger, noticing for the first time a spot on the crown of his head where the hair was thin.

Dropping her bag on the floor, she pulled out a chair and sat down. The table creaked. "Jim . . ." Jim didn't move. The mustard-colored walls closed in. Outside a fire engine wailed. "Jim . . . It's me, Gail. I came back. I just wanted to see how you are before I go for good."

Eerie, like calling "Anybody home? Anybody home?" in an empty house. "I—I heard about Scott," she said, pausing. "Michael says you were a hero. That figures. I used to think so—pretty often. Remember when I got locked in the gym in elementary school on a Friday afternoon and you pried the wire off the window?"

Jim still didn't move.

"I know you don't feel like talking—that's O.K. I hope you won't mind if I do . . . a little."

Maybe it didn't even matter if he wasn't listening. Sitting back in the chair, she stared at the teakettle on the unplugged hotplate. She'd sat here last night, across from Scott. "I—I'm trying to imagine what you're thinking," she said. "But I can't. I've never been through anything like what you've just been through. The suddenness—losing somebody suddenly must be the worst. And the awfulness of the way it happened. And you being the one to—" She stopped. "I guess there's nothing to say, except how much I wish I could help you."

The room was silent. Jim's breathing was deeper now.

"Do you think it's strange that I'm going on like this?" she asked, fixing her eyes on the back of his head. "I feel this incredible need to talk. Maybe it's because I haven't really seen you in so long. Or because of all the stuff I've had to keep to myself this week. Only a week since I first went looking for you —I can't believe that. Or maybe it's the wine I had that's affecting me," she said. "Doug and I just had wine with dinner. Doug's here—I guess you didn't know that. He came looking for me. He's out there somewhere with Michael." She glanced into the hall and then back at Jim. "Doug's helped me a lot. You said last night you wanted me to fill you in on Doug. I don't know if you meant it, but I feel like telling you. Doug and I—it's a very good thing, Jim. I used to like knowing you were around when I was a freshman. I was lucky, I guess, that Doug was at Munro when you left. He's good for me. He helps me have fun and try new things and think for myself. I'm in love with him, Jim."

Jim's shoulders twitched slightly.

"Mom and Dad don't understand how I feel," Gail went on. "A couple of times this year I wished you were around to talk to about Doug. He keeps wanting me to be more open with Mom and Dad. I'll try, I guess. I should have long ago. The longer you wait, the harder it gets. That's why I'm going on like this now, telling you everything that's coming into my head, in case we don't get another chance for a while."

She glanced down at the stained sweater on the floor. "I liked Scott, Jim. Did you?"

Jim's hand moved.

"I spent the whole day with him today, you know. I have one of the poems he threw away. He didn't like it, but I do. Scott wanted to be perfect." She thought for a minute. "I guess he would have kept on being disappointed in himself forever. He was sad and mixed up—very mixed up. But you know, I just realized that, next to you, I liked him best of all the people in the L.O.W. He never lost his *self*. That's what made it so hard for him in the church, I suppose."

Jim shifted in the chair.

"I wish I'd told Scott I liked him," Gail said. "People hardly ever do, except when it's too late, or like now, when something terrible has happened." She sat up. "I love you, Jim," she said in a low voice. "I want to say it before it's too late—before I go. I'm not sure exactly what I mean by it, but I know there's something still there. We were close once. I wish we could be again—" She broke off. "This is a terrible time to talk, I guess. You probably wish I'd stop. I will."

"No," he said, lifting his head slowly, his eyes dull, his face marked with cross-hatched red lines. "Don't stop."

Gail, surprised, reached out and took his hand, felt it tightening over hers. Still holding her hand, he put his head down again and began to sob, his head resting on one arm.

"The look on his face," he whispered. "The *sound*, Gail. There was so much blood, so much blood!"

"You did what you could."

"I held him," Jim said, raising his head again, his face streaked with tears. "I *held* him." He pulled his hand away and looked at his sleeves. "See? The blood's still there."

She laid her hand on his arm.

"The filth in the shaft!"

"What did he say—the inspector?"

"It was overdue, overdue for inspection. . . . Scott was moaning, Gail. Nobody heard him but me. Only me in there with him until the ambulance came."

"Was he conscious?" Gail asked, leaning toward him. "Did he say anything to you?"

" 'I wanted to come with you.' That's all he said, 'I wanted to come with you.' "

Gail tightened her grip on Jim's arm.

Jim's whole body shook. "I knew the moment he died, Gail. It took so long!" He looked up at her suddenly. "Scott was bringing me to you. He wanted to save you, Gail. He was doing Father's work."

Gail closed her eyes for a second.

"He gave his life, Gail. He gave his life for the Light of the World."

"Jim," she said, shaking her head, "you loved Scott, but you have to know something. That's not the way it was."

"What do you mean?" he asked warily.

"I could go without saying this," she went on uncertainly, "but I'm not going to protect you. If I'm any kind of sister, any kind of ally, I've got to tell you this whether you want to hear it or not."

Jim stirred.

"I came here yesterday on my own," Gail said. "I wasn't lying when I told you that. What I didn't tell you was that just the night before, I'd met Mom and Dad and Mat Ferrar in a restaurant to talk about rescuing you."

"Kidnap," he said. "You mean kidnap."

"I know you don't want to hear about rescues or Ferrar, but I'm giving you the whole story. We planned it for Saturday morning, and I agreed to be involved in it."

Jim turned his face away from her.

"But when I got your letter yesterday, it meant a lot to me. I decided to try to talk with you first, to see if the rescue could be called off. They got scared though, when I disappeared and they didn't hear from me, and they arranged to get us both out tonight."

He was clenching his fists.

"It wasn't hard to arrange, Jim," she said, her voice shaking, "because somebody in the L.O.W. gave them information about us."

He shook his head.

"It's true. The same person who gave Mat information about me before. Mat knew I was at Mercy before you did."

Jim's face contorted.

Gail took a deep breath. "Mat wouldn't tell who it was, but now I know, and I think you do, too. The person who was in touch with Mat today. The person I saw in a phone booth this afternoon."

Jim snapped his eyes shut.

"The person who told Mat and Dad what to do from beginning to end," she went on. "He gave the instructions for Doug to come in as a recruit and pull me out when the curtain opened. He told Mat and Dad to wait at the basement exit, and he agreed to bring you down—in the elevator—only neither of you ever got there."

"No! It's not true!" Jim said, rising out of his seat. "Satan's making you say these things!"

"It is true, Jim. And I think I understand why he did it. 'I wanted to come with you'—that's what he said, wasn't it?"

Jim sank into his chair again. "He meant he wanted to help me bring you back!"

Gail shook her head. "He confessed tonight because he felt so terrible about deserting, but he wanted to come with you out of the Light of the World. That must have been what he meant. Mat will know if it's true. I'll ask him tonight."

Jim's lips twitched. "You have no proof, not of anything."

"Only that someone promised Mat to bring you down in the elevator. I'm not telling you this to make you hate Scott. It's just that some people in the church aren't what they seem. Some people need help and they aren't getting it. Scott needed help."

"Glasses—" Jim said, bewildered.

"That's the least of it. Look, Jim," she said, touching his hand again, "I've been honest with you. For God's sake, be honest with me, please? There are so many things I don't understand—from the beginning. Please explain. I want to understand. Did you know right away you were joining the Light of the World?"

Jim hesitated. Sweat was standing out on his forehead. "I thought I was joining the Model Schools Unit."

"And then?"

He stared straight ahead. "In three days I knew it was the Light of the World. By that time it didn't matter. I was involved."

"You signed a pledge?"

"After three days. I gave Father all I had."

"Did they keep you from calling home?"

"No, but there wasn't time to."

"They didn't actually refuse to let you make a call?"

"No, but there wasn't any time, I said."

"Did they tell you what to write home?"

"Yes, they dictated letters to all of us."

"Did they advise you not to see Mom and Dad?"

"Yes. They said parents would try to convince us to leave."

"And what about me? Did they ask if you had brothers and sisters?"

"Yes."

"Did they ask where I was?"

"Yes."

"But they didn't make a move until I came to them?" He nodded.

"The letters," she said suddenly. "Was that a lie, about writing me letters?"

"No, that was true. I wrote you letters."

She paused. "Is it possible that Mom and Dad didn't take them—that they got lost in the mail?"

"I suppose it's possible."

"What else—what kind of life have you had? How many hours of sleep do you get?"

"Four, five."

"And food—the meals aren't regular, are they?"

"Not always."

"And you're not allowed—to be with any girls."

"No."

"No one breaks the rule?"

"No."

"There are things you've found hard to accept, aren't there? Lying to people on the street, for instance, about what money is being used for?"

"Yes."

"And other things they've made you do. You haven't wanted to, have you?"

"No."

"Like what?"

"Writing home for money. Sponsoring three members."

"You told me before there was no quota."

He breathed unevenly. "I lied. There is."

"How many have you gotten?" she asked, her temples throbbing.

"Two."

"You hoped I'd be the third."

He nodded.

She rubbed her eyes, a gesture of her father's. "Then there's been one lie after another, hasn't there? And it *has* been hard not seeing Mom and Dad."

"You're right, it's been hard."

"You've wanted to see them all along, haven't you?"

"Yes."

Gail watched him. His skin was pale, his face muscles rigid, as if he were in a trance. "And it's been hard for you to say all this to me, hasn't it?" she asked quietly.

"Yes."

"I respect you for it—tremendously. I can see just from these two days how easy it is to get involved here. I can see how rough it must be to admit you've made a mistake—"

"Mistake?" Jim said, sitting at attention. He looked at her as if he were just waking up. "I haven't made any mistake," he said.

Gail cleared her throat. "But you just admitted—"

"I admitted there are things that are hard to accept. But *I've accepted them,* Gail!" he said, smiling calmly. "I have to, once I accept Father Adam. All those things are unimportant, means to an end, and the end is a world of love with Father at the helm."

She sat very still. "Jim," she said, *"Scott's dead.* Dead for no reason, because of the way the L.O.W. is. And everybody is sitting up there right now, too holy to know the awful truth—that a kid who was trying to leave here died because an elevator wasn't safe, and because they let him punish himself. And Father Adam—he disappeared, didn't he? In his

Mercedes, so he wouldn't have to answer embarrassing questions." She felt the tears stinging her eyes. "Is *that* what you accept?"

"That's your way of putting it," Jim said, examining the cuffs of his shirt. "Scott's death—you're right—that's hard for me to accept." He trailed off. "No," he said suddenly, shaking his head, "I take that back. I *can* accept it. Even that. If you're right, that Scott betrayed Father, then his death was necessary—as a punishment."

"You believe that?"

"I believe in Father," he said, "with all my heart."

Gail looked at him, her vision blurred. "Then you don't care about us," she said in a low voice, "or about truth, either."

Jim let out his breath. He closed his eyes. "Truth looks different depending on where you're standing. You know that. About you and Mom and Dad—I *do* care."

"Prove it then," she said loudly. "Come home Sunday like you promised. Or was that a hoax, too, to get me to stay, to try to wear me down minute by minute, when you had no intention of keeping up your end of it?"

Jim looked at her. "I agreed to come home overnight before I knew my own parents and sister had hired a Snuffer to kidnap me."

"Wait a minute." She stiffened. "I came here yesterday because you asked me to. I came because I couldn't stand the idea of a kidnapping. I had nothing to do with that attempt tonight. I kept up my part of the deal. I expect you to keep yours."

"Gail, be realistic. How can I go to Laurel Ridge for a day or two?" He smiled ironically. "They'd have the Snuffer waiting on the doorstep. I'd go to have a look at my old room and they'd tie me to the bed. You wouldn't be able to stop them even if you wanted to."

"Meet *me* then," she said quickly. "Here in the city, away from the hotel. For two days, like you promised. Doug'll come. We'll have dinner, walk around, talk like we used to. We'll stay over at Doug's friend's place. No tricks, Jim, I swear. I won't even tell Mom and Dad I'm seeing you. Just a chance to—take a break—to remember what it was like—"

Jim tapped his fingers on the table. "I can't—my work."

"You promised. You promised me *two days*. Didn't you mean it?"

Jim's lips twitched. "Yes, I—"

"Come then," she said. "Meet Doug and me outside the hotel, Sunday at ten. We'll go—boating, maybe, or to a movie. We'll eat chicken cordon bleu." Her throat tightened. "You'll come, Jim, won't you?"

"Yes."

"Word of honor?"

"Yes."

He meant it. He did. They had never broken word of honor. She got up slowly, pushed back her chair. "O.K., then—I've got to go now. Doug and I still have to catch a bus tonight." Her voice was shaking. "Mom and Dad are waiting. I'm going to tell them I saw you—and that you've decided to stay for now." She paused. "Is there anything you want me to tell them?"

"Tell them I'm fine. Tell them—hello."

Gail picked up her bag. Reaching over, she took his hand, felt the dampness of his sleeves. "Sunday, then, ten o'clock." She was afraid to meet his eyes.

"Yes." He got up after her and put his arm around her as they walked to the door. "Gail," he said, leaning against the door frame, "thanks for coming."

She nodded. "See you Sunday," she said. And then, impressing in her memory the way he looked, she squeezed his hand hard before she turned away and let go.

ABOUT THE AUTHOR

ROBIN FIDLER BRANCATO, a native of Pennsylvania, drew upon her childhood in the suburban town of Wyomissing for the setting of her first novel, *Don't Sit Under the Apple Tree*. Her second novel, *Something Left to Lose*, was published the next year, followed by *Winning*, a 1977 ALA Best Books for Young Adults, and a Literary Guild alternate selection.

Ms. Brancato holds a B.A. in creative writing from the University of Pennsylvania and an M.A. from the City College of New York. She has lived in Italy, traveled extensively both here and abroad, and taught high school English for a number of years. She now lives in Teaneck, New Jersey with her husband, John, and their two teenage sons.